VANISHED WORLDS

An Introduction to Historical Geology

To Frank W. Beales

VANISHED WORLDS

An Introduction to Historical Geology

ROY R. LEMON

Florida Atlantic University

WCB **Wm. C. Brown Publishers**

Dubuque, Iowa•Melbourne, Australia•Oxford, England

Book Team

Editor *Craig S. Marty*
Developmental Editor *Robert Fenchel*
Production Editor *Diane E. Beausoleil*
Designer *Elise A. Lansdon*
Art Editor *Jodi Wagner*
Photo Editor *Carol Judge*
Permissions Editor *Gail I. Wheatley*
Visuals/Design Developmental Consultant *Donna Slade*

Wm. C. Brown Publishers
A Division of Wm. C. Brown Communications, Inc.

Vice President and General Manager *Beverly Kolz*
National Sales Manager *Vincent R. Di Blasi*
Assistant Vice President, Editor-in-Chief *Edward G. Jaffe*
Director of Marketing *John W. Calhoun*
Advertising Manager *Amy Schmitz*
Director of Production *Colleen A. Yonda*
Manager of Visuals and Design *Faye M. Schilling*
Design Manager *Jac Tilton*
Art Manager *Janice Roerig*
Publishing Services Manager *Karen J. Slaght*
Permissions/Records Manager *Connie Allendorf*

Wm. C. Brown Communications, Inc.

Chairman Emeritus *Wm. C. Brown*
Chairman and Chief Executive Officer *Mark C. Falb*
President and Chief Operating Officer *G. Franklin Lewis*
Corporate Vice President, President of WCB Manufacturing *Roger Meyer*

Cover photo © John Cancaldsi/Peter Arnold, Inc.

Copyedited by Mary M. Monner

The credits section for this book begins on page 471 and is considered an
extension of the copyright page.

Contents

4

FOSSILS AND EVOLUTION   61

5

ROCKS AND TIME   79

13

THE ORDOVICIAN-SILURIAN: THE WATER PLANET   229

14

THE DEVONIAN: THE GREAT INVASION   257

15

THE CARBONIFEROUS: AN END AND A BEGINNING   279

16

THE PERMIAN   303

17

THE TRIASSIC AND JURASSIC   321

20

THE NEOGENE   401

Preface

This book is written for both nonscience and science majors as an introduction to historical geology. Although it is likely that many students will have already taken an introductory physical geology or earth science course, this background is not assumed. Accordingly, the book stands on its own and presents a comprehensive picture not only of earth's history but also of the geological forces that have shaped it.

In studying the broad field of geology at an introductory level, many students are surprised that the basic concepts can be discussed without reference to geologic time. Although students are told that geology is a historical science, a good deal of the subject matter in an introductory text is concerned with "here and now" geology. Although exciting concepts and fascinating new ways of looking at our world are revealed in such courses, it is when we delve into the past and attempt to read the record in the rocks as a sequential account that the subject matter evokes a new fascination. It was the search for answers to questions about the origin and age of the earth, rather than an interest in observed geologic processes, that laid the scientific foundation of geology.

No investigation of any geologic feature, phenomenon, or process can proceed very far without an awareness of the time dimension. That most people are curious about time is evident when we consider that the first question just about everyone asks when looking at a rock or fossil is "How old is it?" It is such a simple but vital question that a book about historical geology sets out to answer.

Although an account of geological processes and change leads to an awareness of time, fossils do much to reinforce that awareness and help make the immensity of geologic time more understandable and even believable. The fossil record and the story it tells of the evolution of life on this planet are surely what a large part of historical geology is all about. This is why a considerable portion of this text is concerned with such topics. There is no question that it is fossils that often draw people to geology. It is a rare person who has not been intrigued by dinosaurs at some point in growing up and acquiring an education. On the other hand, in many ways the humbler fossil remains of the invertebrate hosts play a more important role in fostering interest, for the simple reason that they are more accessible. They can be found almost everywhere and, so, are *collectible.*

The organization of this book is conventional in the sense that the first part is concerned with the fundamental principles that are particularly relevant to historical geology, whereas the remaining 11 chapters deal with earth history. This approach needs no justification because it is the simplest and, therefore, probably the best. The standard geologic time scale is used as the framework for chapter organization, and no attempt has been made to seek other, so-called natural divisions, such as the sequences used by some authors. It is often forgotten that the original systems of the nineteenth-century geologists were established as biostratigraphic units. For all practical purposes, they still are biostratigraphic units and, because the pace of earth history is measured in large part by the fossil record, a calendar of earth history based on evolving life forms is the only truly natural one.

In an account of earth history, there is always the question of how much of the world to cover. Because the book is intended primarily for North American students, this is where the emphasis should be. At the same time, so much is important outside of North America that some excursions farther afield are often called for. For long periods of history, North America did not even exist as a separate continent; in discussing such times, some expansion of our territorial limits is obviously called for. Paleogeographic maps are the key to understanding the world pictures, and this book is generously supplied with such maps. A key to symbols used on each paleogeographic map is supplied below.

Throughout this text, but particularly in the first part, many concepts are discussed as part of the history of the science of geology, and the personalities involved are introduced. It is important that students realize that science is ongoing; thus, the most recent findings are presented not as cut and dried facts but as hypotheses to be tested. Numerous examples are given of studies that can be described as still on the cutting edge of science and that may yet be discarded. This is the way science works and, even at this introductory level, it is an important point to make; particularly is it necessary in the case of nonscience majors.

A textbook of this type does not require detailed reference annotations. Each chapter closes with suggestions for further reading. At the same time, the authors of many of the more important concepts and advances are introduced informally and their professional affiliations mentioned, although it is realized, and has been pointed out by at least one reviewer, that people have a habit of changing affiliations and that such references tend to "date" the book. It is hoped that the reader makes allowances for this. Be that as it may, science is done by real people, and getting this point across is also important.

Ancillary Materials

Vanished Worlds is accompanied by an instructor's manual, a test item file, a testpak, and a transparency set. The instructor's manual was written to assist the instructor in lecture preparation. It includes instructor's notes to highlight key ideas and themes and answers to the end-of-chapter questions. The test item file is bound with the instructor's manual and includes approximately 500 multiple-choice and true/false questions. The test item file is also available on Testpak, a computerized test bank. Testpak is available for IBM, Macintosh, and Apple computers. There are 40 transparency acetates of selected paleogeographic maps, charts, schematic drawings, and conceptual diagrams.

Acknowledgments

This book owes much to the input of its reviewers; their guidance and many helpful comments and suggestions have contributed a great deal. I sincerely appreciate their help and I extend my thanks to Allen H. Johnson, West Chester University; John R. Huntsman, UNC–Wilmington; John Howe, Bowling Green University; Richard A. Laws, UNC–Wilmington; Gene Robinson, James Madison University; and Mark Camp, University of Toledo.

The manuscript was typed by Cynthia Mischler and without her hard work, enormous patience, and never-failing cheerfulness the project would not have been possible. To her go my most grateful thanks and appreciation.

The support and wise advice offered by the editorial staff of Wm. C. Brown Publishers have been invaluable and my sincere thanks go to Bob Fenchel, Diane Beausoleil, Jodi Wagner, and Elise Burckhardt. Mary Monner's editing of the typescript was truly outstanding, and her contribution has improved the book enormously.

Last but not least the support and encouragement of my wife Mary, my son Christopher, and my friend Beulah are gratefully acknowledged.

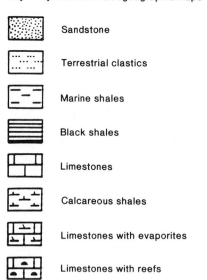

Key to Symbols on Paleogeographic maps

Sandstone

Terrestrial clastics

Marine shales

Black shales

Limestones

Calcareous shales

Limestones with evaporites

Limestones with reefs

VANISHED WORLDS

An Introduction to
Historical Geology

1

A MATTER
OF TIME

Introduction

When Neil Armstrong first set foot on the moon on 21 July 1969 and astronauts later began exploring the lunar surface and sampling rocks, they had, in effect, traveled back in time. As pictured in Figure 1.1, the landscape over which they walked had remained virtually unchanged for more than 3 billion years. Moreover, their footprints on the moon probably will still be discernible millions of years into the future!

Such vast periods of time are almost beyond comprehension, but geologists and astronomers deal with them routinely in their study of the earth, the solar system, and our galaxy. By contrast with the moon, landscapes on the earth are often altered beyond recognition in only a few million years, sometimes even in a few hours (Figure 1.2). Our home in space is a planet where, in the cosmic scheme of things, change is very rapid. On the other hand, in human terms, changes that take place over millions of years are hardly rapid. Even time spans of hundreds of years seem long. Thus, dealing with time is a question of scale, and some adjustment in ordinary thinking is necessary when we consider geologic processes.

During the formative years of geology as a science, the great time intervals involved was one of the most difficult concepts to grasp, and it is still a difficult concept for beginning students today. We will discuss the numerous ways of measuring time in later chapters; however, none is of much concern to us unless there is some kind of record in the rocks.

Historical geology is that vital aspect of geology that considers geological phenomena in the time context and attempts to assemble an account of what has gone before. Drawing upon data from every branch of geology, and also from fields outside of geology, historical geology endeavors to restore vanished worlds (Figure 1.3) and to visit landscapes that have long since disappeared in the mists of time (Figure 1.4). Initially, at least, historical geology is concerned with extrapolation from the present into the past. It is only logical to attempt a reconstruction of the past in terms of what can be seen at the present day.

Many geologic features and processes can be described under the heading of what might be called "here-and-now" geology, usually termed physical geology. Indeed, we can learn a great deal about the basics of geology with little need to refer to the time frame in which

FIGURE 1.1

The lunar surface near the landing site of *Apollo 15*. (NASA Photograph.)

FIGURE 1.2
The Po Shan road landslide, Hong Kong, 18 April 1972.
(Photo courtesy Hong Kong Government, Geotechnical Control Office.)

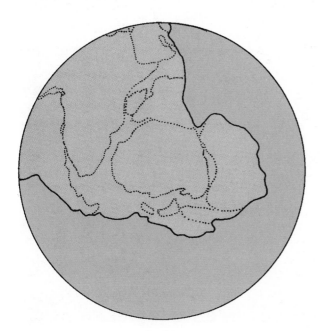 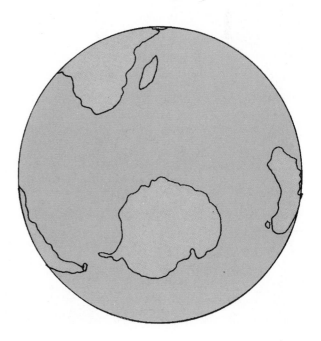

FIGURE 1.3
(a) The ancient continent of Gondwana, a vanished world, viewed from a point over the South Pole. (b) The earth today from the same point in space.

many geologic phenomena operate. Sand accumulating on a lake bed, for example, eventually will likely become sandstone; however, apart from some awareness of processes such as cementation and lithification, the essential features of the sand—its mineralogy, texture, and sedimentary features; its source; and its sedimentary environment—can all be discussed in terms of what we can see actually happening today. Similarly, if the erosional processes responsible for landform evolution can be viewed in progress and over a period of perhaps 50 to 100 years, then probably much of the variability in rate and magnitude of the processes will have been observed.

The Record in the Rocks

The varied surface of the earth can be described in terms of different environments, such as hills and lowlands, river valleys, beaches, shallow lagoons, deep ocean basins, and so on. In virtually all of these places, sediment accumulates—pebbles in the bed of a stream, sand on beaches, muds in ocean basins. Just as such sediments vary today, so did the sediments laid down in environments of the geologic past vary also.

During the first half of the nineteenth century, new ideas on geology and earth history began to emerge. One of the most important steps forward was marked by the realization that the geologic processes observed at the present time have been in operation for countless ages in the past, and furthermore, that past geologic processes were responsible for the rocks and features of the present earth. From this principle of **uniformitarianism**, we can logically assume that many sedimentary environments of the past were similar to those that exist today, and thus that many ancient sedimentary rocks can be compared to modern sediments. This principle is not inviolable, however, because time is inevitably a factor. Many of the geologic processes operating on the earth today do so within great cycles, some of the cycles lasting thousands or even millions of years. It follows, therefore, that conditions that existed at certain times in the geologic past may not necessarily be duplicated on the present-day earth, but presumably will again be evident in future times.

The record of sequential geologic events contained in the sedimentary rocks can often be read only with difficulty. Sometimes, the clues to past environments are very subtle and even ambiguous. In **stratigraphy,** the science of

FIGURE 1.4

A Mississippian landscape, the view that would greet a time traveler arriving 330 million years into the past. Forests of scale trees were spreading across the land, as were the first land-dwelling animals in the form of insects and amphibians. *(From a mural at the Royal Ontario Museum, Toronto, Canada.)*

stratified rocks, two main sources of data are available: One source is the rocks themselves; the other is what is referred to as the **field relationships** of the rocks, including their sequential succession as noted and measured in **stratigraphic sections**, and their areal distribution and lateral changes as pictured in **geologic maps.**

FIGURE 1.5
Sedimentary rock strata. Turbidites of Ordovician age.

In the case of the rocks themselves, their constituent minerals, textures, and many internal structures can be examined with a hand lens, and much can be learned in the field. In the laboratory, more sophisticated analyses are possible. Perhaps the most common procedure is to prepare thin sections in which the rock sample is ground down paper thin, to near transparency. Then, even the smallest mineral grains can be examined under the petrographic microscope. The nature of the mineral grains and their relationships to each other within the fabric of the rock can reveal a good deal about the past history of the rock—not only its depositional environment, but also the earlier history of the grains from their time of origin from a magma or parent rock and the rock's postdepositional history.

Geologic maps and stratigraphic sections demonstrate the gross relationships of bodies of rock to one another. **Sedimentary rocks** are made up of successive strata, each stratum having a particular thickness and character (Figure 1.5). In stratigraphic successions, the geologist is concerned with measuring and sampling outcrop sections (Figure 1.6). Much the same sort of procedure is followed in the subsurface, using borehole samples and constructing logs.

One of the earliest laws promulgated in geology was proposed by Nicolaus Steno in 1669. In his **law of superposition,** Steno pointed out that, in a stratigraphic succession undisturbed by folding, the oldest strata are at the bottom and the youngest are at the top. In measuring the

(a)

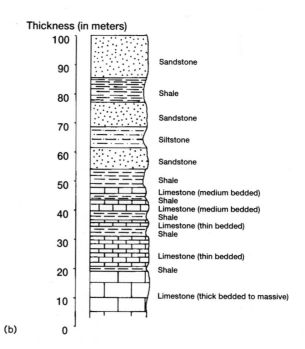

(b)

FIGURE 1.6
(a) Landscape profile of tilted strata. (b) A typical stratigraphic section. The symbols for the different rock types are standard. Thicknesses may be presented on a linear scale, as shown. The irregular line of the section's right margin is a convention to show the relative resistance to weathering. Thus, the shales are soft and recessive compared with sandstones and limestones.

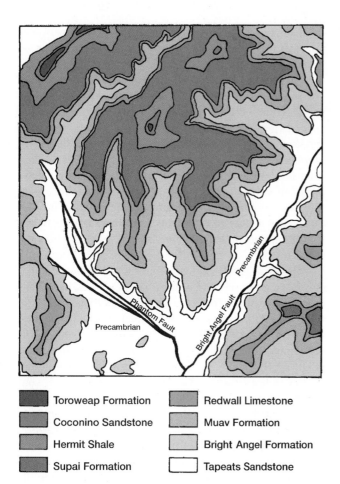

Precambrian

Phantom Fault

Bright Angel Fault

Precambrian

Toroweap Formation	Redwall Limestone
Coconino Sandstone	Muav Formation
Hermit Shale	Bright Angel Formation
Supai Formation	Tapeats Sandstone

FIGURE 1.7
Simplified portion of a typical geological map: the U.S. Geological Survey Grand Canyon sheet.

face of a cliff and noting the changes in the strata from bottom to top, the geologist is, in effect, traveling forward through time.

In geologic mapping, the extent of individual rock bodies, each with its unique characteristics, is plotted and the relationships to other adjacent (overlying and under-lying) rock bodies shown (Figure 1.7). Rock bodies considered as mappable units are referred to as **formations.** Geologic maps show how the physical characteristics of rock formations in an area may gradually or sometimes abruptly change when traced over any distance.

Consider, for example, a modern sea floor. A sandy bottom in one area may give way to a muddy or gravelly bottom somewhere else. This change often is related to variation in water depth. When we consider that most sedimentary rocks are formed from sediments that were originally deposited on a sea floor somewhere, the observed lateral changes in rock formations become more explicable. Almost all sedimentary rocks are stratified, with each stratum, or bed, being separated from the one below and above by a **bedding plane.** Bedding planes are more than just partings along which the rocks split; they represent a

pause in sediment accumulation. For a short span of time—perhaps measured in days, weeks, months, or even years—they were the actual beds of the seas or lakes on which the particular sediments were being laid down. In effect, they are fossil sea floors and commonly also reveal the fossil remains of the animals and/or plants that lived on the ancient sea bottom.

In looking at a modern seabed as an environment both for the deposition of sediment and for animals and plants, geologists describe it in terms of water depth, water temperature, salinity, the amount of sediment in suspension, and so on. To what extent can a sedimentary rock be described in terms of these same environmental parameters? In other words, can geologists reconstruct the environment that existed on some ancient sea floor by studying the rocks? Usually, the combined field data and laboratory results allow this to be done with some degree of confidence. Even when the past environment was likely very different from that of the present, geologists can make a reasonable extrapolation on the basis of known physical and chemical laws.

Gaps in the Record

Unfortunately, the whole of geologic history is not evident in the sedimentary record, laid down layer upon layer as the centuries rolled by. Just as historians frequently find portions of archives missing or destroyed, so do geologists find gaps in the sedimentary record. To express geological history in terms of a diary, most of the pages are blank, torn out, or obliterated by age.

All sedimentary successions represent the result of an alternation between three states: (1) Sediment is being deposited, (2) no sediment is being deposited, and (3) sediment that had been deposited is being eroded away. On a local scale, these three states may alternate over intervals of hours, days, months, or years, being controlled by such factors as the amount of sediment delivered to the area (perhaps by a river) and the strength of the current or wave action, which, in turn, usually is controlled by the depth of the water.

On the whole, therefore, whether sedimentary processes provide a good or poor record of contemporary or past events is a matter of chance. In any event, episodes of uplift and erosion in later time will likely remove the accumulated record, as can be seen in Figure 1.8. Moreover, the older the rocks, the more it seems a minor miracle that they are preserved at all.

Geologists discovered many years ago that, in most geologic successions, there is more gap than record. Although this observation might be taken to indicate that the task of trying to put together a coherent picture is hopeless, in fact, things are not nearly as bad as they seem. While in any one locality, the preserved strata are likely to contain only a fragment of the record of passing time,

FIGURE 1.8
A small-scale erosion surface within a bedded sedimentary succession. This shows that sediment accumulation was not continuous but was periodically interrupted with small-scale erosion and removal of previously formed sediment.

in another place, while the record is probably just as fragmentary, it may contain some account of the time unrecorded at the first locality.

By analogy, if we took a novel and randomly tore out 95 percent of the pages, it would seem reasonable to assume that only a fragmentary, and likely distorted, version of the story could be reconstructed. Now suppose that 95 percent of the pages were also randomly removed from 9 additional copies of the same novel. Putting together the pages from all 10 copies could likely result in a much more complete story. Some of the remaining gaps might be filled, at least partially, by intelligent interpolation.

This analogy illustrates exactly how historical geology is investigated. Nowhere is there a complete stratigraphic record, but piecing together the fragments allows for some understanding of the whole. Even when no real improvement on a fragmentary record is possible (that is, only one novel is available), the situation is not hopeless. After all, even with only 5 percent of the original pages, it might be possible to say whether the novel was a romance, a detective story, a western, or science fiction; almost certainly, most of the main characters would be identified also.

Geologists work with fragments. A proper understanding of the geologic history of a region never results from a single effort; invariably, the history is pieced together bit by bit over many years and incorporates the work of many individuals. One of the most fascinating aspects of geology, particularly on the historical side, is that

something always remains to be discovered. In fact, the more geologists learn about the geologic history of an area, the more they are likely to uncover additional problems to be solved.

Reading the Rocks

All of the data and all of the later interpretation and the piecing together of geologic history begin with rock and fossil samples, field notes, and sketches from field geologists. For purposes of illustration, let us consider a typical geologic section with coal beds in the eastern United States. As shown in Figure 1.9, immediately below the coal bed is siltstone containing plant fossils and, below that, cross-bedded sandstone, the texture and other features of which indicate that it was originally deposited on a riverbed. Above the coal bed is siltstone containing marine fossils and, above the siltstone, is limestone, also with marine fossils. Clearly, the rock types at this locality were deposited over an interval of time during which sedimentary environments were undergoing marked changes. An interpretation of these changes reveals that the area was initially a coastal plain traversed by streams. A progressive subsidence of the land or a rise in sea level (the sedimentary record is ambiguous as to which) gradually turned the area into a swamp. Plant debris from the lush vegetation growing in the swamp accumulated to ultimately form the coal bed. A further encroachment of the sea brought the swamp conditions to an end, and mud was laid down on top of the swamp deposits. The remains of shallow-water marine organisms are found in these sediments. As the water became deeper and increasingly free of suspended sediment, limestone, derived from the skeletal remains of marine organisms, was deposited on top of the muds.

This succession of rock types provides a glimpse of geologic changes that were taking place over a time span of probably several hundred thousand years. What it records is a **marine transgression**, a phase during which sea level rose and flooded inland across the swamp. As will become clear in later chapters, much of geologic history is concerned with sea-level fluctuation, and much of the marine sedimentary record contains evidence of marine transgressions and **marine regressions**, the latter referring to retreats of the sea.

A good deal of the discussion to this point has concerned sedimentary rocks. This is hardly surprising because sedimentary rocks form on the earth's surface, which is where many of the changes through geologic history, not to mention the evolution of life-forms, are taking place. However, geologic history is certainly not recorded only in sedimentary rocks. Other kinds of rocks and a great variety of geologic features also have a story to tell.

For example, among the major happenings in geologic history are continental collisions and the formation of great ranges of mountains. The evidence for these events

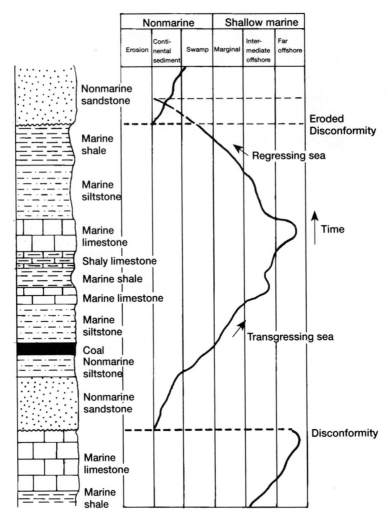

FIGURE 1.9
A stratigraphic succession recording a marine advance
(transgression) and then retreat (regression).

FIGURE 1.10
Highly metamorphosed sediments. What originally was likely
a succession of sandstones, or siltstones and shales is now
highly contorted, altered, and intruded.

is best seen in folded, faulted, and metamorphosed rocks
(Figure 1.10). Large intrusions of granite into the roots
of mountain chains are also characteristic. In the Appalachian Mountains, for example, a much clearer picture
of what happened when Europe and North America collided is derived from a study of the structures and from
metamorphic and intrusive history than from any succession of sedimentary rocks.

Erosion is also part of the story. With respect to the
historic record, it might seem that erosion is akin to tearing
out the pages of the diary, but this is not necessarily the
case. Gaps in the stratigraphic record should not be con-
strued merely as missing pages; they are, themselves, often
significant parts of the history of a region and must be
evaluated as such.

Fossils

In providing a record of past faunas and floras, **fossils**—the remains of organisms from the geologic past preserved in the rocks—play as big a role in deciphering earth history as anything else. Some would argue that the story they tell is the most important because it is the story of life. In the solar system at least, earth appears to be the sole abode of life, which makes our planet unique. The account of the evolution of organisms—from their primitive beginnings early in earth's history to the emergence of humans—makes for fascinating reading. The only setting for this story is the planet itself, and the history of the earth and the history of life are best not separated. Historical geology must give both accounts.

Fossils have many uses. Apart from their general interest, they have provided the evidence for a new way of looking at evolution itself and have led to the emergence of new models in explaining evolutionary mechanisms.

A second role that fossils play is as environmental indicators: They often provide information that even the most detailed analysis of a sedimentary rock cannot. For example, a significant change in a marine environment might be an increase in water temperature, perhaps due to climatic change. Such a change would not necessarily be accompanied by any change in the character of the sediments, but it would be easily detected by changes in the composition of fossil biotas (the flora and fauna of a region).

A third role of fossils is that they can be used to determine the age of rocks—a role that for practical purposes might be considered the most important within the context of historical geology. They do not, of course, contain any intrinsic indicators of their age in terms of real time (that is, time measured in years) and can only establish a relative age. On the other hand, if there is a known relationship between fossiliferous rocks and intrusive rock bodies, the real-time age of which has been established, most commonly through radiometric dating, the fossils can then be used in fine-tuning the real-time chronology. Fossils also provide the means of organizing sedimentary successions and of correlating them across the world. Because they record evolutionary change, an ongoing and nonreversible process through time, fossils can be used to construct what is termed a **biostratigraphic calendar.** Without such a calendar, our understanding of earth history would be much diminished. Reliance on radiometric dating alone would yield only a blurred picture of earth history, especially in the last 570 million years since the first appearance of a usable fossil record.

From Myths to Facts— The Growth of a Science

Historical geology is not about the history of geology but about the history of the earth. Nevertheless, an account of how the science of geology evolved is worthwhile. In earlier times, much of what we call physical geology was taken for granted, and it was more the historical aspects of geology that excited curiosity. Aside from those who believed in some kind of mystical origin for the earth, like that described in the first and second chapters of the Book of Genesis, many people through the years have wondered about the earth's origin. Of perennial interest was the age of the earth.

The discovery of the link between the present and the past was perhaps the most important step in the evolution of the science of geology. It led to an immediate appreciation of the earth's great antiquity and can be said to mark the beginning of modern geology. James Hutton (1726–1797) took this first step when in 1795 he published his great work *Theory of the Earth.*

The story of geology did not begin with James Hutton, however, and instead, we must go back over 2,000 years to gain some insight into what the ancients thought about such subjects as rocks, fossils, and the earth's origin. The growth of knowledge about the earth has been a long and painful process, at certain times advancing and at others slipping into decline. Some of the earliest observations on geological subjects were made, perhaps not surprisingly, by the ancient Greeks.

Science in the Ancient World

Many believe that the classical Greeks were very knowledgeable about science and that much of their knowledge later was forgotten or that their writings were destroyed or lost during the so-called Dark Ages. How accurate is this idea? Did the Greeks, for example, understand the nature of rocks, fossils, and geologic processes? Had they discovered how old the earth was? The answers to these questions are mixed.

Such scholars as Thales, born around 636 B.C., had come to some surprisingly modern conclusions about such things as coastal erosion and river deposition of sediment. The works of other writers also clearly indicate that the Greeks were aware of fossils. On the other hand, despite their often remarkably up-to-date interpretations of natural phenomena, they were no more able to come to any conclusion about the age of the earth or geologic time than were the scholars of later times. Plato (428–347 B.C.), for example, was obliged to fall back on the concept of a deity, a "Divine Craftsman" as he put it. This craftsman supposedly devised and set in motion the universe as a means of imposing order on the raw material of the world, according to timeless mathematical laws. Plato was vague about when this creation took place, but it must have been previous to approximately 9,000 years earlier because Greek legend spoke of a war between the Athenians and the Atlantians at that time. Aristotle (384–322 B.C.), for his part, had no problem with the concept of creation, or of the age of the earth, because he believed in a steady-state universe. In his view, the world and everything on it, together with the heavenly bodies, were eternal.

Above all, what made the Greeks different was that, unlike the thinkers of later times, they were unhindered by restrictions set by a religious establishment. At least in the intellectual sphere, the Greeks did not take their gods very seriously, and so were not continuously looking over their shoulders or forced to retract when their discoveries stepped beyond the bounds of some official religious revelation. The Greeks had access to no more information than did scholars in later times. They had developed no experimental science to speak of and were in no position to acquire data that were unavailable to later generations. What they were able to do was to speculate freely on what they saw. This was a promising beginning to science, but it did not last.

When the Dark Ages began is a matter of debate. To many scholars, their beginning was marked by the decline of the western half of the Roman Empire and the rise of Islam and Christianity. To others, a more definite date was set by the destruction of that great center of learning of the ancient world, the library at Alexandria. A few years before that, in 415 A.D., Hypatia, generally considered the last of the great classical Greek thinkers, had died. Her death, at the hands of a mob incited by Archbishop Cyril, is in some ways symbolic of what was happening in the ancient world. Secular thinking was inundated by the increase in mysticism that was inevitable with the rising power of the Catholic church in Europe.

Medieval Science

Christian philosophy had inherited from the Jews a great preoccupation with history—not history in the sense we think of it today, however. Instead, it was concerned with time, both past and future, and it also was mingled inextricably with prophecy. Many historic events were seen as the manifestations of events prophesied many years before. The world's future was believed to rest on waiting for happenings that would be heralded by certain signs and portents. In general, such matters were considered of much greater importance than any concern with the physical world. The minds of western philosophers and thinkers of the Middle Ages in Europe were occupied with such topics as the next world that would follow the destruction of the present world, the millennium, and the second coming. In many ways, these early ideas considerably influenced later scholars because prophecy was to provide the basis for the calculations used in determining the age of the earth and also the timetable of the ultimate ending. The question of the earth's origin and age were not subjects for scientific speculation; after all, everything was spelled out in the Book of Genesis, and no one, it seemed, was in the least curious as to *when* the seven days of the Creation had been or how long each was.

Oddly enough, it was the rise of fundamentalist Protestantism that eventually led to questions about when the Creation had occurred. Presumably as a reaction to Catholicism, some of the early Protestant clerics paid much closer attention to the Bible, seeing it as a literal account, rather than interpreting it largely allegorically, as many of the great Catholic Christian scholars had done. One example of this meticulous scrutiny of biblical texts was the study made by John Lightfoot, a Greek scholar at Cambridge University, who in 1644 announced that the Creation had begun at 9:00 A.M. on 17 September 3928 B.C. Six years later, Archbishop James Ussher, Primate of Ireland, concluded that Lightfoot's data were incorrect and that the Creation had occurred at the "entrance" of the night preceding October 23, 4004 B.C. The words of Ussher, not unexpectedly, carried more weight than did those of Lightfoot, so Ussher's date came to represent the official Anglican position on the question of the earth's age and even was noted as such in the margin of the Authorized Version of the Bible right up to 1910.

In retrospect, it seems likely that Ussher simply borrowed his data from others, one of whom was Martin Luther. Luther, in the tradition of earlier students of prophecy, believed that the earth would end after 6,000 years—that is, at the millennium in 2000 A.D. His year of creation was thus 4000 B.C. In the meantime, astronomer Johannes Kepler (1571–1630), in correlating the date of the crucifixion with the cycle of solar eclipses, detected an error of four years in the Christian calendar, which meant that the date of Christ's birth actually had been 4 B.C. In taking Luther's date, Ussher simply applied the Kepler correction to arrive at his 4004 B.C. Pronouncements like these meant, of course, that anyone with differing views was guilty of heresy, and in some circumstances, even in danger of imprisonment or worse, such was the power of the church.

One person who apparently was not too bothered by such strictures was Count Georges deBuffon (1707–1788), a distinguished French nobleman. Because he was well known at court, he could get away with statements that other people, perhaps, could not. This was fortunate because, in the course of writing what was to prove, in effect, an encyclopedia of natural science, deBuffon ran into trouble with the religious authorities over some of his views on cosmology and geology. He was forced to write a formal retraction in 1749. Twenty-five years later, he published the results of studies designed to determine the earth's age.

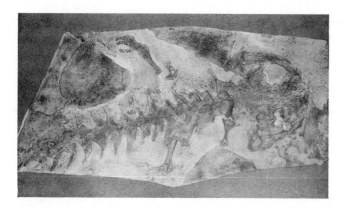

FIGURE 1.11

Homo diluvii testis ("man who witnessed the Flood"). This fossil of a giant salamander, first discovered in the eighteenth century, was believed to be part of a human skeleton—in fact, the remains of someone who had lived before the Noachian Deluge described in the Book of Genesis.

DeBuffon had experimented with the cooling rates of spheres of differing sizes and compositions (iron and other metals). From his observations, he compiled a list of the times needed for the cooling of not only the earth, but all the other planets as well, from white heat down to a temperature where life could exist. His long and involved calculations arrived at 74,047 years for the age of the earth. He later modified this figure to take into account the sun's radiant heat; the final number was 74,832 years. Having already had firsthand experience with the church's displeasure, deBuffon went to considerable lengths to reconcile his calculations with the biblical account and proposed that, as far as the earth was concerned, the seven days of creation were an allegorical reference to what were, in fact, geologic epochs, ranging from 3,000 to 35,000 years in length. Whether deBuffon really believed in the biblical connection is doubtful, but, as it turned out, his figure for the age of the earth made no real contribution in the advance of geology as a science. It was to be some years before any further attempts were made to dispute the "official" age of the earth.

DeBuffon was not alone in trying to reconcile observational data with the biblical account; later scholars turned from the account of creation to another part of the Book of Genesis, that concerned with Noah's Flood. If anything could reconcile geology and the Bible, this would. The evidence for the Deluge was everywhere to be seen in rock strata, contorted rocks, and most particularly, in the fossils that were clearly the remains of animals drowned in the Flood (Figure 1.11). An immediate problem arose, however. Even a cursory study of rock strata showed that they contained successive faunas and floras that were often remarkably different from one another. This observation could lead to only one conclusion: There had been not one, but many floods. The world had been visited apparently by such catastrophes many times in its history.

The Catastrophists

The idea that the earth's history had been spelled out in a series of catastrophic events held considerable appeal to many people during the formative years of modern geology—that is, between 1750 and 1850—for several reasons. For one, the successive faunas and floras found in stratified successions demonstrated marked changes in composition. The most logical explanation for these changes, at least as it seemed to many paleontologists of that time, was that they represented successive creations, each ultimately being destroyed and replaced, in turn, by the next.

One of the strongest advocates of this view was Georges Cuvier, (1769–1832), often considered the founder of scientific paleontology. Cuvier believed that the many discontinuities in the stratigraphic succession were worldwide in extent and marked complete extinction of all species. He also believed that all species were the outcome of distinct creation events and were fixed and immutable. He was vehemently opposed to what he considered the preposterous ideas put forward by Jean Lamarck (1744–1829) and others that species could change over time!

Considerable support for this **catastrophist** viewpoint was found among those (Cuvier included) who sought to reconcile geological observation with the biblical account, as found in the Book of Genesis. To these people, Noah's Flood fit in nicely as the latest of the catastrophes, humans only being present in the two latest epochs. Although still a very long way from an accurate account of earth history, the official catastrophist view did concede a great age for the earth, placing the Deluge at about 5,000 to 6,000 years ago, and with antediluvian time stretching back indefinitely before that. In that sense, at least, it was a considerable improvement on the idea that the earth was only about 6,000 years old.

During the early years of the nineteenth century, the catastrophist view was not by any means the stance of what today some probably would consider a lunatic fringe. It was, in fact, in many ways argued just as scientifically as any other theory. Quite apart from the fossil evidence for successive creations, a catastrophist view of earth history seemed quite plausible to many people for the simple reason that they had experienced natural catastrophes, such as volcanic eruptions, great floods, and earthquakes, firsthand.

The obvious changes in the earth's surface wrought during such catastrophic events could be much more readily appreciated than could the small changes supposedly going on very slowly all the time. Many of these changes take place so slowly that they are imperceptible even over a whole lifetime (Figure 1.12). Even after 100 years, many landscapes seem entirely unchanged. Even in places where changes occur quite rapidly, such as along riverbanks and eroding shorelines, most of the obvious changes happen during times of flood or storms, so again, in the total scheme of things, unusual events

(a)

(b)

FIGURE 1.12
Two views of landscape taken nearly 100 years apart.
(a) Photograph of Bowknot Bend on the Green River in Utah taken in 1871. *(USGS Photograph Hillers 476.)* (b) Photograph taken in 1968 of the same location. *(USGS Photograph Shoemaker 13.)* Note that weathering and erosion over that time interval have made no noticeable change.

sometimes appear to be more important than so-called "normal" events. As it has turned out, geologists today take catastrophic happenings much more seriously than they used to.

Werner and the Neptunists

One of the most controversial figures of eighteenth-century geology was Abraham Gottlob Werner (1750–1817), professor of mineralogy and metallurgy at the mining academy in Freiburg, Germany. A compelling and popular lecturer, Werner attracted a large following of disciples, and his teachings dominated the science of geology during the latter part of the eighteenth century and even into the nineteenth. Unfortunately, much of what Werner taught was incorrect! He believed that all rocks were formed by precipitation from water and that the whole world had once been covered by an ocean that, as it became progressively smaller, left different layers of rock behind. Although Werner did not travel far beyond what is now

Germany, he was aware of the relatively recent emergence of coastlines around the Baltic Sea. This, of course, is due to postglacial rebound of the crust following the disappearance of the Fenno-Scandian ice sheet in the last 18,000 years or so, but to Werner, it probably provided the basis for his hypothesis of a shrinking ocean.

Werner was no catastrophist and not only believed the earth to be very old but was able to construct a timetable of strata based upon his hypothesis. The oldest rocks in his scheme were what he called the Primitive or Primary rocks. Included in this category were granites, gneisses, schists, and all rocks with no fossils. They were found high on mountaintops because they had been precipitated in the oceans when they stood at high levels. Next in age were the Transition rocks, and these comprised sedimentary rocks, such as graywackes, that did contain fossils. According to Werner, these rocks had been formed after the sea had receded somewhat and were often seen to be tilted. Werner ascribed this tilting to their having been precipitated over the old, irregular surface of Primary rocks. Next in Werner's scheme came the Secondary rocks, characterized by being flat-lying and occurring at lower levels. Included here were limestones, sandstones, coals, gypsum, and basalt. Finally came the Tertiary rocks on the lowlands and in valleys, comprising alluvial sands and gravels. Werner's insistence that even lava flows and igneous sills were precipitated in water is hard to understand, his explanation being that they represented rocks heated and melted by the burning of adjacent coal beds.

Werner's pedantic and misguided views were undoubtedly due, in part, to his not having traveled very far beyond his native Saxony; if he had, he might have been influenced by the observations of others, such as Jacques Gueittard (1715–1786), who on visiting the Puy de Dôme in the Auvergne region of France, was much impressed with the importance of volcanic action. Not surprisingly, Italian geologists also had come to the same conclusion that the interior heat of the earth, manifested in volcanic activity, was of great importance in shaping the earth's surface.

Thus, by the close of the eighteenth century, opinions were sharply divided. Werner's teachings became widely disseminated, and his followers became known as "**Neptunists**," while those who focused on volcanic action were dubbed "**Vulcanists**" after the Roman god of fire, or alternately, "**Plutonists**," after the Greek god of the underworld.

James Hutton

Of all the eighteenth-century geologists, it was James Hutton (1726–1797), a Scot and a man of wide interests and liberal education, who made the most significant advance in the science of geology, although his contribution in its entirety was hardly as "scientific" as has been generally believed. Hutton's work has long been believed to be based on observational data but, in fact, this was not entirely the case. His "Theory of the Earth" was largely developed by intuitive means, rather than as a result of the interpretation of field studies. His observations were used to illustrate his theory, rather than the other way around.

Hutton's thesis was that the earth had been created for a definite purpose and that it was, in effect, a sort of world machine whose cyclical mechanisms were seen in the operation of physical processes. According to Hutton, the earth had been constituted as a habitat for the human race, or, as he put it, "peculiarly adapted to the purposes of man," and everything on the earth was subservient to man. In this, of course, Hutton was merely duplicating a familiar Old Testament theme in which man was given "dominion over the earth."

Hutton's teachings had a profound influence because he was the first to point out that the geological features of the earth's surface had been formed by natural processes that still could be observed in operation today. Further, such processes had apparently been going on uniformly for a very long time. Hutton's views were first made public in 1785 in a lecture he delivered before the Royal Society of Edinburgh. When, three years later, they were published in the society's transactions, they were widely criticized. Undeterred, Hutton went on to expand his work into two volumes entitled *Theory of the Earth with Proofs and Illustrations,* published in Edinburgh in 1795. From the geological data he had gathered, Hutton could see no direct evidence for an act of Creation, or for that matter, successive catastrophes, such as Noah's Flood. His statement that "in the economy of the earth, I see no vestige of a beginning, no prospect of an end" summed up his views on the subject.

The vehemence of the criticism leveled at Hutton is somewhat surprising and gives some indication of the strength of the influence of catastrophist views on the one hand and Werner's teachings on the other. It was also undoubtedly due, in part, to Hutton's making no attempt to confront either biblical scholars or proponents of successive creations, global deluges, and the like. He did what was even more infuriating: He ignored them!

For many years into the nineteenth century, all the commanding heights in the intellectual world were held by those with catastrophist views. When Hutton's views became more widely disseminated, however, an opposing or **uniformitarian** school gradually emerged that suggested that all of past geologic history could be interpreted and understood in terms of geologic processes going on and, in many cases, observable at the present day. Much of the credit for this went not to Hutton himself, but to one of his disciples, John Playfair. For all his astute observations and brilliant insight, Hutton's literary style was, to put it mildly, uninspiring, so John Playfair took it upon himself to write *Illustrations of the Huttonian Theory,* which was published, also in Edinburgh, in 1802. Play-

FIGURE 1.13
Sir Charles Lyell (1797–1875).

fair's concise and interesting writing style ensured a wide readership, but it was still many years before the catastrophists, not to mention the Neptunists, were finally routed.

Charles Lyell

While Hutton and Playfair had offered an alternative to catastrophism, they had not, by any means, won the controversy. It was left to Sir Charles Lyell (1797–1875) to win the majority of geologists over to the uniformitarian view of geologic history (Figure 1.13). His *Principles of Geology,* published in three volumes between 1830 and 1833, made an immediate impact. Halfway through the first volume, he had not only demolished the current (that is, nineteenth-century) concept of a special Creation event and biblical chronology, but had disposed of the catastrophists and Neptunists also. He argued that the cumulative effects of step-by-step changes were responsible for all geologic features and that these changes were not always constructive in their effect. Lyell pointed out that erosional processes, for example, are destructive and are responsible for the numerous interruptions in the geologic record. Thus, according to Lyell, the great hiatuses seen by the catastrophists were more or less local in their extent and certainly not caused by global catastrophes. *Principles of Geology* was read so widely that, within 10 years of its first appearance, it was into a sixth edition. Lyell added new findings and refinements constantly, and by the time he died in 1875, 12 editions had been published.

Among those greatly influenced by Lyell's book was Charles Darwin, who read it during his famous voyage on the *Beagle.* He later claimed that no other book made such an impression on him. The relationship between Lyell and

Darwin is a rather curious one because, although implicit in Lyellian uniformitarianism was the concept of a changing and evolving earth, Lyell rejected any ideas of organic progress, believing like Cuvier, that species were fixed and immutable. It was to be some years before he finally came around to Darwin's view, a change duly incorporated into the ninth edition of the *Principles of Geology.*

In one other area of controversy, Lyell never was persuaded to the modern view; this concerned what is now referred to as the Pleistocene glaciation, or the Great Ice Age, as it was known in Victorian times. Louis Agassiz (1807–1873), a Swiss zoologist, had determined correctly that the many erratic boulders, glacial gravels, and moraines in central Europe and elsewhere were evidence for the former extent of glaciers, and being a catastrophist, he concluded that this ice age was one of many catastrophes. He also was a confirmed believer in organic progression, seeing in all of this the working out of a divine plan. Agassiz's views were anathema to Lyell, which may have persuaded Lyell to reject the glacial theory ideas in favor of drifting ice floes and icebergs as the source of glacial deposits. Incidentally, this is why, to this day, such deposits are still referred to as "drift."

The Age of the Earth

To followers of both Lyell and Darwin, and indeed to geologists of all persuasions, the big question of the age of the earth remained unanswered. Believers in uniformitarianism and evolution were convinced that the earth was very old, measured in many hundreds of millions of years. Darwin saw the observable geologic record as representing only a tiny fraction of the sum total of geologic time and concluded that the gaps in the stratigraphic record represented far more time than did the strata between the gaps. This is, as it has turned out, precisely how modern geologists see the stratigraphic record, but to the geologists of the first half of the nineteenth century, it was altogether too pessimistic a view. To Darwin, not only did the magnitude of the gaps in the record point to a very long history for earth, but they were also the reason why the "missing links" between evolving species were not apparent in the fossil record.

Naturally, numerous ideas were put forward in trying to determine the earth's actual age. Thomas Huxley attempted to add up all the sedimentary successions of all ages around the world and to make a master geologic column, the composite nature of this succession supposedly ensuring that it was reasonably complete. In another approach, John Joly,[1] working in England, tried to determine the rate at which salt was added to the ocean and thereby arrive at a minimum age. By coincidence, both

1. In some texts, this salt method is attributed to French physicist Nicholas Joly.

these methods came up with an age of around 100 million years, a figure that no one really accepted.

This was where matters stood when, in 1862, the first of a series of papers by physicist William Thompson (who later became Lord Kelvin) was published, in which he determined the age of the earth on the basis of the laws of thermodynamics as applied to the cooling of the earth from an originally molten state. According to these calculations, even the sun was no more than 500 million years old, whereas the earth had originated somewhere between 20 and 30 million years ago. Even more important, according to Lord Kelvin, the earth would have been cool enough to sustain life no more than a few million years ago. Reminiscent of the calculations of deBuffon of less than 100 years before, the numbers produced by Lord Kelvin's elegant mathematics seemed no more believable.

Matters clearly had reached an impasse, and it was not until the early years of the twentieth century that further progress seemed possible. The discovery of radioactivity by Henri Becquerel in 1896 and the brilliant work by Marie and Pierre Curie around the turn of the century made all the difference. In the course of their decay, radioactive elements give off heat, and minerals containing such elements are quite common in the earth's crust. These discoveries clearly indicated that the earth could no longer be considered as simply a cooling ball obeying the laws of thermodynamics. Not only did radioactivity provide the means of disposing of Lord Kelvin's numbers, but it was to eventually prove to be the key to the riddle of the earth's age.

Although it was some years before the technology necessary for accurate isotopic age determinations was developed, as early as 1902, British physicist Frederick Soddy and New Zealander Ernest Rutherford, at McGill University in Montreal, Canada, had come up with the basic idea. Working with radium, they were able to show that, as decay continued and the number of parent radioactive atoms became fewer, the number of atoms decaying became proportionately fewer (See Figure 6.2). Such information made it possible to determine the rate of decay of a radioactive element. The next step was to ascertain the amount of the accumulated radiogenic material derived from the decay process, and from that calculate the length of time since the decay process started. Following up on the Canadian studies, American Bertram Boltwood, of Yale, who had been working with uranium and its decay products, eventually came up with a formula that would give an age determination. If 1 gram of uranium produces 0.000,000,0076 grams of radiogenic lead per year, the formula would read:

$$\frac{\text{Amount of radiogenic lead} \times 7,600,000,000}{\text{Amount of uranium}}$$

for the number of years since the uranium had begun to decay. By 1907, Boltwood had made determinations using uranium-bearing minerals of many different ages from several parts of the world. His results showed ages as old as 1,640 million years. Although crude by modern standards, Boltwood's ages were certainly in the ballpark, and insofar as the age of the earth was concerned, hinted at many surprises to come.

The long search was almost over. The arguments of so many nineteenth-century geologists and paleontologists for a very old earth finally were vindicated. Scientists now had at their disposal the means of age determination that would grow ever more accurate as technology improved. The big breakthrough came in the late 1920s and early 1930s with the development of mass spectrometers of increasing sensitivity, and age determinations with an accuracy of 3 percent or better are now routine. The subject of radiometric dating is discussed at greater length in Chapter 6.

Uniformitarianism and Actualism

As the science of geology evolved during the nineteenth century, it became clear that, among the clamor of dissenting opinions, those of Hutton, Playfair, Lyell, and the other uniformitarians were the most correct. Yet, in the century or more since the death of Lyell, views on earth history have continued to evolve, and today's ideas are encompassed in what has come to be called an "actualistic" model. **Actualism** embraces what is still, fundamentally, a uniformitarian philosophy, but it takes into account that it is the natural laws that are constant, rather than the results, or processes, themselves. To assume that all the geologic processes of weathering, erosion, deposition, vulcanism, structural deformation, and so on in progress today have always been proceeding at the same rate with the same intensity, or even in the same manner, is certainly incorrect. Even before the end of the nineteenth century, it was obvious that the earth had a beginning that was explicable in terms of celestial mechanisms and crustal evolution. It was also becoming clear that, during the planet's formative years, surface conditions were quite

unlike those of later time. Only in recent years is some understanding of the early evolution of the lithosphere, hydrosphere, and atmosphere emerging. It is possible that plate-tectonic mechanisms, for instance, were somewhat different during the earth's early history, although the details of just how different are still a matter of debate.

Even from much later in the earth's history, the stratigraphic record contains evidence of conditions and events that are not part of the earth as we see it today. For example, at times, there were widespread floodings of the continents by shallow epeiric seas in which thousands of meters of sedimentary rocks were deposited. No such continent-wide seas currently exist, so in this case, the key to the past is certainly not to be found in the present.

There is also the problem of catastrophic happenings in the geologic past. Although the catastrophism ideas that were fashionable in the nineteenth century are not about to be resurrected, geologists are becoming increasingly aware that earth history has not moved along as a continuously flowing stream. Rather, it has, from time to time, been interrupted by cataclysmic changes, the evidence for which is best seen in the fossil record of mass extinctions. It is a widely held view that at least some of these extinction events were triggered by the impact of large meteorites, or possibly comets. Some evidence even suggests that such events have occurred regularly, with a cycle of about 26 million years.

Other unusual or rare events on a smaller scale are also seen as playing a more important role than had previously been supposed. This has raised questions as to the reliability of even the sedimentary record itself. It is suspected that, in some cases, the record of unusual events, such as great storms or floods, is preserved, rather than that of so-called normal events. Rare events, whether they occur only every 26 million years or perhaps every 50 years, appear to have as much, or possibly more, effect on geologic history and on the geologic record than do the day-to-day normal processes that operate in-between. This is hardly uniformitarianism as Charles Lyell saw it.

Summary

The planet earth is a place of change when compared with "dead" worlds like the moon. Both surface and subsurface processes are responsible for the constantly changing conditions on the earth's surface over vast spans of time. Historical geology is that vital aspect of geology that considers geological phenomena in the time context and attempts to assemble an account of what has gone before.

The earth's surface can be described in terms of different environments, such as river valleys, hills, beaches, and ocean basins. Sediment accumulating in these different environments will likely have distinctive features that are diagnostic of these environments. The record of past geological events is, at best, fragmentary, and the gaps in the record often represent more time than does the record itself. However, by piecing together the fragments from many different places, a more complete picture of the geologic history can be constructed.

Fossils play three important roles in historical geology. They provide: (1) evidence for an explanation of the processes of evolution, (2) evidence of past environments, (3) the most accurate means for age correlation.

The story of the growth of geology as a science and earlier ideas on geologic phenomena begins in ancient Greece. Many of the ancient Greek scholars held some quite "modern"-sounding views on such subjects as coastal erosion, sediment deposition, and the nature of fossils. They had, however, little to say about the age of the earth. Unlike later scholars, the Greeks were untroubled by the zealots of an established church.

During the Middle Ages, western scholars turned their thoughts inward, considered the supernatural more important than the natural world, and were more concerned about the end of the world and the second coming.

Some early ideas on the age of the earth were based upon interpretations of the biblical account, and scholars gave a date for the Creation of 4004 B.C. Later, theologians and geologists were concerned with reconciling the account of Noah's Flood with geological evidence. This led many geologists and paleontologists to believe in successive creations, each ended by a great catastrophe. Fossils were considered proof of this hypothesis in representing the remains of animals and plants of past creations.

The Neptunists, led by Abraham Werner, believed that all rocks were formed by precipitation from water and that the whole world had once been covered by an ocean that, as it became progressively smaller, left different layers of rock behind. The Vulcanists believed that the interior heat of the earth, manifested in volcanic activity, was also of great importance in shaping the earth's surface.

The first person to suggest that the earth had undergone slow changes was James Hutton, who in 1795 published *Theory of the Earth with Proofs and Illustrations.* Followers of Hutton were termed uniformitarians, as opposed to catastrophists. Charles Lyell's book *Principles of Geology,* published between 1830 and 1833, quickly popularized the ideas of Hutton and the uniformitarians. Darwin was much influenced by this book.

By the second half of the nineteenth century, the problem of the age of the earth still remained unsolved. Lord Kelvin was the first to apply a scientific method to the problem. In 1862, he calculated, on the basis of the earth as a cooling body and using the laws of thermodynamics, that the earth was no more than 20 to 70 million years old and had likely been cool enough for life only in the past few million years. Few believed these numbers but could find no way to dispute them. The big breakthrough came in 1896 with the discovery of radioactivity and with the later discoveries that heat was generated during radioactive decay and that such heat-generating elements were fairly common in minerals of the earth's crust. Radioactivity not only demolished Kelvin's numbers but eventually provided the means of measuring the earth's age.

The modern view of uniformitarianism is somewhat modified from that of Lyell and others. Today, the concept of actualism is preferred, which suggests that the actual causes, obeying natural laws, are constant and that they control the processes going on at the earth's surface. The rate at which the processes operate and also the manner of their operation have, however, changed through time.

Questions

1. What is the most important difference between the surface of the earth and the surface of the moon?
2. What is the difference between a relative time scale and an absolute time scale?
3. What are the chief controls in the accumulation and preservation of sedimentary successions?
4. What is the law of superposition?
5. The statement is often made that the stratigraphic succession as a whole contains "more gap than record." Explain.
6. What is a marine transgression? Describe how it might be recorded in a sedimentary succession.
7. Name three ways in which fossils help geologists to decipher the past.
8. Describe some of the conflicting ideas on geology in the late eighteenth and early nineteenth centuries.
9. Describe Abraham Werner's stratigraphic classification.
10. Who was James Hutton? How did his work represent a big step forward in our understanding of the earth?
11. Give some account of the contribution made by Charles Lyell to the development of geology as a science.
12. Describe some of the early attempts at measuring the age of the earth.
13. What was the first real scientifically valid evidence for a great age for the earth?
14. What is meant by the actualistic model?
15. Modern geologists accept the fact that earth history has not flowed smoothly but has been periodically interrupted. How do these views differ from catastrophists' views of the early nineteenth century?

Further Reading

Eicher, D. L. 1976. *Geologic time.* 2d ed. Englewood Cliffs, N.J.: Prentice-Hall.

Faul, H., and C. Faul. 1983. *It began with a stone.* New York: Wiley.

Gould, S. J. 1987. *Time's arrow, time's cycles.* Boston: Harvard University Press.

Mather, K. F., and S. L. Mason. 1939. *A source book in geology.* New York: McGraw-Hill.

Press, F., and R. Siever. 1982. *Earth.* San Francisco: W. H. Freeman.

Toulmin, S., and J. Goodfield. 1965. *The discovery of time.* New York: Harper.

Wendt, H. 1970. *Before the Deluge.* Translated from the German by C. Winston. London: Paladin.

2

SEDIMENTARY ENVIRONMENTS— ANCIENT AND MODERN

Introduction

Over geologic ages, sedimentary rocks have been the repository for data about past lands and seas, past climates, past tectonic events, and past life, and many geological findings are based on the record contained in sedimentary rocks. This chapter is concerned with the relationships between sediments, sedimentary rocks, and sedimentary environments, both ancient and modern.

Sedimentary Rocks As a Record of Past Events

"The present is the key to the past." This statement sums up the uniformitarian idea that emerged during the nineteenth century and that has influenced geology ever since. As we saw in Chapter 1, the simplistic version of uniformitarianism required modification, but when it comes to reconstructing ancient environments, geologists still have to begin with the present. After all, they do not possess a time machine to go back and see for themselves, so all they have to work with is the record in sedimentary rocks. In turn, geologists can only understand the sedimentary record by comparing it with modern sediments. What this means in practical terms is that geologists can, for ex-ample, look at a 200-million-year-old Jurassic sandstone and, in comparing it with a modern sand deposit having the same characteristics, be fairly certain that the Jurassic sand was deposited in much the same kind of environment (Figure 2.1). Because nearly all sedimentary rocks can be matched with modern sediments of one kind or another, the sedimentary environments of the geologic past can usually be ascertained. There are, as we shall see, some notable exceptions, where modern analogies do not seem to exist, but in general, this extrapolation from the present into the past and from the past into the present seems to work quite well.

One complicating factor is the **lithification** process that turns sediment into sedimentary rock because it may alter the sediment's original texture or introduce new characteristics that have nothing to do with the original depositional environment. Involved here are what are called **diagenetic processes** that encompass all the changes that occur in the sediment after it is deposited, right up to the time it is destroyed by weathering or altered by metamorphism (Box 2.1).

In sands, lithification is usually due to the precipitation of a chemical cement, commonly calcium carbonate ($CaCo_3$) or silica (SiO_2), in the pore spaces. Muds are transformed into shales as they become more deeply buried. Rising temperature and pressure drive out the

FIGURE 2.1
Comparisons with modern deposits indicate that these Jurassic-age sands in Zion National Park, Utah, were deposited under desert aeolian conditions.

water, and the tiny clay particles then become welded together. The most obvious changes in the lithification of mud involve a 40 to 50 percent or more reduction in volume and the roughly parallel alignment of the flaky clay particles, so that the rock acquires the finely laminated appearance, or fissility, characteristic of shales (Figure 2.2). Compression has little effect on sands because of the roughly spherical shape and also the mechanical strength of the quartz grains. Thus, sandstones rarely show more than a 15 to 20 percent loss of volume. In the case of limestones, the chief diagenetic change is recrystallization— that is, the formation in the solid state of new crystalline mineral grains. Of all the sedimentary rocks, limestones are the most sensitive indicators of depositional environments, but at the same time, they are the most vulnerable to diagenetic change. Their frequent recrystallization into dolostones, particularly in the case of older formations, invariably destroys the original texture (Figure 2.3).

FIGURE 2.2

Pennsylvanian siltstones and shales. Note the extremely fine laminae, dark color, and softness of shales as compared with the lighter and more resistant siltstones.

BOX 2.1

The Origin of Sedimentary Rocks

All sedimentary rocks are derived from earlier generations of rocks exposed to weathering and breakdown at the surface of the earth (the ultimate parent rock being igneous). The only exceptions are the pyroclastic rocks formed from the accumulation of cinders and ash thrown out by volcanic eruptions, a process that does not involve weathering.

Weathering processes can be broadly categorized as either mechanical (for example, frost shattering) or chemical (for example, solution). Mechanical breakdown produces pieces of rock and mineral grains of various sizes, known as clasts. An initial classification of sediment is based on the size of clast (see Box 2.2). Chemical breakdown produces two kinds of material: (1) new minerals, such as clays, formed by the chemical alteration (hydration) of minerals like the feldspars, and (2) material in solution.

Granite is a typical parent rock since it is the most common igneous rock exposed on the continents. A typical granite is made up of the following minerals:

1. Orthoclase feldspar ($KAl.Si_3O_8$), approximately 50 to 60 percent
2. Quartz (SiO_2), approximately 35 to 40 percent
3. Plagioclase (sodic) feldspar ($NaAl.Si_3O_8$), approximately 5 to 10 percent
4. Biotite ($[Mg.Fe]_2K_2Al_2Si_3O_{12}$), less than 10 percent
5. Hornblende ($Ca_2Na[Mg.Fe^2]_4[Al.Fe^3Ti][Al.Si]_8O_{22}[O.OH]_2$), 5 percent or less

How do weathering processes affect granite? The feldspar, hornblende, and biotite (all of which are aluminum silicates) break down into clays (hydrated aluminum silicates), and some proportion also goes into solution. For example, orthoclase breaks down as follows:

(Orthoclase) (Carbonic acid)
$KAl.Si_3O_8 + 2H_2CO_3 + 9H_2O$
(Kaolinite)
$Al_2Si_2Si_2O_5(OH)_4 +$
(Silicic acid)
$4H_4 SiO_4 + 2K$
(Bicarbonate ions)
$+2HCO_3$

Biotite is a mica, extremely friable and brittle, so it is quickly broken up into tiny fragments that are often indistinguishable from clays. Chemically, the micas and clays are also closely related. Quartz is a very tough mineral. Mechanically, it has a hardness of 7 on the Mohs hardness scale and so is harder than steel. Because it has only vague cleavage, it does not split easily. Chemically, it is almost inert. Quartz is, therefore, the only mineral to survive weathering processes and is classified as a **resistate** (a mineral that is extremely tough both in terms of hardness and also in its resistance to chemical attack). Quartz crystals, released from the disintegration of the granite, become sand grains.

Thus, the complete destruction of granite produces three kinds of material:

1. Clays, which eventually become shales
2. Material in solution, ultimately destined to join the other salts in the ocean
3. Resistates, by far the most common being quartz grains, which eventually are deposited and lithified as sandstones

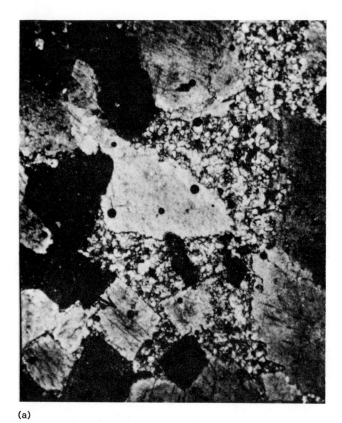

(a)

(b)

FIGURE 2.3

(a) Alteration of limestone by recrystallization involving the process of dolomitization, as seen under the microscope. Note the large, well-formed dolomite crystals growing within the limestone fabric of calcite crystals. (b) Partial dolomitization in the Upper Devonian Palliser limestone, Alberta, Canada. The dark upper part of the bed is dolomitized, the lower pale portion is unaltered limestone.

Except for pyroclastic sediments derived from volcanic eruptions, the ultimate sources of all sediments are earlier generations of rocks exposed at the earth's surface that have been broken down by chemical and mechanical weathering processes (Box 2.1). Complete disintegration of a rock produces material that goes into solution (ending up as salts in the sea) and also solid mineral and rock fragments, known as **clasts.** *Clast* is a general term for any rock or mineral fragment because the term has no size connotation; clasts may range in size from lumps as large as houses to tiny clay particles measured in microns. The Udden-Wentworth size scale for clasts is widely used. (See Box 2.2.) This is a convenient way of categorizing clasts on the basis of their size. Seven major size classes are recognized, ranging from boulders down to the smallest clasts of clay size, which are measured in microns.

History in a Sand Grain

Granite is the most common igneous rock exposed on the continents, so it is the ultimate parent rock of most sediments. As discussed in Box 2.1, simple mechanical breakdown of granite, as a result of frost shattering, for example, produces angular clasts of granite, and these, in turn, break down into mineral grains of quartz, orthoclase (potassium) feldspar, biotite, and any other constituents of the granite. If these mineral grains become deposited as a sediment, they form a special kind of sand, known as arkosic sand, whose total composition likely differs little from the original granite. If, however, the sand is carried away by streams and eventually arrives on a beach, say 2,000 kilometers away, it will have a very different composition and likely consist entirely of quartz. Quartz is extremely tough, having a hardness of 7 on the Mohs hardness scale, and is chemically almost inert. It is hardly surprising, therefore, that it is typically the only mineral to survive 2,000 kilometers of transport and chemical breakdown. Sandstone composition clearly holds important clues, not only as to the nature of the parent rock and the conditions under which it was weathered, but also about the transportational history of the clasts.

If, on the other hand, the granite parent rock was exposed in a wet tropical region and broken down by chemical weathering, only quartz clasts would be produced; the feldspars, micas, and hornblende would be dissolved or transformed into clays. In this case, a pure quartz sand would result without the necessity for long-distance transportation.

BOX 2.2

The Classification of Sedimentary Rocks

There is no simple way of classifying sedimentary rocks, a complex group with diverse origins and depositional environments. One approach is to begin with the material derived from the source rocks (see Box 2.1). This takes care of the majority of common sedimentary rocks. Notably absent because they do not fit into this scheme, however, are the coals and the pyroclastic sediments.

Many different schemes for the classification of sediments and sedi- mentary rocks have been proposed; most are designed for special needs. For our purposes, Box Table 2.1 presents a hybrid classification, partly genetic and partly descriptive (taxonomic).

BOX TABLE 2.1

A Classification Scheme for Sediments and Sedimentary Rocks

Initial Division

Clastic Sediments and Rocks (derived from clasts)

Sediment	Rock	Biogenic	Nonbiogenic (chemical)
*> 256mm Boulders		Most limestones	Evaporites
64–256mm Cobbles } Gravels	Conglomerate		
4–64mm Pebbles		Some cherts	Some cherts
2–4mm Granules			Ironstones
1/16–2mm Sand	Sandstone		Some limestones
1/256–1/16mm Silt	Siltstone		
<1/256mm Clay	Mudrock		

Pyroclastic (derived from volcanoes)

*>64mm Blocks	Volcanic	
Bombs	breccia and	
	agglomerate	
2–64mm Lapilli	Tuff	
< 2mm Ash		

Carbonaceous (derived from plants)

Peat
Coal

Further Divisions

Sandstones (classified on basis of mineral grains)

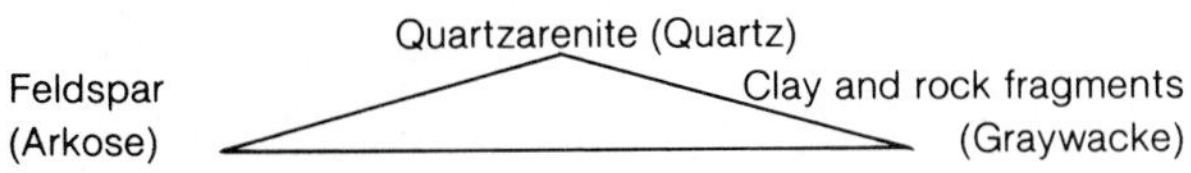

Quartzarenite (Quartz)

Feldspar (Arkose) ——————— Clay and rock fragments (Graywacke)

Note: Triangle depicts proportions of mineral grain types in the three major classes of sandstones.

Limestones (classified on basis of biogenic origins)

Reef limestone
Shelly limestone (Coquina)
Crinoidal limestones
Pellet limestone

Note: More refined classifications of limestones are based on thin-section examination under the microscope.

Siltstones and Mudrocks (classified on the basis of proportions of silt and clay)

	Silt	2/3	1/3	
Nonlaminated	Siltstone	Mudstone	Claystone	
Laminated	Silt shale	Mud shale	Clay shale	
		1/3	2/3	Clay

Udden-Wentworth size classification
Fisher (1961) size classification

These two examples show that mineral composition alone may not always be a reliable indicator of a sediment's past history. Other clues are found, however, in the shape of the mineral grains. The crystalline minerals in a granite are typically angular in shape, and quartz, as the last mineral to crystallize as the magma cools, is particularly irregular in shape and size. In arkosic sand, mentioned earlier, the grains would still be largely angular in shape, whereas in beach sand, they would have become much more rounded and better sorted, with the grains more or less the same size. Such a sand would be described as mature, in contrast to arkosic sand and the sand produced by tropical weathering, both of which would be called immature. Arkosic sand is immature because of the presence of chemically less stable and softer minerals like feldspars and mica; the tropically weathered sand is immature because of the angularity and poor sorting of the quartz grains.

Because quartz grains are so durable, they typically survive many cycles of weathering, erosion, transportation, deposition, and burial. During each cycle, the grains undergo further wear and tear, the weaker grains are broken, and the remainder become ever more rounded. It follows, therefore, that the immediate source of many sands is not a granite but an earlier generation of sandstone, which itself may have been derived from an even older sandstone. Through succeeding cycles, the sands become increasingly mature until, in a so-called supermature sand, the grains consist entirely of quartz or other very resistant grains, such as zircon. Texturally, the sand is very well sorted, with the grains all essentially the same size. Typically also, the grains are all well rounded.

Modern Depositional Environments

On the present-day earth's surface, sediments are accumulating in many different environments, both in the oceans and on land. The most obvious distinction in classifications of sedimentary environments today is the division between land and sea.

In terms of the sedimentary record, sediments laid down in marine environments predominate because they and the fossils contained in them are more likely to be preserved. Terrestrial environments, in contrast, are subject to constant change, so terrestrial sediments are much more likely to be eroded away. Their preservational potential is consequently poor, and it follows that both the sedimentary and fossil records are heavily biased in favor of those of marine origin.

Perhaps, the most natural approach to the study of sedimentary environments is to follow the clastic material derived from the weathering of rocks in a mountain range to its final resting place on the sea floor. En route, it passes through numerous sedimentary environments and may remain in one or more of them for long periods of time, sometimes millions of years.

FIGURE 2.4
Talus slopes of angular debris accumulating at the foot of a cliff.

Nonmarine Environments

In midlatitude mountainous regions, frost shattering is the dominant weathering process, and the initial breakdown of a parent rock produces masses of angular rock fragments that accumulate as talus (rock debris) around the lower slopes (Figure 2.4). Under gravity, this loose material eventually reaches the valley floor and begins its journey as the bed load (the material moved by a stream along its bed) of a stream or perhaps on the surface of, or frozen within, a valley glacier.

Alluvial Environments

Young streams in youthful valleys are typically choked with boulders of all shapes and sizes that constitute a deposit known as a gravel. Wear and tear during downstream transportation of these large clasts, as they are rolled and tumbled along, quickly reduces their size and rounds off sharp corners. As the river expands, the spreads of alluvial gravels become more extensive, and at the same time, the boulders are largely reduced to the size of pebbles. Mixed with the pebbles is coarse sand composed predominantly of quartz grains. Most of the grains are quite angular because water films around small clasts protect the clasts from the attrition that quickly rounds pebbles and boulders. Youthful streams carry most of their load as bed load that only moves intermittently and is typically seen in gravel bars in braided streams and in point bars on the inside bends of streams.

As a river becomes larger and more mature, its course begins to loop and bend in a series of meanders. The valley widens until it is floored by an extensive floodplain, so called because it is periodically covered with water when the river floods and overflows its banks. By this time, the coarser clasts have been left behind, and the alluvial sediment consists mainly of sand- and silt-size particles. The

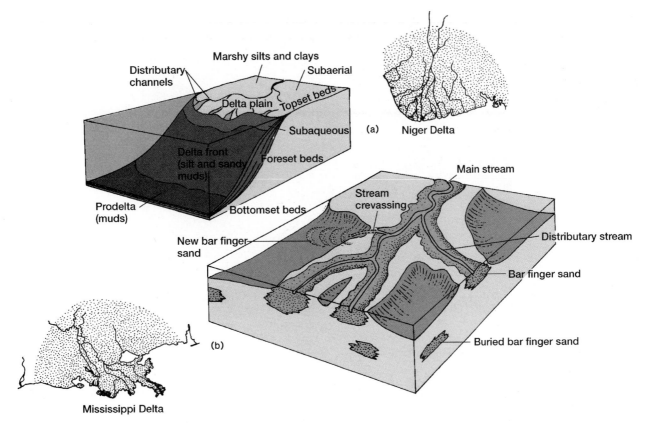

FIGURE 2.5
The sedimentary regimes in (a) a wave-dominated delta and
(b) a fluvial-dominated delta.

sand grains, carried as the bed load, are becoming some-what better rounded. The silt-size and finer material of mica flakes and clay is chiefly carried in suspension, and when the river floods, this suspended sediment is deposited across the floodplain as **alluvium.**

Sands and silts of alluvial origin are quite common in ancient terrestrial successions and can usually be distinguished from marine sands and silts by the presence of mica flakes and feldspar grains; both of these minerals are quickly eliminated once they reach the high-energy environment of the surf zone.

Deltas

A delta is formed when a river drops its load of sediment into a lake or the ocean and the waves and currents do not move the sediment into deeper water or along the coast. The river mouth then becomes blocked, and the main stream splits into many small distributary streams (Figure 2.5).

In terms of sediment volume, deltas are among the most important depositional environments. Smaller, inland deltas in lakes are considered nonmarine because they are formed by rivers and the bulk of their sediment was alluvial in origin. On the other hand, all the major deltas are on the coast, and marine influences are inevitably involved. Indeed, the bulk of the sediment making up the delta mass may actually have been deposited in a marine environment.

In both the short term, measured in only years, and the long term, spanning tens of thousands of years, deltaic sedimentation is typically intermittent and variable. The shifting of distributaries may dramatically alter the configuration of the delta over times as short as months; moreover, shifting of the course of the mainstream and fluctuating sea levels are also responsible for changes over much longer periods.

The delta as a whole is often in a state of unstable equilibrium. It is built out seaward and maintained only by the enormous quantities of riverborne sediment delivered from the continental interior. Once this supply diminishes, coastal erosional processes begin active removal of the sediment until equilibrium is reached between removal and supply. The precarious existence of the delta is further aggravated by the subsidence of the delta silts and muds as the enormous pile of sediment is compressed under its own weight. This alternation of advance and retreat is particularly marked at the mouths of individual distributaries that may be abandoned as a consequence of a pro-

FIGURE 2.6
A cypress swamp in southwestern Florida.

cess known as upstream crevassing. This typically occurs quickly, when the river is in flood and when in overtopping its bank, the river breaks through to establish a new channel (Figure 2.5b).

Maximum sedimentation, characteristically of sands and silts, occurs along the courses of the distributary streams. Between distributaries are swampy lowlands characterized by peats and coals. Ancient delta deposits have been described in successions of many geologic ages. In the Pennsylvanian Period, discussed in Chapter 15, much of the coal of the major coal fields was laid down in deltas, as well as in coastal swamps.

Lacustrine Environments

Along the length of many rivers, local topography or structural features may result in the formation of lacustrine (lake) environments. Some of these lakes fill hollows scoured out by glaciers or formed by structural sagging of the crust. On occasion, a river may be dammed by landslides, lava flows, or glacial ice, although such lakes are, as would be expected, usually short-lived.

Even the largest lakes have life spans that are measured in hundreds of thousands rather than millions of years and so, in terms of geologic time, are considered quite ephemeral features. The reasons for this short life are twofold. As the outlet stream erodes its bed deeper and deeper, the river level and, of course, the lake level drops. From the other direction, the bottom of the lake becomes shallower as it silts up. This is inevitable because streams transport sediment, and as soon as a river enters a lake, the flow ceases, and the sediment settles to the lake floor.

The sedimentary succession and distribution of **facies** (characteristics of a rock that reflect its particular environment deposition) in larger lakes tend to simulate those of many marine environments. Thus, beach sands and deeper water muds are found; even shelly limestones form locally if freshwater mollusks are abundant. Wave energy in a lake, however, is naturally much less than in the ocean, and the differences in water chemistry and lack of tidal movement are also important factors.

Ancient lake deposits are known in successions of various ages but are not common. One of the best known is the Eocene Green River Formation of Wyoming, laid down in a lake that covered large areas of what is now Wyoming, Utah, and Colorado (see Figure 19.5).

In arid and semiarid regions, many lakes are what is known as hydrologically closed because they have no outlet streams. The water that enters the lake can only leave by evaporation, and the lake becomes a salt lake, typically with evaporite deposits made up of gypsum, anhydrite, and sometimes halite. Periodically, such lakes often dry up altogether.

Swamps

On low, flat ground or on coastal plains, where the drainage is poor and the water table high, swamps may extend over large areas. The most characteristic feature of swamps is an abundance of vegetation, growing in the shallow water, and a shortage of dissolved oxygen (Figure 2.6). With only sluggish water movement, the oxygen used up by aerobic bacteria is not readily replaced, which inhibits the decay of dead vegetation. As a result, layer upon layer of leaves, stems, and other vegetable debris accumulate as peat. Under conditions of deep burial and increasing temperature and pressure, peat is eventually metamorphosed into coal.

Desert Environments

Wherever the climate is arid (less than 25 centimeters or 10 inches of rain per year), there are naturally few streams, and the characteristic sediments are rock rubble and windblown sand. Currently, about one-fifth of the earth's land surface is desert. Of this area, about one-fifth again is classified as sandy desert, typified by various types of dune deposits. Elsewhere, the desert surface is rocky or covered with stony rubble transported by flash floods and sheetwash (water flow over a sloping land surface) during rare cloudbursts.

Of particular note in windblown sands is the extremely good sorting of the grains, with the great majority of the grains having a diameter of about 0.2 millimeters. Grains of this size have a terminal velocity of fall that approximates the average speed of the eddies close to the ground as the wind blows across the desert surface. Desert sand grains are also typically well rounded and have a frosted, rather than glassy, surface due to the constant collisions between the grains as they bounce across the desert before the wind, a process known as saltation.

Temporary lakes called playa lakes appear in low areas after rain, and muds, interbedded with thin beds of evaporite minerals like gypsum and anhydrite, are characteristic sediments. Ancient desert deposits of several ages are known from various parts of the world. Spectacular examples of the large-scale festoon bedding typical of desert dunes are preserved from the Permian, Triassic, and Jurassic periods, in particular (see Figure 2.1).

Glacial Environments

Current glacial environments include the Antarctic and Greenland ice caps, which comprise remnants of what were in the very recent geologic past (a mere 20,000 years ago) much larger continental ice sheets that covered almost a third of the world's land surface. This Late Cenozoic Ice Age is still with us, of course, our present relatively mild climate marking one of the several interglacial episodes as the ice sheets alternately grow and shrink, perhaps in response to the earth's orbital cycles. The mechanisms involved are discussed in Chapter 9, and more details about the ice ages themselves are presented in later chapters. Locally, glacial environments are associated with valley glaciers in high mountain ranges, and these also were much larger during glacial episodes.

Glaciers are powerful agents of erosion but are also capable of transporting and depositing enormous masses of sediment. The latest glaciation—the Wisconsin (in Europe, the Weichsel) that ended when the ice began a

FIGURE 2.7
Typical glacial till: boulders of all shapes and sizes in a clayey matrix.

rapid retreat some 18,000 years ago—left an extensive legacy of sediments and landforms. Many of the landscape features over large areas in the midlatitudes are of glacial origin, and large spreads of glacial deposits are found almost everywhere. Glacial action is predominantly destructive in its effect, so it is not surprising that only the latest glaciation has left any significant legacy of glacial features. The landscapes of older glacial advances and even earlier ice ages have in many areas long since disappeared. Thus, any direct record of former glaciations is, for the most part, preserved in glacial sediments.

The most characteristic glacial deposit is till, or boulder clay, made up typically of large boulders and pebbles embedded in a clayey matrix (Figure 2.7). The boulders are often smoothed and striated as a result of being scraped along below the moving glacier. The clayey matrix is actually finely pulverized rock "flour" produced by the immense crushing power of the ice. Deposits of glacial till are found in such geomorphic features as moraines. These are large, sinuous, moundlike features that mark the places where the front of the ice sheet or glacier stood for an extended period, as melting just balanced forward movement of the ice. Many ancient boulder conglomerates suspected of being glacial in origin are known, but some of these may have been formed under other, rather special conditions.

Ice ages have been important features of earth history. Since the beginning of the Cambrian, they account for more than 160 million years, which adds up to a third of Phanerozoic time. Several major ice ages also occurred during the Precambrian.

Marine Environments

The products of weathering and breakdown of rocks of the continental interior, both in solution and as clastic material, eventually reach the ocean. The journey from the parent source rock may have taken a long time, even millions of years, because en route, the sediment may have "rested" in a lake bed, desert dune, or delta before being eroded once more and sent on its way.

On reaching the coastal environment, the mixed load of sand, silt, and mud carried by a river is quickly sorted by the action of waves, tidal movements, and longshore currents. The sands tend to move into the high-energy zone of surf action along the beach (Figure 2.8), while the finer-grained material is both carried out into the deeper offshore or is swept through tidal channels into lagoons and sheltered bays landward of the beach zone.

As ocean waves break near shallow inshore regions, the surge piles up water carrying suspended sand grains onto the beach. The backwash of water is never as strong as the upsurge, or swash, since some water soaks downward into the sand. Thus, under normal weather conditions, a beach is built up. The coarser the sand, the steeper the shoreface slope.

For the past 18,000 years, since the retreat of the last ice sheets, sea levels have been steadily rising. Unless there is local uplift of the crust to compensate for this rise, coastlines are progressively "drowned." This means that the lower ground immediately landward of a beach tends to be flooded by a shallow lagoon, isolating the beach proper from the mainland. Thus, most beaches along tectonically passive "drowned" coastlines are termed barrier beaches. Such a coastline can be seen, for example, along most of the eastern seaboard of the United States (Figure 2.9).

Although during normal conditions, wave action on a beach is largely constructional in its effect, the situation changes during storms. Then the churning action of heavy surf and the powerful backwash cause erosion of the beach, and sand is moved down the shore and out into deeper water just offshore to form one or more longshore bars. Occasionally, very large storm waves throw sand far up onto the back of the beach where, out of reach of normal waves, it gradually accumulates as a storm ridge. Vegetation grows on such ridges and helps to stabilize them, and they are also often augmented by windblown sand in the form of coastal dunes.

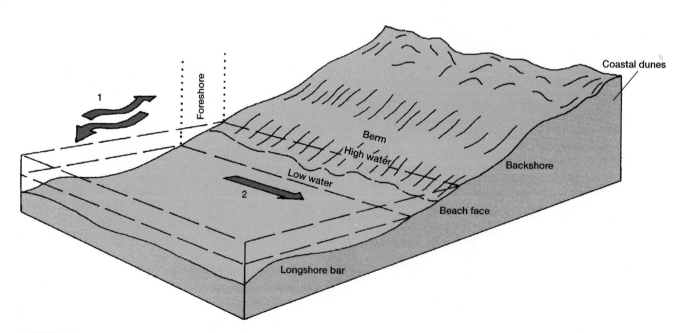

FIGURE 2.8
Sediment movement in the beach environment. (1) Back-and-forth movement between beach face and longshore bars in slightly deeper water offshore. (2) Movement parallel to the shore by longshore currents.

The texture of beach sand differs from that of alluvial sands in that the grains are better sorted and more rounded. There is also a conspicuous absence of the mica flakes seen in river sands. Along the length of a barrier beach are frequent gaps called tidal inlets. With the rising tide, a mixed load of sediment is swept into the lagoon behind the barrier beach, and there it settles during slack water. As the tide turns, most of the sand returns through the inlet on the ebb tide jet, but the finest sediment tends to remain behind because, once it settles out of suspension, it is quite cohesive and more difficult to reentrain than are the coarser sand grains. This process of sorting out by both waves and tidal currents leads to the distinctive sediment types associated with the various elements of the coastal environment. Over longer periods, as sea levels rise or fall, these different sedimentary facies move either inland or seaward, and at any one location, the sedimentary succession should contain a sequential record of these changes (Figure 2.10).

Carbonate Coastlines

Shorelines in tropical regions, especially if no large rivers are bringing terrigenous muds and sands into the coastal zone, often develop their own distinctive sedimentary associations as a result of the activities of lime-secreting animals and plants and are known as carbonate coastlines. The most important organisms, in many cases, are the corals. If the water is shallow (preferably less than 20

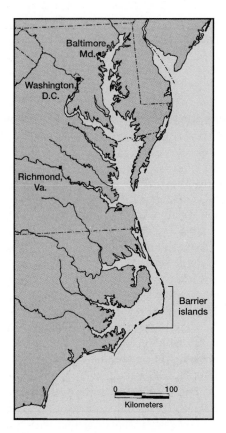

FIGURE 2.9
A drowned coastline along the eastern United States, with barrier islands lying offshore from the mainland.

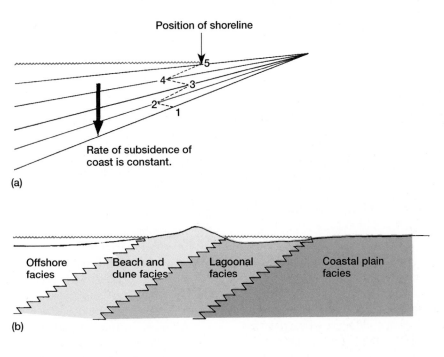

FIGURE 2.10
How the various depth- and energy-related sedimentary facies move with changing sea level. (a) 1–2, 3–4: Sea level falls faster than rate of subsidence. 2–3, 4–5: Sea level falls slower than rate of subsidence. (b) With rising sea level, depth-related facies of shoreline migrate inland.

meters), warm, clear of suspended sediment, of normal salinity, and well oxygenated, corals flourish. Generation by generation, the small, tube-shaped coral animals, or polyps construct a fringing reef along the shore. Again, as with barrier islands, reefs may also grow some distance from the shore as barrier reefs, and a shallow lagoon may form behind them.

The main reef tract is constructed largely of the skeletons of coral colonies (Figure 2.11). Although they are typically the chief frame builders of the reef, volumetrically, they may amount to as little as 10 percent of the total reef mass. The remainder of the reef consists of encrusting masses built up by lime-secreting algae, together with the skeletons and shells of many other reef-dwelling organisms, including bryozoans, mollusks, echinoderms, and arthropods.

Reef masses often form pronounced topographic features on the sea floor and by affecting the movement of currents may influence the distribution of sediment over considerable areas. Seaward of the reef into deeper water, deposits are typically of reef debris broken off by wave action. This material forms a submarine talus slope below the reef and often provides a foundation for the seaward expansion of reef-building organisms. On the landward side of the reef, in the sheltered water of the lagoon, fine-grained lime muds accumulate together with deposits of fecal pellets derived from mud-ingesting organisms.

In the surge channels between reef segments, the typical bottom sediment is an oolitic sand. Ooliths are small spheres built up of concentric layers of aragonite accreted in snowball fashion as the grains are alternatively rolled around by currents on the bottom and buried in the sediment (Figure 2.12). During burial, they are immersed in pore-space water supersaturated in calcium carbonate, and at this time, they presumably acquire a new concentric layer of aragonite.

Reef limestones, because of their open structure, usually have a good porosity and permeability, so in the right geologic setting, they are often reservoirs for oil and gas. Many of the big oil fields of the Middle East are producers from reef limestones, as are the big fields of western Canada; the Williston Basin in North Dakota, Montana, and Saskatchewan; the Michigan Basin, and the Permian Basin of West Texas.

Carbonate Platforms

In some places, large areas of shallow water are found on what are, in effect, submarine plateaus. These are termed **carbonate platforms,** and one such area is the Bahama Banks. Here, isolated from the influence of terrigenous sediments derived from the North American continent by the Straits of Florida, and bathed by the warm waters of the Gulf Stream, conditions are ideal for reef growth. Again, corals are the main frame-building organisms, but over most of the platform, the surface sediments are characterized by lime muds, pellet muds, and oolite shoals.

FIGURE 2.11
Massive reef limestone of the Pleistocene Key Largo Formation, Florida Keys.

Another example of a carbonate platform is the Campeche Bank, north of the Yucatan Peninsula in the Gulf of Mexico. Both the Florida and Yucatan peninsulas are largely limestone plateaus and contribute almost no terrigenous sediment. The Persian Gulf also provides the right conditions for carbonate deposition. Here, the arid climate has resulted in evaporite deposits on the shallow tidal flats, or sabbkhas.

In many ancient reef tracts, such as those in the Michigan and Williston basins, evaporite deposits are commonly associated with reef limestones. With very shallow water, currents restricted by reef banks, and an arid climate, evaporite deposition is almost inevitable.

At times in the past, whole continents were almost entirely submerged under shallow **epeiric seas,** which with the possible exception of Hudson Bay as a small-scale example, are not found on earth today. During the Paleozoic, for example, over vast areas of North America, conditions rather similar to those on the Bahama Banks existed, although there were important differences that are

(a)

(b)

FIGURE 2.12

(a) Oolith grains ×100. General view of typical ooliths, showing subrounded shape. (b) Oolith grains ×250. Oolith composite grain, showing how separate ooliths become cemented together.

described later. Many of the Paleozoic limestones of the craton interior thus are similar to the sediments seen on modern carbonate platforms.

Continental Shelves

The **continental shelves** are the outer margins of the continents that are flooded by the sea. Along passive margins, such as the eastern seaboard of North and South America, the continental shelves are sometimes up to 200 kilometers wide and gently slope from the shoreline out to what is called the shelf break, at a depth of about 200 meters. On the west coast of North America, which is a tectonically active margin, the continental shelf is relatively narrow with irregular topography.

The sediments found on passive margin shelves are typically sands and silts that are in a state of intermittent movement, with submarine bars and ridges forming and reforming under the influence of tidal currents and storm waves. In areas formerly influenced by the Late Cenozoic ice sheets, there may be relict glacial gravels and sands left behind after the glaciers retreated. On the continental shelves of active margins, sedimentary associations are more variable, depending upon the water depth and the degree of stirring of bottom sediments. Anoxic black muds may accumulate in deep basins, whereas in shallower areas, sands are characteristic.

Deep-Sea Environments

Deep-sea environments include the continental slope, submarine canyons, and the deep ocean floor. Beyond the shelf break is the **continental slope,** where the sea-bottom slope increases sharply to a gradient of about 1 in 40 (a drop of 1 meter for every 40 meters horizontally). Sediment set-

tling from suspension onto this slope is in a state of unstable equilibrium and is easily disturbed. Storm waves or earth tremors cause submarine landslides of the unconsolidated material, which often generate turbidity currents, masses of water full of suspended sediment. Turbidity currents are denser than the surrounding water and tend to remain as coherent masses as they flow rapidly down the slope and beyond.

A conspicuous feature of many continental slopes are submarine canyons, great steep-sided valleys that cut deeply back into the shelf, some extending nearly back to the shoreline (Figure 2.13). Submarine canyons are, in effect, giant conduits that channel masses of shallow-water sediments from the shelf above down to the foot of the continental slope and the deep ocean floor beyond.

Along the foot of the continental slope, the gradient gradually flattens across what is called the **continental rise.** This great wedge of sediments is made up of material carried down the slope and down the submarine canyons by turbidity currents. The surface of the continental rise passes imperceptibly out onto the deep ocean floor. Here are the **abyssal plains,** the flattest areas on earth, formed by the blanketing effect of flows of fine sediments carried by the turbidity currents as they reach their furthest limits.

Beyond the reach of the turbidity currents, the deep ocean floor is covered by fine oozes and clays. These are true **pelagic** (oceanic) **sediments,** and the oozes consist of the tiny skeletons of microscopic marine organisms. The chief contributors are the coccolithophores and the foraminifera, particularly the planktonic species that live in the surface ocean waters, especially in tropical and subtropical seas. These creatures secrete skeletons of calcium carbonate, and so the oozes they form are calcareous in composition. Other organisms, such as the microscopic

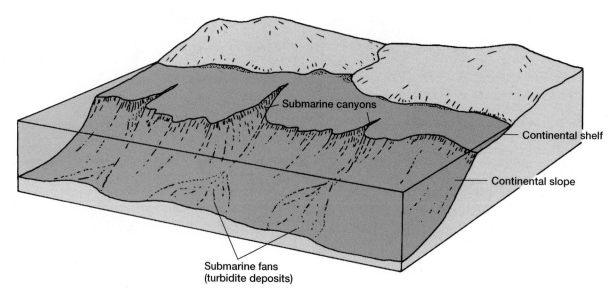

FIGURE 2.13
Submarine canyons cutting back into the continental shelf.

FIGURE 2.14
Regular bedding in Paleozoic limestones.

planktonic plants, the diatoms, and tiny animals known as radiolaria, secrete internal structures of silica, which result in the siliceous oozes, found particularly in deeper parts of the ocean and in high latitudes.

This part of the chapter is concerned with relating modern sedimentary environments with those of the past, as revealed in sedimentary rocks. In the case of deep-sea environments, this is difficult. Although, as a glance at any world physiographic map will show, the deep-sea basins cover two-thirds of the earth's surface, examples of ancient deep-sea deposits in the stratigraphic record are extremely rare. This is because the ocean floors and the sediments on them are all eventually carried down into

subduction zones and recycled within the plate-tectonic mechanism. Sedimentary rocks interpreted as of pelagic origin are found only at a few odd locations, where they are thought to have been scraped off along a continental plate margin as the oceanic plate was subducted.

Ancient Environments

The sediments and sedimentary environments discussed up to this point can be seen on the modern earth. Sedimentary rocks of lithified sediment hopefully preserve some record of a past earth with sufficient of the original sedimentary features that can be interpreted in terms of their depositional environment. In this section, the "here and now" earth is left behind, and the discussion now turns to sedimentary rocks and the way they can provide a record of vanished worlds. The sedimentary rocks are the pages of the book on which is written the geologic history of the earth.

Sediments and the Rock Cycle

Much of earth history is cyclical. Virtually all of the major events, such as continental rifting, continental collision, mountain-building movements, and marine transgressions and regressions, are repetitive. Nowhere is this cyclicity more obvious than in the sedimentary rocks. All rocks, whether igneous, sedimentary, or metamorphic, are involved in the **rock cycle,** in which sedimentary rocks derived from igneous rocks are eventually metamorphosed and then melted to form a new generation of igneous rocks.

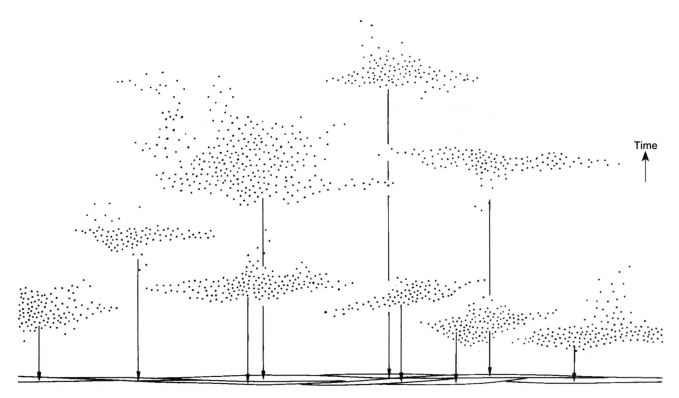

FIGURE 2.15
Sediment is delivered in pulses over time and settles to the sea floor or lake bed. Thus, a single bedding plane varies slightly in age from place to place.

Many sediments take a shortcut and are derived not from an igneous rock but, as described earlier, from an earlier generation of sedimentary rock or possibly from a metamorphosed sediment.

The constant recycling of quartz grains is hardly surprising in view of their toughness, but clay minerals are also very durable. Originally derived from the chemical breakdown and hydration of feldspars and other aluminum silicates, clay minerals are extremely stable under surface conditions and are easily reworked. In recycling, they may add or lose certain ions and be transformed into different clay mineral types, but they are still clays.

In nonclastic sediments, such as limestones and evaporites, recycling is even more direct. Under chemical weathering, such rocks simply pass into solution, and the salts are transferred back to the ocean, where they are utilized by lime-secreting organisms or are precipitated as evaporite deposits.

Beds and Bedding

The most conspicuous feature of sedimentary rocks is usually the bedding. **Bedding** refers to the way the rock is divided up into layers (Figure 2.14). Each layer is termed a bed, or if it is extremely thin, as in shales, a lamina. As mentioned in Chapter 1, a bedding surface represents what was, for a short time, the sea floor or lake bed.

Each bed of a sedimentary formation accumulates over a given time interval, and, other things being equal, a bed that is 10 centimeters thick probably took twice as long to accumulate as did a bed that is 5 centimeters thick. However, many variables are involved in the relationship between time and sediment accumulation. In some situations, such as in a major delta like the Mississippi, enormous quantities of sediment are delivered to a relatively small area. The rate of accumulation is then extremely rapid, and several meters may be deposited in a matter of years or even months. On the other hand, in parts of the ocean basins, far from terrestrial influences, sediments accumulate very slowly, perhaps 1 millimeter per thousand years. Victorian geologist Hugh Miller poetically described the deep ocean floor and "the fine, gray mud, or light micaceous sand that settles upon its unseen bottom, as the impalpable dust that mottles the sunbeam sinks on the floor of some deserted hall or old haunted chamber."

Sediment does not continuously rain down to the sea floor from above, but rather comes in discrete clouds or pulses. Just as with rain showers on land, only limited areas are affected at any one time (Figure 2.15). This is particularly true on shallow shelves and platforms. Thus, bedding surfaces, representing as they do the intervals between the pulses, are not everywhere the same age. Although an individual bedding plane may sometimes be correlated over

(a)

(b)

FIGURE 2.16
Bedding plane features. (a) Desiccation cracks formed in the mud in a drying pond or on a tidal flat. (b) The casts of salt crystals formed in a saline lake in an evaporite basin.

considerable distances, the bed immediately below the surface will vary slightly in age from place to place.

The wide variety of preserved bedding-plane features provide direct evidence of bedding surfaces as fossil sea floors or lake beds. Ripple marks and the tracks, trails, and burrows of bottom-dwelling organisms are commonly seen on any modern seabed.

Not all sediments are laid down in the sea, of course, and other sedimentary environments are characterized by their own distinctive bedding-plane features. Sediments deposited on tidal flats or in desert playa lakes, for example, are identified by desiccation cracks that formed as the muddy surface dried in the sun (Figure 2.16a). Other features include the casts of salt crystals that formed in the soft mud, clearly an indication of an arid climate (Figure 2.16b). Tiny craters left by raindrops and dinosaur footprints are other examples.

In addition to providing clues regarding past environments, certain bedding-plane features can be used to determine the top and bottom of beds. This is of particular importance in areas where the geology is structurally complex—where, for example, flat-lying beds may, in fact, be completely overturned in a recumbent fold.

Mapping Sedimentary Formations

The reconstruction of ancient landscapes begins with geological mapping. Until the areal relationships of the various rock masses are set down, little can be done to construct a paleogeographic map. With regard to the field relationships of rock, the fundamental mappable unit is the **formation.** A formation is a **lithostratigraphic unit** defined solely on a rock's physical features—its lithology, texture, color, bedding, and so on. There is no age connotation in defining a formation; indeed, if it extends over a large area, its boundaries will almost certainly vary in age from place to place and are said to be time-transgressive.

Mapping relies on matching the rock succession in one place with that in another; continuity between the two locations is extrapolated and assumed. In practice, geological mapping is often like trying to complete a jigsaw puzzle with 90 percent of the pieces missing because, except in arid and semiarid areas, such as western North America or arctic regions, surface exposures of rocks are typically few and far between.

When a formation is first measured and described, a standard, or type section (**stratotype**), is selected as being the best place to see the full thickness of the formation, its relationships to other formations below and above it in the succession, and its typical lithologic characters. The formation is assigned a name, very often based on the geographic location of the stratotype. Distinctive units within formations are often recognized as subdivisions known as members. Two or more formations that have features in common that distinguish them from the remainder of the succession may be recognized as a group. Similarly, two or more groups may be lumped together as a supergroup.

Facies

On the modern sea floor, the nature of the sediment varies widely, with the variations often controlled by water depth and, hence, the amount of stirring of the bottom. Thus, in shallow, inshore regions are sands with rounded to subrounded grains. Traced seaward into deeper water, the sand typically passes into silt and mud. Similarly, on carbonate coasts and platforms, as already mentioned, rapid, lateral changes in sediment type are often found in passing from the front of the reef to the back reef and lagoon. The different aspects of the bottom sediment can be referred to as different facies (Figure 2.17). The term *facies* encompasses the total lithologic characteristics of the sediment, together with some implications as to its sedimentary environment. Thus, geologists might speak of a sandy facies passing into a silty or muddy facies, or alternatively, a shallow-water facies passing into a deeper-water facies.

PLATE 1
A thin section in polarized light of an arkosic sandstone. The prominent gridlike pattern is perthitic twinning in a microcline (K-feldspar) grain; other grains are dominantly of quartz.

PLATE 3
Coarse, angular talus derived from the mechanical breakdown, most commonly from frost shattering, of granite. These clasts slide and tumble down from outcrops on the slopes above.

PLATE 2
Mechanical weathering breakdown of granite produces a coarse sand dominantly of quartz and feldspar grains.

PLATE 4
Alluvial gravels in a braided stream, Dolores River, Colorado.
By now, the clasts are becoming rounded as they are tumbled
along the stream bed.

PLATE 6
The floodplain of the Orange River, Namibia. This is a typical
mature stream flowing across a flat floored valley.

PLATE 5
Alluvial gravels in a point bar on the Animas River, Colorado.

PLATE 7
Distributary stream channels flowing across the delta of the
Orinoco River, Venezuela.

PLATE 8
Salt flats in a playa lake, Arizona.

PLATE 9
A "sea of grass" is an apt description for the Everglades of
Southwest Florida.

PLATE 10
A typical cypress swamp in southern Florida.

PLATE 11
Beach dunes at Cabo Blanco, Peru. Note the slip faces developing on the leeward slopes.

PLATE 12
Star dune at Sossos Vlei, Great Sand Sea, Namibia.

PLATE 13
Typical stony desert, Namibia.

PLATE 14
Dune bedding in the Jurassic Navajo sandstone, Zion National
Park, Utah.

PLATE 15
The edge of the Antarctic ice cap, Lemaire Channel, Antarctic Peninsula. (Photographs courtesy of Mary Lemon.)

PLATE 16
A small, tabular berg calved from the ice shelf, Lemaire Channel, Antarctica. (Photo courtesy of Mary Lemon.)

PLATE 17
A closeup view of an iceberg, showing the layering of snowfall increments.
(Photo courtesy of Mary Lemon.)

PLATE 18
The Columbia glacier, Alberta. Note the meltwater stream
flowing from beneath the ice.

PLATE 19
The Columbia glacier. Note the morainic debris and
the ice margin and outwash gravels in the foreground.

PLATE 20
Drumlins are rounded, egg-shaped hills of glacial morainic
material that form beneath continental ice sheets. This example
is at Sunderland, Ontario.

PLATE 21
Eskers are long, sinuous ridges of gravels laid down in meltwater streams that flow
within and beneath glaciers. After the ice has melted, the gravel deposits remain as
"fossil stream beds." This example is at Manilla, Ontario, and was formed beneath the
Wisconsin ice sheet that melted back from this region only about 12,000 years ago.

PLATE 22
A closeup view of current-bedded
meltwater gravels exposed in a gravel
pit excavated in the Manilla esker.

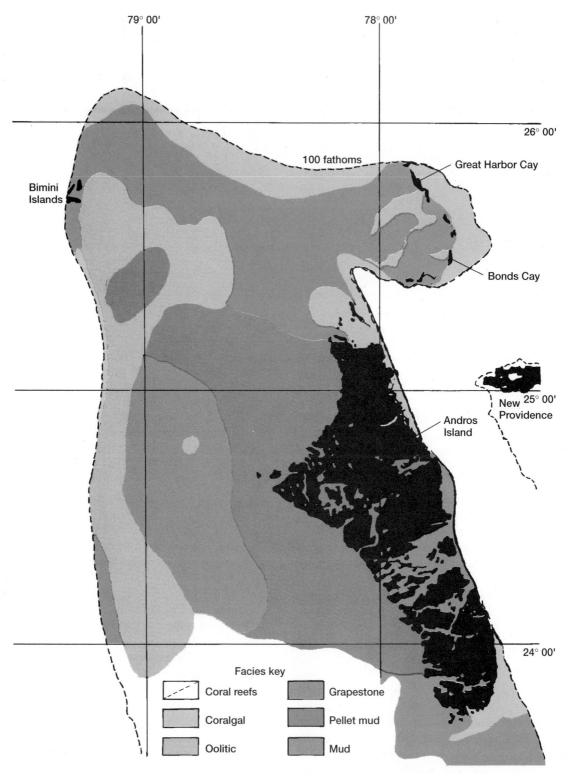

FIGURE 2.17

A sedimentary facies map of a portion of the Bahama Banks, showing various types of bottom sediment. Distribution of the different sediment types is largely controlled by water depth and wave energy input; thus, oolitic sediments are typically found in high-energy areas, where there is vigorous wave and tidal movement. Muds are found in slightly deeper and/or quieter water.

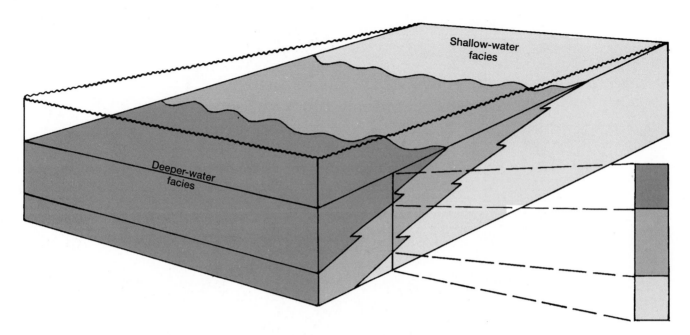

FIGURE 2.18
Walther's Law illustrated by facies migration during a marine
transgression.

The facies concept is useful because it addresses lateral and sometimes vertical changes in lithology, often within a single formation. Facies are often controlled by water depth and, therefore, sea level. If sea level rises at any one place, there will be a change from shallower- to deeper-water facies. At the same time, the shoreline will move inland, as will the parallel depth-related zones. This concept was described over 100 years ago by German geologist Johannes Walther and has come to be known as **Walther's Law.** According to Walther, the different depth-controlled facies seen to lie side by side on a sloping sea floor will, after a rise or fall of sea level, be found at any one place to be repeated in the same order vertically up or down the stratigraphic succession (Figure 2.18).

Depositional Cycles

A large proportion of sedimentary rocks are marine in origin and so are influenced by sea-level changes. Whether due to crustal movements or a rise or fall of worldwide sea level, the relative positions of land and sea are constantly changing over geologic time. Some of these sea-level cycles take place over quite short time periods. Glacio-eustatic movements controlled by the advance and retreat of ice sheets, for example, involve sea-level changes of as much as 80 to 100 meters in 100,000 years. Other sea-level cycles take many millions of years to complete and are due to plate-tectonic movements.

The immediate effect of a relative rise in sea level, for whatever cause, is that shallow-water sediments come to be overlain by deeper-water sediments as the shoreline moves inland. When sea level falls, deep-water sediments are overlain by those of shallow-water origin. The sediments deposited during a single cycle of sea level rise and then fall are grouped into what is termed a **depositional cycle.** When this process is repeated, the various depth-related facies are reflected in a zig-zag diagram as shown in Figure 2.19.

Although this is a useful beginning to understanding sequential facies changes, other factors must be considered. In the first place, the succession marking falling sea level is hardly ever a mirror image of that deposited during rising sea level, as the simple zig-zag diagram in Figure 2.19 implies. Often, a marine regression is due to depositional progradation, which is active outbuilding of the shore by rapid sediment accumulation. This process might even be going on while sea level is still rising and is a frequent phenomenon in actively growing deltas, for example. These regressional sediments are typically quite different from the sediment associated with a marine transgression. Another factor to be considered is that many cycles of sea-level change are asymmetrical—that is, sea level rises faster than it falls, or vice versa. Another reason why thick sedimentary successions do not contain a complete record of the zig-zag sea-level shifts is because a marine regression is typically followed by emergence and erosion. By the time the next cycle of marine advance begins, little or no sedimentary record of the previous cycle may remain, and the new sediments are laid down across an erosion surface.

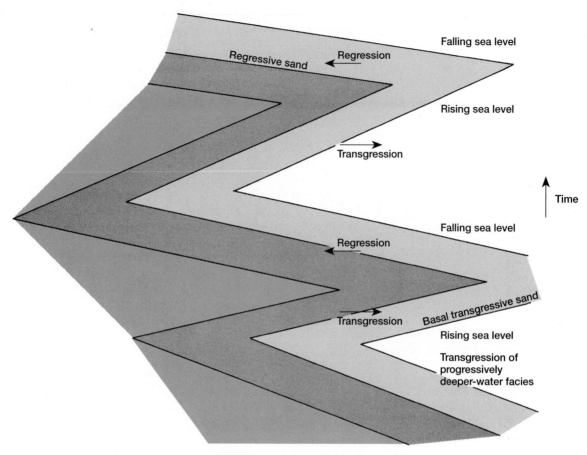

FIGURE 2.19
The shifting pattern of sedimentary facies during marine transgressions and regressions.

Tectonic Settings of Sediment

As we have seen, sedimentary rocks can preserve within them, often with remarkable fidelity, a record of local environments that can be built into the larger picture of distribution of land and sea in the past. Beyond the geographic parameters of physiography and climate, however, geologists must also take into account the major structural controls through time. These are linked, either directly or indirectly, to plate-tectonic movements and to the location of the region relative to plate margins.

Ultimately, the **tectonic setting** of a particular sedimentary environment plays the major role in controlling the nature of the sediment that will accumulate there. Even within a single rock sample, certain textural and mineralogic characteristics can be detected that go far beyond the local depositional environment. *Tectonic settings* refers to the largest natural division on earth—namely, those

boundaries defined by plate tectonics. Within this framework, five first-order divisions, or tectonic settings, are recognized:

1. Passive continental margins
2. Active continental margins
3. Continental interiors emergent
4. Continental interiors submergent (epeiric setting)
5. Ocean basins

Each of these settings is different from the others in all its essential features and its history (Figure 2.20). Each is remarkably self-contained, and there is little overlap, suggesting that they are quite "natural" divisions. A number of subdivisions can be identified within each division, but again, there is little blurring across the major boundaries. Even laboratory analysis of sediments and sedimentary rock samples usually reveals many features that are unique to each of the divisions.

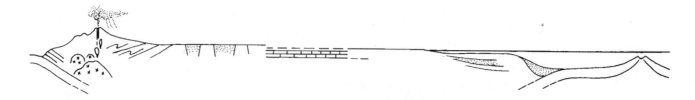

1	Active margin	Craton		Passive margin		Ocean basin		
		Emergent	Submergent					
2	Subduction zone/island arc	Fault basin	Epeiric sea	Coastal plain	Continental shelf	Continental slope/rise	Abyssal plain	Midocean ridge
3	Volcani-clastic	Terrestrial/ clastic/ evaporite	Limestones/ dolostones	Swamp/alluvial/ deltaic	Shallow marine/ shelf carbonates	Turbidites	Pelagic	Volcanics

Key: 1= Tectonic setting; 2= Sedimentary environments; 3= Dominant sedimentary associations.

FIGURE 2.20
Major tectonic settings for sedimentary regimes.

Summary

Because modern sediments can be observed as they accumulate on the sea floor, and in lakes, rivers, swamps, and deserts, the various environmental controls over sediment deposition can usually be assessed with little difficulty. These data form the basis for the interpretation of the environments of the geologic past in which the sedimentary rocks originated. Diagenetic changes (physical and chemical changes that occurred in the sediment after deposition) are part of the lithification process that turns sediment into sedimentary rock. Sand grains become cemented together by the introduction of a chemical cement (most commonly calcite) into the pore spaces. Muds become compressed and lithified as the water is squeezed out and the clay mineral particles become welded together. Lime muds and calcareous skeletal material become cemented and recrystallized to form limestones.

The ultimate sources of all sediments, except for the pyroclastic sediments formed by volcanic eruptions, are earlier generations of rocks broken down by chemical and mechanical weathering. Material in solution goes to join the other salts in the ocean, while more resistant minerals become clasts of various sizes.

The most common resistant mineral is quartz, the dominant mineral of sand-size clasts. From their place of origin, sand grains pass through numerous depositional environments, sometimes remaining for thousands or even millions of years in lake, swamp, alluvial, or deltaic deposits en route to the coast. Beach and offshore deposits eventually become buried and incorporated into the great wedges of sediment many kilometers thick that underlie the continental shelves.

One-fifth of the earth's land surface is arid, and of this, a fifth is sandy desert. Windblown dunes of well-sorted and well-rounded sand grains are characteristic. Elsewhere, desert surfaces are rocky or stony. The present Antarctic and Greenland ice caps are remnants of formerly much larger continental ice sheets that have periodically covered nearly one-third of the earth's land surface during the past 2 million years. The most characteristic glacial sediment is till, a mixture of pebble and boulder-sized clasts in a clayey matrix.

In coastal environments, barrier beaches are separated from the mainland by shallow lagoons. Most sand is deposited on the beach or in the shallow offshore region. Fine muds and silts are carried through tidal inlets into lagoons and coastal swamps. In tropical and subtropical regions and where the water is clear of suspended sediment, coastal deposition is dominated by calcareous sediment consisting of skeletal debris derived from mollusks and other lime-secreting organisms. In shallow water, coral reefs flourish and are important rock builders.

In the deep sea, sediments can be broadly classified under two headings. Close to the continents, the deep ocean floor is covered by sediments carried down the continental slope and through submarine canyons by turbidity currents. Such sediment comprises the bulk of the continental rise (see Figure 1.5). Beyond the reach of turbidity currents, deep-ocean (pelagic) sediments are dominated by fine oozes and clays. The fine-grained oozes consist of the tiny skeletons of calcareous foraminifera and siliceous diatoms and radiolaria.

All rocks, whether igneous, sedimentary, or metamorphic, are involved in the rock cycle, in which sedimentary rocks derived from igneous rocks are eventually metamorphosed and then melted to form a new generation of igneous rocks.

The most obvious feature of the majority of sedimentary rocks is the bedding.

Bedding planes mark pauses or changes in the process of sediment accumulation. They often represent what was for a time the sea floor or lake bed and may exhibit such features as ripple marks or tracks and trails of bottom-living organisms.

The field relationships of sedimentary rocks can be assessed by dividing a stratigraphic succession into formations. A formation is a thickness of rocks which, in lithology, color, grain size, bedding, and so on, is distinguished from other rock units above and below. Such features enable it to be mapped and correlated over an extended area.

The term *facies* encompasses the overall aspect or set of characteristics of a rock that reflects its particular environment deposition. The facies concept addresses lateral and sometimes vertical changes in lithology, often within a single formation.

The majority of sedimentary successions are marine in origin and so are influenced by sea-level changes. These are often cyclical and of several magnitudes. Long-term cycles are due to plate-tectonic movements, while short-term cycles are usually of climatic origin, typically linked to glacial and interglacial periods.

The tectonic setting of a particular sedimentary environment plays the major role in controlling the nature of the sediment that will accumulate there. The five tectonic settings are: (1) passive continental margins, (2) active continental margins, (3) continental interiors emergent, (4) continental interiors submergent, and (5) ocean basins.

Questions

1. What is meant by diagenesis?
2. Explain the maturity concept in sands and sandstones.
3. How does the character of alluvial sediment change in going from the source of a stream down to its mouth at the seacoast?
4. Describe how a delta forms. Why have major deltas of past time become important sedimentary accumulations?
5. What role does climate play in controlling the kind of sediment derived by weathering of a parent rock?
6. What kinds of sedimentary association would normally indicate deposition in a desert environment?
7. What features would you look for to ascertain whether or not a sedimentary deposit was of glacial origin?
8. Describe how the various parts of a modern beach, when seen in profile, reflect wave energy.
9. Why are many coastlines around the world "drowned" coastlines? Describe the main features of a drowned coastline.
10. Describe some of the different kinds of limestones and why they are usually good indicators of bottom environments.
11. How do sediments and sedimentary rocks fit into the rock cycle?
12. What are bedding planes? Explain their significance.
13. What is meant by the facies concept?
14. What is Walther's Law?
15. Draw a diagram to show the relationship between the various shallow- and deep-water sedimentary facies during a marine transgression followed by a regression.

Further Reading

Allen, J. R. 1977. *Physical processes of sedimentation.* London: Allen and Unwin.

Blatt, H., G. Middleton, and R. Murray. 1980. *Origin of sedimentary rocks.* 2d ed. Englewood Cliffs, N.J.: Prentice-Hall.

Friedman, G. M., and J. E. Sanders. 1978. *Principles of sedimentology.* New York: John Wiley.

Laporte, L. 1979. *Ancient environments.* 2d ed. Englewood Cliffs, N.J.: Prentice-Hall.

Selley, R. C. 1976. *An introduction to sedimentology.* New York: Academic Press.

3

THE FOSSIL RECORD

Introduction

Fossils play an important role—some would argue the leading role—in the study of historical geology. Fossils provide, often with great detail, information about past environments and climatic changes. They also remain the most accurate means of determining the age of rocks and of correlating rocks from different parts of the world. Without evidence of former life-forms on this planet, not only would we have no knowledge of the many extinct species of the past, but our understanding of evolutionary mechanisms and pathways would be vague indeed.

Fossils have been the object of speculation for thousands of years, so it is not surprising that they have generated some fanciful ideas (see Box 3.1). One other aspect of fossils also is worthy of mention. Of all geologic phenomena, fossils are what spark many people's interest in geology. From earliest childhood, few have not been intrigued by dinosaur fossils, for example. Since fossils may be the means whereby more people become aware of our planet's past, then perhaps they can also kindle more concern about earth's future as we enter a period of increasing environmental problems.

In this chapter, we examine what fossils are, how they are formed, how accurately they portray the life of the geologic past, and how they can be used as environmental indicators. The subject of evolution and the part played by fossils in age determination and stratigraphic correlation are discussed in later chapters.

BOX 3.1

Fossils: Facts and Fancies

As with so many features of the natural world, the origin and meaning of fossils were apparently well understood by ancient Greek scholars. They presumably had no problem with the idea that the sea had once covered parts of the land, although they did not relate the fossils to the rocks containing them.

During the Dark Ages, fossils were variously held as objects with healing powers, supernatural objects, proof of Noah's Flood, or simply as shells dropped from the pockets of pilgrims. One particularly strange idea was that they were somehow formed by exhalations from the rocks drawn up by the stars. Another was that fossils were placed in the rocks by the devil to deliberately confuse humankind. Yet another was that fossils were rejects tossed out by God during the process of the Creation.

Not everyone held such views, of course. In the sixteenth century, Leonardo da Vinci recognized that fossils were the remains of marine organisms and discounted theologians' suggestion that they were evidence for Noah's Flood by pointing out that many floods must have been responsible.

During the late eighteenth and early nineteenth centuries, geology was beginning to emerge as a science, and geological phenomena (and, of course, fossils) were for the first time being discussed with a sense of curiosity. Breaking free of the old beliefs was not easy, however, and many attempts were made to reconcile the revelations of the early geologists and paleontologists with the biblical account of history.

Ultimately, as the fossil record became better documented, it was clear that faunas and floras of the past were characteristically different from those of the present, so a belief widely held for many years was that there had been not one but many creations. Fossils, therefore, were evidence of former worlds, complete with their landscapes, seas, and living organisms. Each division of the stratigraphic succession, in effect, represented a "paleo-today." On the other hand, some scholars did not see fossils as having any organic origins at all.

One scholar in particular—German professor Johannes Beringer—amassed large collections of fossils, describing and illustrating them in an elegant tome he published in 1726 and dedicated to a local prince. Unknown to Beringer, he was the victim of a hoax because many of his fossils were, in fact, carvings made by his students and deposited where they knew he went fossil collecting. By the time Beringer finally discovered what had happened, his book had been widely read, and in his chagrin, he attempted to buy all of the books back and destroy them. A final footnote to this story may or may not be true: During Beringer's last years, while attempting to retrieve all the copies of his book, he went heavily into debt and died owing a considerable sum. Apparently, so the story goes, his relatives found themselves obligated to pay part of this debt, and to raise the money, they retrieved a surviving copy of Beringer's book and published a second edition!

The Fossilization Process

How representative of past life is the fossil record? To answer this question, we should perhaps begin by asking another: How many of the animals and plants we see around us on the present-day earth would likely be preserved as fossils, perhaps to be discovered by some paleontologist of the far-distant future? In other words, how does the fossilization process work?

Conditions Conducive to Fossilization

Fossils are produced by many different processes, depending not only upon the sedimentary environment in which the animal or plant was buried but also upon what happened to the sediment after it was deposited (Figure 3.1). The branch of geology especially concerned with the fossilization process is called taphonomy.

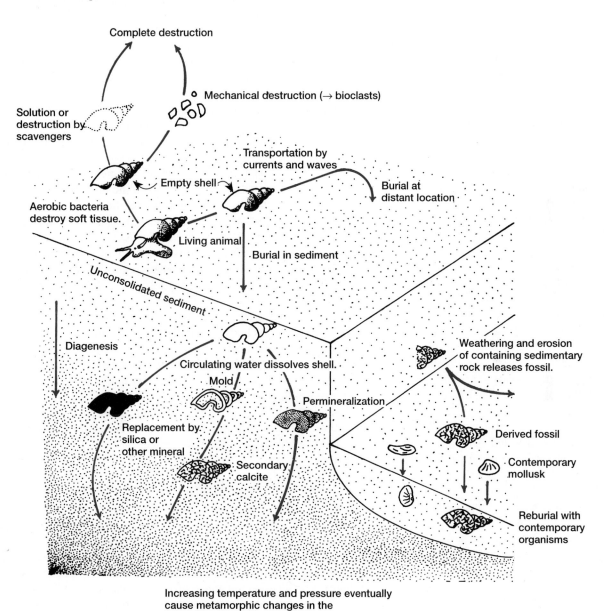

FIGURE 3.1
The possible ways in which fossils are formed.

Once an animal or plant is dead, scavengers often begin a process of destruction that is completed by bacterial decay. In fact, normally, within a very short time after death, very little—or more often nothing—of the once-living organism remains. Soft tissues are the first to break down, but even hard skeletons and shells are not indestructible and, particularly on the surface of the ground or on the seabed, they also are eventually eliminated.

The key to the rate at which the decay process operates is oxygen. In an environment with abundant oxygen, **aerobic bacteria** (bacteria that function only in the presence of oxygen) efficiently break down all kinds of organic matter. Also, higher temperatures speed up decay processes. At below-freezing temperatures, decay processes virtually come to a halt. Water also aids the decay process, and in its complete absence, decay is greatly slowed. Although rare, remarkable examples of mummified skin and other soft tissues have been found in the hot sands of deserts or in dry caverns. To summarize, dead animal and plant material lying on the surface of the earth, seabed, or lake bed— where there are scavengers, where oxygen and water may be abundant, and where temperatures may be elevated—stand little chance of preservation as fossils.

Rapid burial before extensive decay is an essential first step in the fossilization process. In fact, the word *fossil* comes from the Latin word *fossus,* meaning "something dug up." Rapid burial of the dead animal or plant usually ensures an environment in which oxygen is in short supply and in which aerobic bacteria can no longer operate.

The availability of oxygen within the burying sediments depends largely on the sediments' porosity and permeability. In coarse sands, for example, water moves easily through the pore spaces, and oxygen is abundant, perhaps down to a meter or more below the sea floor or lake bed. In fine-grained sediments, such as silts and muds, on the other hand, porosity and permeability are so poor that pore-space water, perhaps only a few centimeters below the sediment-water interface, is essentially stagnant and oxygen deficient.

These differences in porosity have an important bearing on the fossilization process. Under oxygen-deficient (**anoxic**) conditions, decay of organic material trapped in the sediments is much slower and is largely due to the action of anaerobic bacteria. Sulfides rather than oxides tend to form, and hydrogen sulfide is why many muds have a distinctive rotten-egg smell.

Iron is commonly present in many sediments and has a strong affinity to oxygen. In dense muds that lack oxygen, iron sulfides form, and so the mineral pyrite (FeS_2) is a common constituent in black, organically rich shales and may be a replacement mineral of fossils.

Thus, oxygen-deficient muds provide perhaps the best conditions for fossilization, and under favorable circumstances, even impressions of the soft tissues may be preserved. Muds are very compressible, however, and most fossils in shales are more or less flattened out, sometimes being preserved only as paper-thin films on the bedding surface. In special cases, these films may be the carbonized remains of the soft tissues.

The Bias in the Fossil Record

As should be apparent from the preceding section, terrestrial organisms living on dry land are the least likely to become fossils. In contrast, those organisms living in an aquatic environment, where sediment is accumulating, stand the best chance of being buried after death, with the most likely candidates by far for fossilization being those organisms that already live in and on the bottom sediment. Because soft tissue disappears so rapidly, soft-bodied animals such as jellyfishes are very rare as fossils. Inevitably, then, the great majority of fossil remains are of skeletons and shells (Figure 3.2), which results in a bias in the fossil record.

The survivability of the sedimentary rocks containing the fossils also contributes to the bias of the fossil record. As rocks are destroyed by weathering and erosion, so are the fossils contained in them. Because of their widespread extent and often great thickness, sediments laid down in marine environments are far better represented in the overall stratigraphic succession than are terrestrial sediments. Although many terrestrial successions deposited in inland valleys, lakes, swamps, and riverbeds are known, they are generally much less fossiliferous than are the sediments laid down in the sea, particularly those in shallow, offshore environments.

All of these factors explain why the fossil record as a whole is strongly biased in favor of marine organisms with hard skeletons or shells. This bias must be remembered when attempting to compare modern floras and faunas with those whose former presence on the earth is only indicated by the fossil record.

Molds, Casts, and Permineralization

The fossilization process does not end with burial in sediment. After the sediment is laid down on the sea floor or lake bed, diagenetic processes, including compaction, cementation, and other changes, eventually turn the soft sediment into hard sedimentary rock. This process of lithification inevitably affects the fossils entombed within the sediment, sometimes even destroying them altogether.

Sandy sediments, as mentioned earlier, typically are quite porous and permeable, characteristics that persist in many sandstones. Thus, even after the original sand has been lithified and hardened into a sandstone, fossils are likely still exposed to water circulating through the pore spaces. Although sandstones are not usually very fossiliferous, because of their typically good porosity and permeability, they do have one advantage in being relatively incompressible. This means that fossils preserved in them

FIGURE 3.2
Sediment consisting almost entirely of mollusk shells or shell debris.

are not usually squashed flat as they are in many mudstones and shales.

Sometimes, sandstone's porosity and permeability result in solution and removal of the original shelly material, leaving a space in the sandstone in the shape of the original fossil. The outside of the fossil is represented by what is known as an external mold imprinted in the rock, whereas sedimentary infilling of the insides of the fossil is called an internal mold (Figure 3.3). Using plaster or a suitable plastic modelling substance, paleontologists are often able to make good replicas, or casts, of the original shell or skeletal material.

Nature also often forms casts by filling in spaces with mineral materials that are precipitated from solutions circulating through the sedimentary rock. The great majority of fossils are preserved by these secondary minerals, which are introduced during diagenesis. Commonly, the original skeletal material—for example, calcite or aragonite secreted by mollusks—is replaced molecule by molecule by a secondary mineral, usually calcite or silica, but occasionally other minerals, such as pyrite. Thus, although not a single molecule of the original biogenic material remains, the fossil faithfully reproduces every tiny structural feature. Comparisons of modern mollusk shells with many fossil shells show that about the only difference is the lack of color in the fossil, although, on rare occasions, even traces of this may be preserved as light and dark patterns in replacement minerals (Figure 3.4).

FIGURE 3.3
External and internal molds of bivalves.

(a)

(b)

(c)

(d)

FIGURE 3.4

Examples of color patterns preserved in fossil mollusks.
(a) Conus yaquensis, (b) Conus trippae from the Early
Pliocene, (c) Lindoliva spengleri, and (d) Fasciolaria
evergladesensis from the Early Pleistocene. *(Photos courtesy
of E. J. Petuch.)*

To some extent, the state of preservation of a fossil depends also upon the original skeletal material. In scleractinian corals, bryozoans, many mollusks, and other invertebrates, the animal's skeleton is of aragonite, one of the two crystalline forms of calcium carbonate ($CaCO_3$). Aragonite is unstable, and after a relatively short time (often measured in a few thousand years), it changes to calcite, the other form of calcium carbonate. The recrystallization process invariably results in some loss of the finer details of the skeletal structure.

When the original skeletal material is calcite, on the other hand, preservation is typically better. This may explain why the Rugosa and Tabulata groups of corals from the Paleozoic are often better preserved than are scleractinian corals from much younger Mesozoic and Cenozoic rocks. Although not directly provable, the original rugose and tabulate coral skeletons may have been of calcite rather than aragonite, the mineral formed by the Scleractinia.

In a process known as **permineralization,** fossilization is due to additional mineral material precipitated in the pore spaces of the original shell or skeleton. This is commonly the way vertebrate skeletons are preserved.

Fossilization in Anoxic Environments

The process of fossilization is somewhat different in mudstones or shales. Because of the sediment's relatively impermeable nature, water movement through the pore spaces is very sluggish, or the water is stagnant. This means that dissolved oxygen is not renewed and that anoxic (oxygen-deficient) conditions exist in the pore spaces, which slows decay of soft tissues by bacteria. Sometimes, an impression of the soft tissues may be made in the sediment as it hardens, and in rare cases, even impressions of entirely soft-bodied animals have been preserved (Figure 3.5).

Such was the case in the well-known Middle Cambrian Burgess Shale discovered in 1910 by American geologist Charles Doolittle Walcott near Field, British Columbia. Over 35,000 specimens were collected, most of the fossils coming from a single 2-meter-thick layer. During the past 10 years, interest in this fauna has renewed, and the number of specimens has more than doubled. Most of the fossils are of creatures that were apparently swept down, in a submarine landslide, from a shallow-water shelf area where they were living, into deep water at the foot of a submarine slope. Here, they were quickly buried in an anoxic environment unfavorable to bacterial decay. The Burgess Shale fauna is remarkable for the abundance of soft-bodied animals that are not normally found as fossils. They make up 86 percent of the total specimens and include jellyfishes, anemone-like cnidarians, and annelid worms (Figure 3.6).

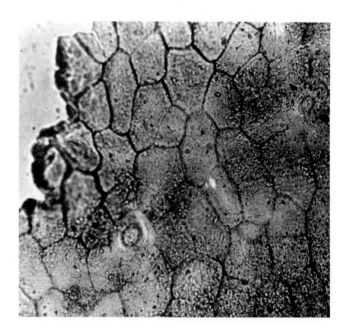

FIGURE 3.5
Plant cuticle tissue preserved in sediments of Lower
Devonian age, Sextant Formation, Northern Ontario, Canada.
This remarkably preserved material is original plant tissue
and is not replaced by chert or other secondary mineral.

An even older fauna, predating the Burgess Shale by
some 30 million years, was found in Yunnan Province,
China, in 1984. Although reported in Chinese scientific
journals, the Chengjiang fauna (as it is known from its
location) only came to the attention of Western paleontologists in 1991. Again, the fauna is characterized by
many soft-bodied marine organisms, apparently buried
quickly in an anoxic environment. Many of the forms are
clearly related to those described in the Burgess Shale assemblage.

Another unusual fauna in sediments apparently laid
down under similar anoxic conditions was discovered in
1984 in rocks of Silurian age at Waukesha, Wisconsin.
Again, the preservation of carbonized films of many soft-
bodied animals is remarkable.

One more example of exceptional preservation is seen
in the famous Mazon Creek fauna of Pennsylvanian age.
This fauna is especially noteworthy in that it contains elements of both marine and nonmarine forms in a deltaic
environment. The delta-plain facies include millipedes,
centipedes, scorpions, insects, fish, amphibians, and plants,
whereas, in the subaqueous delta, in addition to a typical
mollusk and brachiopod assemblage, are worms, holothu-
rians, medusoid coelenterates, and many other soft-bodied
forms. The fossils are found in nodules within the Car-
bondale Formation exposed along Mazon Creek in northeastern Illinois.

(a)

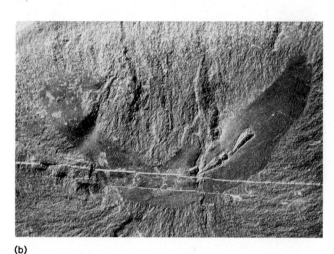

(b)

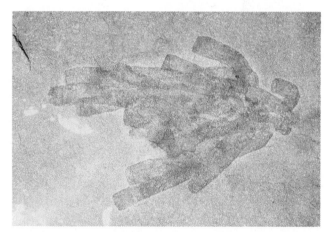

(c)

FIGURE 3.6
Examples of fossils from the Middle Cambrian Burgess Shale
of British Columbia. (a) Aysheaia, (b) Ottoia, (c) Vauxia.
(Photos courtesy of Des Collins Royal Ontario Museum.)

FIGURE 3.7

Fossiliferous limestone. In this example of Miocene age, almost the entire mass of the rock is made up of bioclastic debris, dominated by mollusca. *(Photo courtesy of E. J. Petuch.)*

FIGURE 3.8

A weathered surface of Silurian limestone, showing how the etching action of rainwater causes the fossils to project from the rock matrix.

In many cases, anoxic bottom conditions are only temporary and, perhaps, seasonal. At times, they may be the result of occasional catastrophes. They also may be sometimes linked to algal blooms, or "red tides," that cause mass mortality in the surface water. Such a model has been proposed to explain the occasional "bone beds" and "fish-scale beds" found, for example, in the Rhaetic Series of the European Triassic rocks and the Cretaceous of Colombia. These are veritable graveyards crammed with the remains of fish and other nektonic organisms that normally are rare as fossils. The model suggests that massive mortality of organisms in the water above causes a sudden rain of dead and decaying organic material onto the sea floor so that the aerobic bacterial decay system is temporarily overloaded, resulting in an oxygen deficiency.

Fossilization in Limestones

The most fossiliferous rocks are the limestones, some of which are made up almost entirely of lime-secreting organisms (Figure 3.7). Warm, clear, well-oxygenated waters provide the ideal conditions for an abundance of life-forms, and it was under such conditions that many of the extensive limestone formations of the Paleozoic were formed.

When a piece of limestone is broken with a hammer, the fresh surfaces rarely show any fossils because the rock matrix around the fossil is made of the same mineral (calcite) as the fossil itself. On weathered rock surfaces, however, rainwater (a very dilute carbonic acid) sometimes etches the limestone matrix more readily than the fossils so the fossils tend to stand out (Figure 3.8), or sometimes, the fossils are leached out, and a cavity is left.

In some cases, the original shell or skeleton has been fossilized through a process known as silicification, in which the fossil is preserved in silica. These fossils are especially prized by paleontologists because they typically are well preserved and are also easy to extract from the rock. The rock chunk is simply immersed in an acid bath (dilute hydrochloric acid is the solvent commonly used), and the matrix is dissolved away, leaving even the most delicate structural details of the fossil intact.

Trace Fossils

Not only are the remains of organisms fossilized after their death, but traces of their activities while they were still alive may sometimes also be preserved. Such **trace fossils** include the tracks, trails, and footprints of animals as they moved about over soft sediment. Many organisms also made burrows and borings on the sea floor or lake bed that may be preserved. The most common trace fossils are of **benthos** (bottom-dwelling organisms) (Figure 3.9). Much more uncommon are the imprints left by terrestrial animals as they moved across soft mud flats, among the most interesting being dinosaur footprints. A special category of trace fossils are **coprolites,** the fossil remains of feces.

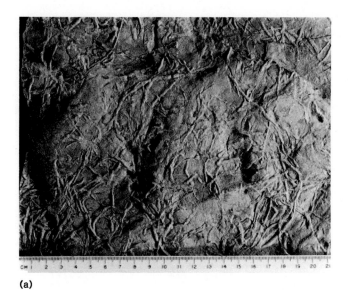

(a)

(b)

(c)

FIGURE 3.9
Tracks, trails, and burrows are common trace fossils on many bedding surfaces. (a) Unidentified worm trails. (b) *Arthrophycus,* possibly a worm trail from the Silurian of Tennessee. (c) Dinosaur footprint from the Jurassic of Arizona.

The animal responsible for trace fossils can only rarely be identified. Indeed, some of the strange markings described in the older literature have, on further investigation, proven to be of inorganic origin and caused by sediment compaction or shrinkage, escaping gas bubbles, and so on.

Nonmarine Fossils

Although the majority of fossils are of marine organisms, the seabed is not the only place where organisms become fossilized. Many great fossils have been found in sedimentary rocks deposited in lakes and riverbeds, but by far the best conditions for fossilization are in swamps. The reason for this should be obvious from what has been said about oxygen and decay processes. In swamps, water circulation is so sluggish that oxygen is in short supply, and again, normal decay processes are inhibited.

It is under such conditions that the world's great coal deposits were formed. Coal is a unique rock in that it is not made up of minerals in a normal sense. It begins as a peat deposit formed of vegetable material that has accumulated in the swamp and there been compressed. Lack of oxygen means that the normal decay that eliminates dead leaves in one's backyard, usually in the space of a single season, is not possible. Year after year, leaves and dead trees tumble into the swamp, where their compressed layers eventually form a semicarbonized deposit. The elevated pressures and temperatures that come with progressively deeper burial finally turn the material into coal.

Surprisingly, the fossil remains of the trees in the coals are usually too altered by the coalification process to be easily recognized, and the best fossils are found in the shales associated with the coals. Most typically, plant fossils are found as carbonized impressions flattened onto the bedding surfaces of mudrocks and siltstones. Even though the fossils are squashed flat, detail preservation is often remarkably good. (Of course, botanists are accustomed to studying flattened specimens because pressing plants is the most common way in which the plants are preserved in herbaria.) Together with the impressions of tree trunks, leaves, seeds, spores, and roots are sometimes found impressions of creatures that lived in these ancient forests. In the Pennsylvanian-age coal beds, described in Chapter 15, fossils of huge cockroaches and of dragonflies with wingspreads of half a meter have been found!

Among the most exciting nonmarine fossils are those of dinosaurs, but again the fossil record is biased in favor of those that lived along the edges of swamps and lakes. With what is known of the adaptability of modern reptiles, it would be surprising if the dinosaurs also had not come to fill a wide variety of habitats. Thus, just as many remarkably adapted reptiles live in modern desert regions, there were, undoubtedly, desert-dwelling dinosaurs. Unfortunately, desert environments of ancient times, although sometimes represented by fossil dune formations, like the Navajo Sandstone of the western United States, are typically unfossiliferous.

The bias in favor of swamp dwellers becomes noticeably less in the case of fossil mammals, probably because of the survival of more complete Cenozoic sedimentary successions, including many of terrestrial origin. In other words, the relatively young age of the rocks containing the record of the great mammalian evolutionary radiation ensures a fairer representation of species.

Birds, because of their delicate skeletons and preferred habitats, have the poorest fossil record of all vertebrates. Again, and rather predictably, the earlier fossils are those of diving birds, such as the flightless *Hesperornis* from the Cretaceous.

Insects in Amber

Our discussion thus far has dealt entirely with fossils buried in sediments of one kind or another. Fossils may be preserved, however, in certain other highly unusual environments. One of these is amber, a fossil tree resin often found to contain fossil insects. Just as with certain modern tree species, the sticky resin oozed out of the bark, and when insects and spiders were caught in its sticky embrace, they became completely coated and so preserved. Fossil amber of various ages is known, but the most famous comes from the Baltic Sea. Amber-containing beds of Miocene age apparently outcrop somewhere on the sea floor and are eroded. Amber floats, so pieces wash up on the shores of Poland and Germany.

Over the centuries, large amber collections were amassed, with the biggest in the museum at Peenemünde in northern Germany. During World War II, Peenemünde was the center of major German rocket research. Inevitably, the town was heavily bombed, and along with the rocket factories, the museum's collection of amber was destroyed.

What makes the insects in amber especially valuable is that, of all living creatures on the planet, the insects have the poorest fossil record, despite the fact that, in terms of both numbers of species and numbers of individuals, they have been by far the most successful of all animals. Some 75 percent of all living species on earth are insects, yet the fossil record accounts for far fewer than 1 percent of described fossil species.

Tar Seeps

Somewhat analogous to the sticky death of insects trapped in amber was the fate of the many animals stuck in natural surface tar seeps. The most famous tar-seep locality is at Rancho La Brea (*brea* is Spanish for "tar"), located in Hancock Park in Los Angeles, California. Here, a variety of Late Pleistocene terrestrial mammals and birds were trapped in the tar, which was probably often covered by a thin layer of water. Animals coming down to drink were quickly mired, and their struggles attracted predators and scavengers, who soon met the same fate. Smaller tar deposits, also of Pleistocene age, have been excavated near Talara, Peru, and on the Santa Elena Peninsula, Ecuador (Figure 3.10).

FIGURE 3.10
Modern tar seeps near Talara, Peru, are still trapping animals.

Preservation of Soft Tissues

Preservation of traces or impressions of soft tissue is, as already mentioned, highly unusual. Even more unusual is the preservation of the soft tissues themselves. In rare cases, the cuticles—that is, the skinlike outer layers of plant stems and leaves—have been preserved intact because this material is almost chemically inert, remaining unaffected by even the strongest acids. A striking example is seen in plant beds of Early Devonian age in northern Ontario, where thin layers of cuticle can be teased apart and handled in the laboratory in the same way as modern plant cuticle (Figure 3.11). That such tissues could survive over some 350 million years is remarkable.

Equally astonishing, although involving much younger remains, are the frozen mammoths of Alaska and Siberia. Exactly how the mammoths came to be entombed in the permafrost is a matter of conjecture. The sediments in which the animals are buried suggest that the animals perhaps broke through river ice or were buried by a falling riverbank.

With such unusual and exciting fossils, it is not surprising that there has been no little exaggeration and no shortage of stories about them, particularly regarding the state of preservation. In one such account, perpetuated for many years, the preservation of the meat was so good as to be still edible. As if that was not enough, it was even reported that mammoth steaks had been served up at a banquet held in St. Petersburg in 1912 during the International Geological Congress. In truth, the soft tissues have always been found in various stages of decay. The skin and fur are sometimes preserved, but other tissues are, in culinary terms, certainly well past the most "gamey" venison.

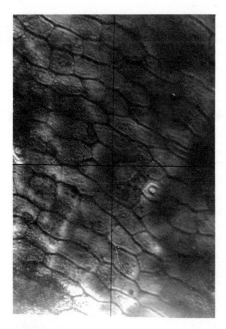 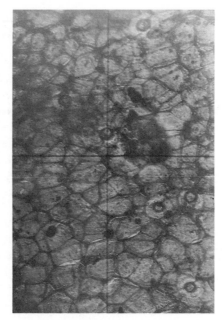 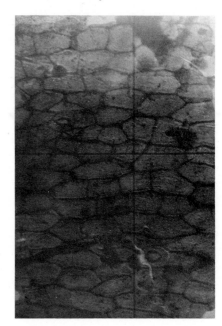

FIGURE 3.11
Plant cuticle tissue of Lower Devonian age from the Sextant formation, northern Ontario, that have been preserved in their original state.

Processes That Destroy Fossils

Every discovered fossil is a minor miracle. As we have seen, the likelihood of any animal or plant becoming fossilized is incredibly small. The odds against the fossil's eventual survival to the present day are increased by several geologic processes that destroy fossils.

One of the most effective ways that the fossil record is eliminated is by metamorphism, whereby rocks are subjected to high temperatures and high pressures and are changed into completely different rocks. As shales are turned into slates, phyllites, and schists, for example, recrystallization of the clay minerals effectively eliminates any fossils that might have been there. The transformation of limestone into marble usually eliminates all but the most massive fossils. Occasionally, traces of animals like corals and stromatoporoids may be discerned in intriguing patterns on polished marble slabs. Clearly, the older the rocks, the more likely they are to have undergone metamorphic change at some time or other. Precambrian rocks, in particular, are rarely found entirely unaltered, and only when fossils are preserved in a special way, such as in cherts, do any traces survive.

In limestones, fossils are often obliterated by dolomitization, which involves the changeover of calcite ($CaCO_3$) to dolomite ($CaMg(CO_3)_2$). In the process, the limestone is transformed into a sugary-textured rock (see Figure 2.3), and all of the limestone's original textural features, including fossils, are eliminated. Fortunately, in some limestones, fossils are preserved in chert nodules, which are unaffected by dolomitization.

Fossil Survival: The Odds

The odds against fossil survival can be estimated from some easily obtained data derived from an assessment of those modern organisms that are likely candidates for fossilization. In one study by G. Thorson of shallow-water benthic organisms off the coast of Japan, researchers counted the number of living mollusks of three species in one-quarter of a square meter. The three species were the bivalves *Macoma incongrua* and *Cardium hungerfordi* and the scaphopod *Dentalium octangulatum*. Inside the study plot, researchers counted 25 individuals of *Macoma,* 160 of *Cardium,* and 12 of *Dentalium*. With an average molluscan life span of two years, simple addition shows that, in ten years, this tiny portion of the seabed would produce approximately 1,000 potential fossils. In 1 million years, the number would be 100 million. Thus, in 1 million years, which, after all, is a relatively short time span in geologic terms, this small area would produce more individuals than all the fossil specimens of all species ever studied!

It is, of course, easy to play with numbers like these to demonstrate the fragmentary nature of the fossil record. Yet, despite the long odds against fossilization, careful and ongoing collecting often provides a reasonable record of past life. For example, in a fauna of 60 species, an estimated 50,000 specimens must be collected before there is a reasonable chance of finding the rarest species in the assemblage.

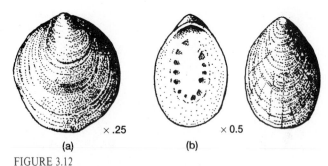

×.25 (a)   × 0.5 (b)

FIGURE 3.12

Comparison of (a) *Neopilina galatheae*, living today, and (b) *Pilina unquis* of Silurian age.

Gaps in the fossil record are also demonstrated with the occasional exciting discovery of "living fossils," organisms that are living examples of species thought to have been long since extinct. In 1938, for example, fishermen off the east coast of South Africa found in their catch examples of *Latimeria*, a coelacanth fish thought to have been extinct for 65 million years (see Figure 14.24a). Another living fossil turned up in 1956 when examples of a primitive gastropod were dredged up 3,600 meters off the Pacific coast of Mexico. Named *Neopilina galatheae*, this species was so similar to *Pilina*, which became extinct in the Late Devonian, that many taxonomists were unhappy about erecting a new genus for it (Figure 3.12).

Despite the huge gaps in the fossil record, much can be done to fill the gaps by extrapolation. Knowledge about modern faunas and floras enables geologists to assess the obvious bias in the fossil record and to make some intelligent guesses about what is *not* represented. New discoveries are being made all the time, and little by little, an ever more complete picture of past life is being assembled.

Taxonomy: The Classification of Fossils

Fossils were once living organisms, so they can be named and classified in the same way as are the animals and plants living on the earth today. The science of classification and naming of organisms is known as systematics, or **taxonomy,** and it not only recognizes the differences between groups of organisms, but also groups together those that are, in one way or another, similar and related to each other.

The system of classification and nomenclature in use today was described in Swedish naturalist Carl von Linné's great work *Systemae Naturae,* published in Stockholm, Sweden, in 1758. The Linnaean system of classification recognizes a hierarchy of groupings of organisms on the basis of their relationships and similarities, beginning with the largest division, the kingdom. In the eighteenth century, only the plant and animal kingdoms were recognized, but since that time, taxonomists have come to establish three additional kingdoms: (1) the fungi (heterotrophic, multicelled, but nonvascular plants), (2) the monera (unicelled organisms with simple **prokaryotic cells** containing no cell nucleus or other internal structures), and (3) the protista (organisms with more advanced **eukaryotic cells** containing a nucleus, organelles, and other structures). Each kingdom is subdivided into phyla, phyla into classes, and so on as set out in Table 3.1.

The fundamental unit is the species, and following the procedure established by Linné, two names are used: the species or trivial name and the generic name preceding it. So, for example, the human species is known as *Homo sapiens;* a dog is *Canis familiaris.* The genus name begins with a capital letter and the trivial name with a lowercase letter. This is the established convention, even when the species is named after someone—for example, *Didymograptus murchisoni* (named for geologist Roderick Murchison). To be strictly correct, and following the directives set out by the International Rules of Zoological Nomenclature, the genus and species name should be followed by the name of the scientist who first described and established the species and the date (for example, *Architectonica nobilis* Roding, 1954).

Normally, members of the same species look more or less alike, although, naturally, individuals differ in many relatively small ways that may be due to environmental influences and other causes. We have only to look at the human species to assess this particular factor. Sometimes, the morphologic differences between different species may not be obvious. Numerous **allopatric species** look alike but are separated geographically and thus are reproductively isolated from one another. **Sympatric species,** on the other hand, may live within the same area but are reproductively isolated by behavioral or other subtle differences.

Even when biologists are working with living populations and have access to data on life history, behavior, ecology, reproduction, and so on, not to mention the soft tissues to dissect, the proper determination of species is sometimes difficult. How much more difficult, then, is the task of paleontologists, who have only the hard parts to work with, and even these are sometimes not too well preserved. In attempting to recognize taxonomic divisions in fossil populations, paleontologists assume that the morphological differences between populations are of the kind and degree that would supposedly indicate reproductive isolation. Although paleontologists freely admit that this assumption is only an educated guess, in practice, it seems to work well enough.

Sometimes, ecologic variants within a single species can look remarkably different, as, for example, with certain scleractinian corals. Those individuals growing on the exposed outer reef tend to form low-growing and compact colonies, in marked contrast to those in the sheltered back reef, where more delicate and branching colonies are found.

TABLE 3.1
The Hierarchical Classification of Organisms

	Human	Pearly Nautilus
Kingdom	Animalia	Animalia
Phylum	Chordata	Mollusca
Class	Mammalia	Cephalopoda
Order	Primates	Nautilida
Family	Hominidae	Nautilidae
Genus	*Homo*	*Nautilus*
Species	*Homo sapiens*	*Nautilus pompilius*

A Guide to the Common Fossils

The bias in the fossil record means that we can only gain a glimpse of what life was really like on earth in past ages. In addition, the fossil record typically is extremely sparse. Many of the species described in the scientific literature have been identified only on the basis of little bits and pieces collected from a wide variety of locations and settings. In some cases, the species described are common, and almost anyone can find specimens with a modest amount of searching. Other species are extremely rare and may be known from only one or two specimens, or perhaps only from fragments. In the case of the famous fossil *Archaeopteryx,* the dinosaur with feathers that was originally hailed (although incorrectly) as the "missing link" between birds and reptiles, only six specimens have ever been found, despite the most diligent search. The extreme scarcity of these fossil finds is often due, not unexpectedly, to the preservational bias. In other instances, the species may never have been abundant in the first place.

As we shall see later, fossils are of great value to geologists as practical working tools. They not only are indicators of ancient environments but also can be used as biostratigraphic markers and index fossils in correlation and age determination. Inevitably, only the common species, such as marine invertebrates with hard shells, can be used in this day-to-day applied paleontology.

In comparisons of fossils with living animals and plants, one fact is immediately obvious: Many groups of modern organisms are entirely unrepresented in the fossil record, or at best are encountered only rarely. Conversely, a list of living groups does not compare very closely with a list of fossils because among the fossils are organisms belonging to groups that are now extinct.

Summary descriptions of the more common fossil groups follow. The groups are listed informally, and their taxonomic rankings are shown in Table 3.2 A taxonomy of all plants and animals, both living and extinct, is contained in Appendix B, and individual fossil species are discussed as appropriate in later chapters.

TABLE 3.2
Taxonomic Ranking of Common Fossil Groups

Fossil Group	Taxonomic Ranking
Cyanobacteria	Phylum of kingdom Monera
Protista	Kingdom
Porifera	Phylum of kingdom Animale
Archaeocyatha	Phylum of kingdom Animale
Cnidaria	Phylum of kingdom Animale
Bryozoa	Phylum of kingdom Animale
Brachiopoda	Phylum of kingdom Animale
Bivalvia (pelecypoda)	Class of phylum Mollusca
Gastropoda	Class of phylum Mollusca
Cephalopoda	Class of phylum Mollusca
Trilobita	Subphylum of phylum Arthropoda
Echinoidea and Crinoidea	Classes of phylum Echinodermata
Graptolithina	Class of phylum (or subphylum) Hemichordata

Cyanobacteria

The Cyanobacteria, formerly referred to, misleadingly, as blue-green algae, are photosynthesizing bacteria. Classified in kingdom Monera, they are unicellular organisms with prokaryote cells—that is, cells having no distinct nucleus, mitrochondria, or other internal structures. That such primitive organisms would be preserved as fossils at all is perhaps surprising, but they are, in fact, responsible for the organosedimentary structures called stromatolites. Stromatolites consist of thin layers of sediment trapped on the surface of so-called "algal mats," made up of colonies of cyanobacteria that grew on the surface of mud in shallow ponds and shoals in both freshwater and marine situations (Figure 3.13). Stromatolites provide the earliest evidence of life on earth: Those found in the Precambrian rocks of the Pilbara region of Western Australia are 3,500 million years old. Similar "algal mats" can be seen today on lakes, in tidal pools, and on intertidal flats in places like the Bahamas and the Persian Gulf. Layer upon layer of sediment is trapped by the sticky filaments of successive generations of cyanobacteria or precipitated by lime-secreting species. Eventually, quite large structures, measuring up to several meters in thickness, can form.

Protista

Most classifications recognize about 14 phyla in the kingdom Protista. Protista are largely single-celled organisms and are more advanced than the monerans in having a eukaryotic cell—that is, a cell with a nucleus containing genes and chromosomes. The most common forms occurring as fossils are the foraminifera (Figure 3.14), the radiolaria, the diatoms, and the coccolithophores. Most foraminifera and the coccolithophores secrete tests of calcium carbonate, while the radiolaria and diatoms secrete tests of opaline silica. Most protists are microscopic, and many species are planktonic in habit. They occur in ocean surface waters in countless numbers, and their remains accumulate on the deep ocean floors to form sediments known as oozes.

FIGURE 3.13
Mud-cracked surface of tidal flat with algal mat formed by cyanobacteria.

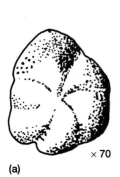

(a)   × 70

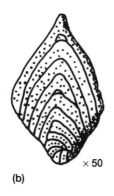

(b)   × 50

(c)   × 40

(d)   × 50

FIGURE 3.14
Representative foraminifera. These protozoans secrete tests of calcium carbonate and, together with the radiolaria and diatoms, are typical microfossils. Such fossils are widely used in the oil industry because they can be identified in well cuttings. (a) *Eponides.* (b) *Palmula.* (c) *Quinqueloculina.* (d) *Globigerina.*

Porifera

The phylum Porifera includes sponges, which are largely soft-bodied animals and which, except for one group (the stromatoporoids), are not particularly common as fossils (Figure 3.15). What *are* fairly abundant as microfossils in sediments of all ages are sponge spicules, tiny rodlike or star-shaped structures that function as loose, skeletal framework supports within the soft tissues of some sponges. The stromatoporoids were lime-secreting forms that are commonly found in Paleozoic reefs as important frame builders (Figure 3.16).

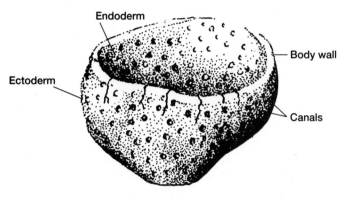

FIGURE 3.15
A simple sponge.

Archaeocyatha

The phylum Archaeocyatha is an example of a group of organisms that is now extinct and whose precise taxonomic affinities are unknown. The archaeocyathids have cone- or tube-shaped bodies with a double perforated wall surrounding an inner chamber (see Figure 12.10d). In many ways, they resemble sponges, but some taxonomists have suggested that they were primitive corals. The problem of which taxonomic division to put them in has been solved by erecting a new phylum to accommodate them. Archaeocyathids were responsible for some of the earliest reef structures in the fossil record and are particularly well represented in the Cambrian of Australia.

Cnidaria

The phylum Cnidaria is best represented among fossils by the corals. Other forms, such as jellyfishes and hydrozoans, are known as fossils, but because they secrete no hard shell or skeleton, they are extremely rare. During the Paleozoic, two major groups of corals—the Rugosa (Figure 3.17a) and the Tabulata (Figure 3.17b)—were important reef-building organisms in the warm, shallow seas that covered many continental interiors. All the skeleton-forming cnidarians became extinct by the close of the Permian, but apparently one or more unknown coral species,

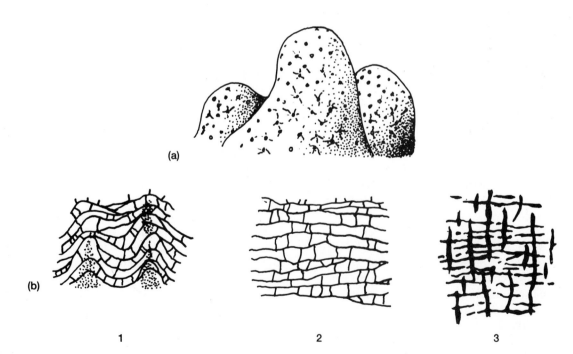

FIGURE 3.16
A stromatoporoid. Only recently have the true taxonomic affinities of these colonial organisms been discovered. They are now considered sponges and placed in the phylum Porifera. (a) External form. (b) As seen in thin section under the microscope. (1) *Stylodictyon columnare* (Middle Devonian). (2) *Clathrodictyon laxum* (Middle Devonian). (3) *Actinostroma expansum* (Upper Devonian).

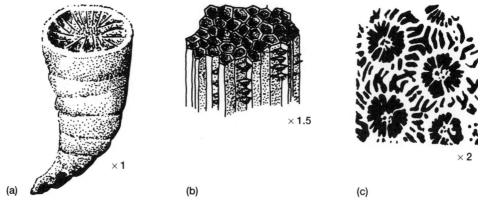

FIGURE 3.17
Representatives of the three main groups of corals.
(a) Rugosa (*Heterophrentis* sp.). (b) Tabulata (*Favosites* sp.).
(c) Scleractinian (*Montastrea* sp.).

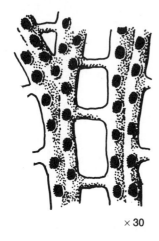

FIGURE 3.18
Portion of a bryozoan colony (lacy form *Fenestella* sp.).

presumably with no skeletons to preserve as fossils, survived to give rise to new reef-building groups, among them the scleractinian (or stony) corals of Mesozoic to Recent time (Figure 3.17c).

Bryozoa

The phylum Bryozoa consists of colonial organisms whose skeletons can be seen as small, lacey structures attached to the shells of other organisms, or as miniature shrublike branches or knoblike structures (Figure 3.18). Under the microscope, the surface of the skeleton is seen to be covered with many small openings, or pores, in each of which lived a diminutive animal, or zooid. The first bryozoans appeared in the Ordovician and have made a modest contribution to the fossil record ever since.

Brachiopoda

The Brachiopoda are exclusively marine animals that secrete a shell consisting of two valves. The brachiopods often bear a resemblance to the bivalves (mollusks). They are, however, anatomically different and belong to a different phylum altogether (Figure 3.19).

Bivalvia

The bivalves, or pelecypods as they are also called, include the clams, mussels, and oysters and belong to class Bivalvia of phylum Mollusca. They are characterized by two valves, left and right, which are joined along a hinge often lined with a series of teeth and sockets (Figure 3.20a). Bivalves have adapted to many modes of life, both in the sea and in fresh water.

The most obvious difference between a brachiopod and a bivalve involves symmetry. In the typical brachiopod, the valves are dissimilar, with one being larger than the other, but each valve is bilaterally symmetrical, as seen in a side view. That is, viewed from the front or the back, a line drawn vertically through the beak or umbo divides the valve into two symmetrical halves (see Figure 3.19). In most bivalved mollusks, on the other hand, each valve is not bilaterally symmetrical, but the two valves look the same, with one being virtually the mirror image of the other.

Gastropoda

Commonly referred to as snails, the Gastropoda are also members of the phylum Mollusca. In most groups, the animal is protected by a single shell, usually spirally coiled (Figure 3.20b). The hollow interior of the shell is fully occupied by the animal's soft tissues, and in most species, there is a muscular foot with which the animal is able to move about. Gastropods are found in marine water and fresh water and on land.

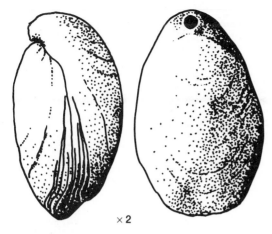

FIGURE 3.19
The brachiopod *Oleneothyris* sp.

Cephalopoda

Class Cephalopoda comprises the most advanced group within the phylum Mollusca and includes the octopus, squid, cuttlefish, and *Nautilus* (Figure 3.20c). All are exclusively marine, and all are active, swimming predators. Of these, only *Nautilus* develops a true external shell, which is plano-spirally coiled and is divided into a series of chambers. *Nautilus,* from the subclass Nautiloidea, is the only survivor of a great variety of closely related shelled cephalopods that lived in the past (Figure 3.20d). Particularly notable were the ammonites (subclass Ammonoidea) that became extinct at the close of the Cretaceous.

Trilobita

The Trilobita were among the earliest representatives of the phylum Arthropoda, appearing during the Cambrian and dying out at the close of the Permian (Figure 3.21). Some trilobites grew to 3/4 meter long, but the majority averaged 2 to 3 centimeters. They had trilobed, articulated bodies, and many developed complex eyes. Exclusively marine, they were adapted to crawling, burrowing, and swimming habits and became widely distributed, particularly in shallow-water environments.

Echinoidea and Crinoidea

The phylum Echinodermata includes starfishes, sea urchins, blastoids, and crinoids (sea lilies) (Figure 3.22). Although unlikely looking relatives, biologists have determined from a study of larval stages that this phylum is closely related to the phylum Chordata, which includes the vertebrates. Six major divisions, or subphyla, are recognized, including the Crinoidea, whose bodies are attached to the sea floor by long, jointed stems, and the Echinoidea, among them the mobile sea urchins.

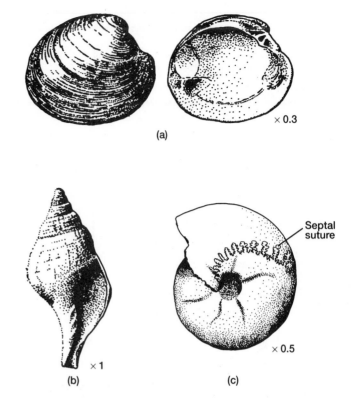

FIGURE 3.20
Typical mollusks. (a) The bivalve (pelecypod) *Merceneria merceneria*. (b) Gastropod *Fasciolaria rhomboidea*. (c) Cephalopod *Cyclolobus oldhami*. (d) Modern *Nautilus*, sectioned to show chambers.

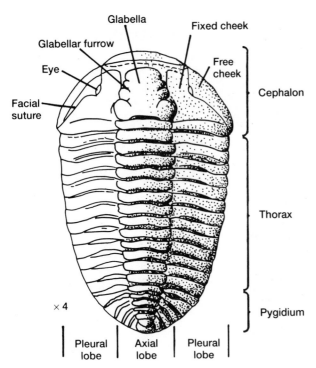

FIGURE 3.21
A typical trilobite, *Calymene* sp.

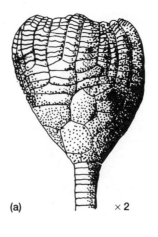

FIGURE 3.22
A typical crinoid, showing (a) calyx with arms folded and
(b) detail of one arm.

Graptolithina

Graptolites are a long-extinct group, and because they look
like nothing alive on earth today, they tended in the past
to be moved by paleontologists from one phylum to another (Figure 3.23). Today, graptolites are known to be
colonial members of the phylum Hemichordata. The
graptolite animal, about which virtually nothing is known,
lived in a small, tubelike sheath known as a theca. All the
thecae in a colony were assembled along one or more stipes,
or branches.

Because some graptolite species are believed to have
been planktonic in habit and to have floated for a long time
after death, they became very widely disseminated. They
also evolved quite rapidly so that, not only are certain species found with almost a worldwide distribution, but they
also had a limited time range, making them excellent
biostratigraphic zone fossils.

Fossils and Ancient Environments

Such is the amazing adaptability of life that virtually every
part of the earth has come to be occupied by organisms
of one kind or another. No place on earth is probably truly
lifeless. Even the deepest ocean depths and the hottest and
driest deserts have their own amazingly adapted inhab-

itants. Around the frozen continent of Antarctica, for example, animals such as penguins survive temperatures of
−70°F and are literally uncomfortable when the temperature rises above the freezing point.

Ecology is the study of the relationships of animals
and plants to their environment. Ecologic relationships involve not only the physical setting of the species on earth,
but also the species' relationship to its food supply and to
other species, some of which may be competitors, para-
sites, or even predators. The natural setting in which the
organism is placed is known as its **ecologic niche.** Ecology
is an important branch of biology and is very clearly a
field science, depending heavily upon observations made
within the **habitats** of the animals and plants being studied.

Paleoecology is the science of ancient environments.
Paleoecologic data are the source of much of the information required in the study of historical geology. Although much can be learned of ancient environments from
the study of sedimentary rocks, only the broadest outlines
of ancient geographies can be discerned in this way. The
fossils contained within the rocks are what provide scientists with the means of filling in the details, sometimes
with remarkable fidelity. Fossils can be used to determine
whether the containing sedimentary formation was deposited under marine or nonmarine conditions, in shallow
water or deep, in cold water or warm, under turbulent
conditions or in quiet water, and so on. In the case of geologically young fossils, extrapolation from what is known
of the habitats and life-styles of living relatives can be done
with some confidence. After all, it is generally assumed
that the scleractinian corals of 50 million years ago lived
under essentially the same conditions as do modern corals.

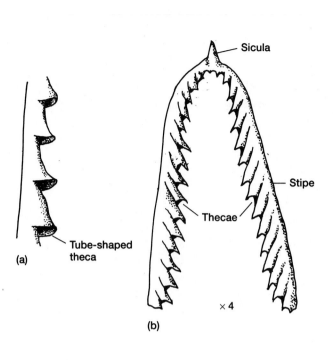

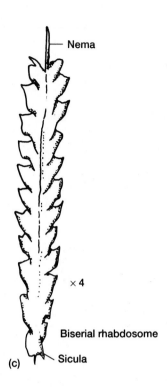

FIGURE 3.23
Typical graptolites. (a) Detail of thecae arranged along stipe.
(b) *Didymograptus protobifidus* (Lower Ordovician).
(c) *Climacograptus ulrichi* (Upper Ordovician).

As we move further back in time, however, the fossil faunas and floras become more alien; many belong to groups long since extinct, and in some cases, even the phylum to which they belonged is in some doubt. The environment in which such organisms lived has to be assessed with more caution. A further complication is that, during the course of evolutionary history, ecologic niches may have changed. For example, once shallow-water organisms may now be found only in deep water, perhaps forced there by increasing competition. For example *Hydnoceras*, the Devonian glass sponge, is found typically in rocks of the Chemung Group, generally interpreted as of relatively shallow-water origin. Today, glass sponges, some remarkably like *Hydnoceras*, are found only in deep water.

Marine Environmental Parameters

In shallow seas, variations in water depth, temperature, salinity, bottom sediment type, and other environmental parameters are reflected most strongly in the bottom-dwelling organisms, or benthos. Eurytopic animals are fairly tolerant and can live in a variety of environments. Stenotopic organisms, on the other hand, can only live in relatively restricted habitats. Corals provide some good examples of the relationship between animals and environment. Indeed, many local variations in sea-bottom environment are caused by the growth of the coral reefs themselves. On the outer reef, only species adapted to exposure to heavy surf can survive. This is in marked contrast to the shallow lagoon behind the reef, where a whole host of organisms adapted to quiet water conditions flourishes.

Many reef-dwelling organisms, including the corals, the main frame builders, show a marked depth zonation in the distribution of various species (Figure 3.24). The polyps of living stony or scleractinian corals are hosts to symbiotic algae that live within their tissues, and so they must live within what is termed the **photic zone**—that is, the zone where the sea is shallow enough for sunlight to penetrate. Some coral species are found in water as deep as 70 meters, but the majority flourish in depths to about 20 meters.

Animals that live in the ocean waters—the **nekton,** or swimming animals, and the **plankton** or floating organisms—clearly indicate little about the seabed environment. They are, however, often quite sensitive to surface water-temperature variations. Among the Jurassic ammonoid cephalopods, for example, there were, at times,

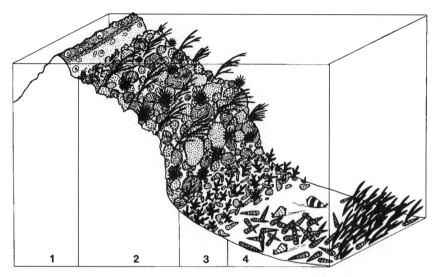

FIGURE 3.24
Depth zonation of various associations of reef organisms. This example is from the Miami reef tract. Zone 1 (*Millepora–Trochita* Zone): High energy, wave-surge reef crest, exposed at low tide. Zone 2 (*Diploria*-Gorgonian Zone): Lower energy reef platform dominated by massive corals and gorgonians.

Zone 3 (*Porites–Septastrea* Zone): Deeper water, low-energy, back-reef area dominated by fragile, branching corals. Zone 4 (*Thalassia–Turritella* Zone): Quiet lagoonal area dominated by turtle grass and *Turritella* beds and soft-substrate mollusks.

FIGURE 3.25
A fish from the Eocene Green River Formation. *(Photo courtesy of E. J. Petuch.)*

two quite distinct faunal assemblages, and these have been interpreted as a boreal, cool-water fauna and a so-called Tethyan or warm, tropical-water fauna. Among planktonic organisms, the foraminifera are particularly temperature-sensitive and have provided paleontologists with a useful means of determining ancient ocean temperatures by reference to the proportions of cold- and warm-water species found in bottom sediment cores. As is described in Chapter 20, the skeletons of these creatures also are used in the oxygen isotope method of determining ancient water temperatures (see Box 20.1). In layered cores of sea-bottom sediment that have accumulated over the past 2 million years, it is possible to record with remarkable precision the successive changes from warm ocean water to cold and back to warm again. These changes mark the alternation of glacial and interglacial periods as the glaciers and ice sheets waxed and waned. Such is the sensitivity of this method that very detailed "paleotemperature" curves can be constructed.

In addition to water depth and temperature, salinity is another important environmental parameter. Corals again are among the more sensitive animals, and in places where there is an incursion of fresh water, as near river mouths, corals are noticeably absent. Brachiopods, except for a few brackish-water forms, are exclusively marine animals, as are the cephalopods among the mollusks and all members of phylum Echinodermata. The discovery of fossils of any of these forms in sedimentary rocks is a certain indicator that the rocks are of marine origin.

Terrestrial Environmental Parameters

Among terrestrial organisms, the distribution of plants is what most closely reflects environmental variations. Unfortunately, plants are not the most common fossils. In certain sedimentary environments, spores and pollen grains can be climatic indicators. The fossil record of nonmarine invertebrates, like that of marine invertebrates, is dominated by those organisms with shells. Bivalves and gastropods are the most common freshwater fossils, but of the mollusks, only gastropods became fully adapted to life on land. On the present-day earth, the arthropods completely dominate terrestrial faunas, of course, with insects comprising the great majority of species. As mentioned earlier, however, the fossil record of insects is, not surprisingly, extremely poor.

Terrestrial vertebrates have a patchy fossil record. Under what must have been unusual bottom conditions, certain ancient lake deposits contain rich fish faunas (Figure 3.25), but in most sedimentary rocks, articulated skeletons are not generally common. Land-dwelling vertebrates are even rarer as fossils, and again, the majority are found in relatively localized environments, such as swamps. Sometimes, the survival of fossil material is due to the action of natural traps, such as sinkholes and caverns in ancient karstic topography developed on limestones. Even tree stumps with the interiors rotted out have been efficient traps for small vertebrates. The tar seeps mentioned earlier are another example.

Problems with Using Fossils As Paleoecologic Indicators

One of the problems with using fossils as paleoecologic indicators is that, quite often, they are found preserved in places far removed from where the organisms lived and died. The shells washed up on a modern beach are a good example. Shallow-water marine organisms may be swept into deeper water during storms or perhaps carried by turbidity currents. Similarly, freshwater and even land animals and plants may be transported down rivers in mats of floating vegetation and subsequently carried far out to sea. Their eventual burial and possible preservation as fossils would clearly be a source of confusion to some paleontologist in the distant future.

Postmortem transportation of this nature means that fossil assemblage may sometimes be a mixture of both species buried in situ (at or near the place where they lived and died) and those derived from some distant place. How do paleontologists solve a puzzle like this? Careful examination of the transported specimens may show signs of abrasion, or the specimens may consist of broken fragments, in contrast to the whole shells or skeletons of the in situ species. Hydraulic effects, like the sorting out of fossils of one particular size by the transporting currents, are also sometimes detectable because, in a living community, one would expect to find all growth stages represented, with juvenile and adults occurring together.

The preceding discussion clearly indicates that, to assume that a fossil assemblage is simply a once-living community frozen in time, as it were, may be completely erroneous. What the biologist calls a **biocoenosis,** or life assemblage (a group of animals or plants that lived together), may not be accurately represented in a **thanatocoenosis,** or death assemblage (fossil remains brought together after death simply as clasts by sedimentary processes).

Fossils can be transported not only in space but also through time. **Derived fossils** are those that are released from their enclosing sediment by weathering and erosion and that may be rapidly reburied in sediment of the current depositional cycle along with the remains of contemporary organisms (see Figure 3.1). After diagenetic changes in the sediment and fossilization of the newer generation of organisms, it might be virtually impossible to distinguish between the derived fossils and those with which they came to be buried.

A thorough paleontologic study, therefore, must go far beyond taxonomic identification and the preparation of a list of species. Not only must the forms be identified, but their relative abundance, their relationships to one another, their state of preservation, the surrounding sedimentary material, their position or attitude within the sediment, and so on, must all come under scrutiny. Only after such painstaking work is there any hope of compiling a meaningful picture of the organisms' life-style and the ancient earth they once inhabited.

Summary

Fossils are important in the study of historical geology because they provide information about past environments and climatic changes. They are also used for the dating and correlation of rock formations.

Because dead animals and plants are usually quickly destroyed by scavengers and bacterial decay, only a tiny fraction of all the organisms that have ever lived on earth have become fossilized. Even then, the soft tissues are invariably destroyed, and only the hard shell or skeleton is likely to survive. Fossilization is most likely to occur under conditions of rapid burial and oxygen exclusion. It follows from this that the fossil record as a whole is strongly biased in favor of marine organisms that secrete a hard shell or skeleton.

After burial in the deposits of a seabed or lake floor, the sediment hardens into rock around the shell or skeleton. Circulating water through the pore spaces of the sedimentary rock usually either removes the organic material in solution, leaving a mold or cast of the exterior form and a mold of the interior, or introduces a new mineral. This secondary mineral, commonly calcite or silica, replaces the original biogenic skeletal material molecule by molecule, faithfully reproducing the tiniest structural details. Sometimes, the fossil is preserved because of the deposition of minerals in the pore spaces of the buried remains in a process called permineralization.

In mudstones with poor porosity and permeability, there is little circulating water and oxygen. This means that the soft tissues of a buried plant or animal—or sometimes even entire soft-bodied animals—may survive long enough to leave an impression in the sediment as it hardens. Sometimes, a carbonized film outlining the soft tissues may be preserved. Under rare circumstances, such as with the Middle Cambrian Burgess Shale fauna, deposition and burial of organisms may occur under anoxic conditions, the elimination of aerobic bacterial decay resulting in remarkably well-preserved fossils of soft animals.

Traces of organisms' activities while they were still alive are also sometimes preserved. These trace fossils include the tracks, trails, and footprints of animals as they moved about over soft sediment. The most fossiliferous nonmarine sediments are formed in swamps and lakes. In addition to burial in sediments, fossils are occasionally preserved under special conditions, such as in amber, tar seeps, and permafrost.

Fossils once formed may be later destroyed by metamorphism, recrystallization, dolomitization (such as when limestone turns into dolostone), and weathering and erosion. Calculations based on counting living animals that are potential fossils show that even one-quarter of a square meter of seabed can produce 100 million fossils in 1 million years, many times the number of all the fossils ever collected. The extremely long odds against fossils being preserved are demonstrated in the occasional discovery of so-called "living fossils," when animals long thought extinct are found still living in obscure or inaccessible habitats.

Because fossils were once living organisms, they are classified in the same way as all animals and plants living on the earth today. Swedish naturalist Karl von Linné invented a binomial system, with a generic and specific (trivial) name applied to every species. Organisms are further grouped into families, orders, classes, and phyla in a hierarchy of divisions. Comparisons of the taxonomic classification of living and fossil organisms show that many divisions seen in the list of living organisms are missing from the fossil list because no fossil remains have ever been found. Conversely, in the fossil list are groups that became extinct and have no living relatives in modern faunas and floras.

Paleoecology is the science of ancient environments. Fossils are often extremely valuable as indicators of environmental conditions on the ancient earth. Fossils can be used to decide whether the containing sedimentary formation was deposited under marine or nonmarine conditions, in shallow water or deep, in cold water or warm, under turbulent conditions or in quiet water, and so on.

These environmental data are obtained by comparing the fossils with living relatives whose present-day habitat can be observed. This is reliable enough with relatively young fossils but becomes increasingly a matter of conjecture with older formations, where many of the fossils belong to extinct groups with no modern affinities. Problems with using fossils as paleoecologic indicators include fossils being preserved in places far removed from where the organisms lived and died and also fossil assemblages that are mixtures of species buried in situ and those derived from a distant location.

Questions

1. Describe some of the conditions required for fossilization and how the process of fossilization works.
2. Describe some of the circumstances under which sediments and organisms accumulate under anoxic conditions.
3. What are trace fossils?
4. Give some examples of how soft tissue may be preserved.
5. Describe some of the ways in which fossils are destroyed by geologic processes.

6. Explain the Linnaean system of binomial nomenclature. Look up the names of five fossil species and give the full nomenclature according to the International Rules of Zoological Nomenclature.
7. What is the difference between allopatric and sympatric species?
8. In comparisons of fossil faunas and floras with current living animals and plants, why is there a bias in the fossil record?
9. Why is it that certain living animal groups have little or no fossil record even though there were presumably ancestral forms living in the past? Cite some examples.

10. What are stromatolites?
11. Why do fossils like the graptolites make good index fossils in biostratigraphic correlation?
12. In what ways can fossils be used as indicators of ancient environments?
13. What organisms have been responsible for building reefs? What environmental parameters most favor reef-building activity?
14. In studying a fossil assemblage, describe some of the ways in which you could distinguish whether it was a biocoenosis or a thanatocoenosis.
15. Why do derived fossils cause problems in biostratigraphic correlation?

Further Reading

Beerbower, J. R. 1968. *Search for the past.* 2d ed. Englewood Cliffs, N.J.: Prentice-Hall.

Lane, G. N. 1978. *Life of the past.* Columbus, Ohio: Merrill.

Levin, H. L. 1975. *Life through time.* Dubuque, Iowa: Wm. C. Brown.

McAlester, A. L. 1977. *The history of life.* 2d ed. Englewood Cliffs, N. J.: Prentice-Hall.

MacDonald, J. R. 1978. *The fossil collector's handbook: A paleontology field guide.* Englewood Cliffs, N.J.: Prentice-Hall.

Raup, D. M., and S. M. Stanley. 1978. *Principles of paleontology.* 2d ed. San Francisco: W. H. Freeman.

Stearn, C. W. and R. L. Carroll, 1989 *Paleontology: The record of life.* New York: Wiley.

4

FOSSILS AND EVOLUTION

Introduction

Historical geology deals with the earth and its inhabitants through time. It describes the stage on which the story of evolution has unfolded, and it also gives some account and interpretation of the fossil record of evolutionary progress. This chapter discusses the concept of evolution and how the idea has itself evolved up to the present day. Of special importance is some understanding of the role that fossils have played in the development of evolutionary theory.

Even the earliest studies of fossils showed that different groups of rocks contained very different fossil assemblages. In moving up through any thick sequence of sediments, the changes in successive faunas were noticeable. In the eighteenth and early nineteenth centuries, as described in Chapter 1, scientists widely believed that such changes were evidence of successive creations. Even at a time when species were believed to be fixed and unchanging, it was becoming recognized that the oldest beds contained the remains of organisms that were more primitive than those from younger beds. In other words, some kind of progress toward ever-more-perfect creations was supposedly demonstrated, even though no evolutionary mechanism or evolutionary progress as such was envisioned. In general, up to the mid-nineteenth century, most biologists and paleontologists believed that species did not change and were the product of a Creation event (or events). This was the view of the greatest nineteenth-century paleontologist, Georges Cuvier, and it was, at first, shared by none other than Charles Lyell.

Pre-Darwinian Evolutionary Ideas

The name of Charles Darwin has come to be linked firmly with the theory of evolution, but he was not by any means the first person to suggest that species could change and evolve. Many of the natural philosophers of ancient Greece, for example, believed that life had evolved and had come out of water. As has happened so often throughout history, however, scholars then took a wrong turn. This was a result of the teachings of Aristotle, who believed in a single act of Creation and in the idea that all species were immutable and had always been so from the beginning. Because the Creation event so envisaged fit in with the account spelled out in the Bible, it was probably inevitable that the immutability of species should become fixed within the body of Christian dogma.

Fortunately, this did not stop many people from believing otherwise. Notable among them was the French diplomat and scholar Benoit de Maillet, who in 1715 wrote a book in which he described how the first life-forms had colonized the earth from space, a remarkably modern idea

that has many proponents today. He went on to describe how fish had gradually evolved into birds. As with so many scholars with unorthodox views, he lived in fear of the power of the Catholic church and went through a great deal of trouble to hide his identity. He even went so far as to leave instructions that his later work should not be published until 11 years after his death!

Although ideas about evolution were widely discussed, most of them were, at best, rather muddled. The object in some cases was simply to circumvent the problem of getting all the animals into Noah's ark! The size of the ark had long been a thorny problem for scholars, so a rather obvious solution was to suggest that only a selection of species had been taken aboard and that the rest had evolved later in the post-Deluge Period.

In the early nineteenth century, discussions of evolutionary changes were slowly edging closer to the truth in that the influence of the environment was being considered. Erasmus Darwin—physician, naturalist, and grandfather to Charles Darwin—maintained, for example, that the most obvious relationships between morphology and environment could be seen in the ways animals acquired their food. According to the elder Darwin, the environment was reflected in the acquisition of given characteristics that were passed on so that future generations would be better adapted to their environment. This sounds very similar to what Charles Darwin was to say, and some have suggested that he was influenced by his grandfather's ideas. Be that as it may, Charles Darwin's early writings indicate that he believed that species were fixed and immutable.

Paramount among pre-Darwinian evolutionists was Frenchman Jean Baptiste Lamarck (1744–1829), professor of zoology at the Musee National d'Histoire Naturelle in Paris. Lamarck proposed the variant idea of evolution (which became known as **Lamarckism**) that implied that characteristics acquired during the lifetime of an individual could be inherited by offspring. Again, the environment was seen as the key. In the Lamarckian model, the giraffe's long neck had been acquired as a result of constant stretching up to reach the leaves of trees over many generations (Figure 4.1). Although Lamarck's views on the inheritance of acquired characteristics were largely discarded by the middle of the nineteenth century, a form of Lamarckism survived into the midtwentieth century in Stalinist Russia in the political doctrine that insists that humans are a product of their environment. Despite the weak scientific foundation of Lamarck's views, he was far ahead of many scientists of his time in recognizing fossils as the ancestors of modern species.

Yet another study showing remarkable insight but, surprisingly, largely overlooked by modern historians was a book by Robert Chambers published in 1844. Entitled

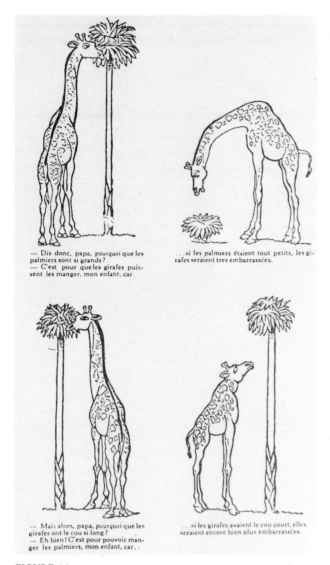

— Dis donc, papa, pourquoi que les palmiers sont si grands?
— C'est pour que les girafes puissent les manger, mon enfant, car.

...si les palmiers étaient tout petits, les girafes seraient très embarrassées.

— Mais alors, papa, pourquoi que les girafes ont le cou si long?
— Eh bien! C'est pour pouvoir manger les palmiers, mon enfant, car..

...si les girafes avaient le cou court, elles seraient encore bien plus embarrassées.

FIGURE 4.1

The Lamarckian model of evolution, a caricature by Caran d'Ache.

Vestiges of the Natural History of Creation, the work reveals an understanding of the broad features of the fossil record and of progressive change through geologic time that is essentially modern. By purely intuitive means and a shrewd interpretation of evidence that was already available, Chambers was asking many of the questions that were to be answered by Darwin. Discussed were such topics as the species concept, the geologic history of species, and their geographic distribution. Chambers also suggested that the fossil record reflects a basic organic continuity, rather than being the product of repeated creations. He even touched upon what for that day and age was a delicate subject—namely, the origin of life. He speculated that, because of the essential chemical commonality of all substances living and nonliving, life must have arisen from nonlife.

A further truly astonishing example of geologic insight was Chamber's discussion of lunar features, in which he correctly interpreted an ordering of events, with older features overlain or intersected by younger. In other words, he clearly had a grasp of the principles of lunar stratigraphy that was fully a century ahead of its time.

It is perhaps a sad commentary on the inhibitions of midnineteenth-century society that Chambers elected not to reveal the authorship of his work, despite its enormous success. The book, in fact, ran to no fewer than 11 editions, the last appearing in 1860, and 23,750 copies were printed in all. The book was widely read, and the mystery surrounding its authorship was a lively topic of speculation in Victorian drawing rooms. The secret was known only to the author's wife, his brother William, and two friends, and was kept even after Robert Chambers died in 1871. It was, in fact, not until 1884, after the death of William Chambers, that the authorship was finally revealed by the sole surviving confidante, Alexander Ireland.

Dawn of Evolution

Charles Darwin's original intention had been to become a doctor, an idea that was soon discarded for the simple reason that he apparently could not stand the sight of blood! He next turned to the church and eventually received his Bachelor of Arts degree in theology at Cambridge University. During his time there, his real interest in biology, or natural history as it was called in those days, became apparent, and this led him to become a student and eventually a friend of Cambridge botanist and geologist Professor John Henslow. This friendship was to change the whole course of young Charles's life. At this time, the British government was planning the itinerary for a world cruise by their survey and research vessel *H.M.S. Beagle.* When the time came to muster the scientific personnel, the captain, Robert Fitzroy, approached Henslow for help in finding a suitable biologist. Henslow suggested Darwin, and so it was arranged (Box 4.1).

H.M.S. Beagle sailed on 27 December 1831, and during the more than 80,000 kilometers and five-year voyage (Box 4.1), Darwin was able to amass a vast quantity of scientific data, not only on animals and plants, but also on geology and fossils. He made large collections of specimens of all kinds, most of which are housed in the British Museum of Natural History. Darwin drew upon this collection as he produced numerous scientific papers and books that eventually culminated in his theory of evolution.

BOX 4.1

Darwin and H.M.S. Beagle

The course of history is, as everyone knows, controlled by a series of events. In retrospect, a very trivial happening is often seen to have had immense significance and even sometimes to have ''changed the course of history.''

In the case of Charles Darwin, his whole life was changed in the late summer of 1831. September 1st, the first day of the partridge-hunting season, happened to be a fine sunny day, which was why Darwin rode to the home of his uncle Josiah Wedgwood (founder of the famous pottery) to take part in a partridge shoot. His conversation with his uncle on that morning was a turning point.

When Darwin was first offered the post on the *Beagle,* his father did not approve because the *Beagle* position was unpaid. Clearly, Darwin needed parental support, as indeed he had during his tenure at Cambridge. Bitterly disappointed, Darwin accordingly wrote to John Henslow at Cambridge, declining the offer. When Darwin told the story to his uncle on that fine September morning, Josiah Wedgwood urged Darwin to write to his father at once to see if he would change his mind, and this Darwin did before leaving for a day of sport. Sensing, presumably, that this was an urgent matter, Josiah Wedgwood then had second thoughts. Accordingly, a servant was dispatched to fetch

Darwin back so that he and Josiah could go to see Dr. Darwin without delay. The combined arguments of son and brother-in-law were obviously too much for the good doctor because he finally gave in.

Overjoyed, Darwin wrote to Henslow, canceling his earlier letter of refusal. Unfortunately, he was too late, and when Darwin went to Cambridge the following day, he was told that someone else had been offered the post but that the captain of the *Beagle,* Robert Fitzroy, would make the final decision. Darwin lost no time in arranging an appointment with Captain Fitzroy, and much to his relief, the two men took an instant liking to one another and Darwin was offered the post.

Fitzroy

Darwin

Henslow

Huxley

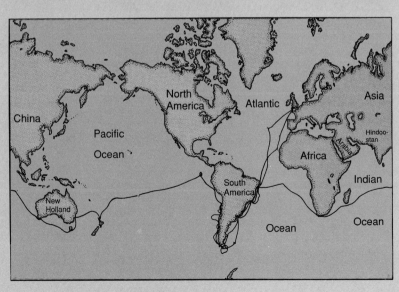

BOX FIGURE 4.1
H.M.S. Beagle and its five-year voyage.

Darwin and the Galápagos

Of all the places that Darwin visited on his epic voyage, none has come to have a closer association with him than the Galápagos Islands that lie some 1,100 kilometers off the coast of Ecuador. On these volcanic islands that had emerged from the floor of the Pacific in Miocene time, some 20 million years ago, Darwin was struck not only by the haunting similarity between island species and those on the mainland, but also by their differences, more particularly by the differences from island to island. These differences could be seen in a whole range of species of reptiles and, especially, in birds.

Darwin took particular note of the finches, the only land birds, of which he found 14 species on the islands (including nearby Cocos Island) (Figure 4.2). While they were clearly related to a species on the nearby mainland (believed by David Steadman of the New York State Museum to be the blue-black grassquit *Volatinia jacarina,* a species found from Mexico to Chile), they were so different as to fill various ecologic niches. These birds reflected **adaptation,** a feature of an organism that better enables it to live in its environment. Some had apparently become adapted to a diet of nuts and had developed heavy beaks with which to crack the nuts. Others were insectivores or vegetarians, while one species had adapted the life-style of a woodpecker and, lacking a long beak, used a cactus spine to reach for insects. Incidentally, this habit gives the species a claim to fame as the only tool-using bird.

All of these various species had apparently arisen from a single parent stock (a common ancestor) of mainland finches that at some time in the remote past had managed to reach the islands. Biologists have noted many instances of long-distance transportation of even small birds by storm winds or hurricanes. Immigration in this manner follows what has been termed the sweepstakes route. Given enough time, even the biggest geographic barriers may be eventually crossed during a chance event. Darwin noticed that many other island populations also had their own peculiar species and similarly had apparently risen from parent immigrant stocks. The absence of those forms that were incapable of any long-distance migration was equally significant. Thus, large land mammals, many terrestrial reptiles, and terrestrial invertebrates are often notably absent from island faunas, unless they have been introduced by humans.

Introduction of the Darwin/Wallace Thesis

Studies of island races led another biologist, Alfred Russel Wallace, to stumble independently upon the same revelation as Darwin. Wallace and Darwin knew of each other's work and agreed to present their findings together, and so before the 1 July 1859 meeting of the Linnean Society in London, they presented a joint paper. Their findings were received with polite interest, but beyond that,

(a)

Group	Diet	Bill	Name
Tree finches (Camarhynchus spp.)	Fruit	Parrot like bill	Vegetarian tree finch
	Insects	Grasping bills	Large insectivorous tree finch (C. psittacula) C
			Small insectivorous tree finch (C. parvulus) E
		Probing bills	Woodpecker finch (C. pallidus) A
Warbler finch			Warbler finch (Certhidea sp.) G
Ground finches (Geospiza spp.)	Cactus	Crushing bills	Cactus ground finch (G. scandens) N
	Seeds		Sharp-beaked ground finch (G. difficilis) L
			Small ground finch (G. fuliginosa) K
			Medium ground finch (G. fortis) J
			Large ground finch (G. magnirostris) I

(b)

FIGURE 4.2

(a) The 14 species of finches indigenous to the Galápagos Islands and nearby Cocos Island. (b) Characteristics of ten representative finches.

nothing much happened. This apparent lack of interest probably gave Darwin the impetus to finish his book, and *On the Origin of Species by Means of Natural Selection or the Preservation of Favored Races in the Struggle for Life* was published in November 1859. The book had an immediate impact and aroused so much interest that the first edition sold out on the day of publication!

Darwin's thesis was not by any means based solely on the observations and specimens accumulated during the voyage of *H.M.S. Beagle.* Much of the evidence he used to explain his theory was, in fact, already well known; he simply reinterpreted it. What made Darwin's thesis so believable was its basic simplicity. His main point was simply this: In any population, those individuals that are better adapted to their environment than their fellows, perhaps because of only small variations in form, or size, or behavior, are more likely to survive and to pass their useful characteristics to their offspring. If this process is continued over many generations, the organism naturally becomes increasingly well adapted to its environment. If the environment changes, other characteristics of the animal are tested, and other variant forms succeed and gradually displace the traditional, or parent, stock. Thus, species are not fixed and immutable products of some creation event, but have arisen from other species. The whole panoply of life from its origin on earth is the result of a progressive and ongoing process of change from ancestral to descendent species.

Controversy over Darwinian Evolution

Because humans were part of Darwin's evolution thesis, there was, not surprisingly, an immediate outcry from the church, particularly from the more fundamentalist elements. Clearly, a belief in the Book of Genesis would not be easy to sustain if humans' relationship to other more primitive animals demonstrated a common ancestry.

Darwin was a shy and retiring man and shrank from the controversy aroused by his book. Thus, renowned vertebrate paleontologist Thomas Henry Huxley, a man who, in marked contrast to Darwin, loved a good debate, took up the cudgels for Darwin. The famous debate in Oxford on 30 June 1860 between Huxley and Samuel Wilberforce, Bishop of Oxford, is now, of course, a matter of record, particularly the closing minutes. When it was clear that the argument was going badly for him, Wilberforce attempted to retrieve the situation with a joke, asking Huxley whether he was descended from an ape on his grandmother's or his grandfather's side. At this, Huxley is reported to have leaned across to a neighbor and whispered, "The Lord hath delivered him into mine hands." (Whether he really said this has recently been a topic for discussion, but be that as it may, if he did not say it, there is little doubt that he thought it!)[1] Upon which Huxley rose to his feet and in his reply said, "If you ask me whether I would prefer to have an ape for my grandfather or a

brilliant man of great importance and influence, who uses his gifts to make mock of a serious scientific discussion, then I unhesitatingly declare that I prefer the ape."

At this there was pandemonium, and it is reported that a Lady Brewster swooned (as was fashionable for Victorian ladies) and had to be carried from the hall. Order was finally restored by the moderator, John Henslow, Darwin's old friend. Joseph Hooker, another botanist, and, incidentally, Henslow's son-in-law, then fired the final broadside in summing up for the evolutionists. That was the end for the Wilberforce contingent, who, it was generally agreed, could be said to have sunk with all hands!

The Influence of Malthus

As mentioned in Chapter 1, Lyell's book *Principles of Geology* made a big impression on Darwin, but another book was equally important. This book, written by English clergyman Thomas Malthus, dealt with the problem of overpopulation. Malthus pointed out that, in natural animal populations, there is typically an overproduction of offspring, but that only a few survive because of competition. His main thesis was that, because humans had virtually eliminated the factor of competition, the human race would go on increasing in geometrical progression, whereas food supplies would increase only arithmetically. In other words, the natural balance that was normally set between populations and food supply was upset, and Malthus forecast a time when humans would no longer be able to provide sufficient food, and there would be widespread famine.

These ideas were new and, to say the least, controversial. Indeed, the author's doubts about their reception were such that the first edition of the book was published anonymously, and only with the second edition did Malthus reveal his identity. The book's reception was mixed, and although Malthus's views quickly gained many adherents, there were others to whom this gospel of doom was downright ridiculous.

Today, Malthus's views sound all too familiar. In the last 20 years in particular, we have all become so aware of the population explosion that the apparent naiveté that existed in the nineteenth century is difficult to accept. On the other hand, this was the time when the western nations were looking at new lands and indulging in that typical Victorian occupation of empire building. All the major European nations were so engaged, and vast colonial territories were being carved out of Africa and Asia. Australia was being settled, as was much of southern South

1. In the days before tape recorders and videocameras, the accounts of speeches and debates were often pieced together from the recollections of several eyewitnesses, and there is little doubt that recollections sometimes varied. This would be especially the case in the informal rough-and-tumble of the Huxley/Wilberforce debate, so it is small wonder that there are several versions of what actually was said during the course of the evening. The version given here is accurate in all essential details and so will suffice.

FIGURE 4.3
A Victorian view of the Jurassic world. Nature "red in tooth and claw" is how Tennyson summed up the concept of survival of the fittest.

America. In North America, the immense spaces of the West beckoned. The supply of available land and space to grow food must have seemed inexhaustible.

As Darwin pondered the enormous mass of data he had acquired on his voyage and his great theory began to take form, a phrase used by Malthus apparently made a great impression on him. "The struggle for life," as Malthus put it, exactly described what Darwin was trying to say. All life was a struggle to survive, and only those individuals best adapted to their environment would succeed in passing on their characteristics to their descendants.

Misinterpretation of Darwin's Thesis

In the intellectual world of the nineteenth century, Darwin's book was, curiously enough, to cause controversy both because of implacable opposition, as we have seen, and also because of what was in many ways an overenthusiastic acceptance. Inevitably, there were misunderstandings of what evolution was all about, and Darwin's use of the word *struggle* (borrowed from Malthus) caused much of the trouble. As Darwin saw it, the struggle for life described what happened as species evolved: It was the struggle for survival of the fittest variants over the less fit. Nowhere in Darwin's work is there any indication that he visualized an actual life-and-death struggle between individuals or species. Unfortunately, many people interpreted Darwinian evolution to be a natural process involving the strong overcoming the weak. In other words, nature "red in tooth and claw," as Tennyson put it, was everywhere seen in constant, competitive struggle (Figure 4.3).

It quickly became fashionable to assess all sorts of human activities—political, sociologic, economic, ethnologic, and even theological—in terms of Darwinian principles. "Survival of the fittest" became a cant phrase used

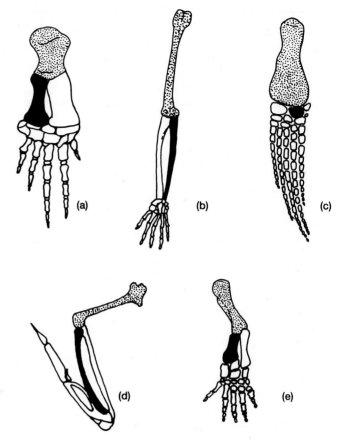

FIGURE 4.4
Homologous bones in the forelimbs of (a) whale, (b) human, (c) plesiosaur, (d) bird, and (e) amphibian (*Trematops*).

to justify questionable activities, many of which are better left unmentioned. The dispossession of native peoples by "fitter" white races in the acquisition of colonial territories, mentioned earlier, was one of these activities. From such origins also arose the ridiculous "master race" cults that were largely responsible for two world wars. That Hitler was an avid believer in so-called "Darwinian principles" should come as no surprise.

Evolution Applied to Biology

Many biological phenomena, already known for years, could be reinterpreted in the light of evolution.

Homologous and Vestigial Organs

Particularly interesting to Darwin was the evidence of **homologous organs.** Thus, two very different animals often have similar-looking bones that serve very different functions. Homologues of the five digital bones of the human hand can be seen in the limbs of such diverse creatures as whales, reptiles, and birds (Figure 4.4). Evidence for a common ancestry is also often seen in **vestigial organs,** which are those structures in an animal that no longer serve

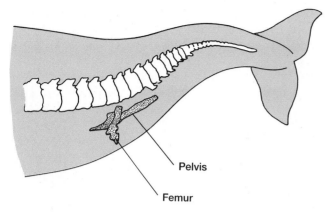

Pelvis

Femur

FIGURE 4.5
Vestigial pelvic bones in baleen whale skeleton.

any useful purpose but that can be compared with those of functioning organs in other animals (Figure 4.5). That whales, for example, evolved from a four-legged ancestor is clearly demonstrated by the presence of small pelvic bones, representing vestigial limb elements.

Although evolution is synonymous with change and clearly implies the disappearance by extinction of ancestral forms, the genetic blueprints are apparently not destroyed, and, on rare occasions, still have an influence. Whales with nonfunctioning hind limbs, horses with three toes, and humans with tails are among rare but fascinating glimpses of ancient genetic codes still affecting **ontogeny** (the growth and development of the individual).

Haeckel's Law

In Germany, strong support for Darwin's ideas came from a different field of investigation, that of embryology. Eminent embryologist Ernst Haeckel (1834–1919) had noticed that, as a mammalian embryo went through successive developmental stages, it exhibited various features reminiscent of animals that presumably formed part of the species' ancestral lineage. Thus, the human embryo in its early stages possesses gill slits and a very fishlike tail. In other words, the embryo's developmental stages reflect the evolutionary stages of **phylogeny** (the evolutionary history of the species). This seemed to be convincing proof of evolution from more primitive ancestors and became known as **Haeckel's Law,** often simply stated as: "Ontogeny recapitulates phylogeny."

The close resemblance between early embryos from widely different animals had also long been noted, and one of the people to remark on this was zoologist Louis Agassiz of Pleistocene Ice Age fame. Although opposed to Darwin's views on religious grounds, he did not believe in immutable species and rather saw organic progression as part of some grand design.

The Birth of Genetics

Perhaps, the missing link in Darwin's chain of evidence for evolution was his inability to explain the mechanism of inheritance. By a strange twist of irony, unknown to Darwin, a discovery made by Moravian[2] monk Gregor Mendel in 1869 would have provided him with the answer.

Mendel's Pea Experiments

Working with sweet peas, Mendel showed that the flower's colors were controlled by hereditary factors derived from the parents. In the strains of plants he used, two forms of the same factor were apparently present, one red and one white. When they were combined during breeding, the result was not a pink flower, as would have been suggested by what was known of inheritance at that time, but all red flowers. This was because the red factor was the dominant one, while the white was recessive. In the second generation of offspring from interbreeding of the red flowers, Mendel found that one white flower was produced for every three red ones. In this further mixing, the factors were combined as follows: red/red, red/white, white/red, and white/white. Only when both white factors were present were white flowers produced. Generation by generation, Mendel was able to mathematically predict the ratios of red and white flowers. Unfortunately, he published his results in an obscure journal that no one in the West ever read and then apparently did no further studies along these lines. Mendel's study was not unearthed until the early 1900s, after other workers had independently come to the same conclusions.

Mendel's hereditary factors came to be called genes, and so was born the science of **genetics.** The most significant feature of Mendel's work was his discovery that the hereditary factors, or genes, retain their separate identity through many generations. If Darwin had known this, he would have held the key to understanding why the favorable characteristics manifested in one generation could persist through following generations without being diluted during successive breeding cycles. He knew that, somehow, the favorable characteristics were retained—indeed, his basic thesis demanded it—but he could not explain how. Darwin's opponents, not unnaturally, made much of this and held it to be the fatal flaw in the theory of evolution.

Genetic Advances

As genetics progressed during the first half of the twentieth century, the most important advances came in genetic chemistry, as the molecular structures of the genetic material finally came to be understood. The culminating

2. Moravia was once part of Czechoslovakia.

study, published in 1953, was the description by Cambridge biologists James Watson and Frances Crick of the **DNA molecule.** Chemically, genes are made up of long molecules of the compound deoxyribonucleic acid. Called DNA for short, this compound contains chemically coded instructions for an organism's growth and development. Even the slightest changes in this chemical coding result in the appearance of new instructions and, in turn, of new characteristics in the organism.

Sources of Genetic Variability: Reproduction and Mutations

Offspring receive half of their genetic material from each parent and thus are never identical to one parent. Most of the differences among individuals are due to recombination during the meiotic stage of cell division in sexual reproduction, which involves the exchange of chromosomes and also changes in the positions of genes and gene fragments on the chromosomes. Because it is responsible for a rapid reshuffling of gene combinations, sexual reproduction is the primary cause of variability and genetic diversity, and as such, it provides the potential for change, generation by generation. It is, in fact, the main driving force in evolution.

A second source of genetic variability involves gene **mutations,** in which the cell's DNA molecules are changed. At cell division, then, the new cells may receive an imperfect copy of the parent cell's genetic material. Such "misprints" can and do apparently occur at random. External effects, such as bombardment by radiation or the influence of chemical agents, can also slightly alter genetic instructions.

Mutations introduce a random variable into the process of sexual recombination, thereby continually producing new genetic combinations. Most mutations are detrimental, but result in changes in the new generation that are so subtle as to be undetectable. Occasionally, on the other hand, the new variant may inherit a trait that gives it a distinct advantage over the rest of the population. From here on, Darwin would have been quite at home; clearly, the statistical odds for the survival of the new variant and its ability to pass on that trait would be measurably improved.

One of the best examples of this principle at work is seen in the oft-cited case of industrial melanism in moths. Because butterflies and moths have been favorites of collectors for many years, large collections were available for studying variation within a species. Of special interest is *Biston betularia,* the peppered moth, studied in England. In its natural woodland habitat, the normal gray and speckled moth was almost perfectly camouflaged against the bark of the sycamore tree, its usual habitat. This was clearly a big defensive advantage over predatory birds. Occasionally, collectors noted and eagerly sought a mutant

dark variety of the moth. During the nineteenth century, as the Industrial Revolution produced great manufacturing cities like Birmingham and Liverpool, the smog resulting from the burning of coal not only blackened all the buildings in the cities, but also spread a dark pall over the surrounding countryside. This introduced a significant change in the peppered moth's environment. On the soot-blackened trees, its gray color was no longer a protective camouflage against birds, and so populations were significantly reduced. Not so for the mutant dark variety of the moth; they were now the invisible ones, and so their numbers increased. In recent years, with the reduction of coal-burning and the introduction of new clean-air policies, the balance of gray and dark varieties of peppered moth is returning to normal. The **selection pressure** (the influence of the environment) illustrated in this example can only operate if there is a reservoir of variants whose potential for survival is tested.

Gradualism

One overriding requirement for evolutionary change, as expounded by Darwin, is time and plenty of it. This, as we saw in Chapter 1, was one of the reasons why Lord Kelvin's calculations for the age of the earth were brushed aside by most geologists and paleontologists. For progressive evolutionary change to result in the eventual appearance of new species would require the accumulation of small changes over many tens of thousands of generations. It also would require changes in the environment and, preferably, the reproductive isolation of portions of a population. All of these factors were built into a model that, during the first half of the twentieth century, was assembled to explain Darwinian evolution.

Gene Pools and Selection Pressure

At the heart of this model was the concept of the **gene pool,** defined as the sum total of genetic components in a population (Figure 4.6). Within the gene pool existed the potential for the free exchange of genetic material. In other words, all members of the population were potentially capable of interbreeding. Provided that the environment did not change, such a gene pool would presumably remain essentially conservative. The random emergence of new variants as a result of mutant genes, would, theoretically at least, not be tested, and the population would remain unchanged because it was, presumably, well adapted to its environment—that is, no selection pressure was operating.

If, on the other hand, the environment was changing, selection pressure, operating by virtue of the emergence of variant genes, would presumably cause shifts in the genetic makeup of the gene pool, and the population would "adapt" to the new environment. Taxonomists might see

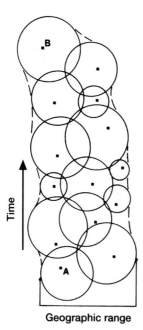

FIGURE 4.6
The gene pool in space and time. Circles represent local populations; dots are individuals within successive generations. While B is descended from ancestor A, no morphologic difference between A and B is implied or necessary.

sufficient differences in the new population when compared with the old to recognize a new species. In other words, the original species evolved into a new species by a process that biologists call **cladogenesis.**

Geographic isolation of portions of the gene pool—for example, when a rise in sea level isolates an offshore island—would also result in significant changes. If a hypothetical island race of mice found itself isolated from the mainland gene pool and, at the same time, was faced with different selection pressures because of its isolation—say, the absence of a particular predator—then new variant strains probably would emerge. If the island mice were isolated for long enough, the accumulated differences might mean that, even if they were reunited with the mainland race (by a fall in sea level), interbreeding would no longer be possible, and a new species would have emerged. In other words, it was the small changes resulting from genetic and mutational input into a population, accumulating over a sufficient number of generations, that eventually produced a new species. This, in essence, was the **gradualistic** model of most biologists.

Again, vast spans of time would be required for such changes to occur, and, above all, the changes would occur *gradually.* Because scientists realized that time was the most important factor, they did not expect to see the emergence of new species within the time frame that could be observed in dealing with extant faunas, even if manipulated in the geneticist's laboratory. Only in the fossil record would the real proof be found.

Gradualism and the Fossil Record

Even in Darwin's day, fossils were known to contain a hidden record of the long ages of change that had eventually resulted in the species that inhabit the earth today. Darwin was not optimistic that the "missing links" between ancestral and descendent species would be found, but he was generally reconciled to the fact that far more of the geological record was missing than was preserved and that it would probably remain missing forever. When his opponents asked for the proof that the fossil record of intermediate forms would have supposedly produced, Darwin could only speak rather disparagingly of the "imperfections of the geologic record."

The fossil record does seem to be imperfect. The relationships among fossil species, their ancestors, and their descendants are largely a matter of guesswork based on the degree of difference or resemblance. Through thick successions of strata, representing the passage of long spans of time, paleontologists can sometimes pick out "trends" and draw family-tree type diagrams showing not only the likely descent of one species from another, but the probable relationship between species descended from a common ancestor. At any one time horizon, an assemblage can be arranged into groupings of species and genera on the basis of resemblances and differences: If two species look very much alike, they probably belong to the same genus; if two genera are similar and different from other genera, they can be placed in the same family; and so on (Figure 4.7).

With only skeletal material to work with, and with fossils often fragmentary, this purely morphologic approach to taxonomy is inevitable. Many of the family trees constructed are probably valid enough as far as they go, but it would be wrong to assume that more than a few of the gradational intermediate forms between ancestral and descendant species are preserved as fossils. The fossil record indicates otherwise.

The Decline of Gradualism

Gradualism—the evolutionary model of Darwin, as modified by Mendelian genetics—required that **speciation events** (that is, the appearance of new species) occurred gradually. They supposedly resulted from the accumulation of many subtle and additive changes wrought in the lineage, generation upon generation, through the action of selection pressure. The fragmentary nature of the fossil record could naturally be expected to provide only very occasional glimpses of this supposedly continuous and ongoing process.

What had been increasingly apparent to paleontologists for many years, however, was that the fossil record, even allowing for its many gaps, did not do a good job of demonstrating gradualistic evolution in metazoans. Only in certain Cenozoic foraminiferan and radiolarian groups was there evidence for gradualistic lineages. Even in places

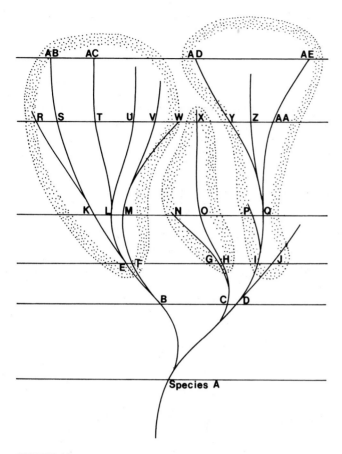

FIGURE 4.7

How gaps in the stratigraphic record can be used to define species within a hypothetical gradualistic lineage. This traditional family-tree diagram is widely used in demonstrating phylogenetic relationships in fossil lineages. The six time horizons depicted here are represented in one particular succession or area. The tree's various branches are drawn by connecting those species that have the most morphological features in common and separating those that are least similar. For example, species C and D are more similar to one another than either of them is to species B, but they are all similar enough to species A, found in older strata, to be considered descendants of this common ancestor. The shaded areas are possible groupings of species within three genera.

with a better-than-average sedimentary record, it was the same story. Lineages showing progressive morphologic change through thick stratigraphic successions were conspicuously absent. On the other hand, there were many well-documented successions in which a new species suddenly appeared, persisting through great thicknesses of strata, before suddenly disappearing, never to be seen again. Often, the time spans involved amounted to millions of years, and during all this time, the species showed no detectable morphologic change. **Stasis** (morphologic stability), rather than change, seemed to be the rule.

To take some typical mollusks as examples, the *average* range of Cenozoic bivalve species is 7 million years. Among the ammonites, the species *Phylloceras serum* lasted for 20 million years, while *Phylloceras thetys* was around for nearly 25 million years. In many cases, not even microevolutionary changes are discernible. Indeed, this longevity of species and their persistence through thick successions were the very features of the fossil record that had persuaded many people that Darwin was wrong. The great Canadian geologist, J. William Dawson, for example, a vehement opponent of Darwin on religious grounds, claimed that such features were clear evidence for the immutability of species, and he remained so convinced to the end of his days.

Punctuated Equilibrium

Niles Eldredge of the American Museum in New York and Stephen J. Gould of Harvard wondered if perhaps the reason why the fossil record shows so few examples of gradual evolutionary change is because the changes were not gradual in the sense that they demonstrated an insensibly graded series. Perhaps, evolution did not work that way. Then how did it work? In a new model, first proposed in 1972, Eldredge and Gould suggested that evolutionary change proceeded in a series of steps. When a new species arose, it remained unchanged, sometimes over long periods, but from time to time, under environmental stress, portions of the gene pool underwent rapid speciation events, resulting in the appearance of new species. Such newcomers sometimes reinvaded the ancestral species range and either successfully displaced the parent stock (which would then abruptly disappear) or coexisted with the parental species over all or part of the range. This was certainly what the fossil record seemed to show.

In other words, what Eldredge and Gould did, in effect, was, instead of trying to find evidence for gradualism among the fossils when it obviously was not there, they took the fossil record as their starting point. Their new model, which they labeled **punctuated equilibrium** seemed to make much more sense than did the earlier model of gradualism. While Darwin had been right about the scarcity of "missing links" in the fossil record, he had been right for the wrong reasons!

The model of punctuated equilibrium suggests that, around the periphery of the geographical range of a species, environmental stress tends to be higher than in the heartland of the species' range (Figure 4.8). Selection pressure is then greater, and new variant genes are likely to respond to new opportunities for adaptation. New characteristics would likely appear in small, isolated populations that, from time to time, became cut off from the main gene pool. This was the essential mechanism of the model for allopatric speciation suggested by Ernst Mayr in 1963, in which he referred to such populations as peripheral isolates. New species would arise over a relatively short period

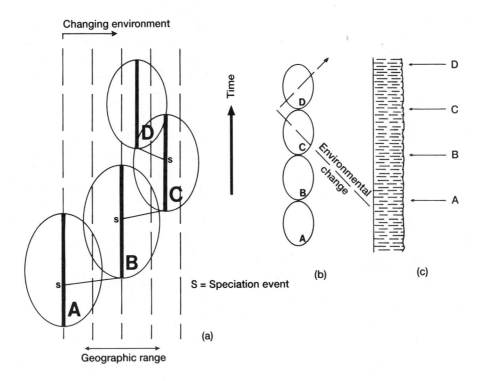

FIGURE 4.8

The punctuated equilibrium model. (a) Species *B* arises from a speciation event in a parent population of species *A*. For a time, it exists alongside species *A* and even overlaps in its geographic range. A progressively changing environment favors the new species produced at each speciation event, at the expense of parent species. (b) How the succession of species appears in the stratigraphic succession. (c) The location of the new species within an actual sedimentary section containing more gaps than record and numerous, largely undetected hiatuses.

among these populations. Their isolation, the comparatively small numbers of the evolving stock, and the rapidity with which the speciation event occurred would all be factors in reducing the likelihood of a fossil record. Sometimes, the new species would exist alongside the parent stock, but the fossil record seems to indicate that the new species most often would displace the parent stock.

In later work, Mayr pointed out that isolated populations were not necessarily peripheral but could also occur as geographic entities within some (perhaps unsuitable) portion of a species' range. Mayr called such populations peripatric isolates.

The chances of the speciation process being "caught in the act," as it were, are thus extremely small. Nevertheless, Peter Williamson of Florida Atlantic University, who worked in the molluscan faunas of the Plio-Pleistocene deposits of Lake Turkana in East Africa, was able to record not one, but numerous speciation events in freshwater mollusks (Box 4.2). Although the stratigraphic and sedimentary setting was ideal, evidence for a gradualistic mechanism to explain the evolutionary changes seen in the fauna was conspicuously absent. Instead, all the evidence supported the punctuated equilibrium model.

As Williamson pointed out, the punctuated equilibrium model envisages significant evolutionary change occurring only in miniscule portions of a given species population within peripatric isolates. In contrast, the traditional gradualistic model emphasizes a gradual transformation of entire species' lineages—that is, the entire population of the species across the entirety of its geographic range.

Microevolutionary changes arising from mutations would seem likely not to give rise to new species simply by their steady accumulation over long periods of time. Instead, however, the changes noted over relatively short periods may, in fact, be oscillatory. Ecologic factors of local significance probably are the cause of the numerous observed examples of local "races" or geographical variants within a species. Over the short term, such subspeciation events might seem to lead to accumulated change, but over the long term, the descendants are essentially the same as their predecessors (or conspecifics as biologists would say). Within the fossil record, this would be seen as stasis.

Background Extinctions

As new species appear, others become extinct. As environments progressively change, species are eventually displaced by better-adapted variants. In this **background extinction,** as it is known, local extinctions are occurring all the time—perhaps due to sudden environmental change, increased predation, pathologic organisms, or competition with new or other species.

BOX 4.2

A Demonstration of the Punctuated Equilibrium Model

In a succession of sands and silts laid down on an ancient lake bed in northern Kenya, East Africa, Peter Williamson (then at Harvard) discovered a virtually complete record of numerous speciation events in freshwater mollusks. Covering a time span of over 3 million years in the Turkana Basin, the fossil record shows no evidence of gradual evolutionary change from one species to another. Instead, the evidence in the lineages of 13 species is for long periods of genetic stability, or stasis, interrupted by brief periods of from 5,000 to 50,000 years when new species arose from parent

stocks. These speciation events occur mainly at two periods when, due to climatic change, lake levels dropped abruptly, and the environment was under stress.

Many of the fossil species are still extant, and living representatives can be seen in modern lakes in the region. From studies of these living species, Williamson concluded that the speciation events he had noted in the fossil lineages had taken, on average, about 20,000 generations to complete.

Most biologists would agree that 20,000 generations would probably be sufficient for evolutionary changes of

the order seen in the Williamson study to occur within the generally accepted gradualistic mechanism of evolution. Perhaps the controversy between gradualists (most biologists) and proponents of punctuated equilibrium (many paleontologists) hinges on questions of scale and timing. Periods of thousands of years involving thousands of generations may seem like a long time to biologists, whereas to paleontologists, the 50,000 years during which a new species arose in Williamson's study represent only about 1 percent of the species' time range.

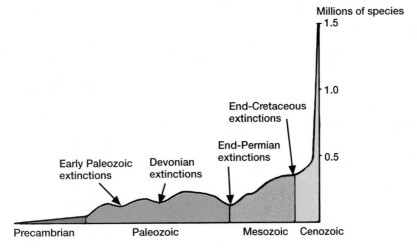

FIGURE 4.9
The supposed increasing diversification of species through geologic time.

In explaining what she called the effect hypothesis, Yale biologist Elizabeth Vbra described how a given environment may support few generalized species but numerous specialized ones that are not in competition. On the other hand, the more specialized species are less likely to survive environmental changes than are the generalists. The main cause of extinction throughout earth history apparently has been loss or change of habitat. The environment plays the key role.

Background extinction may have kept the total number of species fairly constant over extended periods. Although some scientists argue that the total number of

species at any one period has grown through geologic time, as shown in Figure 4.9, others point to the preservational bias in the fossil record as reflecting a lower than actual number of species. Clearly, in moving forward through time, greater volumes of successively younger rocks are preserved, along with the fossils in them. Conversely, the older the rocks, the more likely they are to have been metamorphosed and their fossils destroyed. Similarly, in limestones, the older they are, the more likely that they will have been recrystallized by dolomitization. Many factors must be considered in this argument, and it may never be resolved.

Yet another factor remains to be built into the evolutionary equation, and many scientists believe that it is the most important of all in the history of life on earth. This is the mass extinction factor (Figure 4.10).

Mass Extinctions

Even the most cursory view of the geologic column in terms of fossil species cannot fail to discern times when the extinction rate rose dramatically over relatively short periods (Figure 4.11). Two of these **mass extinctions**—that at the close of the Permian Period and the other at the end of the Cretaceous—are so obvious that their significance was recognized even in the nineteenth century. John Phillips used them as important biostratigraphic markers to set boundaries for the Paleozoic and Mesozoic Eras, respectively. At the Permian extinction event, an estimated 90 percent of all species became extinct. The mass extinction at the close of the Cretaceous was only slightly less destructive, with 75 percent loss of species. In recent

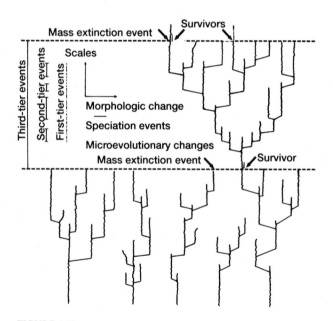

FIGURE 4.10

Tiers of time. A representation of the three sets of evolutionary events or changes that occur on markedly different time scales, as described by Steven Gould of Harvard. The short term (microevolutionary) changes of the first tier are seen as wiggly lines. The occasional line leaning to left or right represents a case of so-called "genetic drift," a progressive morphologic trend supposedly reflecting selection pressure. The sudden shifts of much greater magnitude represent speciation events, as described in the punctuated equilibrium model, and are events in the second tier. Third-tier events, occurring at infrequent intervals (tens of millions of years), are mass extinctions. These represent "bottlenecks" in the large flow of evolutionary change.

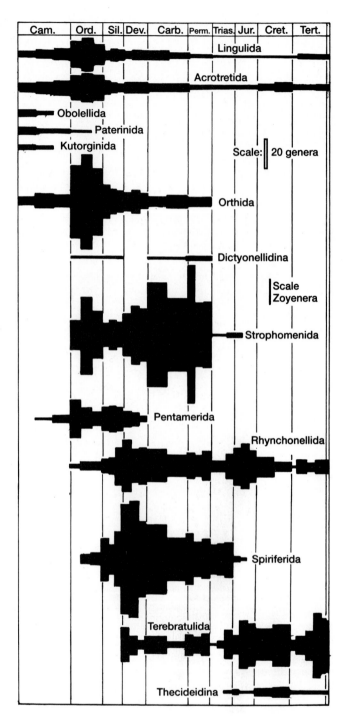

FIGURE 4.11

Stratigraphic distribution of Brachiopoda in orders or suborders and proportionate to the number of genera. Note abrupt terminations in some cases, particularly at the close of the Permian.

TABLE 4.1

Major Extinction Events during the Phanerozoic

| Extinction Event | Animal Groups | | Percentages of Families Extinct |
	Extinct	Greatly Reduced	
End-Cretaceous	Ammonites Rudistid mollusks Dinosaurs Large marine reptiles	Belemnites Corals Bryozoans Echinoids Sponges Planktonic foraminiferans	26
Late Triassic	Conodonts	Brachiopods Ammonites Fish Reptiles	35
Late Permian	Rugose corals Trilobites Blastoids Inadunate, flexibiliate, and camerate crinoids Productid brachiopods Fusulinid foraminiferans	Bryozoans Reptiles	50
Famennian-Frasnian (Late Devonian)		Corals Stromatoporoids Trilobites Ammonoids Bryozoans Brachiopods Fish	30
Late Ordovician		Trilobites Brachiopods Crinoids Echinoids	24
Late Cambrian		Trilobites Sponges Gastropods	52

Sources: Data from A. Hallam, *Facies Interpretation and the Stratigraphic Record* © 1981 W. H. Freeman and Company; and N. D. Newell, "Revolutions in the History of Life," *Geological Society of America Special Paper 89*, 63–91.

years, as biostratigraphic and radiometric dating techniques have improved, other mass extinctions in earth history have been identified. At least six are well documented (Table 4.1), and some believe that such events may even be regularly recurring phenomena. One hypothesis estimates an approximately 26-million-year cycle.

On the other hand, not everyone has been persuaded that mass extinctions occur. Some scientists argue that the extinctions were actually spread out over extended periods and were not triggered by cataclysmic mechanisms. They suggest that the so-called "events" are merely artifacts of statistical analysis of faunas, or of errors in dating methods, and are perhaps not very different from background extinctions. Circular thinking has also been cited. If the end of the Cretaceous is defined by the extinction

of the dinosaurs, then obviously the dinosaurs finally became extinct at the close of the Cretaceous! These are minority views, and there is now a fairly general consensus as to the validity of mass extinctions. Any display of unanimity disappears, however, when the possible causes of mass extinctions are examined.

Possible Causes of Mass Extinctions

Many possible causes of mass extinctions have been proposed, and, broadly speaking, they can be categorized as: (1) terrestrial causes, (2) biological causes, and (3) extraterrestrial causes. In the first category, suggestions range from changes in continental configuration because of plate-tectonic movements, to mountain-building events, to volcanic episodes. The problem is that they all involve extremely slow processes that are difficult to envisage as causes of the sudden and major environmental changes apparently called for in an explanation of mass extinctions. However, some sort of threshold effect may have been involved that perhaps triggered other events. Progressive changes in ocean basin configuration, for example, may have eventually reached a critical stage when oceanic circulation became restricted and oxygen levels declined. The resultant anoxic event would cause mass mortality in essential parts of the food chain.

This trigger, or domino effect, is almost certainly necessary if biological mechanisms are to be considered as causes of mass extinctions. The intimate links between many organisms and between the organisms and their environment are so complex and often so delicately balanced that relatively small changes in one parameter could have enormously magnified effects through a wide range of organisms.

Extraterrestrial causes of mass extinctions are, in contrast to terrestrial and biological causes, relatively simple. The mechanism preferred is that of a meteorite impact. Evidence is growing that the best-known mass extinction event, at the close of the Cretaceous, was caused by just such an impact. The impacting of extraterrestrial bodies—be they meteorites or comets—has the requisite suddenness required for a mass extinction event. However, the animals that disappeared did not do so overnight, which again suggests the domino effect, with collapsing food chains.

One reason why meteorite (or cometary) impacts are among the favorites in the list of causes is that they provide the only means of explaining the apparent periodicity of mass extinctions seen by some scientists. According to David Raup of the University of Chicago, mass extinctions occur approximately every 26 million years and are

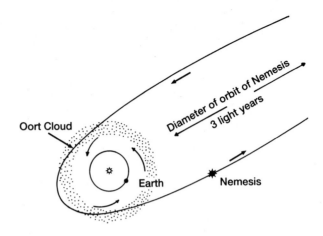

FIGURE 4.12
The Oort Cloud and its relationship to the sun and the Nemesis star.

caused by the in-fall of comets derived from a swarm—the so-called Oort Cloud—that lies beyond the orbit of Pluto. This hypothesis suggests that the sun has a dim companion—called the Nemesis star—that sweeps into the solar system on a highly eccentric 26-million-year orbit (Figure 4.12). In so doing, it disturbs the Oort Cloud so that many comets are ejected into earth-intersecting orbits. No one has seen the Oort Cloud or the Nemesis star, but some astronomers have started an active search of the heavens. It has recently been suggested that Nemesis may, in fact, be what is known as Barnard's star.

The preceding discussion contains much pure conjecture because the subject of mass extinctions is very much an area of active research, with new discoveries reported on an almost monthly basis. Mass extinctions are clearly important crises in earth history and are discussed in chronologic sequence in the chapters that follow.

Summary

In the eighteenth and early nineteenth centuries, the generally held view was that species were fixed and immutable, an idea that likely had its origin in the teachings of Aristotle. On the other hand, there were Greek thinkers and many scholars in later years who believed otherwise. Benoit de Mallet, for example, in 1715 wrote a book describing the evolution of birds from fish.

Another Frenchman—Jean Baptiste Lamarck—proposed that characteristics acquired during the lifetime of an individual could be inherited by offspring, that the giraffe's long neck, for example, was due to constant stretching to reach the leaves of trees.

Charles Darwin became interested in biology while studying theology at Cambridge University. His friendship with

Professor John Henslow led to his appointment as naturalist on the British research ship H.M.S. Beagle. During a five-year voyage around the world, Darwin made many observations and amassed an enormous collection of animal, plant, fossil, and rock samples. On the Galápagos Islands, his studies of finches that were apparently derived from a common ancestor that had arrived from South

America millions of years before led him to believe that one species could evolve into another. In 1859, Darwin, together with biologist Alfred Russel Wallace (who had come to similar conclusions on island races) presented a paper to the Linnean Society. In November of that year, Darwin's book *On the Origin of Species* was published, selling out on the day of publication. Darwin's thesis was that, in any population, those individuals better adapted to their environment are more likely to survive and pass on their characteristics to offspring.

Darwin was influenced by a book on population and food supply written by Thomas Malthus, and Malthus's phrase "struggle for survival" made a big impression on Darwin. This led many people to misinterpret Darwin's work. Apart from those opposed to evolution on religious grounds, others believed that "survival of the fittest" was a universal law and the justification for exploitation and the idea that "Might is right."

Many biological phenomena, already known for years, could be reinterpreted in the light of evolution. Thus, homologous organs, often serving very different functions, are found in many diverse animals. Sometimes, they have ceased to be functional and now occur only as vestigial organs, one example being the pelvic bones of whales. The field of embryology also

provided support for Darwin's ideas. Developmental stages in mammalian embryos exhibit features reminiscent of animals that presumably formed part of the ancestral lineage. For example, the human embryo passes through stages where it possesses gill slits and a fishlike tail. This phenomenon can be summarized as "Ontogeny recapitulates phylogeny" and is known as Haeckel's Law. The resemblance between the embryos of widely different species had also long been noticed, providing further evidence for origin from a common ancestral stock.

Unknown to Darwin, the mechanism of evolution had been discovered by Moravian monk Gregor Mendel, who had experimented in the breeding of sweet peas. Mendel showed that flower color was controlled by hereditary factors, some being dormant and others recessive. Mendel's work was not noticed until the early twentieth century, by which time others had made the same discovery. The hereditary factors were called genes, and their study became known as genetics. The importance of genes in the mechanism of evolution is that they retain their identity from generation to generation. In 1953, genes were discovered by Watson and Crick to be made up of long molecules of deoxyribonucleic acid (DNA). Mutations are produced when new cells receive an imperfect copy of the parent's genetic material. They introduce a random variable

into the process of sexual recombination and, together with sexual recombination, provide a mechanism for selection pressure and are the driving forces of evolution.

Biologists in particular once believed that new species arose as a result of the gradual accumulation of many small differences over thousands of generations, a model called gradualism. The fossil record, however, indicates otherwise. Despite many gaps, the fossil record shows that new species appear suddenly, persist unchanged for millions of years, and disappear just as suddenly. This led Eldredge and Gould to suggest that evolution was not gradualistic, and they proposed a new model of punctuated equilibrium, in which new species appear as a result of environmental stress in peripheral populations and eventually replace or coexist with the parent stock.

Background extinction describes the way that species are eventually displaced by better-adapted species as environments change. Whether this means that the total number of species has remained more or less unchanged through geologic time is still a matter of controversy. What does seem certain is that, from time to time, there have been mass extinctions; at least six are known. While many theories speculate as to the causes of mass extinctions, one of the most plausible suggests giant meteorite (or cometary) impacts.

Questions

1. What is meant by Lamarckism?
2. What made a big impression on Darwin in the Galápagos Islands and why?
3. What feature of Darwin's theory of evolution caused so much opposition from certain church authorities?
4. Which two books influenced Darwin in his theory of evolution, and in what way did they influence him?
5. Who was Thomas Malthus, and what was the significance of his work?
6. What are vestigial organs?

7. Explain what is meant by Haeckel's Law.
8. What contribution did Gregor Mendel make to the theory of evolution?
9. What are the sources of variation within a species that provide the potential for evolutionary change?
10. Explain what is meant by selection pressure.
11. Name a feature of the fossil record that was cited by Victorian critics of Darwin to discredit the theory of evolution.

12. Why does the punctuated equilibrium model for evolution seem to be supported by the fossil record, whereas a gradualistic model is not?
13. What are mass extinctions? What role do they play in the evolution of life?
14. David Raup claims that mass extinctions occur at regular intervals. Explain the evidence for this conclusion, and give some account of a possible mechanism.
15. Why do biologists and paleontologists often disagree over the mechanisms of evolution?

78 Chapter 4

Berra, T. M. 1990. *Evolution and the myth of creationism.* Stanford: Stanford University Press.

Chambers, R. 1844. *Vestiges of the natural history of creation.*

Darwin, C. R. 1859. *On the origin of species by means of natural selection or the preservation of favored races in the struggle for life.* London: Murray.

Eldredge, N. 1989. *Time frames.* New York: Simon and Schuster.

Hoffman, A. 1989. *Arguments on evolution.* New York: Oxford University Press.

Raup, D. M., and S. M. Stanley. 1978. *Principles of paleontology.* 2d ed. San Francisco: W. H. Freeman.

Stanley, S. M. 1981. *The new evolutionary timetable: Fossils, genes, and the origin of species.* New York: Basic Books.

Stebbins, G. L. 1982. *Darwin to DNA, molecules to humanity.* New York: W. H. Freeman.

5

ROCKS AND TIME

Introduction

Just as human history relies upon the measurement of time, so does any account of historical geology. Without a calendar to mark off successive events, construction of a coherent, worldwide account of geologic changes is impossible. Methods of time measurement fall into one of two categories: They either work by reference to a cyclical or regularly recurring phenomenon, or by reference to an ongoing nonreversible process. The passage of the hands around a clock face and the daily, lunar, and annual cycles are all familiar examples in the first category, while sand in an hourglass, the burning of a candle, the decay of radioactive elements, and evolutionary change are examples in the second. Clearly, only those phenomena that leave some trace in rocks are of any use in time measurement to geologists (Figure 5.1).

Although the geologic time scale in its present form has been in use for more than 100 years, reasonably accurate age determinations measured in real time—that is, in years before the present—were not available until the late 1920s and early 1930s. Until then, the geologic time scale had been a **relative time scale**—that is, one in which geologic events are set out in the order they occurred, without reference to the actual time measured in years. The ordering of geologic events and the age of geologic phenomena relative to one another were known with considerable accuracy, but the actual ages, measured in years, could only be guessed.

This chapter is concerned with relative time and gives some account of the beginnings of time measurement using fossils. The chapter also discusses other stratigraphic methods of time measurement. The measurement of geologic time in terms of real time (that is, in years before the present) is examined in Chapter 6.

As described in Chapter 1, one of the most important advances in the science of geology was the realization that the earth was very old. Once the idea of a special creation event and an "instant" earth had been discarded, some kind of calendar of earth events was needed.

The Calendar in the Rocks

In human history, events and time are connected. When speakers refer to the Victorian Era, for example, it is clear that they are referring to a specific time interval during which Queen Victoria reigned. In geologic history, however, rocks contain the physical record of past events, and rock units are defined on the basis of purely physical characteristics that normally have no time connotation. Many rock formations, in fact, that are known from their relationships to other rocks to vary markedly in age from place to place contain no intrinsic age indicators. For example, Cretaceous sandstone may look very much like Devonian-age sandstone and may have been deposited under essentially the same conditions. In any stratigraphic succession,

(a)

(b)

FIGURE 5.1

Glacial varves in the Don Valley, Toronto, Canada. (a) Each dark/light pair, or couplet, represents an annual increment. (b) Close-up of annual varves in glacial lake deposits. *(Photo courtesy of Paul F. Karrow.)*

TABLE 5.1
The Hierarchy of Chronostratigraphic and Geochronologic Terms

Equivalent Units	
Chronostratigraphic*	**Geochronologic****
Eonothem	Eon
Erathem	Era
System	Period
Series	Epoch
Stage	Age
Chronozone	Chron

*Defines a body of rock unified by being formed during a specific interval of geologic time; represents all rocks formed anywhere during a certain segment of earth history
**Defines a unit of geologic time determined by geologic methods; may correspond to the time span of a stratigraphic unit

FIGURE 5.2
The eruption of Mount St. Helens, 18 May 1980. *(Photo courtesy of Jim Quiring, Mt. St. Helens National Volcanic Monument.)*

provided it is not structurally disturbed, only relative time can be discerned, with the oldest strata at the bottom and successively younger strata laid on top.

Paleogeography

Much of historical geology is concerned with **paleogeography,** the reconstruction of ancient worlds in terms of the distribution of land and sea, the climate, and life-forms. A paleogeographic reconstruction, based on an interpretation of the rocks and their contained fossils, ideally provides a view of the world as it appeared at a particular time. An essential first step in paleogeographic reconstructions is establishing time equivalency among widely scattered stratigraphic successions, regardless of how different the rocks are in terms of lithology and depositional environment.

Chronostratigraphic Units and Isochronous Surfaces

From the earliest days of geology, a connection between time and rocks was made by means of **chronostratigraphic (time-rock) units,** rock units whose boundaries are set by time horizons, or **isochronous surfaces.** In other words, a chronostratigraphic unit contains all the rocks deposited during a given time interval. Thus, the Cambrian, Ordovician, and Silurian **systems** are chronostratigraphic units formed during the Cambrian, Ordovician, and Silurian **periods,** respectively. The hierarchy of **geochronologic** (time) and chronostratigraphic (time rock—geologic time defined by rock units whose boundaries are set by isochronous surfaces) terms is summarized in Table 5.1.

Chronostratigraphic units are not easy to define. The problem lies with identifying the isochronous surfaces that delimit the units and carry them from one area to another. What do geologists look for in the rock? Theoretically, an isochronous surface represents an instant in time; however, any brief event, except on a local scale, is unlikely to leave a record in the rocks. On the other hand, some geologic events occur very quickly and sometimes leave a record over a considerable area. An excellent example is the ash fall from a large volcanic eruption, like that of Mount St. Helens in 1980 (Figure 5.2). This eruption spread a layer of ash over tens of thousands of square kilometers within a few days. A record of those few days exists wherever the ash layer is present in seabed deposits, lake sediments, or soil profiles. Not an *instant* in time certainly, but few would argue that in the great sweep of geologic time, we might concede a day or two!

In the recent geologic past, there have been many volcanic eruptions far more violent than that of Mount St. Helens. Ash falls derived from massive eruptions in Central America, for example, have been found far out in the Pacific and provide invaluable time markers within deep-sea sedimentary successions. We return to the subject of time correlation by volcanic ash beds, or tephrochronology as it is called, later in this chapter.

Although volcanic ash falls provide excellent isochronous horizons, they are too infrequent and local in their extent for use in regional or worldwide stratigraphic studies. Instead, the stratigraphic record of other phenomena that occur over brief, or at least relatively brief, time intervals are used. The only two ways of establishing isochronous, or at least quasi-isochronous horizons, on anything approaching a worldwide scale are by means of fossils (biostratigraphy) and by using reversals in the earth's magnetic field (magnetostratigraphy)—both of which are discussed in more detail later in the chapter.

Today, the relationship between time and rocks is generally well understood. Perhaps the most outstanding feature of the modern view is the realization that the stratigraphic record contains many more gaps than it does any sedimentary record of elapsed time. This has been mentioned in earlier chapters and is discussed again later.

History of the Concept of Geologic Time

The concept of geologic time and its relation to rock has evolved over the last 300 years, beginning with the work of Nicolaus Steno and William Smith, followed by many others.

Steno's Laws of Rock Strata

Perhaps the earliest account of geological phenomena that considered the passage of time is in a book written by Danish physician Nicolaus Steno and published in 1669. Steno is considered by many to be the founder of modern geology, and few men have excelled and been honored in such widely separate fields as medicine and geology. In addition, Steno is almost certainly the only geologist who is now a candidate for sainthood! Born Nils Stenson in Denmark in 1638, he went to Italy as a protégé of the Medici family of Florence. At the age of only 28, he had already made a name for himself in medicine. He became the archduke's personal physician and tutor to his sons, a post that apparently gave him opportunities to travel and to indulge his interest in natural history. In particular, he made detailed observations of rocks and fossils and concluded that the region of Tuscany had been submerged beneath the sea at least twice and had twice been uplifted and the rock strata tilted. In the sense that he was describing distinct phases of geologic history, Steno's book could be considered the first historical geology text.

Although Steno's book contained remarkably advanced views on fossils, which were the book's chief topic, Steno's work is remembered primarily for his "laws" pertaining to rock strata. His **law of superposition** states that, in any succession of stratified rocks, the oldest are at the bottom, and the youngest are at the top. Today, this sounds so obvious as to be hardly worth mentioning, but in the seventeenth century, it was a new concept. A second law—that of **original horizontality**—states that all strata, however tilted and folded, were once lying flat. Third, the **law of original continuity** deals with the loss of strata by erosion. For example, the strata exposed along one side of a valley were once continuous with those on the other, the missing portion having been removed by the erosional processes that excavated the valley.

Steno's remarkably modern-sounding interpretations of his observations were contained in what was, in effect, a uniformitarian setting. However, like so many scholars of his time, he was constrained within an essentially biblical chronologic framework. In other words, he had to try to compress his timetable of geologic events into that of recorded history. In fact, he searched for historical references to events that could account for what he thought had happened in Tuscany; for example, he believed that fossil mastodon bones were the remains of elephants that Hannibal's army brought across the Alps.

Faced with what must have seemed two irreconcilable philosophies, Steno apparently turned to the church. He converted to Catholicism, was ordained a priest, and shortly thereafter, was consecrated bishop of Munster. From there, he moved to the Duchy of Mecklenberg and for the rest of his days lived a devout and ascetic existence.

William Smith and the Time-Stratigraphic Significance of Fossils

Although Steno showed the way to the historical narrative approach to geology, he clearly had no concept of the scale of geologic time. Indeed, this whole subject was to remain a closed book until the early twentieth century. In the meantime, however, a relative time scale (essentially, a dimensionless calendar of events) evolved, and by the midnineteenth century, all the essentials of the time-stratigraphic concept were in place. The real beginning of stratigraphy as it is known today came near the end of the eighteenth century with the work of William Smith (Figure 5.3).

Smith was, apparently, the first to realize the time-stratigraphic significance of fossils and to be aware that a given species could be found only through a particular thickness of strata and, therefore, had only a finite existence in time. For that day and age, this was a remarkable breakthrough and laid the foundation for **biostratigraphy,** the study of how fossils can be used to demonstrate the

FIGURE 5.3
William Smith (1769–1839).

age equivalency of widely separate and often lithologically distinct stratigraphic successions. With Smith's discovery, geologic mapping and the establishment of a geologic time scale became possible.

William Smith was born in the village of Churchill, Oxfordshire, in 1769. Largely self-educated, he began work as a land surveyor but soon became involved in civil engineering, mostly canal building and land drainage. Traveling widely and with access to newly excavated quarries, cuttings, and tunnels, Smith was able to pursue his great interest in collecting fossils. He kept careful notes, not only of his collections but also on the local geology, and began to assemble a table of all the strata underlying central and southern England. In naming his various rock formations, he often used the local names familiar to the quarry workers, like Kellaways Rock, Cornbrash, and Forest Marble, some of which have been retained in modern stratigraphic tables (See Appendix A9).

Around 1797, Smith met Reverend Benjamin Richardson, also a fossil collector, and amazed that gentleman by unerringly locating the places and formations from which his specimens had been collected. It quickly became clear to Richardson and also to an associate, Reverend Joseph Townsend, that Smith must write a book. Smith had actually been planning a book for some years but had never found the time to spare. Now, with the collaboration of his friends, a table of strata was published in 1798, and later, a detailed geologic map was finally completed and published in several sheets during 1814 and 1815. Other publications followed as well.

Smith was engaged in several business enterprises, not all of which were successful. Indeed, financial problems grew, and in 1819, he even spent 10 weeks in debtor's prison! Meanwhile, he was becoming well known in scientific circles and was often invited to give lectures. In 1831, formal recognition came from the most prestigious of all geological organizations—the Geological Society of London—which awarded him the first Wollaston Medal (an annual award for outstanding contributions to the science of geology). In the following year, he was granted a government pension. To the end of his days, Smith remained something of a "character." Shabbily dressed, his pockets stuffed with fossils, and ever ready to share his knowledge and experience, he undoubtedly deserved the title of "Father of British Stratigraphy."

Birth of the Geologic Time Scale

Early nineteenth-century geologists began to apply biostratigraphic methods to the whole of the geologic column, beginning above the ancient basement rocks and continuing up to the youngest sediments (Table 5.2). Among the leading geologists of this time were Roderick Murchison, later to be director of the British Geological Survey, and Adam Sedgwick, professor of geology at Cambridge University. These two friends spent summers together in the field, working mainly in west-central England and in Wales. Year by year, often accompanied by their wives, they assiduously measured and mapped the great thicknesses of limestones, sandstones, and shales underlying the hilly countryside.

Murchison chose as his starting point the base of the Old Red Sandstone at the bottom of Smith's stratigraphic table. Over many seasons of work and by measuring downward in the succession, he was able to describe and classify a great thickness of strata to which he applied the name Silurian System, after the name of an ancient British tribe, the Silures, who had lived in the Welsh border country at the time of the Roman occupation.

Sedgwick, for his part, started his stratigraphic studies with the oldest fossiliferous rocks he could find. These were sandstones and shales lying unconformably over ancient crystalline and metamorphosed rocks exposed in North Wales and elsewhere. Measuring upward in the succession, although doing little of the systematic fossil collecting that marked Murchison's work, Sedgwick applied the name Cambrian System to his rocks, after the ancient name for Wales: Cambria.

TABLE 5.2

Origin of the Geologic Periods and Systems

Quaternary	Name first applied in 1829 by Paul A. Desnoyers, although incorrectly, to Tertiary sediments of the Seine Valley; redefined in 1833 by H. P. I. Reboul.
Tertiary	First used as a period name by Charles Lyell in 1833; had been used earlier by Giovanni Arduino and others in the eighteenth-century simple division of rocks into Primary, Secondary, and Tertiary.
Cretaceous	From the term *Terrain Cretace* used in 1882 by d'Omalius d'Halloy for chalk and greensand of northern France.
Jurassic	Some Jurassic formations termed Jura Kalkstein by von Humboldt in 1799; modern use introduced as Jurassique in 1829 by French and Swiss workers for occurrences in the Jura Mountains.
Triassic	Used in 1834 by Fredrich von Alberti for the three-division sequence of Bunter, Muschelkalk, and Keuper of Germany.
Permian	System first defined by Roderick Murchison in 1841; based upon a type section near Perm, Russia.
Carboniferous	Named in 1822 by W. D. Conybeare and William Phillips in their *Outlines of Geology of England and Wales*.
Devonian	Named by William Lonsdale in 1837 after the county of Devon, England, for the marine facies of the Old Red Sandstone; first published by Sedgwick and Murchison in 1839.
Silurian	System first defined in 1835 by Roderick Murchison and named for the Silures, an ancient tribe that had inhabited the type area in the Welsh borderland region.
Ordovician	Name adapted by Charles Lapworth in 1879 from that of an ancient tribe, the Ordovices, to apply to a system of rocks in Wales and adjacent England that occurred between two unconformities within the Cambro-Silurian sequence of Sedgwick and Murchison.
Cambrian	So-called after the ancient name for Wales and applied as a system name by Adam Sedgwick in 1835; no characteristic fossils were described, so the system was not fully recognized until the faunas were described by Frederick McCoy and J. W. Salter in the 1850s.
Pennsylvanian and Mississippian	In North America, the marked twofold division of the Carboniferous; recognized as the Pennsylvanian, named in 1858 by H. D. Rogers, and the Mississippian, named by A. Winchell in 1870; both these divisions were given system/period status in 1905 in Chamberlin and Salisbury's *Textbook of Geology*.

Source: Data from W. B. N. Berry, *Growth of a Prehistoric Time Scale*. Copyright © 1968 W. H. Freeman & Company, San Francisco.

Inevitably, with Murchison adding successively older strata to his Silurian System as he worked downward in the succession, and with Sedgwick discovering progressively younger Cambrian strata, a disagreement arose as to where the boundary between the two systems should lie. The disagreement between the two men grew into a dispute that destroyed their friendship, and they died unreconciled. The problem of the Cambrian-Silurian boundary was not resolved until 1875, when Charles Lapworth, professor of geology at Birmingham University, proposed that a third system, the Ordovician, be recognized between the Cambrian and Silurian.

Lapworth's contribution more or less completed the division of the geologic column, at least that part with fossils, above the Precambrian. Geologists everywhere quickly realized that recognition of the various geologic systems anywhere in the world depended upon finding the characteristic fossils and that the erosional breaks seen in the original type sections, and that had been used in establishing the boundaries of the systems, were of no more than local significance.

Thus, the final vestiges of catastrophism, with successive creations terminated by events of worldwide extent, were at last laid to rest. Sedgwick himself had once been

a catastrophist but was finally persuaded that the uniformitarian approach was the correct one.

The primary divisions of the geologic column are the systems, established for the most part on the basis of their contained fossils (Table 5.3). Thus, although defined as chronostratigraphic units (bodies of rock formed during a specific period of time and bounded by isochronous surfaces), they were, and for that matter still are, essentially biostratigraphic units (bodies of rock defined on the basis of their fossil content). A case in point is the Cambrian/Ordovician boundary in North Wales. At its type section, the upper boundary of the Cambrian is placed at a pronounced erosional discontinuity or disconformity at the top of the Tremadoc Shales (See Box 12.1). Because these shales contain fossils that elsewhere are considered characteristically of Ordovician age, the Tremadoc Shales should, more correctly, be included in the Ordovician System (see Appendix A2). The extension of the systems from their various type sections to all parts of the world has involved many compromises and modifications of this nature. Further discussion on the definitions of the various geologic systems is postponed until each one is dealt with in its proper place in the chapters that follow.

TABLE 5.3

The Geologic Time Scale

Eon	Era	Period		Epoch	Millions of Years Ago
Phanerozoic	Cenozoic*	Quaternary		Holocene	
				Pleistocene	
		Tertiary		Pliocene	
			Neogene	Miocene	
					23.7
			Paleogene	Oligocene	
				Eocene	
				Paleocene	
					66.4
	Mesozoic	Cretaceous		Late	
				Early	
					144
		Jurassic		Late	
				Middle	
				Early	
					208
		Triassic		Late	
				Middle	
				Early	
					245
	Paleozoic — Late	Permian		Late	
				Early	
					286
		Carboniferous	Pennsylvanian	Late	
			Mississippian	Early	
					360
		Devonian		Late	
				Middle	
				Early	
					408
	Paleozoic — Early	Silurian		Late	
				Early	
					438
		Ordovician		Late	
				Middle	
				Early	
					505
		Cambrian		Late	
				Middle	
				Early	
					570
Proterozoic	Late Middle Early	Precambrian: Further subdivision is based essentially on local successions, and no worldwide standard has, as yet, been agreed upon.			
					2,500
Archean	Late Middle Early				
					3,500?

Source: Data from Geological Society of America *1983 Time Scale.*
*Cainozoic or Kainozoic are variants (particularly in British usage).

Correlation

In studying and particularly mapping the regional extent of sedimentary formations, geologists must invariably compare the succession in one locality with that in another (or compare one well log—that is, the stratigraphic succession as recorded from drill cuttings, or drill cores—with another). This is necessary because, except in rare cases—most often in places like deserts or the arctic where exposures are exceptionally good—outcrops are not continuous.

The process of comparison is often erroneously referred to as correlation. In this situation, what is really meant is that the different successions can be *matched*. The term *correlation* should be reserved to mean *time* correlation. The formations or other stratigraphic units only correlate with each other if they are the same age—that is, are coeval.

Age equivalency can be demonstrated by reference to isochronous horizons, and these can be established in several ways:

1. By reference to distinctive fossil species (biostratigraphy)
2. By reference to known magnetic polarity events—that is, magnetic reversals (magnetostratigraphy)
3. Locally and, occasionally, regionally, by reference to a known volcanic ash fall (tephrostratigraphy)
4. By reference to a known cycle or part of a cycle, such as a sea-level change or a climatic cycle (cyclostratigraphy)
5. By reference to a major event that may even be global in extent, perhaps marked by a mass extinction or a geochemical marker (event stratigraphy)

Biostratigraphy: Time Correlation by Fossils

Evolution makes biostratigraphic correlation possible (Box 5.1). Because evolutionary changes are progressive and nonreversible, when a given species appears in a stratigraphic succession, it is only found through a finite thickness before it becomes extinct and disappears forever.

Biozones

The fundamental unit used in biostratigraphy is the **biozone,** a body of rock defined by the presence, absence, or relative abundance of selected species. Different kinds of biozones have been defined. A range zone, for example, consists of the strata containing the entire life of a species. Because of the vagaries of deposition, erosion, and nonpreservation of fossils, the actual range of a species through time is probably unknowable, and the observed time range is always somewhat shorter. Due to the fragmentary nature of the fossil record, the earliest fossils found are extremely unlikely to be the first representatives of the species, and the situation is similar when a species disappears. In the case of mass extinction, however, the latest fossils found may indeed mark the demise of a species.

The sensitivity of biostratigraphic zonation can be greatly improved if several different species are used together. Each species has its own particular stratigraphic range, which, when combined into overlapping range zones, are called concurrent range zones. As illustrated in Figure 5.4, any single species may have a considerable range through time, sometimes lasting for 1 or 2 million years or longer. In contrast, the time range during which a number of selected species are all present together is likely much shorter. Thus, each concurrent range zone is characterized by a unique assemblage of species that differs from the assemblages contained in zones that are lower and higher in the succession.

When possible, the species selected as zone fossils should be those that are known to have relatively short life spans. In addition, they should not be restricted to a particular sediment type. Correlating a sandstone with a shale of the same age would be impossible if each contained its own peculiar facies-linked fauna and showed no species in common. Nektonic and planktonic species often provide the best zone fossils because their distribution is not influenced by bottom sediment type, and their remains may be found in whatever sediment existed on the sea floor at the time they died.

Biostratigraphic Units: Quasi-Chronostratigraphic Units?

In the search for isochronous horizons, geologists are, of course, looking for time markers identifiable over extended distances, preferably worldwide. As we saw, William Smith used the appearance and disappearance of species to establish time equivalence, and in doing this, he assumed that a particular species would appear and disappear everywhere at the same time. How valid was this assumption? Perhaps, over the hundreds of kilometers of Smith's maps, it was valid, but what about thousands of

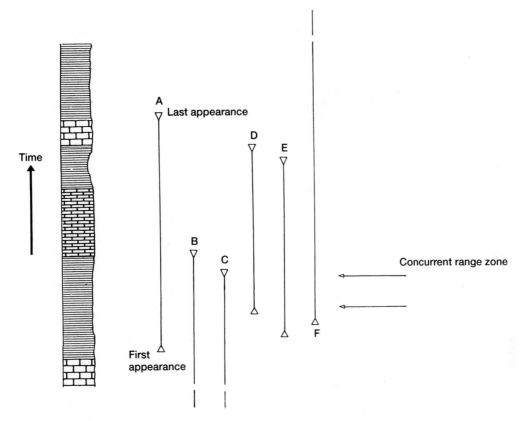

FIGURE 5.4
How a concurrent range zone involving several species
delineates a shorter time span than that of a single species.

kilometers? When a new species appears, it does so in a
restricted area; how long is it before the species extends
its range into all suitable habitats, perhaps over extended
distances? The answers to these questions are fundamental to biostratigraphy.

Studies of the distribution of living species, particularly marine organisms, show that, given the opportunity,
a species may expand its geographic range over great distances in time spans measured in only thousands or even
hundreds of years. The gastropod *Littorina littorea,* for
example, was introduced to Nova Scotia around the thir-
teenth century, presumably by the Norsemen, and since
that time has spread southward along the eastern seaboard of the United States. Its expansion from Maine to
New Haven, Connecticut, a distance of nearly 600 kilometers, apparently took no more than 12 years. The rapid
spread of insect pests and weed plants across entire continents after their accidental or deliberate introduction is
well known.

When compared with the periods involved in the deposition of thicknesses of sedimentary rock, time periods
of hundreds of years can be considered virtually instantaneous. Thus, biostratigraphic units can be considered
quasi-chronostratigraphic units.

Long-Distance Biostratigraphic Correlation

Because historical geology is concerned with events and
changes that are often of worldwide significance, the divisions of the geologic calendar must be recognized worldwide. At the large scale of the geologic systems and series,
there is usually no problem, except sometimes with the
precise placing of the boundaries. Can smaller divisions
be established to give better time definition and still be
recognizable everywhere?

Series are divided into stages, and theoretically, at
least, stages are also recognizable on a worldwide scale.
In practice, however, it is usually a matter of recognizing
local stages, based on more or less endemic forms (organisms that are restricted in their geographical range or confined to a specific region or environment), and trying to
make them match with other local stages with their own
endemic faunas. To be truly worldwide in significance, a
stage defined, say in England, should be recognizable in
North America or New Zealand by virtue of having the
same fauna with identical index species. In practice, this
never happens. While in rare cases, certain species of
floating organisms, like ammonites and graptolites, have
come to have almost a global distribution, the more usual

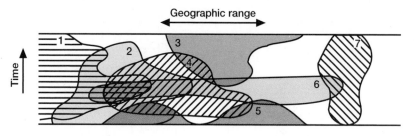

FIGURE 5.5
How the ranges of various species overlap through space
and time.

situation is that the zonal species are more or less local in their distribution, being limited by temperature, salinity, geographic, or other barriers.

When a stage is defined at a particular place, it is described in terms of a selection of index species. Traced laterally, these species disappear one by one as they reach the limits of their geographic range, and their places are taken by other local species. For example, water temperature may be a factor, and in passing from tropical to subtropical water, the warm-water species give way to cooler-water species. Approximate time correlation can be maintained by observing the ways in which the ranges of species in one zonal assemblage interfinger with zonal species of an adjacent area. By tracing the local interfingering relationships, biostratigraphers are able to maintain a reasonable semblance of age equivalence, sometimes over thousands of kilometers, proceeding step-by-step and linking many local faunas (Figure 5.5). In practice, other, nonpaleontological methods, such as magnetostratigraphy and isotopic dating, are sometimes used to improve the accuracy of long-distance biostratigraphic correlation.

Magnetostratigraphy: Time Correlation by Magnetic Reversals

While so far we have discussed isochronous horizons defined by fossils, **magnetostratigraphy** involves establishing isochronous horizons by **magnetic reversals** (180-degree changes of polarity of the earth's magnetic field). The earth, by virtue of its metallic core and its rotation, behaves as a great dipole magnet, with the magnetic poles located close to the rotational (true or geographic) poles. Due to an apparent instability in the field, the position of the magnetic poles varies year by year. This is known as the magnetic declination.

Quite early in the study of the earth's magnetic field, scientists discovered that certain minerals, such as magnetite, behave as natural magnets and, if free to move, the mineral grains align themselves with appropriate polarity orientation in the earth's field. In igneous rocks, the magnetic crystals acquire thermoremanent magnetism as the

magma cools and passes through what is known as the Curie point; this varies from 600°C to 800°C, depending on the mineral. As the magma solidifies, the grains become locked in place so that, in effect, the direction of the earth's magnetic field at that time and at that place is "frozen in." Magnetic mineral grains in sediment similarly become aligned in the magnetic field as they settle to the bottom and are incorporated into the sedimentary rock. This magnetism is termed detrital magnetism. The characteristics of fossil, or remanent, magnetism in terms of field strength and polarity can be determined by suitable laboratory techniques, and so-called paleomagnetic directions can be plotted on a map.

The apparent movement of the magnetic poles over geologic time was very puzzling in the early days of magnetic studies but was later discovered to be an effect brought about by movement of the continents. Apparent polar-wandering (APW) curves (see Box 9.1) have been plotted for all the continents and have proven invaluable in determining the timing and direction of continental drift in past geologic time. The apparent movement of the poles is discussed in later chapters.

In addition to the apparent movement of the poles, scientists discovered another peculiarity of the earth's magnetic field: In any succession of rocks containing magnetic minerals (such as lava flows), approximately half of the paleomagnetic determinations show normal polarity (that is, with the north-seeking pole pointing north), whereas the other half show a reversed polarity (Figure 5.6). Self-reversal in magnetic minerals, consequent on internal molecular reordering, is known but is not a common phenomenon, and its occurrence in 50 percent of the rocks would be too much of a coincidence. Clearly, what was indicated was not a self-reversal, but an actual reversal of the earth's magnetic field.

Dating the magnetized rocks showed that such reversals happen at intervals ranging from tens to hundreds of thousands of years (Figure 5.7). The exact cause is unknown but is presumably due to irregularities in the movement of material in the earth's outer core.

Because a reversal in the earth's magnetic field is obviously worldwide in its effect, and because the reversal event can often be detected in the rocks, it quickly became

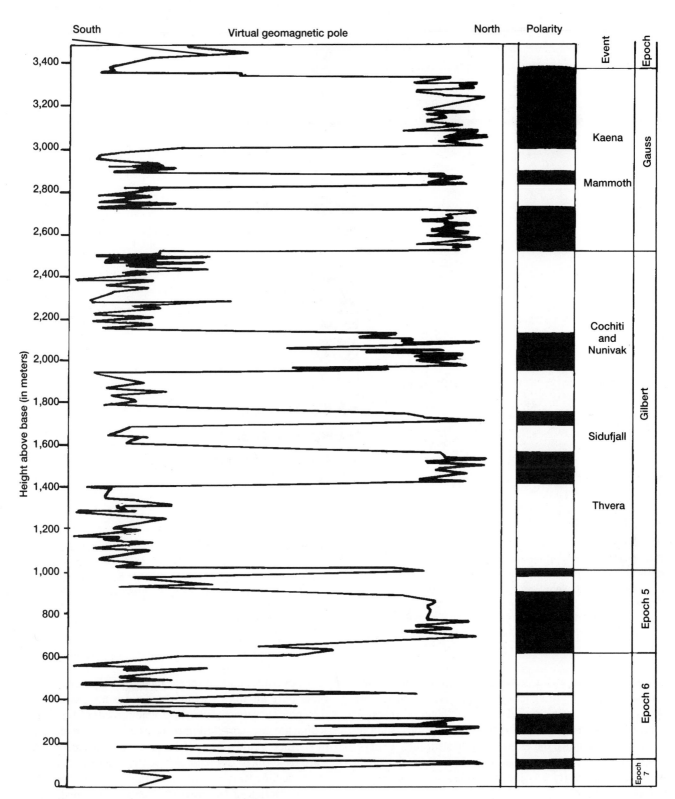

FIGURE 5.6
Magneto-stratigraphic section through a 3,500-meter
succession of Late Cenozoic lava flows in western Iceland.
Determinations to the left show reversed polarity. The
standard names for polarity chrons (time intervals) are shown
on the right.

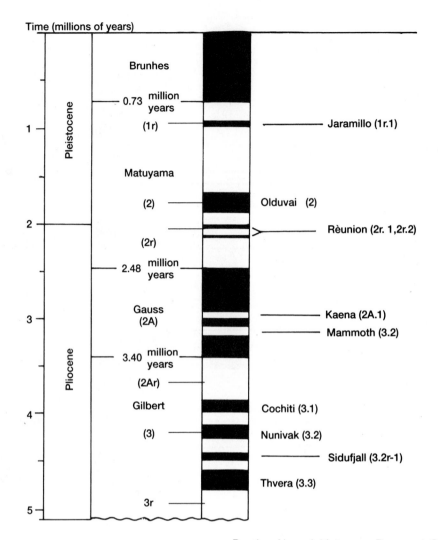

FIGURE 5.7

Time scale for the most recent magnetic reversals. The time scale is divided into chrons and subchrons, formerly referred to as epochs and events, respectively. Although originally the practice was to name magnetic epochs after well-known geomagnetists, for reversals beyond about 5.1 million years ago, a numbering system has been adopted. Counting the Brunhes Normal, Matuyama Reversed, Gauss Normal, and Gilbert Reversed Epochs as 1 through 4, the normal epoch preceding the Gilbert becomes number 5 and so on. Reversal events within epochs are lettered A, B, C, and so on, with increasing age and smaller excursions within events identified by a further letter or numerical subscript.

obvious that here was a powerful new stratigraphic correlation tool. The magnetic reversal is not instantaneous—it occurs over a period of several thousand years—but just as with the time of dispersal of species, such a time span is usually too short to be measurable. Everywhere a particular magnetic reversal can be detected within a sedimentary succession or igneous rock is an isochronous horizon.

Although this was an exciting discovery, it soon became clear that it was not a panacea for the time-correlation problem. For one thing, magnetic reversals are simply flip-flop phenomena: Every change from normal to reverse and back again looks like every other one. There is nothing unique about magnetic reversals, as there is with the appearance and disappearance of species. Because reversals are all alike, sorting them out is not easy. If stratigraphic successions were complete records of continuous sedimentation, correlating reversal events from one place to another would simply be a question of counting backward from the most recent one. Unfortunately, many gaps in the sedimentary record mean that, at many locations, only a fraction of the reversal events is recorded. If, for example, four reversal events are recorded in a given deep-sea core, there is no guarantee that they are the same four reversals documented in a core 100 kilometers away. In practice, biostratigraphic indicators, tephrochronologic markers (discussed in the next section), and radiometric dating methods (see Chapter 6) are used to supplement magnetostratigraphic data.

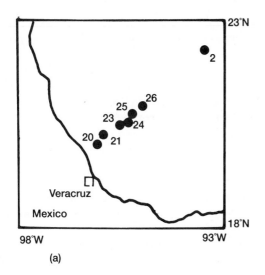

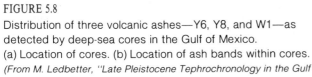

(a)

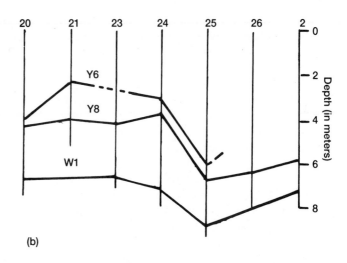

(b)

FIGURE 5.8

Distribution of three volcanic ashes—Y6, Y8, and W1—as detected by deep-sea cores in the Gulf of Mexico. (a) Location of cores. (b) Location of ash bands within cores. *(From M. Ledbetter, "Late Pleistocene Tephrochronology in the Gulf*

of Mexico Region," in Nancy Healy-Williams, ed., Principles of Pleistocene Stratigraphy Applied to the Gulf of Mexico, *p. 124,* © *1984 International Human Resources Development Corporation. Adapted by permission of Prentice Hall, Englewood Cliffs, New Jersey.)*

Tephrochronology: Time Correlation by Volcanic Ash Beds

The value of volcanic ash deposits or tephra as a stratigraphic correlation tool is indicated by their isochronous nature, as discussed earlier. In recent years, the science of tephrochronology (the study of stratigraphic correlation and the dating of tephra) has grown considerably. Clearly, a discrete ash band—wherever it occurs and in whatever stratigraphic succession it is interbedded—represents the few days or weeks of a volcanic eruption and ash fallout. On the scale geologists use in dealing with geologic time, this can obviously be considered an instant in time. Although in volcanic regions, local eruption histories can be established from ash bands in soil horizons, swamp and lake deposits, glaciers, and the like, the most important application of tephrochronology is in the study of deep-sea sediments.

Many ash bands in Pleistocene and Recent deep-sea sediments were first discovered as subbottom reflectors in acoustical sounding surveys. Volcanic ash is a relatively strong reflector of acoustic energy when compared with successions containing marine muds, so ash bands can be detected over wide areas of the sea floor. The Worzel Band, first located as a subbottom reflector in 1959 in the eastern equatorial Pacific, for example, although not a single ash band as originally thought, marked a series of enormous eruptions in Central America. Even 500 kilometers out into the Pacific, the Worzel D ash has a thickness of 6 to 8 centimeters. Because it is virtually ringed by volcanic arcs and mountain chains, most tephrochronologic studies have been conducted in the Pacific basin.

The distribution of volcanic ash is influenced by the vagaries of wind and ocean currents, and because the potential sources are numerous both in space and time, sorting out different ash bands in a given sedimentary succession and correlating them from core to core in deep-sea sampling programs is not always easy (Figure 5.8). In practice, electron probe examination of the volcanic glass shards that make up the bulk of the ash usually reveals a distinctive chemical signature. This often enables the volcanic source and even the particular eruption cycle to be identified. Isotopic dating of volcanic ash provides further evidence. In addition, tephrochronology is typically used in conjunction with other tools available to the stratigrapher, so magnetostratigraphic, biostratigraphic, and oxygen isotope data (see Box 20.1) are all used to establish a coherent account of sea-floor depositional history.

Other Stratigraphic Methods of Time Correlation

Unconformities

When the geologic systems were first described at their type sections during the nineteenth century, unconformities (surfaces representing a considerable break in the succession of rocks and an interruption of sediment accumulation) were often used to establish some of the stratigraphic boundaries. Although geologists first thought that some of the larger breaks in the succession might be worldwide in their significance, this idea was soon dispelled when the missing strata were eventually found at other localities. In recent years, unconformities have made something of a comeback in stratigraphic classification schemes because some, at least, of the major discontinuities—the **regional unconformities**—appear to be synchronous on almost a global scale. Clearly, this opens up exciting possibilities for stratigraphic correlation and time-scale calibration.

The apparent synchroneity of unconformities is linked to mechanisms of sea-level change. Fluctuations in sea level have been an important feature of earth history for most of geologic time, and at many places, the geologic column typically contains a sedimentary record of marine transgressions and regressions. Some of them mark **eustatic** (worldwide) **sea-level changes;** others are more local in their effect and are due to regional tectonic movements of the crust. Sorting them out is not easy because the sedimentary record at any one place is usually ambiguous.

If the sea-level changes and especially the unconformities produced during periods of low sea level are to be used as worldwide time markers, then only the record of eustatic sea-level changes is of interest. In practice, if regional unconformities on several different continents are found to be coeval, they are considered to be of eustatic origin. From such data, a eustatic sea-level curve can be constructed (see Box 9.2 and Figure 9.5). As is discussed later in this section, there are some problems with this idea, and it must be approached with caution.

Sequences

During past periods of high sea level, extensive sheets of limestones, shales, and sandstones were deposited across the interiors of **cratons** (central stable cores or nuclei of ancient basement rocks of a continental block). At times during the Ordovician, for example, epeiric seas (shallow seas covering continental interiors) may have covered up to 90 percent of the North American continent. In some cases, individual formations can be traced over thousands of square kilometers. When sea level eventually fell again, the continents became emergent dry land, and weathering and erosional forces began to remove the sediments laid down during the marine incursion.

Many of these episodes of marine transgression and regression are described in detail in later chapters. The important point here is that, when sea level rose again and the next cycle of marine inundation began, the new sediments were laid down on an erosion surface bevelled across what was left of the previous marine sedimentary cycle.

The erosion surface represented a hiatus in the sedimentary record represented by an unconformity. As this process was repeated over tens of millions of years, the total sedimentary record of the cycles of marine incursion came to form extensive envelopes of sedimentary formations, each one separated from the next below or above by an unconformity of regional extent.

The significance of these major sedimentary units in the geologic history of North America was first pointed out by Lawrence Sloss of Northwestern University. He applied the term **sequence** to these units and suggested that they represent a special kind of stratigraphic entity. This is because, although bounded below and above by major unconformities whose age varies from place to place, sequences do have a certain chronostratigraphic significance, being everywhere younger than the bounding unconformity below and older than the one above. Sequences typically represent long periods of time, according to Sloss, roughly of the magnitude of geologic systems. Many scientists have suggested that if, indeed, the sea-level fluctuations responsible for the sequences are worldwide in their effect, then they are more "natural" chronostratigraphic units than are the systems that came to form the basis of the geologic time scale.

In North America, six sequences—representing six major marine transgressions—have been described (Figure 5.9). If the original geologic time scale had been assembled by American rather than European geologists, the major divisions would undoubtedly have been selected somewhat differently.

On the other hand, there are two difficulties with the idea of using sequences rather than systems as worldwide chronostratigraphic units. First, on the other continents, the sequences are often not as well developed as in North America, frequently due to modification by local tectonic movements (Figure 5.10). Second, it is not known with absolute certainty that all the sea-level fluctuations responsible for the epeiric sequences were entirely eustatic in origin. They may, in fact, involve a noneustatic component and, thus, not be simultaneous on a worldwide scale.

Nevertheless, although now defined in several ways that differ from Sloss's original concept, sequences have found a place in stratigraphic classification because, as unconformity-bounded units, they can be detected by seismic surveys. Thus, they have become the fundamental divisions used in seismic stratigraphy.

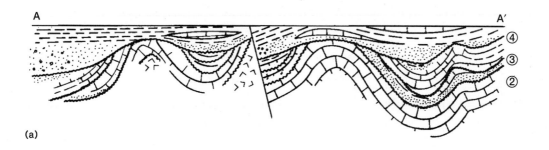

(a)

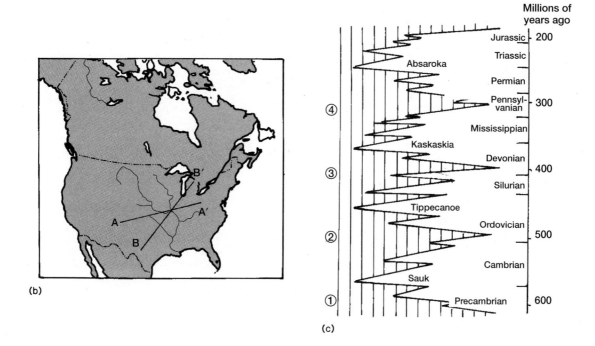

(b)

(c)

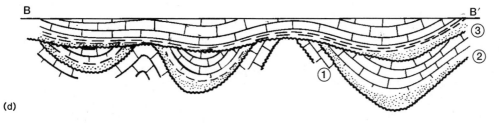

(d)

FIGURE 5.9

Sequences on the North American continent, as described
by L. L. Sloss (1963). (a) Diagrammatic cross section of the
craton along line A–A'. (b) Location map for cross sections.
(c) Time scale of the North American sequences.
(d) Diagrammatic cross section of the craton along line B–B'.

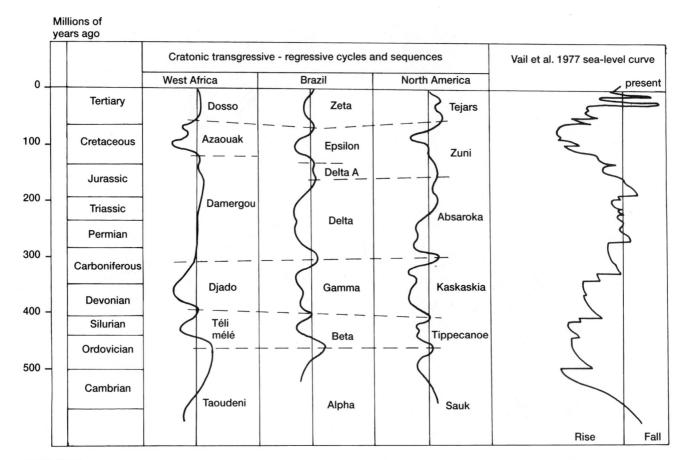

FIGURE 5.10
Regional unconformities on three continents mark major
eustatic sea-level changes. The Vail sea-level curve,
discussed in Chapter 9, has been added for comparison
purposes.

Seismic Stratigraphy and a Sea-Level Curve

Seismic stratigraphy is a method of probing the various
layers in the earth's crust by means of sound waves. The
sound waves are generated by small explosions set off at
the earth's surface. They travel downward in all directions and are reflected back to the surface, where they are
picked up by sensitive microphones (geophones) placed in
interconnected arrays on the ground (Figure 5.11). The
principle involved is rather like the echo-ranging systems
used by bats, whereby they can avoid obstacles in complete darkness. As the signals are picked up by the geophones, they are transmitted by cables to a recording truck
and the pulses translated into the printed record of the
seismic survey (Figure 5.12). The seismic survey record
allows interpretation of the attitude and to some extent
the nature of the rock strata deep below the surface.

Used most widely in the exploration for oil and gas,
seismic surveys were most successful in finding buried
structures, such as anticlines (arching folds) synclines
(trough-shaped folds), and faults (fractures in crustal
rocks along which there has been a relative displacement
of the rocks). As techniques and knowledge increased,
however, geologists discovered that the reflection characteristics of certain rock types were sufficiently distinctive as to be identifiable. Thus, the contrast between
massive reef limestones and their surrounding shales was
so marked that reef trends, many containing oil and gas,
could be located. One of the first successes of this exploration technique came in 1947 with the discovery of the
Devonian Leduc field in western Canada.

In more recent years, seismic surveys have found
major unconformities in the subsurface, especially in the
thick sedimentary successions that underlie the continental shelves. Some of these have proven to be the same

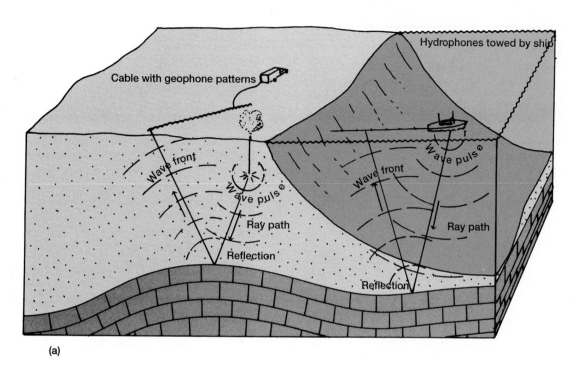

(a)

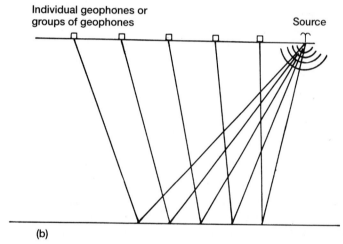

Individual geophones or
groups of geophones   Source

(b)

FIGURE 5.11

Principle of seismic surveying. (a) Sound waves generated
by explosions on the ground surface, or nonexplosive
devices in the water, travel downward and are reflected back
to the surface from buried stratal surfaces. (b) At the
surface, the pulses are picked up by geophones (or in the
water, by hydrophones).

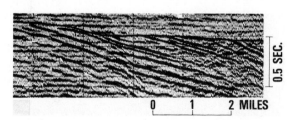

0   1   2 MILES

0.5 SEC.

FIGURE 5.12

Typical seismic section. The dark lines are combinations of
wiggle traces produced by sonic vibrations picked up by
geophones. The individual reflections seen as light or dark
zones across the section do not usually represent individual
strata but are combinations of reflections from many beds
within a given thickness of strata. *(Courtesy of American
Association of Petroleum Geologists.)*

FIGURE 5.13
Reflection "packages" in a seismic section. The packages
are separated from each other by discontinuities, or
interruptions in the reflection patterns. On this section, such
package boundaries are marked by heavier lines.
(LK = Lower Cretaceous; J = Jurassic.) *(Courtesy of American
Association of Petroleum Geologists.)*

unconformities that separate the cratonic sequences mentioned earlier. Along the continental margin is found the
most complete sedimentary record of marine transgressions and regressions, and oil explorationists, using data
from hundreds of offshore seismic surveys, as well as offshore wells, have claimed that many of these transgressions and regressions are of eustatic origin (Figure 5.13).

They arrived at this conclusion because they were able
to correlate the same unconformities among several continents, and, as a result, it became possible to draw up a
master sea-level curve. The curve was calibrated by using
biostratigraphic markers from the stratigraphic succession recorded in drill cuttings from the subsurface (well
logs), and it looked as though the sea-level curve itself
might become an important tool for stratigraphic correlation.

On the other hand, there are some good reasons to be
cautious. In the first place, fluctuations on a sea-level curve

suffer from the same weakness as do magnetic reversals.
There is nothing unique about them, and their age must
be confirmed by biostratigraphic methods or other means.
In addition, and as with surface and borehole stratigraphy, the accuracy of the biostratigraphic data varies
widely, resulting, quite possibly, in miscorrelation. There
is also the question of the basic mechanism involved. The
sea-level curve can only be used as a worldwide correlation tool if it is truly a eustatic curve, and this is by no
means certain. The apparent coincidence of sea-level rise
and fall at locations thousands of kilometers apart on either
side of an ocean may be simply a reflection of a similar
basin history. For example, it would hardly be surprising
to find that the geologic history of the western margin of
Africa and the eastern margin of South America were
similar, following the breakup of Gondwana and their
drifting apart from a spreading center. In Chapter 7, the
mechanisms involved are discussed in detail.

Summary

The passage of time and the deposition of sedimentary rocks are linked. Until the late 1920s and early 1930s, little was known about the true age of rocks and geological events in terms of real time (measured in years). Sedimentary successions and their contained faunas were described only in terms of relative time, based almost entirely on the fossil content within a scheme of evolutionary development. The more species two stratigraphic sections had in common, the more likely they were to be the same age.

A chronostratigraphic unit contains all the rocks deposited during a given time interval. The first defined chronostratigraphic units were the geologic systems. The Cambrian, Ordovician, Silurian, and so on, established by nineteenth-century geologists, were each deposited during a period, a geochronologic unit. The systems were actually defined in the field on the basis of their contained fossils and so, strictly speaking, are biostratigraphic units.

The first person to describe geologic phenomena in terms of time and to begin to observe stratigraphic relationships was Nicolaus Steno in Florence. In a book published in 1669, he proposed three laws: (1) the law of superposition, (2) the law of original horizontality, and (3) the law of original continuity. The use of fossils as stratigraphic correlation tools to demonstrate time equivalence was first suggested by William Smith, a civil engineer and paleontologist, often referred to as the "Father of British Stratigraphy." The first stratigraphic column of rock formations in England was published in 1798, and the first geologic maps were issued in 1814 and 1815. After Smith's work, the remainder of the geologic columns containing fossils were described during the first part of the nineteenth century by Murchison, Sedgwick, Lapworth, and others. During this time, all the geologic systems and periods recognized today were defined.

More detailed biostratigraphic divisions are based on the ranges through time of particular species or assemblages of species, selected as being widely distributed in sedimentary rocks of all kinds and preferably having relatively short species' range spans. Such zone fossils are used to establish biozones, each characterized by and named after selected species.

Biozones are used as the basis for recognizing stages. Stages are, theoretically, at least, chronostratigraphic units and the smallest such units supposedly recognized worldwide. In particular, stages are defined on the basis of relatively local faunas and can thus only be correlated approximately with faunas in distant places, particularly those in different climatic zones.

In addition to being defined by fossils, isochronous horizons within stratigraphic successions can be established by magnetostratigraphy. The earth, because of its metallic core and its rotation, behaves as a dipole magnet. Certain minerals, notably magnetite, are natural magnets and acquire thermoremanent magnetism as they crystallize in a cooling magma. The earth's magnetic polarity and its direction when and where the magma cooled are thus "frozen in."

Over time periods ranging from tens to hundreds of thousands of years, the earth's magnetic field reverses itself. In a succession of rocks that contain magnetic minerals, roughly half of the magnetic samples will, when studied in the laboratory, show normal polarity (that is, the north-seeking pole points north, as at the present day), and the other half will show reversed polarity.

Magnetic reversals occur quite quickly—within a few thousand years—a time interval so short as to be considered instantaneous in geologic terms. Because magnetic reversals are global phenomena, the succession of normal/reversed polarities recorded in a stratigraphic succession at one place can be correlated with the same succession in another. However, magnetic reversals are also flip-flop phenomena and are not unique; therefore, they must be used in conjunction with biostratigraphic, tephrochronologic, isotopic, or other dating methods.

Tephrochronology is based upon the recognition of discrete bands of volcanic ash found, for the most part, in deep-sea successions. A single ash band, derived from the fallout of a volcanic eruption, is, essentially, an isochronous horizon. If the various ash bands found in deep-sea sediment cores can be recognized and correlated among sampling sites, then tephrochronology is a powerful stratigraphic tool. In practice, ash bands are tied in with biostratigraphic and magnetostratigraphic markers.

Major unconformities of regional extent separate sequences of sediments laid down during extensive marine incursions onto the continental margins and even the craton interiors. The time-stratigraphic significance of sequences is supported by the idea that some of the sea-level changes responsible for successive marine transgressions, seen in many stratigraphic successions, have been of eustatic origin and, therefore, are of worldwide significance.

Because the bounding unconformities of a sequence can be widely recognized in seismic surveys, sea-level fluctuations are among the most important phenomena recognized in seismic stratigraphy. A master sea-level curve based upon the apparent time equivalence of many local sea-level curves may become an important tool for stratigraphic correlation.

Questions

1. In what two ways can time be measured? Give examples.
2. What is a chronostratigraphic unit? Give examples, and list the hierarchy of units of different rank.
3. Give examples of geologic phenomena that would be recorded in the stratigraphic succession as isochronous (or approximate isochronous) surfaces.
4. What big breakthrough did William Smith make in studying fossils?
5. Why was there a controversy between Murchison and Sedgwick? How was it finally resolved in terms of the geologic time table?
6. What are zone fossils? Explain their relationship to biozones.
7. Although stages are theoretically biostratigraphic units of worldwide extent, explain why this is impossible.
8. Describe how magnetostratigraphy works.
9. How might regional unconformities be used in continent-to-continent stratigraphic correlation?
10. What is the sea-level curve? Why might it be a primary tool in stratigraphic correlation?
11. Describe the concept of sequences.
12. Explain the principle of seismic stratigraphy. How can it be used in stratigraphic studies?
13. Why have seismic stratigraphic studies been of special value in understanding the stratigraphy of the continental shelf successions?
14. Compare the strengths and weaknesses of the various methods used in stratigraphic correlation.
15. In your local stratigraphic succession, how many major unconformities occur? What portion of the geologic time scale do they represent?

Further Reading

Ager, D. V. 1981. *The nature of the stratigraphical record.* 2d ed. New York: John Wiley.

Berry, W. B. N. 1968. *Growth of a prehistoric time scale.* San Francisco: W. H. Freeman.

Eicher, D. L. 1976. *Geologic time.* 2d ed. Englewood Cliffs, N.J.: Prentice-Hall.

Krumbein, W. C., and L. L. Sloss. 1963. *Stratigraphy and sedimentation.* 2d ed. San Francisco: W. H. Freeman.

Schneer, C. J., ed. 1969. *Toward a history of geology.* Cambridge, Mass.: MIT Press.

Wendt, H. 1968. *Before the Deluge.* New York: Doubleday.

6

REAL-TIME DATING IN GEOLOGY

Introduction

Among the topics reviewed in Chapter 1 was the age of the earth—in particular, the role played by the discovery of **radioactivity** (the spontaneous decay of unstable atomic nuclei). In this chapter, we return to this important subject and discuss the various dating methods that increasingly are providing accurate geologic ages measured in **real time**—that is, in time calibrated in years before the present. A time scale based on measurements in years is usually termed an **absolute time scale,** in contrast to the **relative time scale** that evolved during the nineteenth century in which geologic events were set out in the order they occurred without reference to the actual time measured in years. The study of these real-time dating methods has come to comprise a subdiscipline in geology termed **geochronology.** Many of the methods used involve the radioactive decay of certain elements and are often referred to as **radiometric** or **isotopic dating methods.** Other dating methods examined in this chapter include amino acid racemization and dating by radiation damage.

Isotopic Dating Methods

As discussed in Chapter 1, radiometric dating began in the early years of this century with the discoveries of Rutherford and Soddy at McGill University in Montreal, and Boltwood at Yale. The basic principles of radioactive decay, as they could be applied to the problem of age determination, were known even at this early date, and since that time, geochronology has advanced largely as a result of improvements in technology. Particularly important was the invention in 1929 of the **mass spectrometer,** a device that makes it possible to determine the relative abundance of different isotopes, an essential first step in making the calculations necessary to determine the length of time the radiometric clock has been running or, in other words, the age of the enclosing mineral or rock. Our discussion begins with a brief overview of the basic principles of isotopic dating.

Principles of Isotopic Dating

Isotopes

Although for a given element, the number of protons (positively charged particles in the atomic nucleus) of each atom is constant, the number of neutrons (particles with no electrical charge in the atomic nucleus) may vary. Thus, nearly all elements have two or more nuclear variants, called **isotopes.** Isotopes for a given element differ from one another in the number of neutrons in the nucleus, yet their chemical behavior, which only involves the electrons (negatively charged particles found outside the atomic nucleus), is unaffected. Thus, the isotopes of a given ele-

ment have similar chemical properties, and changes in the nucleus—for example, those resulting from radioactive decay—are unaffected by the element's physical or chemical environment. It follows that the differences between isotopes of a given element cannot be detected by normal chemical analyses.

Radioactive Decay

Isotopes were originally discovered because the isotopes of certain elements were unstable and change spontaneously, or "decay," into new isotopes. In so doing, they make their presence known by the effects produced by particles emitted from their nuclei.

Frenchman Antoine Bequerel detected the emission of these high-energy particles in 1896. He discovered that photographic plates became exposed, or "fogged," when placed in proximity to samples of the uranium ore pitchblende (uraninite), even though the plates were carefully protected from the light. Some kind of radiation, invisible to the eye and capable of penetrating solid materials, exposed the plates. New discoveries soon followed, and Marie Curie and her husband Pierre were able to show that the changes in nuclei of the uranium atoms not only caused the emission of the mysterious radiation but also led to the formation of the new chemical elements radium and polonium.

In the years that followed, scientists discovered that nearly all elements have at least two isotopes. Oxygen, for example, has three (oxygen-16, oxygen-17, and oxygen-18, with mass numbers of 16, 17, and 18, respectively), iron has four, and tin has as many as ten stable isotopes.

When isotopes with unstable nuclei undergo radioactive decay, a series of spontaneous changes take place until, eventually, the configuration is stable. In this decay process, the nuclei of the **parent isotopes** change as a result of the emission of particles and radiant energy. The particles are the so-called alpha particles (helium nuclei) and beta particles (free electrons). Gamma rays (similar to X rays) are also given off (Table 6.1). Sometimes, a parent isotope decays to a stable **daughter isotope** in a single step; in other cases, a **decay series** of steps is involved.

One of the more complex decay series is that for the uranium isotope uranium-238 (U-238), shown in Figure 6.1. As can be seen, after passing through a whole chain of unstable isotopes, of which some blink into and out of existence in a fraction of a second, a final stable isotope of lead (Pb-206) is produced. The total number of alpha particles involved in all the stages is eight, each having a mass number of four (being helium nuclei), so that there is a total reduction in mass number of 32, which is the difference between the values for parent uranium-238 and radiogenic lead-206 at the end of the series. In discussions of decay series, the usual convention is to ignore the intermediate isotopes; thus, the U-238 to Pb-206 series would be shown as U-238 $\rightarrow$ Pb-206 + 8^{4}HE.

TABLE 6.1

Summary of Decay Processes

Decay Mode	Change	Result	Example
Alpha decay	Emits alpha particles	Reduces atomic number by 2; reduces mass number by 4	$_{92}U^{238} \rightarrow {}_{90}Th^{234}$
Beta decay	Emits negatively charged beta particle (electron)	Converts neutron into proton + electron; atomic number increased by 1; mass number unchanged	$_{37}Rb^{87} \rightarrow {}_{38}Sr^{87}$
Electron capture	Captures electron	Converts proton into neutron; atomic number decreased by 1; mass number unchanged	$_{19}K^{40} \rightarrow {}_{18}Ar^{40}$

TABLE 6.2

Decay Constants and Half-Life Values

Radioactive Isotope	Half-life (years)	Decay Constants
Potassium-40(K^{40})	$1,250 \times 10^9$	5.543×10^{-10}
Rubidium-87(Rb^{87})	48.8×10^9	1.42×10^{-11}
Uranium-238(U^{238})	$4,468 \times 10^9$	1.55125×10^{-10}
Uranium-235(U^{235})	0.7038×10^9	9.8485×10^{-10}
Uranium-234(U^{234})	2.47×10^5	2.806×10^{-6}
Thorium-232(Th^{232})	$14,010 \times 10^9$	4.9475×10^{-11}

TABLE 6.3

The Half-Lives of Phases in One of the Uranium-238 Decay Schemes

Phase of Decay Scheme	Half-Life
Uranium-238 to Thorium-234	4.5×10^9 years
Thorium-234 to Protactinium-234	24.5 days
Protactinium-234 to Uranium-234	1.14 minutes
Uranium-234 to Thorium-230	2.7×10^5 years
Thorium-230 to Radium-226	8.3×10^4 years
Radium-226 to Radon-222	1,590 years
Radon-222 to Polonium-218	3.82 days
Polonium-218 to Lead-214	3.05 minutes
Lead-214 to Bismuth-214	26.8 minutes
Bismuth-214 to Polonium-214	19.7 minutes
Polonium-214 to Lead-210	1.4×10^{-4} seconds
Lead-210 to Bismuth-210	22 years
Bismuth-210 to Polonium-210	5.0 days
Polonium-210 to Lead-206 (stable)	14.0 days

Decay Constants and Half-Lives

For a given element, the process of radioactive decay proceeds at a constant rate proportional to the amount of material still present, and this is expressed in terms of what is called the **decay constant** (λ), defined as the probability that an atom will decay within a given period of time. That is, the actual *number* of atoms that will decay in a given time is not constant, but the *proportion* of atoms that will decay *is*. Thus, as time goes on, the number of decaying atoms becomes progressively smaller, so the absolute rate of decay decreases with time (Figure 6.2).

Because the number of atoms to decay decreases at an ever-diminishing rate, in theory, at least, it would take an infinite amount of time for all the radioactive atoms in a given series to decay. The length of time required for the decay of half the atoms, however, is measurable, and this is why the decay times of radionuclides (isotopes subject to spontaneous radioactive decay) are always expressed in **half-lives.** Thus, the isotope uranium-238 is said to have a half-life of 4.5×10^9 years, which means that, after 4.5 billion years, one-half of the uranium originally present will have been transformed into radiogenic lead-206. After another 4.5 billion years, half of the remaining uranium will have been transformed, and so on. Every radionuclide has its own half-life; the value of the half-life, usually expressed as T, and the decay constant (λ) are related and expressed as $T = 0.69315/\lambda$ (Table 6.2).

As can be seen from Table 6.3, the half-lives of some isotopes are so fleeting that they clearly are of no use in any isotopic dating procedure. Almost as unsuitable are those radionuclides having extremely long half-lives, perhaps measured in trillions of years, because except perhaps in the very oldest rocks or in lunar or meteorite samples, the amount of accumulated daughter isotopes that must be measured for any dating is so small as to be difficult to detect. In practice, the radiometric method involving a radionuclide with a half-life of about the same order of magnitude as the age of the rocks to be dated is likely to be the most satisfactory.

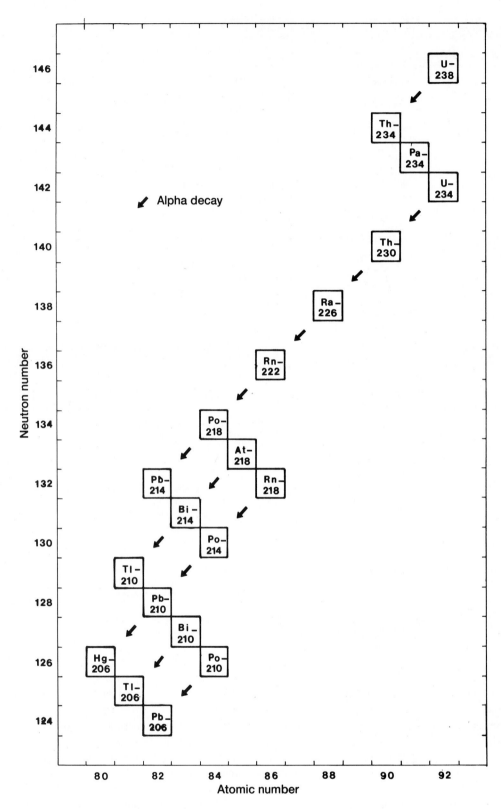

FIGURE 6.1

Radioactive decay series of uranium-238 through eight alpha
decay steps and six beta steps and ending with a stable
isotope of lead (Pb–206). At each alpha step, the mass
number is reduced by four (8 × 4 = 32, the difference
between 238 and 206). *(Source: Data from G. Faure,* Principles of
Isotope Geology, *2d ed. Copyright © 1986 John Wiley & Sons, Inc.)*

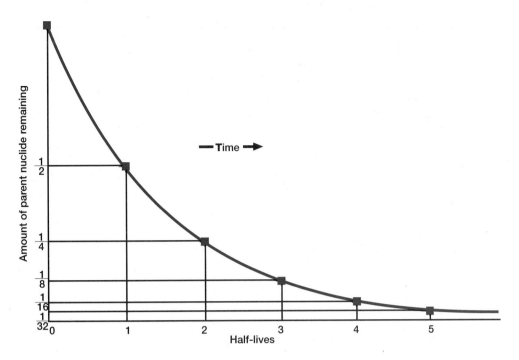

FIGURE 6.2
Graph of time and decay. During each half-life, one-half of
the remaining radioactive element decays; thus, the time
required for the decay of all the element is infinite.

Although most of the radionuclides were created
within stellar masses, perhaps 10 billion years ago, long
before the solar system even existed, they could only begin
to function as radiometric clocks when they became incorporated within minerals so that their decay products
could accumulate and thus be measurable. This is why
they are sometimes termed **accumulation clocks.**

Radionuclides cannot be of any use in age determination unless the proportions of parent nuclide and
daughter isotopes produced by decay can be measured.
Unfortunately, as is described later, many geologic processes, like metamorphism, cause the loss of some of the
decay product, and ages determined from such samples
are, obviously, too young. Sometimes, all the daughter isotopes are lost, and the clock is, in effect, then reset to zero.

The principal isotopic dating methods are uranium-
lead dating, potassium-argon dating, rubidium-strontium
dating, thorium-230 dating, and carbon-14 dating. We examine each of these methods in detail in the sections that
follow.

Uranium-Lead Dating

Early Studies

Studies of uranium-bearing minerals by Ernest Rutherford, and Bertram Boltwood provided the first real inkling
of just how old the earth is. Rutherford measured the

amounts of radiogenic helium produced in the alpha steps
of the uranium decay series and had, as early as 1905,
come up with dates of about 500 million years.

Meanwhile, Boltwood, working at Yale, noted in comparing uranium-bearing minerals of different relative ages
that, the older the mineral, the more lead it contained.
This led to the discoveries that the uranium produced the
lead and that lead was the eventual stable end product of
uranium decay. After determining the uranium-lead ratios
in three samples of uraninite, Boltwood was able to calculate the length of time it had taken for the lead to accumulate, and the first isotopic ages based on this **uranium-
lead dating** method were published in 1907.

What Boltwood did not know was that his samples
actually contained a mixture of three different isotopes—
two of uranium and one of thorium—each decaying at different rates to produce different lead isotopes as stable end
products. The means of separating the various isotopes had
to await the development of the mass spectrometer, which
could determine the mass of charged particles by measuring the curvature of their paths through a powerful
magnetic field. Scientists can now summarize the decay
schemes that produce radiogenic lead as follows:

Uranium-238 $\rightarrow$ Lead-206   (Half-life: 4.5×10^9 years)
Uranium-235 $\rightarrow$ Lead-207   (Half-life: 0.7×10^9 years)
Thorium-232 $\rightarrow$ Lead-208   (Half-life: 13.8×10^9 years)

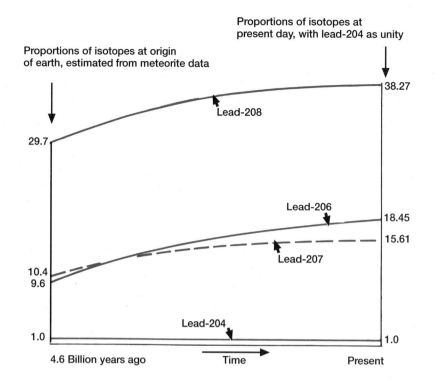

FIGURE 6.3

How the relative proportions of radiogenic isotopes of lead have changed over time. Because the decay rates of the parent isotopes uranium-238, uranium-235, and thorium are known, the time required to reach the present ratios can be calculated. The time calculated for all three isotopes gives a reliable age for the origin of the earth of 4.6 billion years.

Potential Errors in Uranium-Lead Dating

As mentioned earlier, a radiometric accumulation clock is only accurate if all the radiogenic decay product is retained within the mineral or rock—in other words, the rock has remained a closed system. While Rutherford had shown in 1905 that helium, as a stable by-product of the alpha decay steps in uranium, could be used in age determination, in general, radiogenic lead is less likely to suffer leakage or loss.

Another potential source of error—this time in the opposite direction—arises if there is an excess of lead. Ordinary lead is made up of a mixture of the three radiogenic isotopes—lead-206, lead-207, and lead-208—and a further isotope, lead-204, which is never produced radiogenically. Because the proportions of the various isotopes are known, the presence of lead-204 can be used to ascertain the presence of any radiogenic lead retained from an earlier clock setting and that would naturally result in erroneously old dates.

Lead-204 is not radiogenic; thus, its total abundance in crustal rocks, unlike that of radiogenic lead, has presumably remained unchanged. It follows that progressively younger rocks will have accumulated more and more radiogenic lead released from parent rocks by weathering, melting, and so on, as time and decay have proceeded. Lead-204, lead-206, lead-207, and lead-208 currently exist

in the ratios 1.0, 18.45, 15.61, and 38.24, respectively, but in the past, the degree of dilution of the earth's original nonradiogenic lead would have been less. The shift in ratios has been progressive with time, and in a given sample, the ratios among the lead species are systematically linked to the age of the sample (Figure 6.3). Extrapolating lead values back through time, incidentally, points to a date of about 4.6 billion years for the age of the earth, a useful cross-check on figures obtained by other means.

The Concordia Curve

The accuracy of lead dating methods is greatly enhanced if the ages derived from uranium-238 → lead-206 decay can be checked against those of the uranium-235 → lead-207 series (Figure 6.3). If the mineral being dated has remained a closed system, the two calculations will agree and give concordant dates. Such dates are plotted on a graph, with the uranium-238/lead-206 ratio as the ordinate and the uranium-235/lead-207 ratio as the abscissa. The loci of concordant dates defines a curve known as the concordia (Figure 6.4).

Loss of radiogenic lead from the system might seem to introduce an uncontrolled variable, but the concordia diagram allows the date of the lead-loss event to be ascertained. In a given rock body subjected to an episode of metamorphism, intrusion, structural stress, leaching, or

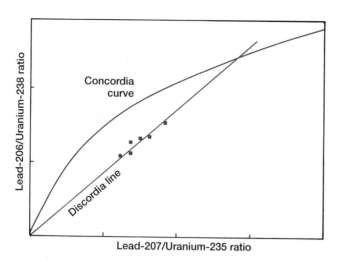

FIGURE 6.4

Typical concordia plot. The curve plots the changing ratios of uranium and lead isotopes through time in a uranium-mineral sample. The concordia curve is plotted so that the amount of radiogenic lead increases upward for lead-206 and to the right for lead-207. The straight line (discordia line) passes through the results of analyses of several uranium minerals from one deposit. The point of interception of the discordia line with the concordia curve yields the age when the uranium minerals formed.

other cause of lead loss, lead loss is unlikely to be the same from all parts of the rock. The values from different samples can be plotted as a series of points marking discordant dates on a straight line below the concordia. The line, known as the discordia, intercepts the concordia curve at two points: one marking the time of initial crystallization of the mineral and one marking the lead-loss event.

Materials Used for Uranium-Lead Dating

Uranium-rich minerals are uncommon, but the element does occur in trace amounts in a number of rock-forming minerals. Zircon, a zirconium silicate ($ZrSiO_4$) found in many igneous rocks, particularly granites, contains up to 0.1 percent uranium in its structure and is the most widely used mineral in uranium-lead dating.

Surprisingly, uranium-lead dating also can be used with certain calcareous skeletal materials and carbonate sediments. Corals, for example, apparently do not discriminate among calcium, strontium, radium, and uranium in secreting their skeletons, and some of these elements become incorporated in the structure. The proportion of calcium in uranium in corals is the same as that in seawater, in which dissolved uranium is enriched in the daughter isotope uranium-234 over the parent uranium-238. Measurement of the thorium-230 derived from alpha decay of uranium-234 allows for the determination of ages

ranging up to 350,000 years. The success of this method depends, of course, upon the biogenic aragonite of the coral skeleton remaining a closed system. The most common failure in this regard is recrystallization and alteration of aragonite to calcite. Certain calcareous sediments, such as oolites and cave deposits, also have been dated by this method.

Potassium-Argon Dating

Potassium is the seventh most abundant element in crustal rocks and is a constituent of many common rock-forming minerals, including the potassic feldspars that comprise 60 percent of most granites and pegmatites. The micas, many clay minerals, and such minerals as hornblende, nepheline, and leucite also contain potassium.

Of the three naturally occurring isotopes of potassium (potassium-39, potassium-40, and potassium-41), only potassium-40 (comprising about 0.1 percent) is unstable. Most potassium-40 (about 89 percent) decays to calcium-40 and the remainder to argon-40. Radiogenic calcium-40 is indistinguishable from common calcium, so that particular decay scheme is unusable for dating. Argon, on the other hand, is an inert gas, so any argon-40 found in a potassium mineral is virtually certain to be of radiogenic origin.

Even though the half-life of potassium-40 is 1.25×10^9 years, minerals as young as 50,000 years have been found to contain measurable amounts of argon-40 because even small quantities can be detected. Dates from young rocks are, in fact, often more accurate than older ones because of the possibility of argon loss from the older minerals. Argon loss is particularly likely if a rock has been heated, perhaps during a phase of metamorphism, and the older the rock, the more likely that it has been heated.

Unless it can be positively shown that no heating or extensive crushing or cracking has occurred, the ages derived from **potassium-argon dating** are generally considered minimum dates only. For this same reason, igneous rocks that cooled quickly, such as lava flows or small intrusions, are preferred for potassium-argon dating over those in deep-seated plutons. Plutons are large rock bodies that may have taken millions of years to cool below about 300°C (termed the blocking temperature), at which point the mineral becomes a closed system. In the case of fine-grained igneous rocks, it is virtually impossible to separate individual crystals, so the entire rock is dated in what is called the **whole rock method.**

Potassium-argon dating can also be used in marine sediments that contain glauconite. A distinctive green-colored mineral, glauconite is a complex potassium iron-aluminum silicate that is precipitated within the pore spaces of sediments or as a replacement for other mineral grains, skeletal material, ooliths, and fecal pellets. The calculated age is obviously that of the glauconite formation and not the sediment, but because glauconite apparently forms only within a shallow depth below the sea floor, the sediment could not have been deposited much more than a few thousand years earlier, depending on the rate of deposition.

Rubidium-Strontium Dating

Rubidium is not a common element in crustal rocks, but it often substitutes for potassium in various crystal structures. It is found in trace amounts in the potassium feldspars, for example, and also in the micas, amphiboles, pyroxenes, and olivine. The strontium originally present in a rubidium-containing rock consists of a mixture of strontium-86 and strontium-87; however, only the radiogenic strontium-87 is used in age calculation. The strontium-86/strontium-87 ratio is accordingly determined by first analyzing a rubidium-free sample that clearly contains no *new* radiogenic daughters. Then, the rubidium-containing samples with their varying amounts of radiogenic strontium-87 can be dated by calculating the parent/daughter ratios as is done in other accumulation clocks.

Because these additional analytical steps introduce potential sources of error that are proportionately greater in younger samples, rubidium-strontium dating is most accurate in very old samples and works best with Precambrian rocks.

In an additional refinement applied to this method, several samples from the same suite of igneous rocks are used to construct what is called an isochron diagram (Figure 6.5). All the rocks derived from a single body of magma can be assumed to have had the same initial strontium-87/strontium-86 ratio, or, in other words, are isotopically homogeneous. This means that, in the isochron diagram, in which the abscissa is the rubidium-87/strontium-86 ratio, all the samples will plot along the line representing time zero (the time the magma crystallized). Samples representing a range of rubidium content are selected so as to give a spread of points. As time passes and radiogenic strontium-87 accumulates in each sample, its isotopic evolution is depicted by a line moving up and to the left at a rate appropriate to its relative content of rubidium. At any one time, the points on the graph will lie along a straight line—the isochron, meaning equal time—whose slope will indicate the age of the suite of rocks.

Thorium-230 Dating

As discussed earlier, the decay of uranium-238 to uranium-234 and thorium-230 can be used to date certain carbonate sediments and skeletons. This spin-off technique has been particularly useful in dating geologically young ocean-floor sediments of a few hundred thousand years,

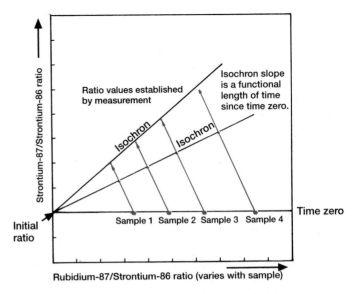

FIGURE 6.5

Isochron diagram. At the time of crystallization (time zero), the ratio of rubidium-87 to strontium-86 will vary from sample to sample, but the initial ratio of strontium-87 to strontium-86 will be the same. As time passes, the decay of rubidium-87 will reduce the amount of rubidium-87 and increase the proportion of strontium-87, since it is produced radiogenically. The changing isotope ratios of four samples are shown and can be plotted to establish an isochron line after the passage of a given time. The intersection of the isochron lines with the strontium-87/strontium-86 axis indicates the initial ratio of strontium-87 to strontium-86.

which are beyond the reach of the carbon-14 dating method described in the next section.

The thorium-230 dating technique relies on the fact that, whereas uranium mostly remains in solution in seawater, the thorium-230 arising from uranium decay becomes incorporated in the bottom sediments by absorption onto mineral grains or incorporation within new minerals. Thorium-230 decays with a half-life of 75,000 years; thus, the sediment sampled in cores at successively greater depths below the sea floor would be expected to contain progressively smaller amounts of thorium-230. Over the relatively short time periods involved, both thorium-230 precipitation in the muds and the sediment accumulation rate can be assumed to have remained constant. This thorium-230 method is not an accumulation clock, dependent upon measuring the ratio of parent to daughter isotope, but instead is termed a **decay clock,** in which only the amount of parent isotope remaining is measured.

Thorium can be used in a second dating method in which its abundance relative to protactinium-231 is measured. Just as thorium-230 is a decay product of uranium-238, so protactinium-231 is produced by decay of uranium-235, via the daughter thorium-231; like thorium-230, protactinium-231 also is precipitated in

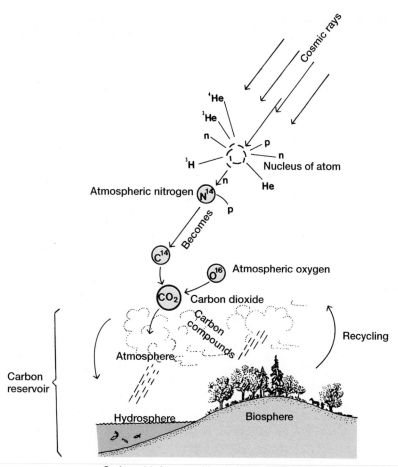

Carbon-14 decays with a half-life of 5,730 years.

FIGURE 6.6
Carbon-14 is formed from nitrogen in the atmosphere. It then combines with oxygen to form radioactive carbon dioxide and passes through the carbon cycle into all living organisms. When the organism dies, it is no longer coupled to the carbon reservoir; thus, carbon-14 lost by decay is no longer replaced. The remaining carbon-14 grows measurably smaller with the passage of time and eventually becomes undetectable.

deep-sea sediments. Because the ratio of uranium-238 to uranium-235 has been constant in the oceans, the thorium and protactinium daughters have also presumably been produced in the same proportions. The half-lives of thorium-230 and protactinium-231 are markedly different; thus, their ratios within progressively older sediments become increasingly at variance with their "natural" ratio at the time of deposition.

Carbon-14 (Radiocarbon) Dating

The **carbon-14 (radiocarbon) dating** method differs from those discussed earlier in being largely applicable to materials that were once living. It can be used to date wood, charcoal, seeds, bones, peat, shells, cloth, and paper, as well as cave deposits, freshwater limestone, and the deposits of mineral springs.

Carbon has three isotopes: carbon-12, carbon-13, and carbon-14. Only carbon-14 is unstable, and it spontaneously decays to nitrogen-14 with a half-life of 5,730 years. Such a short half-life means that only very young

materials can be dated, so, in general, carbon-14 dating is only of interest to archaeologists or geologists studying the Late Pleistocene.

As with the thorium-230 method mentioned earlier, the radiocarbon method is a decay clock, relying on the direct measurement of undecayed carbon-14 rather than on an accumulated daughter isotope. This is why, until recently, the effective limit of the method was 40,000 to 50,000 years, a limitation set by the counting device; older materials contain so little radiocarbon as to be undetectable. However, a technique developed in the 1970s that uses particle accelerators for direct counting of atomic ratios has yielded radiocarbon dates of up to 100,000 years.

Radioactive carbon is produced in the upper atmosphere when cosmic ray bombardment of nitrogen (N^{14}) atoms causes them to absorb a neutron and emit a proton and so change into carbon-14 (Figure 6.6). The proportion of carbon-14 to the stable isotope carbon-12 and carbon-13 is very small and, at least over moderate time periods, remains constant. The carbon-14 produced in the

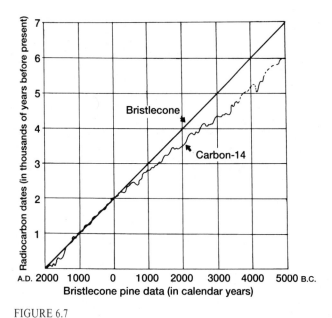

FIGURE 6.7

Calibration curve of radiocarbon dates based on dendrochronological records for the period around 5000 B.C. to the present day. The carbon-14 dates were obtained from groups of 10 annual rings, and the curve is based on nearly 300 samples. Note that, from beyond 2000 B.C., there is an increasing divergence between the carbon-14 date and the calendar date based on tree rings.

atmosphere becomes incorporated in carbon dioxide molecules and quickly becomes mixed within the atmosphere, the oceans, and the biosphere. It thus comes to be incorporated in equilibrium proportions in all carbon compounds, in plant tissues, and, subsequently, in animals through the food chain. Provided there is a constant recycling of carbon, as in atmospheric and oceanic circulation and in the metabolism of living organisms, the proportion of carbon-14 to stable carbon remains the same. When a living organism dies, however, it is no longer recycling carbon, and its supply of radiocarbon is not renewed. The carbon-14 existing in the tissue at the time of death decays so that, as time passes, the proportion of carbon-14 in the dead organism grows progressively less.

On a day-to-day basis, decay is balanced by the production of new carbon-14 in the atmosphere, so equilibrium proportions are maintained. Over extended periods, the rate of production of carbon-14 in the atmosphere varies by small amounts as a consequence of cyclical perturbations in solar activity and changes in the intensity of the earth's magnetic field. These deviations—checked by dating historical and archaeological material of known age and by dating wood, using the tree-ring counting methods employed by dendrochronologists—are now fairly well understood and are taken into account (Figure 6.7).

The burning of fossil fuels since the beginning of the Industrial Revolution has increased the amount of "dead" carbon dioxide in the atmosphere and is known as the Suess Effect. The atmosphere has also been contaminated by artificially produced radiocarbon as a consequence of the detonation of nuclear devices and the operation of nuclear reactors and particle accelerators. Suitable corrections for these essentially random effects are made by reference to the radiocarbon content of wood dated from before the Industrial Revolution.

Amino Acid Racemization

Amino acid racemization is another time-dependent phenomenon and a potential tool for dating fossils in terms of real time. The method is based on the fact that, when an organism dies, the proteins begin to break down, releasing their constituent amino acids. The amino acids also begin to change—from the dominantly L-type isonomers that are almost the exclusive forms in living organisms to D-type isonomers. This conversion process, or racemization as it is called, occurs at a fixed, although temperature-dependent, rate.

The D-type/L-type ratio provides a measure of the elapsed time since the beginning of racemization. Physical and chemical factors in the environment, particularly temperature, apparently influence the rate of racemization and obviously reduce the method's reliability. A temperature uncertainty of only ± 1°C can produce errors of up to 20 percent, for example. In stable environments, such as deep caverns, the method is potentially useful, and according to its proponents, dating back to 200,000 years is feasible.

Dating by Radiation Damage

During the radioactive decay of certain unstable isotopes, the atomic nucleus occasionally undergoes spontaneous fission. In uranium-238, for example, fission events occur approximately once every 2 million decay emissions by alpha particles. The energy released by fission is considerable, and as the nuclear fragments, strongly repelled by each other, travel apart, they collide with adjacent atoms and strip electrons from them. The consequent radiation damage is used in three dating methods: (1) fission-track dating, (2) thermoluminescence, and (3) electron spin resonance.

Fission-Track Dating

Trails of radiation damage can be detected in certain minerals, volcanic glasses like obsidian, and pottery after the items have been cut and polished and their surfaces etched with acid. Such fission tracks, as they are called, can be counted under high magnification, and their density within a unit surface area is a direct function of the age of the material and its concentration of uranium (Figure 6.8). In older samples, there may be several thousand tracks per square centimeter.

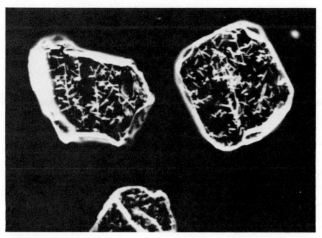

(a)

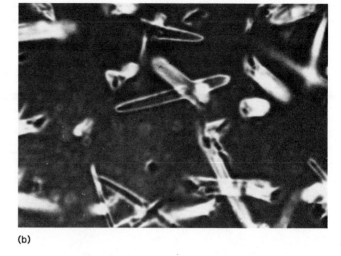

(b)

FIGURE 6.8

Fission tracks in an apatite crystal from Tioga Ashbed, Old Fort Pennsylvania. (a) Three grains of apatite. The grains are approximately 100 micrometers across and the tracks are the short linear features seen scattered throughout the grains. (b) Fission tracks in one apatite grain, etched for 20

seconds at 20° C in 5% nitric acid. In the center of the photograph is a horizontal, confined track produced by etchant flowing down a vertical track which shows as a bright region. The confined track is 13.5 micrometers long. *(Provided by M. K. Roden and D. S. Miller, Department of Earth and Environmental Sciences, Rensselaer Polytechnic Institute Troy, NY.)*

If heated, fission tracks gradually become annealed and fade so that, as with the radiometric accumulation clocks described earlier, phases of metamorphism may cause clock resetting. In practice, accuracy is improved by comparing fission-track dates with calibration standards derived from minerals whose ages have been established by other means. Zircons derived from rapidly cooled rocks with no history of subsequent heating are used for this purpose.

Thermoluminescence

Radiation damage is also used in another dating technique, based on the phenomenon of thermoluminescence. Again, as with fission-track damage, electrons are displaced from their parent atoms by particle collisions, and some become trapped in certain disordered states within the crystal lattice, retaining the excess energy acquired at collision. On heating the mineral, the electrons return to the stable configuration and, in the process, release energy in the form of light. The amount of luminescence is proportional to the amount of radiation damage and, hence, to the age of the mineral. This method is used mainly on such archaeological materials as ceramics, glasses, flints, and bones.

Electron Spin Resonance

Yet another method based on radiation damage is the electron spin resonance method. In this technique, the trapped metastable electrons are exposed to a powerful

magnetic field, and their absorption of microwave radiation at specific frequencies is measured by a spectrometer.

Dating Sedimentary Rocks

As we have already seen in earlier chapters, much of the earth's past history is contained within sedimentary rocks. The problem is that, with few exceptions, the radiometric dating methods described to this point apply to igneous rocks. A historical account is of little use without dates, so it is important to relate the relative time scale manifest in the stratigraphic record to the real time scale obtained from radiometric and other techniques.

Sedimentary rocks can be dated in real time in three ways:

1. In a few special cases, they can be dated directly. As described in previous sections, the uranium-235/lead-207 method can be used in certain carbonate rocks and fossils. The potassium-argon and rubidium-strontium methods are usable with glauconite, while radiocarbon dating of Late Pleistocene and Recent peats is a common technique.
2. Lava flows and pyroclastic deposits, such as volcanic ash bands, are invariably interbedded with sediments. Provided that they and the sediments within the succession as a whole can be shown to be contemporaneous, dating of the sediment with varying degrees of accuracy is feasible.

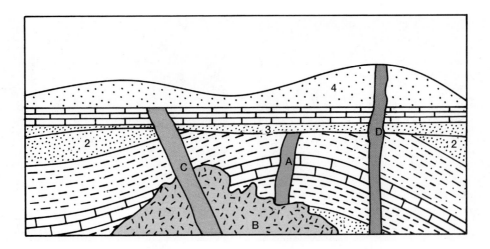

FIGURE 6.9
Relative time dating by bracketing, using the field
relationships between country rock and igneous intrusions,
mineralization, and lava flows. The oldest rocks are the
gently folded beds between sandstone 1 at the base and
sandstone 2 at the top. These were intruded by dike A,
which is, therefore, younger. Intrusion B is younger than A
but predates C. Sandstone 3 postdates succession 1–2 and
intrusion A; its age relationship to intrusion B is ambiguous.
Intrusion C postdates sandstone 3 and the limestone above,
but predates sandstone 4. Dike D is the youngest of all the
units.

3. Obviously, all igneous rocks have some
   relationship to sedimentary rocks—either by
   intruding them or being overlain by them; their
   relative ages can be ascertained by what is called
   bracketing. Bracketing, for example, determines
   that the country rock intruded by igneous rock is
   clearly older than the igneous rock, while any
   sedimentary rock lying nonconformably above
   dated igneous or metamorphic basement rocks is
   obviously younger than they are (Figure 6.9). In
   practice, other more conventional stratigraphic
   correlation methods, involving biostratigraphic
   and magnetostratigraphic data, also are utilized.

Accuracy of Real-Time Dating

Isotopic dates are usually followed by a plus-and-minus
figure that indicates the range in the precision of the age
determinations. For example, a figure of 510 million years,
± 7 million years means that repetition of the age determinations will likely result in a date within a 14-
million-year time range. In other words, the magnitude of
the ± value is a measure of the standard deviation of
values derived from many age determinations.

In the accumulation clocks that comprise the majority of isotopic dating procedures, the chief source of
error lies, as we have seen, in the possibility that the mineral used for dating has not remained a closed system since
it crystallized. Clearly, leakage or leaching of any of the
daughter decay products will result in an age determination that is too young. By the same token, if the mineral
at the time of its crystallization incorporated any preexisting radiogenic material, the age calculated on the basis
of isotopic ratios will be too old.

Several references have been made in the chapter to
the "resetting" of radiometric clocks. Most frequently, this
is due to the heating or mechanical stress endured during
a metamorphic event. What ends up being measured, then,
is the date of metamorphism. This is not necessarily bad—
knowing the age of metamorphic events is often just as
important as knowing the age of the rocks themselves.

In addition to these factors, certain other sources of
systematic error must be considered. Clearly, all the dates
derived from isotopic analyses involve the decay constants
of the respective elements used, but these constants are
known only to an accuracy of within 1 or 2 percent. Also,
there is always a minor degree of uncertainty in the calibration of the mass spectrometers as well as in the standards used in this work. These kinds of variables, taken
altogether, add up to interlaboratory differences of perhaps 3 percent, a figure that most geochronologists can
accept.

Summary

The discovery of radioactivity around the turn of this century led to the use of radioactive isotopes for the dating of rocks and minerals. The dates obtained by these various radiometric or isotopic methods are measured in real time—that is, in years before the present.

Most elements have two or more nuclear variants, called isotopes, whose nuclei contain differing numbers of neutrons. In some elements, certain isotopes are unstable and decay spontaneously—either directly or through intermediate daughter isotopes—to a more stable configuration in a radiogenic daughter isotope. The rate of change from parent to daughter isotope is measured in terms of the isotope's half-life: the time needed for one-half of a parent element to become transformed into its stable decay product.

The first isotopic ages were obtained by Rutherford in 1905 from samples of uranium in which he compared the ratio between one of the stable decay products to the undecayed uranium parent. By 1907, Boltwood had discovered that the ratio of uranium to radiogenic lead (the eventual stable end product of uranium decay) could also be used in age determination, and he published the first dates based on the uranium-lead method.

The invention of the mass spectrometer in 1929 made it possible to separate the different isotopes involved, and scientists found that three different decay series produced isotopes of lead at different rates: (1) Uranium-238 decaying to lead-206, (2) uranium-235 to lead-207, and (3) thorium-234 to lead-208. Because these radiogenic lead isotopes are produced in different decay schemes, their relative proportions have changed systematically through time. Presumably, at the time of the earth's origin, 4.6 billion years ago, only a nonradiogenic isotope—lead-204—existed. Since that time, the amounts of lead-206, lead-207, and lead-208 have grown, but at different rates. The presence of lead-204 can be used to ascertain the presence of any radiogenic lead retained from an earlier clock setting and that would naturally result in erroneously old dates.

The accuracy of lead dating methods improves when the uranium-238 → lead-206 and uranium-235 → lead-207 decay series are compared. The loci of concordant dates from the two decay schemes, when plotted on a graph, describe a curve known as a concordia. Dates from the two schemes that do not agree are discordant and plot below the concordia.

Zircon is the most widely used mineral in uranium-lead dating. Although most uranium-lead methods are applied to igneous rocks, certain calcareous skeletal material and carbonate sediments containing uranium can also be used.

Of the three isotopes of potassium, only potassium-40 is radioactive and decays to argon-40. Because argon-40 is relatively easy to detect in even small amounts, potassium-argon dating can be used for rocks of nearly all ages. The method's chief disadvantage is that radiogenic argon may be lost in subsequent heating of the rock, such as during metamorphism, resulting in erroneously young ages. If all the argon-40 is lost, the isotopic clock is reset at zero. Potassium-argon dating can also be used with the mineral glauconite in marine sediments.

Rubidium-strontium dating is based on the determination of radiogenic strontium-87. Because original strontium consists of a mixture of strontium-86 and strontium-87, this ratio must first be determined by reference to rubidium-free samples. Appropriate corrections are then made in calculating dates for samples with rubidium and that have produced new strontium by decay. Several samples containing different amounts of rubidium and derived from the same isotopically homogeneous parent magma can be used to construct an isochron diagram, which shows the progressive accumulation of radiogenic strontium-87 in different samples.

Other dating methods use relatively short-lived daughter isotopes. The alpha decay of uranium-234 in seawater produces thorium-230, which, unlike the uranium, accumulates in seafloor sediments. At successively deeper horizons within a core, systematic reduction in the amount of radiogenic thorium-230 is proportional to the age of the sediment. Thorium can also be used for dating by comparing the abundance of its isotope thorium-231 relative to the decay product protactinium-231.

Carbon-14 (radiocarbon) dating is used on wood, charcoal, paper, cloth, seeds, bones, and other materials of organic origin. Radiocarbon is produced by neutron bombardment of nitrogen atoms in the upper atmosphere and decays with a half-life of 5,730 years. Thus, after about 40,000 to 50,000 years, the amount of remaining radiocarbon is too small to detect. A new technique using direct counting of atoms has pushed the range back to around 100,000 years, however.

Also used on once-living material, the amino acid racemization method involves the conversion of amino acid isonomers at a fixed, although temperature-dependent, rate. The method has a potential range back to 200,000 years.

Fission-track, thermoluminescence, and electron spin resonance dating methods rely upon detection of radiation damage in minerals containing radioactive elements.

Most radiometric dating methods apply to igneous rocks. Sedimentary rocks can be dated in real time in three ways: (1) by direct-dating in special cases, (2) by correlation with lava flows and pyroclastic deposits interbedded with sediments, and (3) by bracketing.

The accuracy of isotopic dating depends upon such factors as the loss of radiogenic products or the inclusion of original isotopic material. Systematic errors in the values of the decay constants of the elements involved also must be considered. Interlaboratory errors are believed to add up to about 3 percent.

Questions

1. Why has the development of radiometric dating been tied so closely to technological advances?
2. How do the isotopes of a given element differ from one another?
3. What is meant by a decay series?
4. What is meant by the term *half-life*?
5. What is the difference between a decay clock and an accumulation clock? Give examples of each.
6. Describe the various lead ratio methods used in dating.
7. Explain how the concordia curve works.
8. In potassium-argon dating, why are data from fine-grained rocks, such as lavas, invariably more reliable than those from coarse-grained plutonic rocks?
9. Describe the rubidium-strontium dating method.
10. What isotopic-dating methods are peculiarly suited to relatively young deep-sea muds? Explain.
11. Describe the carbon-14 radiocarbon method of dating. In what ways does it differ from most of the other isotopic methods?
12. Describe the dating techniques that are based on radiation damage.
13. How can sedimentary successions be dated in real time by isotopic methods?
14. Name three possible sources of error in measuring ages by isotopic methods.
15. Metamorphism often causes a "resetting" of isotopic clocks. Why does this sometimes supply useful data in understanding the geologic history of an area?

Further Reading

Eicher, D. L. 1976. *Geologic time.* 2d ed., Englewood Cliffs, N.J.: Prentice-Hall.

Faul, H. 1966. *Ages of rocks, planets, and stars.* New York: McGraw-Hill.

Faure, G. 1986. *Principles of isotope geology.* 2d ed. New York: John Wiley.

7

ORIGINS—THE EARTH AND LIFE

Introduction

No account of earth history would be complete without some reference to our planet's origin and its place in the solar system. In the past 20 years, more extraterrestrial geological data have been acquired about the moon and planets than in all of previous history. New information is being obtained on an almost daily basis from space probes and flyby missions, and the input of data likely will grow exponentially as the space programs planned for the next several decades come to fruition.

One result of this information explosion has been the evolution of the new science of planetology—in effect, "extraterrestrial geology." For the first time, scientists can begin to compare some of the geologic features and processes observed on the earth with those on other planets and, in so doing, obtain a better perspective of their observations. With a better understanding of the other planets has come a much clearer picture of the origin and early history of the solar system and, of course, of the earth itself. Not only do scientists better understand earth's very early history, but it is becoming increasingly clear that the earth also has retained a "cosmic connection" throughout later history. This is seen not only in the form of repeated impacts by extraterrestrial bodies but in the influence of certain astronomical cycles on the climates of the past. These events have played a very important role in earth history, and discussing the earth and its history in isolation from its neighbors in space is no longer possible.

In this chapter, we discuss origins—of the solar system, of a star, of the earth, and of life. While most of the theories presented cannot, as yet, be directly proven, scientists are getting ever closer to solving such universal mysteries.

Origin of the Solar System

During the eighteenth and nineteenth centuries, as the science of geology evolved, astronomy was already a discipline with a history dating back several thousand years. On the whole, however, it contributed little to geology and the study of the earth, being for most of its long history concerned with mapping the heavens and describing the movements of heavenly bodies.

During the nineteenth century, various theories describing the origin of the solar system were proposed. As early as 1755, German philosopher Immanuel Kant suggested that the earth and solar system had formed from a cloud of hot gas. Kant believed that, as the solar system cooled and shrank, it rotated at ever-increasing speed, just as dancers or skaters spin faster when they bring their arms close to their sides. According to Kant, as the speed of rotation increased, the mass of gas flattened into a disk that gradually separated out into a series of rings that eventually condensed into smaller aggregates.

The mathematics of the rotational speeds and orbital velocities were worked out in detail by French mathematician Pierre Laplace around 1795, and this so-called **nebular hypothesis** was generally accepted through the nineteenth century. One serious problem with the nebular hypothesis, however, concerned the sun's speed of rotation. According to the law of conservation of angular momentum, the sun should be spinning at a much greater speed than it actually is.

In an alternative hypothesis, University of Chicago astronomer Forest Moulton, together with geologist Thomas Chamberlin, proposed around 1900 that the earth and planets had a cold rather than a hot beginning, being formed by the aggregation of smaller bodies as a consequence of mutual gravitational attraction. One of the novel features of the Moulton-Chamberlin model was that it proposed an encounter between the sun and a wandering star from outer space. The model suggested that this star, in coming too close to the sun, had, through its gravitational attraction, pulled out from the sun a great plume of solar material that formed into a ring around the sun, where it eventually condensed into solid asteroid-sized **planetismals** that were destined to become the planets of the solar system.

It was generally accepted that such cosmic near-misses must be very rare phenomena. This inevitably led to the view that, in the cosmic scheme of things, planetary systems were also rarities. In turn, it followed that life itself must be a rare phenomenon or, it was felt by many, even unique to earth. Needless to say, this idea fit in rather nicely with the comfortable anthropocentric view of the universe that the new discoveries in geology and paleontology had, as yet, done little to dispel.

Today, the most generally accepted model of the origin of the solar system—the solar nebula hypothesis—is in many ways a combination of ideas from earlier hypotheses. As in the nebular hypothesis model, the sun and planets are seen as all forming at the same time, but with a cold rather than hot beginning. First proposed in the 1950s by astronomers von Weizacker and Kuiper, the solar nebular hypothesis suggests that the solar system began as a revolving, disc-shaped cloud of dust and gas and that gravitational clumping of this material led to the accretion of progressively larger masses (Figure 7.1). These, in turn, are believed to have collected into objects the size of asteroids known as planetismals, perhaps similar in composition to comets. Within this great swarm of objects, it is thought that eddies caused many centers for local collision events. In this manner, larger **protoplanets** formed.

It probably took 10 million years to reach this stage, but no solid planetary bodies had yet appeared. The protoplanets were actually individual clouds of cosmic debris, but gradually, they coalesced by mutual gravitational attraction and became smaller. At the same time, their density increased, and their gravity fields were such that they

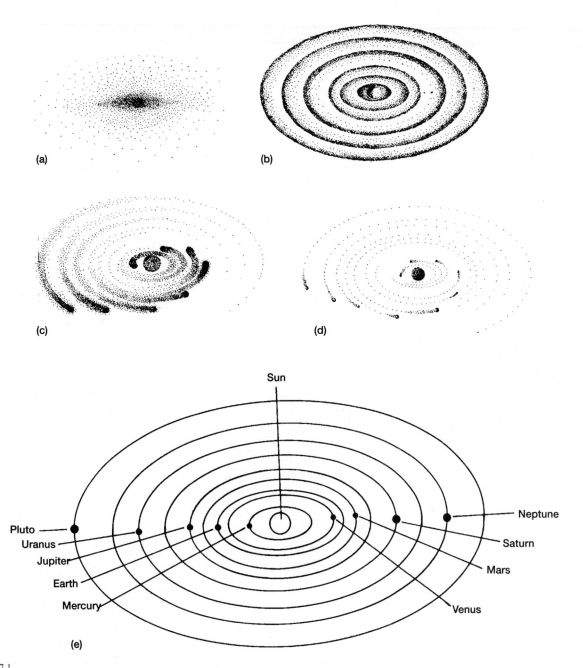

FIGURE 7.1

The von Weizacker and Kuiper model to explain the origin of
the solar system. (a) Gravitational clumping. (b) Planetismals
form. (c) Local collision events lead to protoplanets. (d) The
final stage as modern planets form. (e) The modern solar
system.

BOX 7.1

A Guide to the Solar System

The orbits of the planets of the solar system are not apparently spaced at random distances from the sun, but seem to have a mathematically significant arrangement that was first described in 1776 by the German astronomer Johann Bode (1747–1826), although the arrangement had been noticed earlier in 1772 by another German astronomer, Johann Titius of Wittenberg. What became known as "Bode's Law" states that the proportionate distances of the various planets from the sun may be represented in the series 0, 3, 6, 12, 24, and so on, in other words each number after the first is double the preceding one. By adding 4 to each of the numbers and then dividing by 10, a number sequence is obtained that approximates the mean distances of the planets from the sun in astronomical units (the mean distance from the sun to the earth).

When considered together the planets have numerous features in common; they all rotate about the sun in a counterclockwise direction (when viewed from above the north pole), and they all (except for Venus and Uranus) rotate on their axes in the same counter-clockwise direction. Except for Pluto, all the planets have orbits that lie near the plane of the sun's rotation (the plane of the ecliptic).

BOX TABLE 7.1
Solar System Statistics

Planet	Mass (Earth = 1)	Density (Water = 1)	Rotation Period	Orbital Period	Known Satellites	Inclination to Plane of Ecliptic
Mercury	0.06	5.44	58.65 days	88 days	0	7.0°
Venus	0.81	5.25	243.0 days	225 days	0	3.4°
Earth	1.0	5.52	23 hours, 56 minutes	365 1/4 days	1	0.0°
Mars	0.11	3.93	24 hours, 37 minutes	687 days	2	1.8°
Jupiter	317.9	1.35	9 hours, 50 minutes	11.86 years	16	1.3°
Saturn	95.2	0.69	10 hours, 14 minutes	29.46 years	17	2.5°
Uranus	14.6	1.28	10 hours, 49 minutes	84.01 years	15	0.8°
Neptune	17.2	1.64	15.7 hours	164.89 years	8	1.8°
Pluto	0.003	2.06	6.4 days	247.7 years	1	17.2°

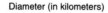

Diameter (in kilometers)

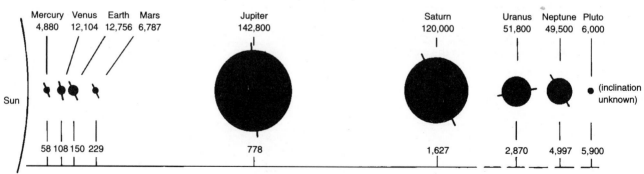

Mean distance from sun (in millions of kilometers)

BOX FIGURE 7.1
A guide to the solar system.

could continue to sweep up cosmic debris in orbit about the sun. Gravitational collapse and shrinking eventually resulted in the formation of a solid planetary body. The mass of the largest bodies was sufficient to attract gas, so they became surrounded by thick, gaseous envelopes that made up the bulk of the planetary mass (Box 7.1).

Origin of a Star

Most stars evolve through five stages: (1) protostar, (2) main-sequence star, (3) red giant, (4) white dwarf, and (5) black dwarf. Some stars, however, explode as supernovae.

Protostar Stage

The sun is a medium-sized star, consisting almost entirely of hydrogen and helium that formed, it is believed, about 5 billion years ago as a cloud of dust and gas. As with all stars, gravitational forces caused the cloud to coalesce and collapse inward, and the cloud became progressively hotter in the process. During this early or protostar stage, the sun was not luminous. When temperatures in the cloud's interior had risen to about a million degrees celsius, thermonuclear reaction began in which hydrogen nuclei combine under intense pressure to produce helium nuclei. At this time, the sun became luminous, and a star was born.

During the gravitational collapse that gives birth to a star, gravitational potential energy is converted into the kinetic energy of heat and light. As the star's interior heats up, so does the pressure within the star increase until it is sufficient to balance the effect of gravitational collapse of star-forming material.

The time from initial gravitational collapse to when the star reaches this equilibrium state and begins to grow varies, depending upon the mass of the initial collapsing dust nebula. In general, the smaller the initial dust cloud, the longer it takes to reach the equilibrium stage and become what astronomers refer to as a **main-sequence star.** For a star with one-tenth the mass of the sun, the time involved is approximately 100 million years, whereas for massive stars, perhaps 100 times the size of the sun, the process is greatly accelerated and may take only 10,000 years, which, in astronomical terms, is virtually instantaneous.

Main-Sequence Star Stage

Once a star reaches an equilibrium state in which collapse and expansion are balanced, the rate of stellar evolution slows, and the star may remain in this main-sequence stage for billions of years. Again, however, this time span varies considerably, depending, apparently, on the star's size. The smaller the star, the longer it will remain in the main sequence. Stars the size of the sun have sufficient hydrogen fuel for about 10 billion years. Paradoxically, larger stars, although their fuel supplies are much more abundant, burn fuel at a much faster rate, sometimes exhausting it within only a million years.

Red Giant Stage

When the hydrogen of a star's core becomes depleted, the state of balance between expansion and gravitational collapse can no longer be maintained, and the star's core begins to collapse. For a time, the star's luminosity increases, and the star even expands again as the energy released by the collapse heats the core to a higher temperature. Expansion of the star's outer regions is, however, also a cooling process, so although the core has become hotter, the star's outer envelope expands to become what is known as a red giant. When our sun eventually reaches this stage, as one day it will, its outer surface will reach beyond earth's orbit.

Meanwhile, the star's core continues to heat up until, at about 100 million degrees, the hydrogen fusion process gives way to a new fusion process in which helium is converted to carbon. In this way, successively heavier elements, such as aluminum, silicon, phosphorous, sulfur, and eventually iron, are formed. The ability of such stellar furnaces to produce ever heavier elements depends upon the size of the star. It is generally believed that the formation of elements heavier than iron requires reactions only found in the most massive stars and in the most awesome of all catastrophes—that of exploding stars or supernovae.

White Dwarf and Black Dwarf Stages

The red giant stage of stellar evolution ends when the star's outer envelope has become so bloated that the bonds of gravity can no longer contain the stellar matter, which is progressively shed as a series of great shells of gas expanding outward. Many stars at this stage in their lives can be observed in our part of the galaxy and are termed **planetary nebulae.** (These actually have nothing to do with planets, but with some stretch of the imagination, they do resemble the outer planets when seen through a telescope.) At the core of the expanding halo of the planetary nebula is a small, intensely hot star known as a white dwarf.

The star has now reached old age. It remains in this state, cooling slowly over billions of years, until eventually, its light blinks out, and it dies as a black dwarf—in effect, a burned-out cinder.

Supernovae

As mentioned earlier, the overall evolution of a star depends on the star's initial size. Very large stars, considerably more massive than the sun, run through their fuel supplies very rapidly in almost a runaway phenomenon

FIGURE 7.2

The Crab Nebula in the constellation Taurus. *(Photo courtesy of the Carnegie Institution of Washington.)*

that ends, not surprisingly, in the spectacular explosion called a supernova. In galactic terms, supernovae are fairly common phenomena, although in human terms, they are uncommon, at least in our own galaxy, with one occurring about every 500 years. The most recent supernova was observed in the Large Magellanic Cloud (a close neighbor of our own Milky Way Galaxy) on the night of 24 February 1987. Other supernovae have been observed and recorded through history: For example, the star of Bethlehem is believed to have been a supernova; another was observed and described by Chinese astronomers in 1054 A.D., and its remains can be seen today as the great Crab Nebula in Taurus (Figure 7.2).

A supernova or perhaps several supernovae played some role in the formation of our solar system. Not only did the heaviest elements of the earth originate within a supernova, but astronomers believe that the shock waves sent out by the exploding star caused eddies or ripples in cosmic dust clouds, which triggered the initial coalescence and gravitational collapse that began our history.

Star Cyclicity

As will become abundantly clear as we discuss the history of our planet, many of the processes and phenomena observed on earth are cyclical. What is truly fascinating is that the mechanisms involved in the birth and death of stars are also cyclical. The material lost to space in planetary nebulae or blasted from the explosion of a supernova

becomes part of the dust clouds that are the stuff of which later generations of stars and planetary systems are made. Virtually all of the elements on earth had their origin in the interiors of stellar masses, and only the daughter elements produced by radioactive decay and trapped within the minerals in crustal rocks can be said to be of truly terrestrial origin.

Origin of the Earth

How did the earth form? How did it become capable of sustaining life? The answers to these questions require discussions of the differentiation of the planet into different zones and the development of the earth's atmosphere.

Homogeneous and Heterogeneous Differentiation

The earth is not simply a great ball of rock but is markedly differentiated into a dense core of iron-rich material surrounded by a mantle of relatively lighter silicates. The separation into a denser inner zone and lighter outer zone probably began quite early in the accretion process described previously. As to the actual mechanism involved, in the differentiation process, opinions are divided.

The most widely held view is that the solid material had already condensed into objects of various sizes and consisting primarily of iron and silicate early in the development of the protoplanet clusters. In the early stages of accretion, the earth was probably a homogeneous mixture of both iron and silicate, and only later did the materials separate to form an iron-rich core. Some support for this idea comes from iron meteorites, many of which have been dated at 4.6 billion years. The crystal structure of these meteorites indicates that they cooled quite slowly, which could only have come about in the interior of asteroid-size bodies.

In a homogeneous planet growing by accretion, the interior would be getting progressively denser as iron material settled toward its center. Heat produced by the release of gravitational energy would eventually cause melting. This, in turn, would speed up the density differentiation process. This so-called **homogeneous differentiation** model proposes that the core was forming quite early in the earth's development, even before the earth was fully formed (Figure 7.3).

An alternative **heterogeneous differentiation** model suggests that the earth formed as a solid mass in two stages: First, the core formed as a consequence of the selective accretion of the iron material in the protoplanet mass, and second, the mantle was added later as the silicate material of the protoplanet accreted to it. For several reasons, this model is considered less likely.

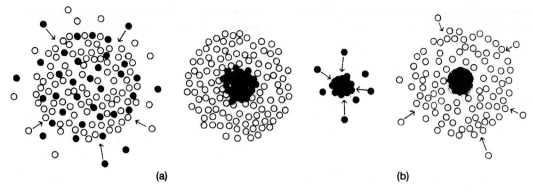

(a)   (b)

FIGURE 7.3
Models describing accretion hypotheses in the formation of
the earth. (a) Homogeneous differentiation.
(b) Heterogeneous differentiation.

BOX 7.2

The Origin of Life—An Alternative Model

The discovery in 1977 of submarine hydrothermal vents has introduced a new dimension to the debate on the origin of life. The vents occur along the crest of mid-ocean ridges where cold sea water percolates downward into the rift zone, is heated as it comes in contact with rising magma from below, and eventually returns to the surface as a submarine hot spring. The hydrothermal solutions, in which temperatures of 350 degs. C have been measured, are rich in dissolved minerals leached from the magmas and these are precipitated as the hot solutions come into contact with sea water. In particular metallic sulfates of iron, copper, zinc, and other metals accumulate in mounds around the vents. In some places tiny particles of the sulfate precipitates form black turbulent suspensions spewing from the vents and are aptly referred to as "black smokers".

Although naturally of considerable interest to geochemists seeking to understand the origins of metallic ore deposits, in the present context hydrothermal vents are seen as providing the setting for the synthesis of complex organic molecules. Some scientists believe that it was around such hydrothermal vents on the sea floors of 4 billion years ago that life began.

Of particular interest among living organisms is a group known as archaebacteria (or simply archea), that are so different from other life forms that some workers place them in a separate kingdom. One of the three cell types seen in these organisms are the so-called thermoacidophyles that live in hot sulfur springs and hydrothermal vents. The thermoacidophyles metabolize sulfur and form the base of a complex food chain embracing a variety of animals that live around the sea floor vents. Because their energy source is the internal heat from the earth, they are, in fact the only major animal communities that are not ultimately dependent on sunlight.

The thermoacidophile archaebacteria live in an environment similar to that postulated for the earliest cells. They also metabolize sulfur just as the earliest cells did in the absence of oxygen. How these first cells appeared is a matter of conjecture. Perhaps the first organic molecules formed as two dimensional layers on the surface of minerals such as pyrite that is commonly found around hydrothermal vents. Other workers suggest that clay minerals played an important role. The next stage was likely the formation of membranes that isolated the increasingly complex molecules and permitted the selective movement of "nutrient" material into an enclosed environment. Perhaps the next step was the breaking away of membrane-enclosed droplets, or coacervates that would eventually take on the attributes of living cells.

TABLE 7.1
Principal Gases of Dry Air

Constituent	Percentage of Air
Nitrogen (N_2)	78.084
Oxygen (O_2)	20.946
Argon (Ar)	0.934
Carbon dioxide (CO_2)	0.034
Neon (Ne)	0.00182
Helium (He)	0.000524
Methane (CH_4)	0.00015
Krypton (Kr)	0.000114
Hydrogen (H_2)	0.00005

TABLE 7.2
Composition of Volcanic Gases from Kilauea, Hawaii (Volume Percentages at 1,200 °C)

Gas	Sample 1	Sample 2
Water vapor (H_2O)	36.18%	61.56%
Carbon dioxide (CO_2)	47.68	20.93
Carbon monoxide (CO)	1.46	0.59
Sulfur dioxide (SO_2)	11.15	11.42
Sulfur trioxide (SO_3)	0.42	0.55
Sulfur (S_2)	0.04	0.28
Hydrogen chloride (HC1)	0.08	0.00
Hydrogen (H_2)	0.48	0.32
Nitrogen (N_2)	2.41	4.13
Argon (Ar)	0.14	0.31

(Source: Data from S. James Shand, *Eruptive Rocks.* Copyright © 1949 John Wiley & Sons, Inc., New York.)

The Atmosphere

Like the earth itself, the earth's atmosphere has also gone through several stages of development, and its evolution is not only linked with that of the earth, but also with the evolution of life.

The Early Atmosphere

During the earth's early stages of development, its atmosphere consisted predominantly of hydrogen and helium from the original gaseous nebula that produced the solar system. This **primitive atmosphere** is believed to have been soon blown away by the outpouring of high-energy particles from the sun known as the **solar wind.** In the outer or gaseous planets, on the other hand, much of this early atmosphere was retained, not only because the solar wind was less effective with greater distance from the sun, but also because the much larger size of the outer planets and their much stronger gravitational fields enable them to hold onto the lighter gases of their primitive atmospheres.

Interestingly, direct confirmation of this early stage is seen in the extreme rarity in the modern earth's atmosphere of inert gases, such as neon, krypton, argon, and xenon (Table 7.1), in contrast to their much greater abundance in the solar system as a whole. Such inert gases do not form compounds in nature; therefore, unlike other gases that are part of heavier molecules (for example, hydrogen and oxygen in water), they were unprotected from the solar wind and easily swept away. For a time, the earth probably had no atmosphere.

Outgassing and the Earth's Second Atmosphere

At this stage in the earth's development, internal differentiation into a denser, hotter core and lighter, cooler mantle of silicate layers was underway, and internal changes were manifested in volcanic activity. Enormous quantities of a variety of gases poured out during volcanic eruptions, a process known as **outgassing.** These gases began to evolve into the earth's second atmosphere, which was very different in composition from the first.

Modern volcanoes and hot springs expel large quantities of carbon dioxide and water vapor; in fact, these two gases typically make up 80 percent or more of the gaseous phase (Table 7.2). Carbon monoxide, nitrogen, and certain sulphurous gases are also produced. Strong evidence suggests that the mixture of modern volcanic gases is a clue to the composition of the earth's second atmosphere.

Also during this stage, the decay of radioactive elements in crustal rocks was an important source of heat within the earth. Since helium and argon gases are among the products of radioactive decay, these gases were also added to the atmosphere.

Importance of Water

Assuming that the other inner planets and the moon also underwent phases of volcanic activity (and there is abundant evidence that they did), they all presumably produced secondary atmospheres by the outgassing process. In their further evolution, however, the inner planets followed different paths, partly because of initial differences in size and internal structure and activity, and even more important because of the role played by water.

Earth is unique in that it is the only planet on which water is found in all three states; gaseous, liquid, and solid. Particularly important is the presence of liquid water, which is the great universal solvent and apparently essential for life. Without water, life—at least the carbon-based version of life seen on earth—probably would not have evolved. The other requirements for various life-forms in terms of chemistry and energy are many and varied, but scientists are generally agreed that water is the one essential ingredient.

Water vapor was such an abundant product in the earth's outgassing process that, on condensation, it began to gather in low places on the earth, and so were born the oceans. Indirect evidence of marine processes and running water is seen in the rounded pebbles and sand grains in many Early Precambrian sediments. Only rolling and jostling in moving water produces this rounded shape.

Lack of Free Oxygen

Although this second atmosphere was a true planetary atmosphere and quite different from that of the giant gaseous planets, it was still very different from the earth's atmosphere today, its chief characteristic, many geologists believe, being the lack of free oxygen. Oxygen is not a component of volcanic gases. While it was present in water vapor, only a very small amount was released by a photo-dissociation process that split the oxygen from the hydrogen. In the modern atmosphere, however, oxygen comprises 20.95 percent. Where did it come from?

The answer is that oxygen is the product of life. Except for certain primitive and highly specialized forms, modern life requires oxygen to survive, but it was life itself that produced the oxygen. The early planetary atmosphere produced by outgassing was what is called a chemically reducing atmosphere—consisting of such gases as methane, ammonia, and carbon monoxide—that to humans and most other forms of modern life was completely unbreathable. Nevertheless, life apparently began in this chemically alien environment.

Origin of Life

How far back can the record of life on the earth be traced? What are the oldest fossils? What kind of life existed in these early times? When did life begin? These are all questions that geologists who study the Precambrian Era have been seeking to answer for many years. Little by little, a picture is emerging.

The Early Fossil Record

Not surprisingly, the Precambrian fossil record is poor, when compared with the fossil record from Cambrian time to the present. As discussed in Chapter 3, fossil preservation is controlled by many factors, not the least of which is the age of the rocks. Clearly, Precambrian rocks are so old that they have likely been metamorphosed at least once and sometimes several times. Thus, even if fossils had been initially preserved, they have long since been obliterated. In addition, the primitive, soft-bodied, and usually microscopically sized life-forms of Precambrian days were extremely unlikely candidates for fossilization in the first place.

When the Precambrian fossil record is reviewed in its entirety, two rather surprising features emerge. One is that the earliest evidence of life is found in rocks dating back 3,400 to 3,500 million years; in other words, life must have appeared very early in earth's history. The second surprise is that, after that early beginning, it apparently took a very long time for more advanced life-forms—that is, multicelled animals, or **metazoans**—to appear. The first direct evidence of metazoans is found in rocks less than 700 million years old. Indirect evidence in the form of sedimen-

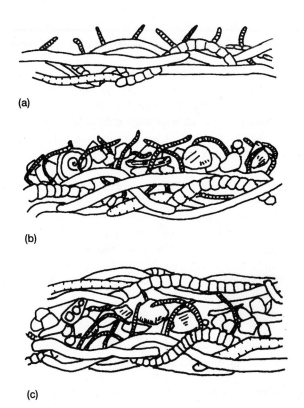

(a)

(b)

(c)

FIGURE 7.4

Day-night accretion in stromatolite-forming algal mats. During the daylight, there is upward growth (a) and sediment trapping (b). Darkness encourages horizontal growth and sediment binding (c).

tary layers disturbed by burrowing organisms begins in rocks not very much older—certainly much less than 1,000 million years. Apparently, the progression from the first fossils of primitive life-forms to metazoans took more than 2,500 million years. This is a staggeringly long period of time, even by geological standards.

The earliest of all proven fossils are of **stromatolites,** made up of successive laminations of sediment-forming, cabbagelike mounds or irregular mats (Figure 7.4). Far from belonging to a long extinct and unknown life-form, as might be expected for such very old organisms, stromatolites can still be seen forming today in many shallow-water environments along seacoasts, in tidal pools, and in freshwater lakes. Unlike many fossils, stromatolites are not the fossil remains of organisms as such, but are layers of sediment accreted by generations of algal mats, and they are, therefore, referred to as organosedimentary structures. The organisms responsible for these structures are associations of **cyanobacteria,** formerly known as blue-green algae. Typically flourishing in quiet, shallow-water situations, they spread as mats across the sediment surface, and either by trapping fine sediment in sticky filaments or by causing precipitation of calcium carbonate, they build up successive layers generation by generation.

Stromatolites have been found in Precambrian rocks in many parts of the world, but the oldest so far discovered come from a place called North Pole in the Pilbara region of Western Australia. Age determinations show the rocks to be about 3.6 billion years old. At that remote time, the earth was a very different place from the current one. It was certainly much warmer than it is today, the atmosphere was more turbulent and stormy, and volcanic activity was probably more common. Perhaps the most important difference was in the composition of the atmosphere: There was little or no free oxygen. Although in the modern world all the higher animals depend on oxygen, certain primitive organisms, such as the anaerobic bacteria and cyanobacteria that are found in swampy muds and stagnant water, thrive in places from which oxygen is excluded (anoxic environments). On the early earth, such anaerobic organisms were presumably the only life-forms.

Chemical Evolution of Life-Forms

Having pushed the fossil record back 3.6 billion years, geologists' search for even earlier evidence for life clearly becomes much more difficult, requiring reliance on indirect evidence and also, to some extent, conjecture. Various lines of evidence point to certain conclusions about the physical and chemical environment on the early earth. With this as a starting point, geologists' task is to chart out the possible chemical pathways along which, somewhere and at some time, the gap between life and nonlife was first bridged. In other words, the discussion here focuses on the chemical evolution that occurred during the early ages that preceded the appearance of the first life-forms.

From a strictly chemical viewpoint, one of the chief differences between life and nonlife is in the size and complexity of the molecules involved. Even the most complex inorganic molecules usually are made up of only a relatively few atoms, whereas typical organic molecules often consist of thousands of atoms and invariably contain carbon in their structure. Stated simplistically, inorganic processes produce simple molecules of a few atoms, whereas organic processes produce giant, carbon-based molecules. Analysis shows that, whether the molecules are simple or complex, they are all made up of the same atoms or combinations of atoms of relatively few elements in simple compounds. A reasonable assumption, therefore, is that an early step in chemical evolution probably involved the synthesis of larger and more complex molecules from smaller, simpler ones. How did this happen?

Amino Acids: The Building Blocks of Life

Among the organic molecules found in all life-forms are a special class of compounds that were early recognized as being of "first importance"—hence, their name, proteins. Proteins are vital components in all higher organisms and, as is well known, are essential in the food humans

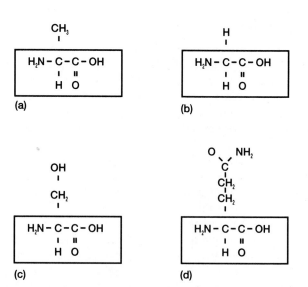

FIGURE 7.5
Structures of four amino acids. (a) Alanine. (b) Glycine. (c) Serine. (d) Glutamine.

eat. Although other essential molecules, such as DNA and RNA, are more complex, proteins are so universally present in all living tissues that they are, perhaps, the best example for discussing the chemical basis of life.

Even before the end of the nineteenth century, the tens of thousands of different proteins were all known to be made up of combinations of simple molecules that, because of certain chemical and physical properties, were collectively known as **amino acids.** An important feature of amino acids is that they have remarkably stable molecular structures, their configuration resulting from shared electrical charges of adjacent atoms, including a very strong tendency to link up with other amino acids to form long, chainlike molecules. A typical protein, for example, consists of a specific sequence of amino acid molecules usually linked together into a linear configuration or twisted into elaborate skeins. By the early twentieth century, 20 different kinds of amino acids had been identified, and amino acids were known to be the only structural elements in proteins.

Amino acids, in turn, are made up almost entirely of only four elements: carbon, hydrogen, oxygen, and nitrogen (Figure 7.5). Structurally, they are all very similar; in particular, their central structures all consist of an arrangement of two carbon atoms, two hydrogen atoms, and one each of oxygen and nitrogen in a very stable configuration.

Is it possible that the first complex molecules necessary for life were synthesized on the early earth from amino acids? If so, where did the amino acids come from? In 1953, in an attempt to answer this question, University of Chicago chemist Stanley Miller prepared a mixture of methane, ammonia, hydrogen, carbon dioxide, and water vapor at a pressure of 1 atmosphere and subjected it to electrical discharge (Figure 7.6). The experiment, designed to simulate conditions on the primitive earth, ran

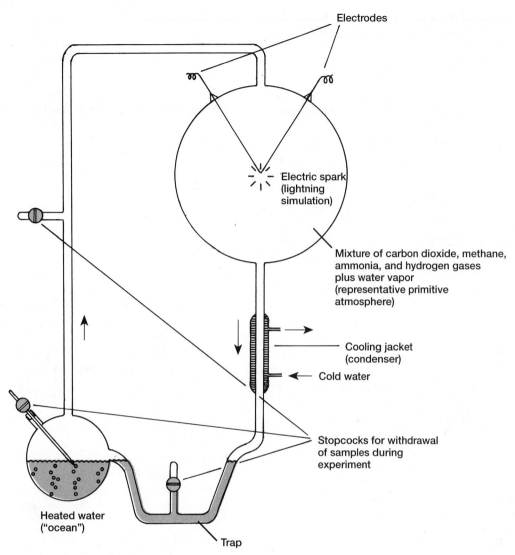

Electrodes

Electric spark
(lightning
simulation)

Mixture of carbon dioxide, methane,
ammonia, and hydrogen gases
plus water vapor
(representative primitive
atmosphere)

Cooling jacket
(condenser)

Cold water

Stopcocks for withdrawal
of samples during
experiment

Heated water
("ocean")

Trap

FIGURE 7.6

Diagram of the apparatus used by Stanley Miller at the
University of Chicago. The experiment was designed to
simulate conditions on the primitive earth and resulted in the
synthesis of amino acids.

for one week. During this time, Miller noticed that the
color of the liquid phase of his mixture slowly changed to
a pale yellow; clearly, something was happening. On analyzing the liquid after the experiment, Miller found that,
among the primary constituents, were now more complex
molecules, including various sugars and carbohydrates
and, significantly, several kinds of amino acids. Miller's
experiment showed that, under certain conditions, complex molecules could be synthesized from simple ones.

Modifying and elaborating on Miller's experiment,
other chemists introduced other elements that likely were
present on the primitive earth. They also simulated the
early earth's more turbulent conditions by using heat, ultraviolet radiation, and radioactivity as energy sources.
Virtually all of the experiments demonstrated the syn-

thesis of amino acids and other complex molecules. On the
modern earth, amino acids—the essential building blocks
of proteins—are produced naturally by life processes. On
the early earth, they were apparently produced by abiotic
synthesis. Clearly, one of the possible chemical pathways
toward life was becoming discernible.

A model describing abiotic synthesis of organic molecules is still a long way from explaining the first life-forms.
To arrive at ever-more-complex and significant molecules
by random synthesis must have taken countless billions of
what were, in effect, miniature chemical experiments.
However, the molecular linkage necessary in synthesis
occurs very rapidly, and because tens of millions of years
are available for this process of chemical evolution, the
overall model remains within the bounds of credulity.

It is a widely held belief that life began in the oceans, but this may not be true. Many scientists believe that the first life appeared in a pond or lake; in fact, Darwin thought this also. Because of accidents of local geology, topography, and climate, virtually every pond would have its own chemical individuality, just as do many modern salt lakes. Certain clay minerals in the sediments may also have had a role in some of these processes of molecular synthesis. Some of them, for example, likely contained metallic catalysts, substances capable of enormously speeding up chemical reactions. In certain ponds, such clays may have been responsible for selectively encouraging particular chemical reactions. With the continuing synthesis of amino acids and other complex molecules, the seas, lakes, and ponds began to take on the character of what has been described as a "hot, dilute soup," in which existed virtually limitless opportunities for chemical synthesis. For an alternative model to describe the origin of life see Box 7.2.

The Chemistry of Coacervates

The opportunity for experimentation also occurred in other locales of chemical activity. Certain substances, usually of large molecular weight and including proteins, have a tendency to spontaneously form discrete droplets of water. These droplets, or **coacervates** (from the Latin, meaning "to heap up"), form as a consequence of molecular electrical forces that impart to the spherical surface of the droplet the characteristics of a semipermeable membrane. That is, certain compounds in the water surrounding the coacervate may pass into the coacervate, perhaps causing it to grow in size, whereas other kinds of molecules are excluded.

Inside the coacervate, isolated from the surrounding water, new molecular exchanges occur. Each coacervate has its own chemical personality, so again, opportunities for chemical experimentation are magnified enormously. As the chemical bonding experiments result in new compounds, certain substances may be unwanted and so pass out through the coacervate membrane. If the water surrounding the coacervate is plentifully supplied with the components required, the droplet will grow and eventually may split to form more coacervates.

As long ago as 1922, Russian A. L. Oparin considered such droplet behavior significant in tracing the steps toward the first living cells. In more recent years, experiments by American Sidney Fox have pointed in the same direction. It certainly does not take too much of a stretch of imagination to see coacervates "feeding," "excreting," and "reproducing."

Even at this prebiotic stage, some kind of selection mechanism likely was operating. Many different kinds of coacervates were forming, and some were more efficient at absorbing substances from the surrounding water than others. They would, therefore, flourish at others' expense. In a sense, Darwinian principles were already at work.

From Nonlife to Life

Approximately 4 billion years ago, chemical evolution and the formation of ever-more-complex organic molecules apparently resulted in the first primitive living cells. How and when the gap between nonlife and life, as we are accustomed to defining it, was bridged is a matter for conjecture. Four lines of investigation and evidence, however, converge on this conclusion:

1. The model of the early earth's chemical and physical environment
2. The experimental evidence pointing to likely chemical pathways from nonlife to life (the work of Miller and others, the evidence of coacervates, and so on)
3. The presence on the modern earth of living examples of primitive organisms, such as stromatolite-forming algal mats and anaerobic bacteria (discussed in the next section)
4. The fossil evidence of stromatolites in 3.6-billion-year-old rocks, as well as the microspheres and other microscopic structures in banded iron formation (BIF) cherts discussed later in this chapter.

Early Life-Forms

In the oxygen-deficient atmosphere of the early earth, the first life-forms were anaerobic, and because they acquired their food by taking in organic molecules from the surrounding water, they are termed **heterotrophs.** Although, as described earlier, organic molecules were constantly being produced by chemical synthesis, the demand likely began to exceed the supply. In any event, among the emerging organisms, those that could feed directly on simpler compounds were more efficient and flourished. In other words, these **autotrophs,** as they were called, were able to manufacture their own food from the simpler ingredients present in the surrounding water. Clearly, this had great survival value.

Some autotrophs apparently utilized sunlight as an energy source in a process of **photosynthesis** in which atmospheric carbon dioxide was dissociated into carbon and oxygen, the carbon being utilized as a nutrient. The oxygen was merely a waste product and, in fact, poisonous to the photoautotrophs. This earliest photosynthesis was anaerobic and presumably appeared in mutant strains of bacteria as a crisis response to a growing food shortage.

This particular step in the progress of life was probably the most important because it led directly to the evolution of life as we know it and also to the atmosphere of the modern earth. Virtually all the free oxygen in the earth's atmosphere is a by-product of aerobic photosynthesis, seen today in cyanobacteria, algae, and all other higher plants. The evolution of life and the evolution of

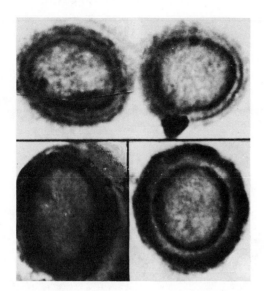

FIGURE 7.7

Microfossils from the Bitter Springs formation of the Amadeus Basin, Australia. *(Photo courtesy of J. W. Schopf.)*

The Free Oxygen Controversy

At what point in the earth's history free oxygen became abundant is a matter of controversy. Earlier models suggested that, during most of the Archean, there was little free oxygen in the atmosphere and only a slow buildup. The evidence cited for this is the apparent lack of abundant redbeds—that is, sediments stained by iron oxides. Instead, iron sulphide minerals, such as pyrite, together with iron carbonates are common in many Archean rocks and suggest a chemically reducing rather than an oxidizing environment. Iron has a strong affinity for oxygen, as indicated by the speed with which iron and steel go rusty. The presence of iron in an unoxidized state in so many Archean rocks is considered highly significant.

On the other hand, others have argued that anoxic environments still exist today and that iron sulfides and carbonates are forming in them even though the atmosphere is an oxidizing one. Some geologists believe that, once photoautotrophs appeared—and evidence indicates that this was early in the Archean—the buildup of oxygen was quite rapid.

A significant part of the controversy concerns redbeds. They are relatively common in rocks younger than about 1.8 billion years but very uncommon before that time, so it is argued that 1.8 billion years marks the time of first oxygen abundance and that, before that, there was just not enough oxygen to satisfy the needs of all the iron in the crustal rocks. Proponents of an early oxygen buildup counter the redbed argument by suggesting that, during the Archean, there were few shallow-platform sedimentary environments and thus a dearth of shallow-water environments where oxidation was possible.

Although this controversy is as yet unresolved, any model of the evolving atmosphere must include some explanation of **banded iron formation (BIF).** These are distinctive, thinly laminated alternations of chert and jasper (hematite-rich chert) (Figure 7.8). The laminations are typically very regular and often have the appearance of red and gray varves (annual glacial clay beds). Sometimes, distinctive, alternating laminae can be traced over distances of hundreds of kilometers and indicate a remarkably widespread and uniform depositional environment.

Enigmatic microspheres, rods, filaments, and other structures often found in BIF cherts suggested to Preston Cloud of the University of California that photosynthesizing organisms, growing in shallow marine waters, were responsible for BIF. According to the Cloud model, the alternations of iron-rich bands with chert represent annual or seasonal cycles in which algal mats periodically "bloomed." The oxygen they produced caused precipitation of the ferrous iron that was in solution in the water. Because oxygen was a waste product and toxic to these anaerobic algae, the ferrous iron acted as an oxygen receptor or "sink" and thus played a vital role in the algae

the atmosphere since Precambrian times have proceeded in parallel, the one being dependent on and caused by the other.

The early carbon-dioxide-rich atmosphere was probably cloudy, perhaps like Venus today. As the atmosphere cleared, aerobic photosynthesis evolved, with organisms living at water depths that were shallow enough to receive sunlight but deep enough to offer protection from deadly ultraviolet radiation. A by-product of photosynthesis is oxygen, a gas that is toxic to anaerobic life-forms. However, anaerobic life-forms did not disappear, and many forms moved into environments that excluded oxygen, such as anoxic muds and stagnant water, where their living descendants can be seen today. Among the Precambrian organisms were presumably mutant strains that became adapted to an aerobic existence. If they did not need oxygen at first, they at least tolerated it.

These early organisms had only a very elementary level of cell organization and are termed prokaryotes. More advanced cells eventually appeared, and these eukaryote cells, found today in protists, fungi, plants, and animals, have a distinct cell nucleus as well as other structures within the cell interior. In contrast to prokaryote metabolism, which is based on relatively simple fermentation processes, eukaryote respiration involves oxygen in the breakdown of sugars. Reproduction is another important area of difference between the two levels of cell organization. Prokaryotes reproduce only by fission, whereas sexual reproduction is apparent in eukaryotes (Figure 7.7). The appearance of eukaryotes marks an important stage both in the evolution of life and in the evolution of the atmosphere because eukaryotes could not have evolved in the absence of oxygen.

FIGURE 7.8
Folded, interbedded iron formation and metasedimentary
rocks of Precambrian age, Beresford Lake area, Manitoba.
(Photo courtesy of Geological Survey of Canada, Ottawa.)

life cycle. BIF are found in all Archean terrains, and at their peak, made up as much as 15 percent of the sedimentary succession. Today, they constitute by far the biggest source of iron ore.

The appearance of BIF about 2.5 billion years ago marked a stage in the evolution of the atmosphere at which oxygen levels were becoming significant, in step with the evolution of photosynthesizing anaerobic autotrophs. The sudden disappearance of BIF at about 1.8 billion years ago is also claimed to have evolutionary significance. At this time, a mutant strain of cyanobacteria may have appeared with an oxygen-mediating enzyme, capable of handling the oxygen without the need for a nonbiological sink, and so the precipitation of BIF ceased. From about this time, redbeds proper became increasingly common (Box 17.1).

Those geologists who believe that free oxygen was present in the Archean atmosphere offer an alternative explanation for banded iron formations, suggesting that they reflect repeated upwelling of iron-rich water from reservoirs in deep, stagnant ocean basins.

Summary

New data from the rest of the solar system are adding much to our knowledge of earth and of the beginnings of the solar system. No study of the earth can be conducted without considering earth's neighbors in space. Although nineteenth-century theories regarding the origin of the solar system generally favored a hot beginning for the earth, later theories suggested a cold beginning, with the solar system forming within clouds of dust and gas.

The essential mechanism involved in stellar evolution is gravitational collapse onto a nucleus. As the mass grows in size and density, it accretes still more cosmic dust and debris, and internal temperatures rise. At the center of the nebular mass, the nucleus eventually grows hot enough for nuclear reactions, and the star becomes luminous. Most stars evolve through five stages: (1) protostar, (2) main-sequence star, (3) red giant, (4) white dwarf, and (5) black dwarf. Very large stars that run through their fuel supplies very rapidly and then explode are called supernovae.

In the same way, the planets formed from local concentrations of dust and gas within the nebula. As the earth grew by accretion of cosmic debris, differentiation into a dense, nickel-iron core and an outer, less-dense shell probably began. Further differentiation resulted in an inner and outer core surrounded by a mantle of largely silicate material.

Development of the earth's atmosphere can also be described in a series of evolutionary steps. The earliest primitive atmosphere was likely part of the solar nebula, consisting predominantly of hydrogen and helium. This atmosphere was quickly stripped away by the solar wind. Following this, the earth may, for a time at least, have had no atmosphere.

Once differentiation into an iron-rich core and mantle of silicate material began, internal temperatures rose, and melting occurred. Heat was also generated by the decay of radioactive elements. Internal changes were manifested in volcanic activity, and a variety of gases poured out during volcanic eruptions, a process known as outgassing. The denser gases, like carbon dioxide and water vapor, were retained by the earth's gravity and came to form the second planetary atmosphere. The most notable feature of this atmosphere was its lack of free oxygen.

Evidence of life on earth is provided by the earliest fossils—stromatolites from rocks dated at 3.6 billion years. Stromatolites are still forming today and are, in fact, organosedimentary structures built up by the accretionary or precipitating activity of cyanobacteria. On the early earth, in the absence of oxygen, presumably all the first life-forms were anaerobic.

What the first living organisms were like and when they appeared are unknown. It is certain, however, that the appearance of life was preceded by a long history of prebiotic chemical evolution. The chief difference between life and nonlife at the chemical level involves the size and complexity of the molecules. Life processes typically form very complex carbon-based molecules, but they are formed from simple compounds, including amino acids. In turn, amino acids, which seem to be the sole chemical building blocks of important components like proteins, are made up only of carbon, hydrogen, oxygen, and nitrogen.

In a benchmark experiment, chemist Stanley Miller was able to show that, under conditions that existed on the primitive earth, in an atmosphere produced by volcanic outgassing, simple compounds of carbon, hydrogen, oxygen, and nitrogen could be induced to form more complex molecules, including amino acids. Clearly,

this was one of the possible pathways from nonlife to life. Coacervates—certain substances, usually of large molecular weight and including proteins, that tend to spontaneously form discrete droplets in water—also are considered significant in tracing the steps toward the first living cells.

Probably about 4 billion years ago, after billions of random chemical experiments, the first living cells appeared. At first, the organisms were anaerobic heterotrophs, utilizing the amino acid and other molecules synthesized by processes in the atmosphere and oceans. Later, as the supply of these nutrients was unable to keep up with the demand, autotrophs (those organisms capable of manufacturing their own food from the simplest molecules) clearly had a big advantage. Those autotrophs that were able to utilize the energy provided by sunlight in a process of photosynthesis were especially favored.

Photosynthesis results in a waste product of oxygen. Because oxygen is toxic to anaerobic organisms, the anaerobic organisms of the early earth moved into environments that excluded oxygen, such as anoxic muds and stagnant water. Presumably, some mutant strains became adapted to an aerobic existence.

At what point in the earth's history free oxygen became abundant is a matter of controversy. One theory suggests that, as a consequence of photosynthesis, oxygen levels in the atmosphere built up quickly, and iron minerals in rocks became oxidized to produce redbeds. The first abundant redbeds appear in rock about 1.8 billion years old, so this time is assumed to mark the rapid increase of atmospheric oxygen levels. However, this controversy is, as yet, unresolved.

Questions

1. Describe the initial stages in the birth of a sun-type star.
2. Describe the current model for stellar evolution for main-sequence stars.
3. Explain the two alternative models that describe the early stages in the formation of the earth.
4. Describe the evolution of the earth's atmosphere.
5. What geological evidence is there for establishing the time of the first oceans?
6. What is the nature of the first indirect evidence for metazoans? When did metazoans first appear?
7. What were the earliest fossils?
8. Describe the basic architecture of amino acids.
9. Describe Stanley Miller's experiment at the University of Chicago. What did it show?
10. Discuss the statistical aspects of the model that describes the production of amino acids by random chemical synthesis.
11. What are coacervates? Why might some scientists see them as the precursors of the first primitive cells?
12. Summarize the evidence available to explain the progression from the earliest stages of chemical evolution to the first primitive organisms.
13. What is the difference between prokaryote and eukaryote cells?
14. What is meant by the free oxygen controversy?
15. How do iron minerals provide clues as to the oxygen content of the atmosphere?

Further Reading

Cloud, P. 1978. *Cosmos, earth, and man: A short history of the universe.* New Haven, Conn.: Yale University Press.

Ebbighausen, E. G. 1976. *Astronomy.* 3d ed. Columbus, Ohio: Merrill.

Hamblin, W. K. and Christiansen, E. H. 1990, *Exploring the planets.* New York, Macmillan.

King, E. A. 1976. *Space geology, an introduction.* New York: John Wiley.

Skinner, B. J., (ed.) *The solar system and its strange objects: Readings from* American Scientist. Los Altos, Calif.: Kauffman.

Snow, T. P. 1985. *The dynamic universe: An introduction to astronomy.* 2d ed. St. Paul, Minn.: West.

Taylor, S. R. 1987. The origin of the moon. *American Scientist* 75:468–77.

Wooldridge, D. E. 1966. *The machinery of life.* New York: McGraw-Hill.

8

PLATE TECTONICS

Introduction

The birth and development of the concept of plate tectonics during the 1960s marked, perhaps, the most important development in the science of geology since the early discoveries of Hutton and Lyell and the abandonment of the catastrophist idea in the early nineteenth century. The evidence for continental drift, the most obvious manifestation of the plate-tectonic mechanism, had been discussed by geologists from the early days of the twentieth century. While they had many of the puzzle pieces, too many pieces were still missing to make a coherent picture.

In science, discoveries are often made in a series of steps. Sometimes, advances are needed in one field before progress is possible in another. Often, it is a question of technology. For example, as mentioned in Chapter 6, isotopic dates were being calculated as early as 1905, but really accurate dating only became possible with the invention of the mass spectrometer in 1929.

In this chapter, we discuss the discoveries that eventually led to the plate-tectonic model. With plate tectonics, the key to understanding lay in the ocean basins. The development of acoustical sounding devices enabled geologists to get their first really good look at ocean floor topography. The technology required for deep-sea drilling, culminating in the JOIDES (Joint Oceanographic Institutes Deep Earth Sampling) program, provided another exploration tool. Finally, the great improvements in seismic survey techniques and survey expansion during the 1970s and 1980s into the offshore regions provided the means to study the great sedimentary accumulations along the continental margins. All of these technologically based developments opened the door to the advances in marine geology that were to lead, ultimately, to the current plate-tectonic model.

Early Evidence for Continental Drift

Continental drift is the concept that, over time, the continents have shifted in position, relative to each other, over the earth's surface. Over a number of decades, geologists and others amassed incontrovertible evidence for continental drift. As we see in this section and later parts of the chapter, their sources were varied and, inevitably, convincing.

Geographic Evidence

The most obvious indication of continental drift lay in the strange coincidence in shape between the eastern coastline of South America and the western one of Africa (Figure 8.1). With a little more juggling, the Australian and Antarctic continents, together with peninsula India, could be assembled into a large supercontinent, like the pieces of a jigsaw puzzle. As early as 1898, Eduard Suess of Vienna had named this landmass *Gondwanaland*.[1]

Although Alfred Wegener in Germany is usually cited as the first person to suggest continental drift, the idea had been put forward some half a century earlier by American Anton Snider-Pellegrini in a book published in 1858.

Wegener, on the other hand, was the first to involve all the continents in a single landmass he called **Pangaea** and to discuss possible mechanisms (Figure 8.2). His book—*On the origin of continents and oceans*—was published in 1915 but aroused little attention, presumably because of World War I. A third edition, published in 1924, was translated into English, and the idea of continental drift began to gain wider attention.

---

1. *Gondwanaland* is, in fact, a tautology because **Gondwana** means "land of the Gonds."

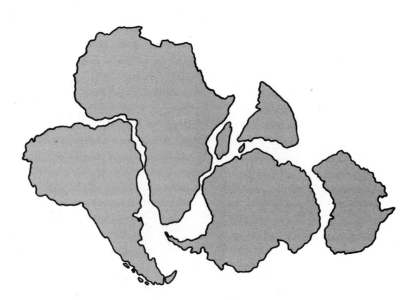

FIGURE 8.1
Predrift reconstruction of the southern continents.

In any event, although some dismissed the similarity of coastal configuration as coincidence, many geologists and paleontologists began to search for further confirmation of the possible joining of the continents. The evidence, particularly in the Southern Hemisphere, was not hard to find.

(a)

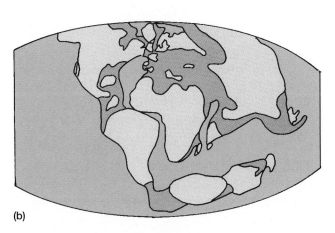

(b)

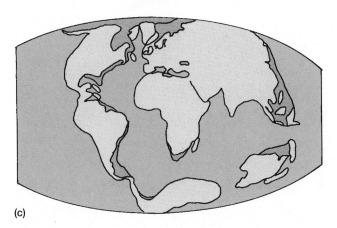

(c)

FIGURE 8.2

Alfred Wegener's reconstruction of continental configuration at three past times: (a) Late Carboniferous (300 million years ago). (b) Eocene (50 million years ago). (c) Early Pleistocene (1.5 million years ago). *(Source: After Alfred Wegener, On the Origin of Continents and Oceans, 1915.)*

Faunal and Floral Evidence

Paleontologists and zoogeographers had long noted certain peculiarities in the distribution and relationships of animals and plants on the southern continents. For example, a comparison of freshwater fishes of South America with those in Africa shows that, although they differ at the species and generic level, slightly higher in the taxonomic scale, virtually every family can be recognized on both continents. How could this be?

One idea was that the fishes may have arisen independently from common marine ancestors in the Atlantic, with descendant forms adapting to a freshwater habitat and evolving along parallel lines. This theory is considered so unlikely that it can be discarded. A much more feasible explanation was to assume the former existence of a **land bridge** that lay where the South Atlantic now lies and that connected the continents (Figure 8.3). In the lakes and rivers of this great, sprawling African-South American landmass lived the ancestors of the modern freshwater fishes. According to the theory, when the land bridge foundered, separating the African and South American populations, the two faunas evolved over time to become more and more distinct, although they retained broad similarities consequent on their common ancestry.

A land bridge was also postulated in the Indian Ocean, connecting India to Madagascar. This was necessary to explain why the fauna of Madagascar is very similar to that of distant India (some 3,600 kilometers away), yet is totally dissimilar to that of Africa only 400 kilometers away, with familiar African mammals like lions, giraffes, and zebra being conspicuously absent. A third faunal connection concerned lungfishes, the order Dipnoi being represented by only three genera: (1) *Neoceratodus* of Queensland, Australia; (2) *Protopterus* of Africa; and (3) *Lepidoriven* of South America. Again, a former land connection between the continents seemed the most logical explanation for this distribution.

The fossil record also contains evidence of former intercontinental connections. One of the best examples is the small lizard like aquatic reptile *Mesosaurus*, whose fossil remains have turned up in the Permian rocks in both Africa and South America (Figure 8.4). *Mesosaurus* was a freshwater species and so was clearly incapable of swimming across the South Atlantic. Particularly striking among plant fossils is the distribution of the so-called *Glossopteris* flora, an association of broad-leaved plants together with certain fernlike species. Well-preserved fossils are found in Permo-Carboniferous rocks on all southern continents as well as in India, and *Glossopteris* was clearly not dispersed by the wind because its seeds are too big and heavy.

While some kind of former land connection between the southern continents clearly was indicated, the faunal and floral evidence alone provided no clue as to whether the connection involved land bridges or continental shifting.

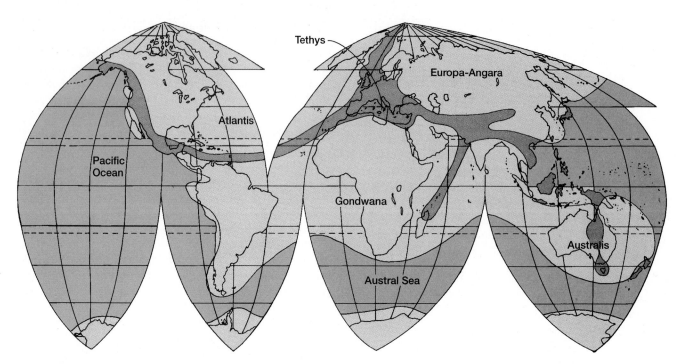

FIGURE 8.3
Typical paleogeographic reconstruction, using land bridges and seaways, to explain the distribution of fossil faunas and floras without recourse to continental drift. This particular reconstruction dates from 1949 and depicts the supposed distribution of land and sea in the Early Jurassic.

FIGURE 8.4
Mesosaurus, a small, freshwater aquatic reptile from the Permian. *(Photo courtesy of E. J. Petuch.)*

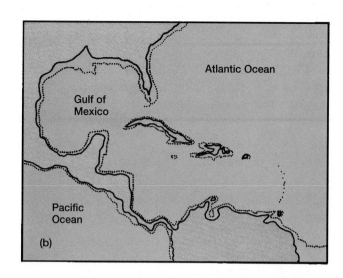

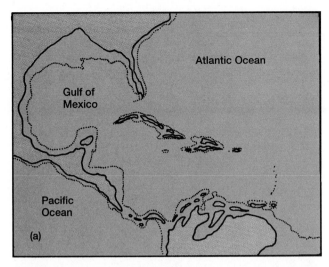

FIGURE 8.5

History of the Panama land bridge. (a) Configuration in the Miocene. (b) Configuration in the Late Pliocene.

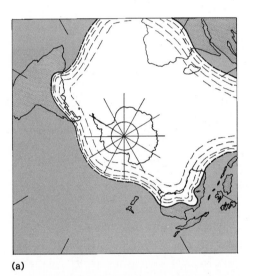

(a)

Many land connections between continents have existed in the geologic past and still exist today. A Bering land bridge during times of glacially lowered sea level was a migration route for many North American immigrants (including humans) from Asia. The Panama land bridge between North and South America emerged from a seaway that had connected the Caribbean and Pacific less than 2 million years ago (Figure 8.5).

The problem with a South Atlantic land bridge was that it raised more questions than it answered. While it could be a valid explanation for the observed zoogeographic relationships, how did it disappear? The impossibility of eliminating masses of sialic crust of subcontinental size, in effect, clearly eliminated the land-bridge theory.

Glacial Evidence

In the late nineteenth century, from rocks of Permian age of southern Africa, came unequivocal evidence of glaciation. Later, similar discoveries were made in the other southern continents and India. The presence of glacially striated pavements and glacial deposits like boulder clays in areas that are now in the tropics and subtropics could conceivably be explained by mountain glaciers. However, the sheer size of the ice cap necessary to produce the hundreds of meters of glacial tills rendered this theory untenable. On the other hand, in a world of fixed continents, with or without land bridges, an ice cap large enough to embrace all the known evidence for glaciation would have had to cover almost half the earth (Figure 8.6). Refrigeration of this magnitude would surely have had an effect on the world climate as a whole, and yet in the Northern Hemisphere, Permo-Carboniferous deposits contained evidence of tropical and subtropical faunas and floras.

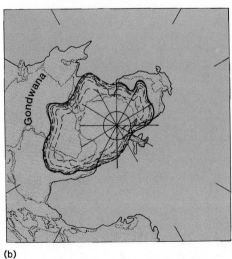

(b)

FIGURE 8.6

The Gondwana ice cap in the Permo-Carboniferous. (a) In a nondrifting world. (b) With a Gondwana reconstruction.

Again, alternative explanations either raised more problems than they solved or were just downright ridiculous. For example, a theory suggesting the possibility of several small ice caps would have required the earth's axis of rotation to change rapidly enough to move the South Pole over distances of thousands of kilometers in a few million years. The law of conservation of angular momentum clearly did not allow for that.

Early Arguments for and against Continental Drift

Evidence like this began to generate a considerable body of opinion in favor of continental drift, and at a conference held in 1928, all the evidence—both pro and con—was presented in papers submitted by a wide spectrum of specialists, including geologists, paleontologists, and geophysicists. From the Southern Hemisphere, in particular, the evidence for drift was convincing. To the paleontological and glaciological evidence were added examples of matching geologic structures between former pieces of the supercontinent as well as evidence of matching stratigraphic successions, similar geomorphic cycles, similar tectonic history, and so on.

In 1932, South African geologist Alexander Du Toit, in a book entitled *Our Wandering Continents,* presented an overwhelming body of evidence for the reality of continental drift. Although many Northern Hemisphere geologists were proponents of continental drift, American, Russian, and European geologists generally preferred to accept the views of the geophysicists, who insisted that there was no conceivable mechanism whereby the continents could be moved.

Early attempts at describing a mechanism for continental drift usually took as a starting point the relative difference in density of the continental crust as compared with the basaltic oceanic crust. The continents were seen as "floating" on the denser oceanic crust; thus, to move, they had to "plough through" the denser crust. On this point, geophysicists were adamant, and they were able to demonstrate quite easily that such movement was impossible. On the other hand, just as with the nineteenth-century controversy over the age of the earth, many geologists simply dismissed the opinions of the geophysicists and continued to insist on the reality of continental drift.

As early as 1928, British geologist Arthur Holmes was suggesting that convectional movements in the molten interior could be the cause of movements of the earth's surface, an idea that turned out to be very close to the truth. Yet, world interest in continental drift waned, despite continued accumulation of evidence. In fact, right up to the late 1960s, the idea was still viewed with suspicion. A geology textbook published in 1963, for example, devoted less than one page to "this interesting idea."

FIGURE 8.7
In regions of folded strata, beds are often turned into a vertical attitude, as shown in this example of Pennsylvanian strata in eastern Tennessee, or even turned upside down.

Accumulating Evidence for Continental Drift

A variety of data continued to provide evidence for continental drift. In some cases, however, the data's significance to continental drift was unrecognized for decades.

Fold Mountains

Well before the end of the nineteenth century, the great **fold mountains** of the world—the Alps, Rockies, Himalayas, and Andes—had been closely scrutinized and numerous theories proposed to account for them. Rock exposures in mountains are generally good, and even the earliest studies in the Alps, Rockies, and other mountain ranges indicated that great compressive forces had been at work squeezing and folding and thrusting the strata on a gigantic scale (Figure 8.7). "Crustal shortening" was a key phrase. One explanation proposed that, as the earth cooled through its long history, it also contracted. Fold mountains in this hypothesis were wrinkles produced on the surface of a shrinking crust, like the wrinkles on a deflating balloon.

Even more remarkable than these early analyses of the fold mountain structures were the detailed studies of the stratigraphy of the sedimentary successions that had

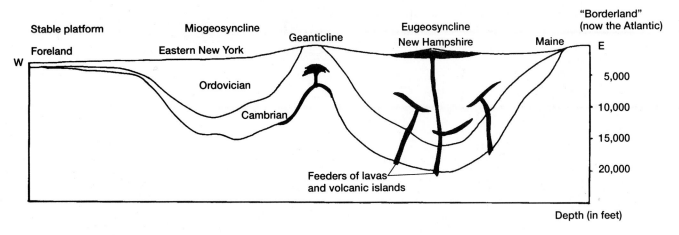

FIGURE 8.8
Restored section of the Appalachian geosynclinal belts prior to the Taconic orogeny. This was the classic interpretation of Marshall Kay of Columbia University in 1951.

been caught up in the folds, often metamorphosed, and complexly folded and faulted. Painstaking work over many years finally began to result in what are called palinspastic maps, maps that show the original setting of the sedimentary successions contained in the fold mountain belts. In other words, the wrinkles were pulled out flat and the crust restored to its former extent.

Geosynclines

It was already apparent over 100 years ago that the rocks involved in the mountain-building episodes had originally been laid down in large downwarped troughs in the earth's crust in which had accumulated tens of thousands of meters of sediment. These great "canoe-shaped welts," as someone once described them, were typically several thousand kilometers long and hundreds of kilometers wide. With the exception of the Ural Mountains and parts of the Himalayas, they all lay at or near the margins of continents. They were called **geosynclines** (Figure 8.8).

Further discoveries during the 1940s and 1950s were based largely on work in the Appalachians—in particular, that of Marshal Kay of Columbia University. It was found, for example, that the geosyncline was not a single downfolded welt, but actually consisted of two parts: an inner welt (on the continent side), known as a **miogeosyncline,** and an outer welt, on the ocean side, called a **eugeosyncline.** The two downfolds were separated by what appeared to be regional upfold termed a **geanticline.**

The sediments that filled the two troughs were discovered to differ in many important ways; quite clearly, the depositional environments had been different. Miogeosynclines were characterized by sandstones, lime-

stones, and shales—often quite fossiliferous—that had clearly been laid down in shallow water. Given that the total thickness of the sediments was 10,000 to 15,000 meters, the geosyncline obviously had been subjected to long, continued subsidence and had probably never been a deep topographic trough on the sea floor.

In the case of eugeosynclines, deeper-water deposits were indicated by dark shales and siltstones; thin, dark limestones; and graded beds of a dark-colored sandstone called graywacke. Also often present were pyroclastic sediments and volcanic rocks.

Detailed studies of facies changes in the stratigraphic successions of geosynclines frequently indicated that the source of the sedimentary infilling lay on the ocean side of the geosyncline. In a nondrifting world, it became necessary to postulate landmasses, or "borderlands" as they were called, in areas that are now oceans (Figure 8.9). As with the transoceanic land bridges, explaining their subsequent disappearance was, to say the least, something of a problem.

Not only were geosynclines of immense areal extent, they also were involved in major slices of earth history. One of the puzzling features of geosynclines was that they apparently underwent two historic phases. For long periods, perhaps 200 to 300 million years, they were simply sites for the passive accumulation of sediment, undergoing slow subsidence in the process. Then this accumulative phase was ended by a relatively short (measured in a few tens of millions of years) orogenic phase, a period of mountain building during which all the sediments accumulated in the geosynclines were squeezed, thrust-faulted, folded, metamorphosed, and intruded by large granite batholiths.

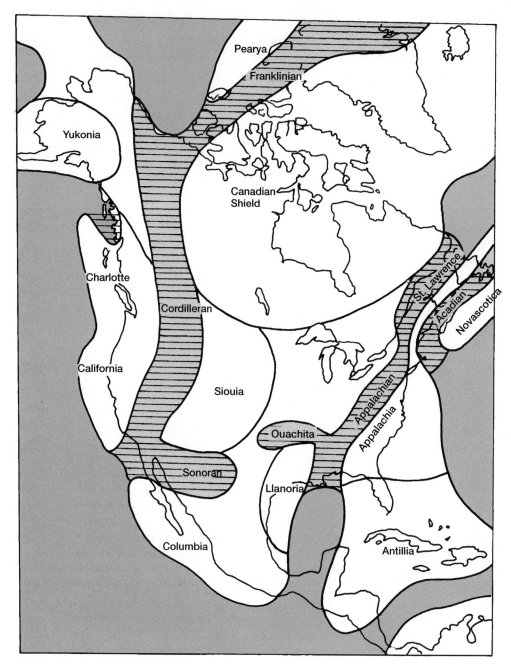

FIGURE 8.9
Borderlands and geosynclines during the Paleozoic, as
envisaged by Schuchert in 1923.

One geosynclinal problem was that there did not seem
to be any modern geosynclines around to provide scientists with a firsthand look at the sedimentary environments and processes. Raised as they were in the nineteenth-
century doctrine of uniformitarianism, geologists of the
first half of the twentieth century were much more comfortable when they could find a present-day example as
"the key to the past." Although some scientists toyed with
the idea that the deep ocean trenches were modern geosynclines, few people were convinced.

Continental Margins

During the 1950s and 1960s, a growing body of information derived from seismic surveys and deep boreholes
was throwing a great flood of light on the stratigraphic
successions and history of the continental shelves, slopes,
and rises, the three great geologic and topographic elements to be found, with some variations, at all continental
margins. Obviously, these were also major planetary features, but here the problem was, in many ways, the opposite of that encountered with geosynclines: Where were

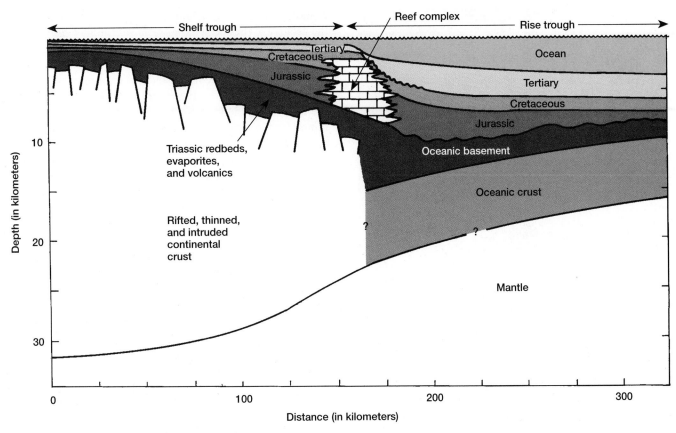

FIGURE 8.10

Schematic cross section through the continental shelf based on seismic reflection data. The line of section passes through the east end of the Long Island region.

the continental shelves and rises of past geologic time? It turns out that the answer to this question was also the answer to another question because in terms of their overall stratigraphy, the miogeosyncline/eugeosyncline couplet and the continental shelf/rise couplet are really one and the same (Figure 8.10). In short, a miogeosyncline was an ancient continental shelf, and a continental shelf is a modern miogeosyncline. The ultimate fate of past geosynclines is discussed later in the chapter.

Polar Wandering

Quite early in the study of paleomagnetism (the study of the earth's magnetism preserved in rocks), scientists discovered that the magnetic poles of the geologic past were apparently in different places at different times. As described briefly in Chapter 5, the orientation of magnetic minerals in rocks provides the means of determining the strength and direction of the earth's magnetic field, "frozen in" as it were, at the time the rock formed.

As the accuracy of magnetometers improved and the number of measurements from all parts of the world and from rocks of all ages grew, a startling picture emerged. The former positions of the magnetic poles in the geologic past, while typically often nowhere near the modern poles, were not scattered randomly about the globe; instead, they

could be plotted along lines that indicated progressive movement of the poles with time (see Box 9.1). From observations taken on all the continents, these **polar-wandering curves** could be plotted from the present back to the early Precambrian.

Well entrenched within the general magneto-dynamo theory that explains the earth's magnetism, or the main field, as it is called, is the link between the earth's core and the earth's rotation. The earth's magnetic field is generated by movements in the liquid outer core. These movements are believed to be a combination of flow generated by the earth's rotation and convective flow. Movement of the metallic core through a weak magnetic field (caused by compositional changes in the earth that produce a battery effect) generates an electric current (the dynamo effect). This current, in turn, generates the strong geomagnetic field. The position of the magnetic poles, allowing for a small nondipolar component, must coincide approximately with that of the rotational (geographic) poles (Figure 8.11).

The paleomagnetic observations indicating moving poles raised some very awkward questions. If the magnetic poles really did move, then so did the axis of rotation. Again, as we saw earlier with the Permo-Carboniferous ice cap, the law of conservation of angular

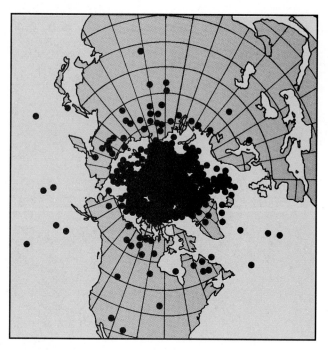

FIGURE 8.11
Paleomagnetic poles for the last 7,000 years, plotted on
polar projection. *(Source: Data from D. H. Tarling,*
Paleomagnetism: Principles and Applications in Geology,
Geophysics and Archaeology. *Copyright © 1983 Chapman and Hall
Ltd., London.)*

momentum applies some very definite constraints. Yet,
freeing the magnetic poles from the rotational poles was
not really a viable alternative because it meant disman-
tling the magneto-dynamo theory. After a brief flirtation
with the idea that the earth's crust was somehow slipping
over an interior that continued to rotate with no wobble,
scientists finally agreed that polar wandering was only an
apparent phenomenon and that it was the continents that
actually moved.

To make things even more interesting, pole position
determinations of the same age but from different continents often indicated more than one pole. A multiplicity
of poles at any one time again would require the abandonment of conventional models and the construction of
nonsensical and unacceptable alternatives. This was really
the end for advocates of the fixed-continent idea, but more
was to come. A mechanism for continental drift still needed
to be found, and paleomagnetic phenomena provided another key to the puzzle.

Evidence from the Oceans

Despite the wealth of data available from observations on
the continents and the clear demonstration that continental drift had occurred, the mechanism responsible

would not have come to light without an understanding of
the geology of the ocean basins. The years following World
War II saw an enormous expansion in the investigation of
the oceans, and while many questions were answered, they
were just as quickly replaced by new questions.

Until well into the twentieth century, knowledge of
the deep ocean floor was confined to what could be obtained from soundings and dredgings. With water depths
of 5,000 meters or more over large areas of the ocean (and
in places twice that depth), sounding and dredging was
clearly a tedious business. The ship had to stop, and the
paying out of cable and the recovery of samples was a
lengthy process. Small wonder that spot soundings of deep
ocean floors were extremely sparse.

All of this changed with the development of echo
sounders of increasing sophistication during the 1930s and
1940s. With this technique, sound waves transmitted from
the ship travel down to the sea floor, where they are reflected back to sensitive ship microphones. By timing the
interval between transmission and receipt of the sound
pulse, scientists can determine the depth of the sea floor.
The big advantage of this method is that the ship can keep
moving and a continuous profile of the seafloor topography plotted. As ships carrying depth recorders criss-
crossed the oceans, a detailed picture of the sea floors
began to emerge.

Midocean Ridges

The North Atlantic was the first ocean to give up its se-
crets, and the most important feature discovered was a
great rifted chain of mountains running roughly down the
North Atlantic's middle and continuing into the South
Atlantic. Ultimately, these mountains were found to be
part of the 64,000 kilometer-long chain that extended
through all the world's oceans (Figure 8.12). Seismologists had known for years that many shallow earthquake
epicenters had been plotted in the central Atlantic; now
they found that the epicenters clustered significantly close
to this **midocean ridge.** Midocean ridges were also places
where geophysicists had discerned a higher-than-average
flow of heat from the earth's interior. Deep-sea drilling,
dredging, and underwater photography along midocean
ridges showed them to be made up of basaltic volcanic
rocks, especially pillow lavas characteristic of submarine
eruptions.

Isotopic age determinations of the seafloor volcanics
resulted in some new surprises. In a traverse at right angles
away from a midocean ridge, scientists found that the rocks
sampled become progressively older, there being a direct
correlation between age and distance from the ridge. A
second traverse in the opposite direction away from the
ridge revealed an age/distance relationship that is approximately a mirror image of the first (Figure 8.13). In
addition, the further one goes from the ridge, the greater
is the depth to the ocean basement rocks. In other words,

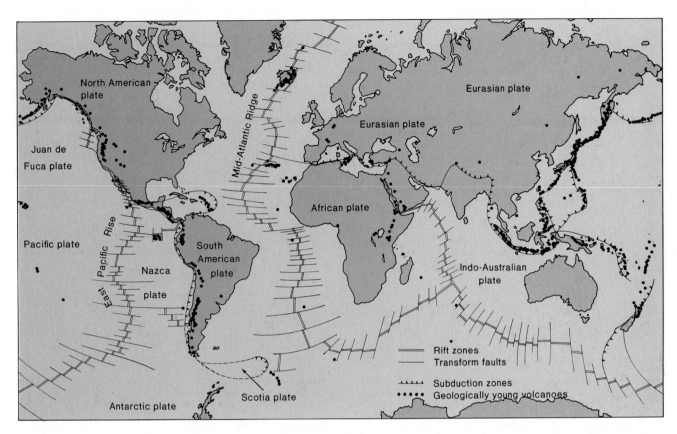

FIGURE 8.12

Locations of midocean ridges and trenches. Note the numerous offsets in the ridges caused by transform faults.

*(Source: Data from R. Decker and B. Decker, *Volcanoes*. Copyright © 1981 W. H. Freeman and Company.)*

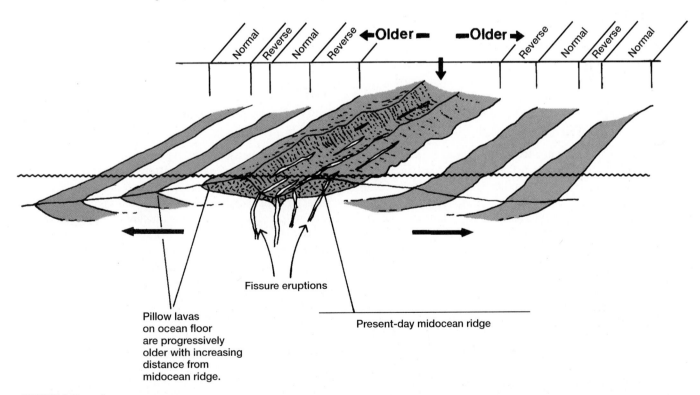

FIGURE 8.13

In a traverse at right angles away from a midocean ridge, rocks become progressively older, there being a direct correlation between age and distance from the ridge. Also, magnetic polarity switches from normal to reverse and back again, with the pattern of magnetic anomalies at a midocean ridge showing up as a series of stripes parallel to the midocean ridge.

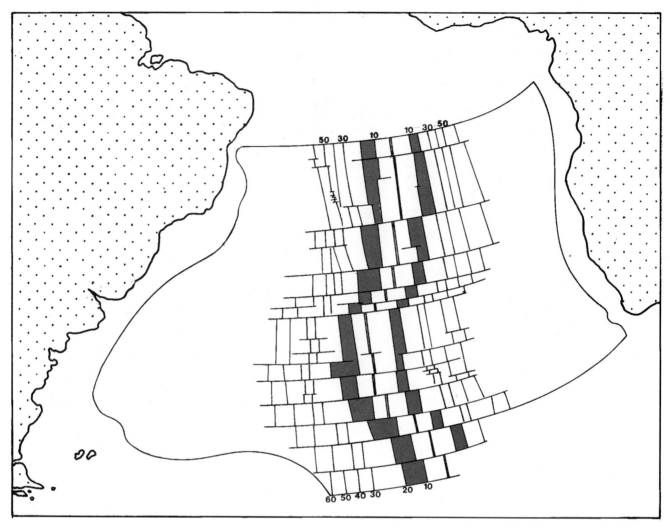

FIGURE 8.14

Linear magnetic anomalies and isochrons on a portion of the South Atlantic sea floor. (Numbers refer to millions of years before present.) (Source: Data from J. R. Heirtzler, et al., ''Marine *Magnetic Anomalies, Geomagnetic Field Reversals and Motions of the Ocean Floor and Continents,''* Journal of Geophysical Research *73:*2124. Copyright © 1968 by the American Geophysical Union.)

with increasing distance from the ridge symmetrically in either direction, the ocean floor becomes systematically both older and deeper. Lines (known as isochrons) joining points of equal age of ocean floor rocks show up as a series of lines parallel to midocean ridges (Figure 8.14). As mapping of the oceans continued, it was found that no-where was there any rock older than Early Jurassic, about 200 million years old.

Magnetic Anomalies

Magnetic surveys of the ocean floor, obtained by towing magnetometers behind ships, began to add further data. Mapping of the magnetic field strength showed a distinctive pattern of magnetic anomalies on the sea floor. These, it turned out, reflect reversals of polarity as the earth's field underwent repeated switches in polarity direction

every few thousand years. At an onshore locality with a succession of lava flows, the pattern of reversals would be seen in a vertical succession, with lava flows with normal polarity (the north-seeking pole pointing to the north magnetic pole) alternating with flows showing reversed polarity (see Figure 8.13). On the sea floor, with lavas becoming progressively older in a horizontal direction away from a midocean ridge, the repeated switching from normal to reverse and back again, shows up as a series of stripes parallel to the midocean ridge and, of course, corresponding to the pattern of isochrons.

Seafloor Spreading and Convection Cells

Based on these data, a hypothesis of seafloor spreading was proposed in 1961 by Canadian geologist L. W. Morley. In his model, new oceanic crust formed along midocean

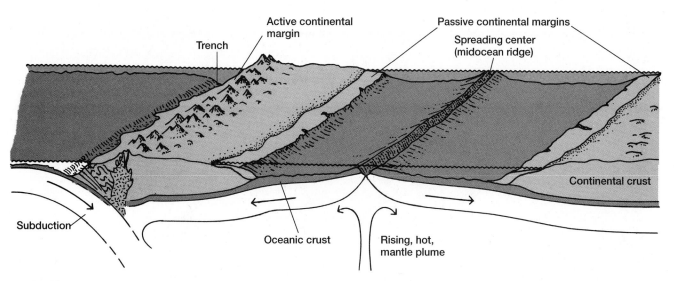

Trench

Active continental margin

Passive continental margins

Spreading center (midocean ridge)

Continental crust

Subduction

Oceanic crust

Rising, hot, mantle plume

FIGURE 8.15
Conveyor-belt model for the plate-tectonic mechanism.

ridges as lavas welled out from fissures onto the sea floor, where the lavas were then carried away in a sort of conveyor-belt fashion. The data used by Morley provided the first hard evidence of a seafloor spreading model that had actually been suggested by Harry Hess of Harvard the previous year. Hess's proposal, in turn, was an attempt to update the convectional flow model suggested by Arthur Holmes 30 years before.

The last pieces of the puzzle were beginning to drop into place, although not without some difficulties. Morley's paper was rejected by first one and then a second scientific journal as being too farfetched! Meanwhile, working in Britain, geophysicists Fred Vine and Drummond Matthews had come up with the same idea and, presumably encountering a more liberal editorial review, their paper was published first.

It was a relatively short step from seafloor spreading to a comprehensive model in which the fundamental driving force was heat from the earth's interior, the motion of the lithosphere (the earth's rigid, outermost layer) being part of a **convection cell** mechanism. The midocean ridges were obvious places where hot material was rising from below.

Clearly, however, there had to be places where cool material descended again into the mantle, and this dilemma finally provided the explanation for deep-sea trenches. The big question, in fact, had always been why did these trenches exist at all? For example, the Peru-Chile trench located off the west coast of South America would seem destined for a very short life. Lying just offshore, it should have been quickly filled by sediment derived from the adjacent continent. Trench regions had other puzzling

features as well. They were also places of considerable seismic activity, although, unlike those at midocean ridges, the earthquakes had deeper foci. In addition, trenches were characterized by abnormally low heat flow from the earth's interior. Here, then, was the other end of the convection cell (Figure 8.15). Trenches and the chains of volcanic islands or mountain ranges associated with them were the surface manifestations of what came to be called **subduction zones.**

In its simplest form, the convection mechanism could be largely described in terms of rising, hot material from below at midocean ridges, or spreading centers as they were aptly called, and sinking, cool material at subduction zones, the horizontal component of movement in the convection cell being movement of the lithosphere. The comparison with a conveyor belt is, although an oversimplification, nevertheless apt. Just as the conveyor-belt machinery stays put, bolted to the floor, and only the belt itself moves, so do the spreading centers and subduction zones remain more or less in place for long periods. The lithosphere, however, like the conveyor belt, moves by virtue of new crust forming at one margin and old crust being destroyed at the other.

The Theory of Plate Tectonics

From all of the accumulated evidence for continental drift emerged the theory of **plate tectonics**—the concept that the earth's surface is divided into distinct, rigid, slowly-moving plates. A map of worldwide spreading centers and subduction zones, more or less divides the earth's surface

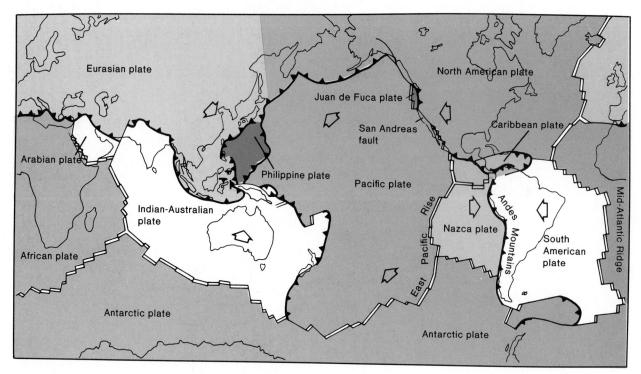

FIGURE 8.16

Distribution of the lithospheric plates. *(Source: After W. Hamilton, U.S. Geological Survey.)*

into distinct areas. These are the rigid **lithospheric plates,** of which there are seven major plates and numerous smaller ones (Figure 8.16). As the spreading centers and subduction zones that form the plates' margins appear and disappear, the plates (especially the smaller ones) change in size and shape.

Lithospheric Plate Boundaries

Three types of lithospheric plate boundaries are possible. Adjacent plates may be separating from one another (divergent boundaries), colliding (convergent boundaries), or simply sliding past each other (translational boundaries).

Divergent Boundaries

As already described, spreading centers are places where new crust is forming and the plate surfaces on either side are moving away in both directions. This type of plate boundary is often called a **divergent** (or "trailing edge") **boundary.** The structural style along such a boundary is one of extension or stretching, with normal block faulting, in which blocks of crust subside between faults.

Although such boundaries on the ocean floor have been directly observed by the use of submersibles and remote television, a far better idea of the regional picture can be gained by going to Iceland. Iceland is actually an emer-

gent portion of the mid-Atlantic ridge, and here can be seen evidence of crustal extension, block faulting, active vulcanism, and all the other features of a typical spreading center.

A spreading center beneath a continental mass causes the landmass to split apart, as Africa and South America were severed in the Cretaceous. The trailing edges become what are known as passive continental margins, on which are constructed the great sedimentary edifices of the continental shelf and the continental rise, facing onto the growing ocean basin that forms between the continental pieces.

Convergent Boundaries

Convergent (or collision) boundaries are found at or near subduction zones, and there are three different kinds, depending on the proximity of continents to the margins: (1) ocean-to-ocean collisions, (2) ocean-to-continent collisions, and (3) continent-to-continent collisions.

Ocean-to-Ocean Collisions When both sides of a lithospheric plate boundary are formed by oceanic crust, the edge of one plate overrides the other, and the downturned plate is carried deep into the mantle (Figure 8.17a). As lithospheric material is carried downward and melts, a considerable amount of water is also mixed in, which helps to build up gas pressures that force magma upward. The resultant volcanism produces what is known as an **island arc,** a curving chain of islands of volcanic origin. The Aleutians, the Kurile Islands, and the Japanese Islands are all examples.

Ocean-to-Continent Collisions   Along an ocean-to-continent (Andean-type) boundary, continental crust is too buoyant to be subducted, and the plate edge carrying the continent rides up over the adjacent oceanic plate (Figure 8.17b). As the descending plate melts, the magma works its way upward and becomes mixed with molten continental rocks. The result is a mixed-composition magma—in effect, a hybrid between basaltic (oceanic) crust and granitic (continental) crust. The resultant rock, called andesite (named after the Andes Mountains), is the characteristic rock type of all the volcanoes that surround the Pacific Ocean along the so-called "andesite line."

Continent-to-Continent Collisions   In a continent-to-continent (Himalayan-type) collision, one plate overrides the edge of the other, resulting in an extremely thick mass of continental crust (Figure 8.17c). The Himalayas and the Tibetan Plateau, in fact, represent the thickest continental crust anywhere; consequently, because of isostatic uplift, the highest mountains and plateaus occur there.

Whenever continental crust is involved in a convergent plate boundary, the structural style is obviously one of compression, and fold mountains are the result. All the fold mountains of the world are a consequence of ancient plate collisions.

Translational Boundaries

The third type of plate boundary, called a translational boundary, involves two adjacent plates sliding past each other in a horizontal direction. One plate does not override the other, and no lithosphere is lost or gained. The actual margin is represented by a fault zone. The relative movement that occurs between the two sides has a dominantly horizontal component, resulting in what is called a strike-slip fault. Along its length, however, the fault may separate adjacent plates whose direction of movement changes. Because such faults may connect either convergent-to-convergent boundaries or convergent-to-divergent boundaries, or any combination thereof, the direction of movement may be changed or *transformed* along its length; hence, they are called transform faults (Figure 8.18).

Transform faults often trend roughly at right angles to the other two kinds of plate boundaries, convergent or divergent, and appear to offset them. For example, one of the most obvious features of the North Atlantic basin topography is the great series of east-west trending fracture zones that repeatedly offset the line of the mid-Atlantic ridge and break it into many short segments.

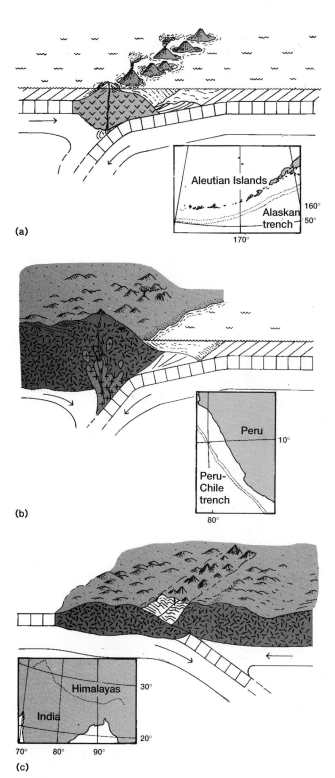

FIGURE 8.17

Comparison of the three types of collision margins: (a) Ocean to ocean. (b) Ocean to continent. (c) Continent to continent.

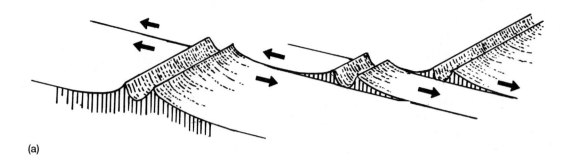

(a)

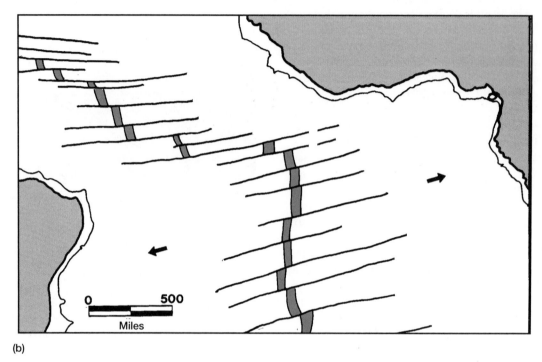

(b)

FIGURE 8.18
(a) Offsets in a midocean ridge mark the locations of
transform faults. (b) A portion of the mid-Atlantic ridge,
showing displacement along transform faults.

The Wilson Cycle

One of the first persons to look beyond plate tectonics and
its implications was geophysicist J. Tuzo Wilson of the
University of Toronto. He suggested that the movement
of continental blocks on lithospheric surfaces is cyclical:
A continent that lies above a newly formed spreading
center is split apart, and a new ocean forms between the
pieces. The ocean becomes larger and larger, but eventually, a subduction zone replaces the spreading center between the continents, and they begin to move back toward
each other until they collide.

In a nutshell, the **Wilson Cycle** explains the mystery
of geosynclines and why they apparently went through an
accumulative phase followed by a compressive stage.
During all the time that the new ocean is widening, the
continental margin (the trailing edge) facing onto that
ocean accumulates typical passive-margin continental
shelf and continental rise sedimentary prisms (the accumulative phase of the geosyncline). This continues during
the beginning of ocean closing, provided that the margin
is still distant from the subduction zone. As the continent
collides with the adjacent plate, the result is the compression and crustal shortening seen by nineteenth-century
geologists as the compressional phase of geosyncline
history.

Movement in the Mantle

The movement of the lithospheric plates is the surface
expression of large-scale movements in the mantle. The
movements are, as described earlier, convection currents

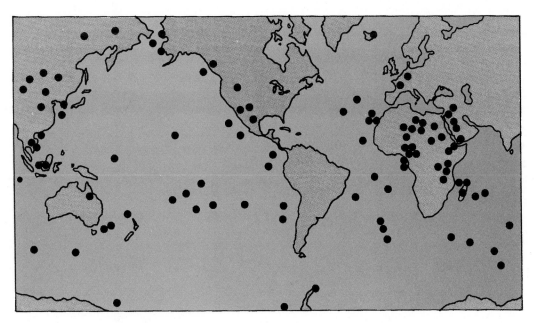

FIGURE 8.19
World map showing the location of major hot spots.

produced from rising, hot material and sinking, cold material. The relationship between the movements seen on the surface as plate motion and the deeper movements down in the mantle, however, is far from simple.

Two-Tiered Convection System

While the midocean ridges mark the locale of rising hot material, the movement is part of a secondary system of motion apparently driven by circulation in the deeper mantle. This occurs within small-scale convection cells, the distance between rising and sinking segments being typically about 1,500 kilometers. Upwelling regions in the mantle are distributed all over the ocean floor, so the large-scale movement responsible for plate motion seems to be superimposed on a smaller-scale system of convection cells deeper in the mantle. The key to the relationship between what are, in effect, two tiers of convection systems is the rigidity of the lithospheric plates in contrast to the ductile nature of the mantle. The motion of the lithospheric plates reflects the average of the forces generated in deeper mantle movements below.

The nature of the deeper mantle movements are clearly well beyond the reach of any direct observation, but in the early 1980s, scientists discovered that sensitive radar altimeters in orbiting satellites could measure fluctuations of sea level on a global scale. They also found that the distribution of bulges and hollows on the sea surface were indications of gravitational anomalies and that these, in turn, provided the clues to the distribution of mantle convection cells. Positive gravity anomalies reflect hot, rising currents in the mantle, while negative anomalies are found where the mantle is sinking in a cool region.

Hot Spots

Any model of mantle convection systems must also take **hot spots** into account. Hot spots mark the location of plumes of rising, hot mantle material that apparently remain stationary over long periods. More than 200 active or recently active hot spots have been located, and at the earth's surface, they are typically marked by a volcano or thermal activity of some kind (Figure 8.19).

One of the first hot spots to be discovered is under the island of Hawaii and is the heat source below the magma chamber feeding Kilauea and other vents on the island. This hot spot has apparently remained stationary for the past 10 million years or more as the Hawaiian chain of islands, together with the seamounts (volcanic hills rising a kilometer or more above the sea floor) to the northwest, passed over it. In moving along the Hawaiian chain, there is a progressive decrease in age from northwest to southeast. Kauai, the oldest island in the group, was formed as it passed over the hot spot some 5 1/2 million years ago. The other islands mark the Pacific plate's movement in a generally west-northwest direction (Figure 8.20). Clearly, new islands are destined to appear east-southeast of Hawaii, and the next island in the chain is already located and named Loihi, although its emergence from the sea is still probably several thousand years into the future.

Hot spots are not confined to ocean basins—the largest concentration is found in Africa. A half dozen or so are located in North America. One hot spot under Yellowstone National Park in Wyoming is responsible for the hot springs and geysers, all that remain of relatively recent volcanic activity.

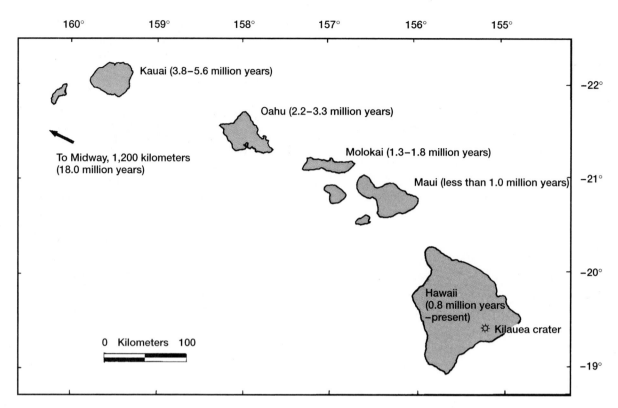

FIGURE 8.20
Map showing movement of the Hawaiian Islands over a hot spot. Note the progressive decrease in age from west-northwest to east-southeast.

Summary

The concept of plate tectonics provides answers to many problems that geologists have struggled with for over 100 years. In particular, it suggests a mechanism to explain continental drift.

From the early years of this century and before, geologists have noted evidence of close geographic, zoogeographic, botanical, and glacial correlations among continents that are now separated by thousands of kilometers of oceans. The jigsaw-puzzle fit of some continents, the puzzling resemblances between living faunas and floras on different continents and unequivocal evidence of widespread glaciation—especially in the Southern Hemisphere landmasses—could only be explained by assuming that these continents were all once joined together.

Although numerous people, chief among them Alfred Wegener, had suggested continental drift, many geologists refused to believe that it was possible. This was particularly the case in the Northern Hemisphere, where the evidence for former continental connections is admittedly less obvious. Instead, nondrifters proposed that transoceanic land bridges had formerly connected the continents. While solving the problem of zoogeographic and botanical relationships, this suggestion raised the question of what had happened to the land bridges. Disposal of large masses of continental crust was not feasible.

Evidence for an ice age in Permo-Carboniferous time raised further problems for nondrifters. If the continents were indeed fixed, the ice cap that produced the glacial deposits must have covered half the globe. This would have cooled down the whole earth, yet in the Northern Hemisphere, Permo-Carboniferous rocks contain fossils of tropical and subtropical species.

Explanations for fold mountain belts, geosynclines, and continental margins also presented many problems in a nondrifting world. Continental drift *per se* did not solve these problems, but the mechanism of plate tectonics did.

The idea of continental drift was finally accepted after paleomagnetic evidence showed that the poles of the geologic past had moved about the globe. The evidence also pointed to multiple poles at any one time. The constraints set by fundamental laws of physics, such as the law of conservation of angular momentum, not to mention the accepted models to account for the earth's magnetic field, clearly indicated that the continents had moved, not the poles. There was no alternative but to accept continental drift, even though geophysicists were unable to agree on a possible mechanism.

By the middle of the twentieth century, geologists had gone about as far as they could on the basis of what they knew of the geology of the continents. Further advances had to await the exploration of the ocean basins. In turn, the deep-sea investigations were largely dependent upon technological developments, including acoustical sounding methods, deep-sea drilling, and seismic surveys.

The ocean basins revealed a wealth of new data. An understanding of the significance of midocean ridges, reinforced by paleomagnetic studies of the sea floor that revealed magnetic stripes parallel to the ridges, led to the concept of seafloor spreading, which described the creation of new oceanic crust along the midocean ridges.

The distribution of heat flow relative to midocean ridges and deep-sea trenches indicated some kind of convectional mechanism for seafloor spreading. Seismological, geomagnetic, and gravity studies also pointed in this direction. Surface manifestations of this convection mechanism are midocean ridges, or spreading centers, as well as trench regions that mark zones of subduction. Hot mantle material rising below the spreading centers creates new oceanic crust. Movement from this hot, rising segment of the convection cell to the cool, descending segment at the subduction zone is seen as movement of the surface of the lithosphere.

From all of the accumulated evidence for continental drift emerged the theory of plate tectonics—the concept that the earth's surface is divided into distinct, rigid, slowly moving lithospheric plates. Three types of lithospheric plate boundaries are possible: divergent boundaries at spreading centers, convergent boundaries at subduction zones, and translational boundaries where two adjacent plate surfaces are sliding past each other.

Continental drift occurs because the continental blocks form part of the lithospheric plates. As the surfaces of the plates move from spreading centers, where new plate material is generated, to subduction zones, where it is destroyed, the continents move also. Plate collision at subduction zones involves the sinking of one plate below the other. As lithospheric plate material is carried down into the mantle, it melts and produces magma that moves upward. When a continent is involved at a collision margin, whether it is a continent-to-ocean or continent-to-continent collision, compressive forces produce fold mountains.

Wilson suggested that the movement of continental blocks on lithospheric surfaces is cyclical, a theory that also explains the mystery of geosynclines and why they go through an accumulative phase followed by a compressive phase.

The movement of the lithospheric plates is the surface expression of large-scale movements in the mantle. A two-tiered convection system, in which a broad convectional system is driven by more complex convectional movements deeper in the mantle, is likely. Positive gravity anomalies reflect hot, rising currents in the mantle, while negative anomalies are found where the mantle is sinking in a cool region. Hot spots mark the location of plumes of rising, hot mantle material that apparently remain stationary over long periods of time.

Questions

1. Discuss some of the earliest ideas on continental drift. Who is usually associated with the first scientific approach to the problem?
2. Why were land bridges in places where there are now major oceans an unacceptable explanation of some of the peculiarities in animal and plant distribution from continent to continent?
3. Why, despite an abundance of evidence, was the idea of continental drift so long in gaining acceptance?
4. What are fold mountains? List as many examples as you can, and indicate their location on a world map outline.
5. What was an early, preplate-tectonic model suggested to explain fold mountains?
6. Why did early workers find it so difficult to explain the evolution of geosynclines?
7. Describe how geosynclines were discovered in the nineteenth century and how modern discoveries have explained their evolution.
8. Other than paleontological/biological evidence for continental drift, what other direct evidence is there?
9. Why was the development of the modern plate-tectonic model only possible after the invention of echo-sounding devices for mapping the ocean floor?
10. In moving away from a midocean ridge in either direction, the ocean floor becomes progressively older and deeper. Why?
11. What special role did the oceanic trenches play in understanding the mechanism of plate tectonics?
12. On a world map, mark in and name the major lithospheric plates.
13. Describe the different kinds of lithospheric plate boundaries.
14. What is a Wilson Cycle?
15. What kind of evidence points to small-scale convectional movement in the mantle?

Further Reading

Bonatti E. 1987. The rifting of continents. *Scientific American* 256:96–103.

Briggs, J. C. 1988. *Biogeography and plate tectonics*. Amsterdam, Netherlands: Elsevier.

Nance, R. D., T. R. Worsley, and J. B. Moody. 1988. The supercontinental cycle. *Scientific American* 259:72–79.

Windley, B. F. 1977. *The evolving continents*. London: Wiley.

9

THE NEW UNIFORMITARIANISM

Introduction

As discussed in Chapter 1, the nineteenth century began with the idea that earth history could be defined by a series of catastrophes and successive creations. Because of the work of Smith, Lyell, Darwin, and others, the century closed with a very different view of the world: A very old age for the earth had been established, and geologic processes were seen as uniformly continuous. In short, the overall philosophy was one of uniformitarianism. To be sure, catastrophes happened occasionally, but they were seen as only minor interruptions in a smooth flow of history.

In recent years, it has become increasingly clear that geologic history is not uniformly continuous, and so the simplistic version of uniformitarianism has been largely abandoned. Instead, a modified philosophy is emerging in which not only are periodic interruptions of the otherwise smooth flow of geologic history being recognized, but they are seen as equal in importance to the periods between them. In particular, many of these "interruptions" are, in fact, related to or parts of cycles of varying magnitude. Cycles, both terrestrial and extraterrestrial, profoundly influence earth history. They are of differing periodicity, and their interactions often result in complex and not always easy to discern consequences. Geologic history and virtually every geologic process are markedly episodic and cyclical.

As the traditional uniformitarianism model underwent modification, the term *catastrophic uniformitarianism* was suggested for the new doctrine. In fact, a much better label for the new ideas is **cyclical uniformitarianism** because cyclical events are evident in virtually everything we observe—even many of the so-called catastrophes seem to fit into a cyclical framework.

Because of the cyclicity of geologic history, many historical geology texts are criticized for engaging in needless repetition, for simply giving an account of "the seas went in, and the seas went out." This chapter discusses the common denominators of the many cycles—both large and small, terrestrial and extraterrestrial—discerned in geologic history so that repetition can be minimized in subsequent chapters. An important objective is to see how cycles interact and how the connection between cause and effect may not always be obvious.

Extraterrestrial Cycles

Events on the earth cannot be divorced from what is happening beyond the earth. Definite connections are sometimes apparent.

Studies of the behavior and motions of moons, planets, and stars show a number of extraterrestrial cycles, from the simple daily cycle of the earth's rotation to cycles measured in hundreds of millions of years. For example, the galactic year—the time during which our galaxy completes one rotation—has been variously calculated as 200 to 400 million years. Most of the cycles are concerned with the relative positions of the heavenly bodies, but at least two apparent cycles in the behavior of the sun have been determined: One is the 11-year cycle of sunspot activity, and the other is a maxima and minima cycle of sunspot of approximately 1,000 years.

Few of these extraterrestrial cycles appear to be related to events on the earth. Of course, this has not stopped people from trying to find connections. In fact, the search for matches between cycles detected in terrestrial phenomena and extraterrestrial cycles of the same frequency has been the excuse for innumerable papers since the early days of science. Sometimes, there does seem to be a match and, presumably, a cause-and-effect relationship, even though the mechanism involved is, as yet, undiscovered. The lunar cycle, for example, can be matched with numerous cycles on earth, physical and biological, as well as with those involving a whole range of human activities, from the behavior of those unfortunate people formerly termed "lunatics," to liquor sales. Various biological cycles of 11 years also have been described, although the mechanisms of the connection with sunspot cycles are, as yet, obscure. In some cases, there is, presumably, a linkage through several other, perhaps subtle, cycles in weather or climatic variables.

Insolation Cycles

Astronomers had known for many years that the distance from the earth to the sun varies over given time intervals and that the obliquity of the earth's axis of rotation also varies through time. In 1855, mathematician Urban-Jean-Joseph Le Verrier was the first to calculate the lengths of the cycles, and his work was later refined in 1904 by Ludwig Pilgrim. There are three cycles:

1. The so-called **precession of the equinoxes** is a cycle of about 19,000 to 23,000 years, during which the time of the year when the earth is closest to the sun (at **perihelion**) varies systematically. Currently, the earth is furthest from the sun (at **aphelion**) during the Northern Hemisphere summer and closest during the Southern Hemisphere summer; hence, the seasons differ more noticeably in the Southern Hemisphere than they do in the Northern Hemisphere.
2. The obliquity of the earth's axis of rotation also varies cyclically. Currently, the earth's axis is inclined at 23.5° from the vertical, but in the past, it has varied from 21.8° to 24.4°, going from maximum tilt to minimum and back to maximum again in 41,000 years. The greater the obliquity, the greater the contrast between summers and winters.

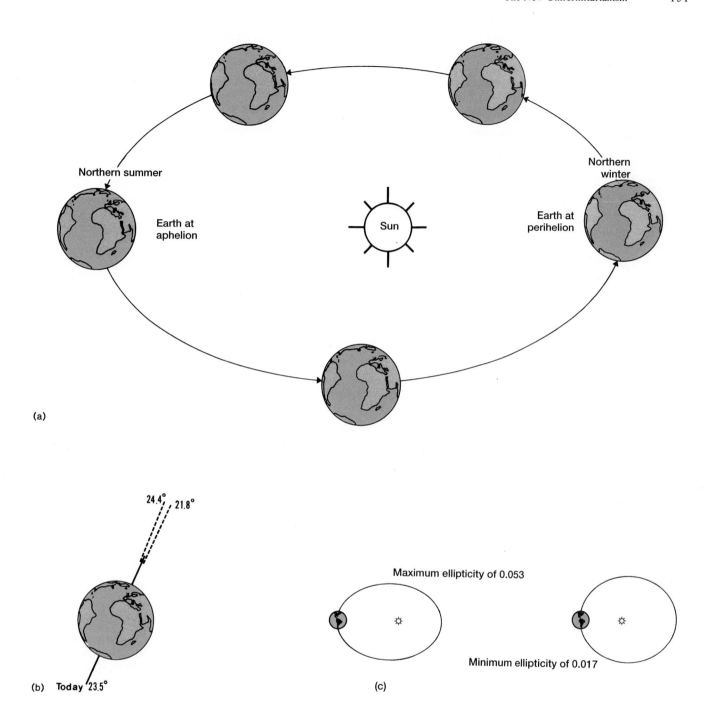

FIGURE 9.1

Insolation cycles. (a) The precession of the equinoxes, 19,000 to 23,000 years. (b) Axial tilt, 41,000 years. (c) Ellipticity of the earth's orbit, 90,000 to 100,000 years.

3. The ellipticity of the earth's orbit changes cyclically over an interval varying between 90,000 and 100,000 years. The shape of the orbit ranges from one that is almost circular (ellipticity of 0.017) to one with an ellipticity of 0.053 (that is, an ellipticity of from less than 1 percent to over 6 percent).

Each of these cycles influences the amount of the sun's energy that reaches various parts of the earth, so the cycles are manifested in what are known as **insolation cycles** (Figure 9.1). The effects of the aphelion/perihelion cycle, for example, are felt most at the equator and have little influence in high latitudes. On the other hand, the wobble in the earth's axis has a small but noticeable effect that is at a maximum at the poles and that diminishes equatorward. Calculations indicate that the earth's elliptical orbit cycle may cause variations in overall insolation values of as much as 30 percent.

The Milankovitch-Köppen Effect

Because the insolation cycles have different effects and are, moreover, of different frequencies, they sometimes cancel each other out and sometimes augment each other. The three cycles plotted together allow the calculation of a master curve showing their cumulative effects. Yugoslav meteorologist Miluntin Milankovitch did this in 1941 and, in collaboration with German climatologist Wladimir Köppen, proposed a master curve to depict the likely effects on world climate over extended intervals. Because the insolation cycles probably have not changed much since the early days of the solar system, the **Milankovitch-Köppen effect** has presumably been affecting world climates through much of geologic history.

The effects are most noticeable during ice ages. Better documentation and dating of the advances and recessions of the ice sheets during the Late Cenozoic glaciation, together with many other climatic indicators, show that the changes occur within rhythmic cycles that correspond to the insolation cycles of the Milankovitch-Köppen effect. More recently, climate-sensitive sedimentary successions, even during nonglacial periods, also are being shown to demonstrate rhythmic changes of similar frequency (Figure 9.2).

Terrestrial Cycles

As described in Chapter 8, the plate-tectonic paradigm proved to be a great unifying theory that solved many geologic mysteries. Although plate-tectonic mechanisms have come to be fairly well understood, what is not clear is why spreading centers and subduction zones appear and disappear. Are they random events or self-regulating, as when a subduction zone apparently becomes "smothered" by a continental mass? Alternatively, is some kind of terrestrial cyclical behavior involved?

The Wilson Cycle

As mentioned in Chapter 8, J. Tuzo Wilson of the University of Toronto suggested that the Atlantic Ocean (the result of the rifting of the North American continent from Eurasia and Gondwana) had replaced an earlier ocean that had closed when the ancestral North American and European blocks had collided above a subduction zone. This was the basis of what became known as the Wilson Cycle (as discussed in Chapter 8), encompassing the total life history of an ocean basin—from its birth at the sundering of continents along spreading centers to its eventual disappearance as two continents collide. Based on the history of the North Atlantic, a Wilson Cycle apparently lasted an estimated 400 million years. The problem with such long cycles is that, within a second cycle, we are back into the Precambrian, where the geologic record rapidly becomes much more obscure.

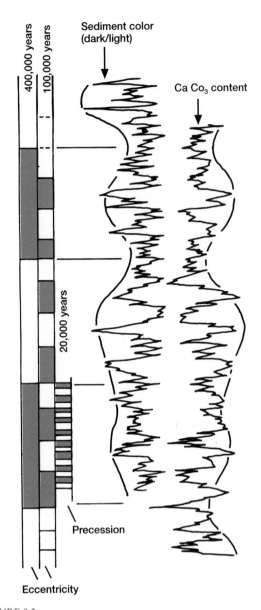

FIGURE 9.2

Signatures of the Milankovitch-Köppen effect in a nonglacial succession. The 400,000- and 100,000-year eccentricity cycles contain "bundles" of high-frequency (precession-related) 21,000-year cycles seen in low-carbonate/high-carbonate bedding couplets. This example is from a core taken in an Albian (Cretaceous) limestone succession in Italy.

In Precambrian terrains, the direct evidence for continental drift in terms of ancient rifts and collision sutures is not easy to find. One of the most useful approaches in deciphering cycles of crustal movement in these very old rocks involves using the apparent polar-wandering curve (see Box 9.1). Because, of course, the continents moved and not the poles, the wanderings of the ancient cratons as far back as the late Archean are becoming known.

BOX 9.1

Cycles and the Apparent Polar-Wandering Curve

The apparent polar-wandering curve plotted from observations at North American sites consists of several relatively smooth segments separated by sharp bends. Over long periods, ranging from 200 to 600 million years, the continent moved along in a uniform path but then suddenly changed direction, often almost doubling back on itself.

In 1972, the smooth segments of the curve were named "tracks" by E. Irving and J. Park, and the sharp kinks "hairpins." Irving and Park then proposed a division of Precambrian time based on the apparent polar-wandering curve (Box Figure 9.1). They identified the following five superintervals, or tracks, each one separated by a hairpin:

	Hairpin 50	2,500 million years
Track 5	2,500–1,950 million years	
	Hairpin 40	1,950 million years
Track 4	1,950–1,300 million years	
	Hairpin 30	1,300 million years
Track 3	1,300–1,100 million years	
	Hairpin 20	1,100 million years
Track 2	1,100–450 million years	
	Hairpin 10	450 million years
Track 1	450 million years	
	Hairpin 6	320 million years
	Hairpin 2	90 million years

This pattern of continental drift could possibly be linked with the Worsley, Nance, and Moody model with the hairpins marking orogenies due to continental collision and Pangaea accretion.

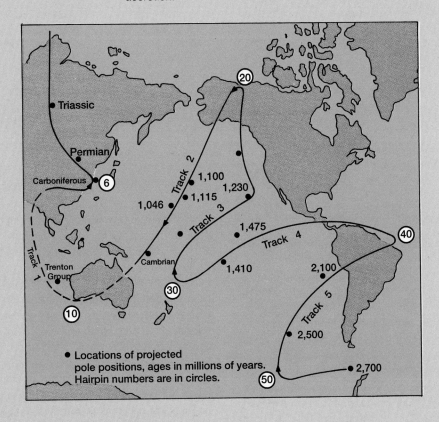

BOX FIGURE 9.1
Apparent polar-wandering curve for North America, showing the tracks and hairpins used by Irving and Park (1972) as the basis for a division of Precambrian time.

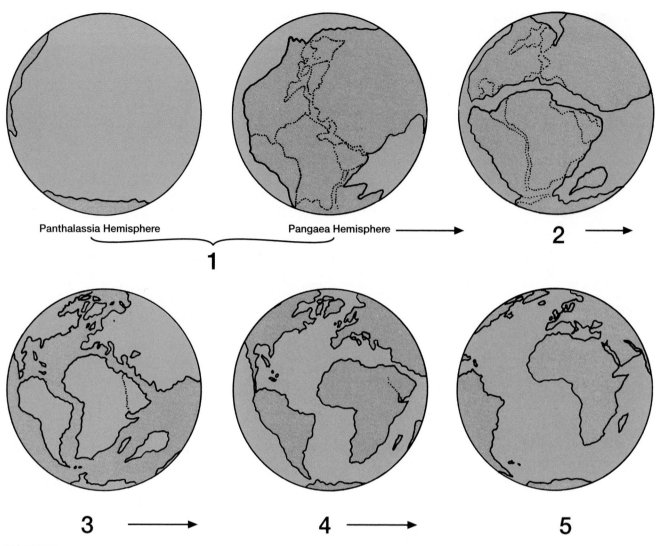

Panthalassia Hemisphere   Pangaea Hemisphere ⟶   2 ⟶

1

3 ⟶   4 ⟶   5

FIGURE 9.3

Worsley, Nance, and Moody model: from Pangaea
configuration to continent dispersal.

The Worsley, Nance, and Moody Model

The search for an underlying mechanism for the Wilson
Cycles led to the possibility that plate-tectonic movements as a whole are not random but occur in cycles. According to the **Worsley, Nance, and Moody model,**
developed by Worsley, Nance, and Moody at Ohio University, the cycles—each lasting about 440 million years—
can be traced back to a beginning over 2,500 million years
ago. They are the result of an initial global asymmetry in
the distribution of continental and oceanic crust, one
hemisphere being dominated by ocean (the **Panthalassia
Hemisphere**) and the other by continent (the **Pangaea
Hemisphere**) (Figure 9.3). The asymmetry of ocean and
continent distribution was reflected in a corresponding
asymmetry in the pattern of heat transfer from the earth's
interior, heat transfer being more efficient through the
ocean hemisphere so that it is, essentially, a permanent

area of mantle upwelling. On the present-day globe, this
area is marked by the Pacific Ocean.

A Pangaea assembled by collision of cratons is potentially self-destructive and relatively short-lived. This is
because the poor heat transfer through such a large continental mass results in a buildup of heat and an expansion
of the crust known as **thermal doming,** and eventually,
Pangaea is rifted, and new continental fragments drift
apart. The newly formed rifts and progressively widening
ocean basins effectively cool the thermal dome. Once
thermal dome heat dissipation is complete, the convectional pattern associated with the oceanic Panthalassia
hemisphere becomes dominant again, and the cratons are
driven back toward collision and the assembly of a new
Pangaea.

In the present-day configuration of continents, Africa
is believed to be the remnant of the former thermal dome
of Pangaea. Interestingly, the global distribution of hot

TABLE 9.1

Causes of Relative Change of Sea Level

Eustatic (worldwide) changes	Noneustatic (local and regional) changes
Changes in volume of ocean water	*Regression*
Changes in volume of land ice (up to 150 meters at 1 centimeter/year)	Epeirogenic upwarping (broad, regional uplift)
Desiccation of basins (15 meters + at 1 centimeter/year)	Postglacial rebound
Changes in mean oceanic temperatures (1 meter/°C)	Uplift and/or faulting in tectonically active areas
	Depositional progradation
Changes in volume of ocean basins	*Transgression*
Variations in volume of oceanic ridge (300 meters at 1 centimeter/1,000 years)	Epeirogenic downwarping (broad, regional subsidence)
Flooding of continental crust and formation of ocean trenches	Sinking along hinge line of postglacial uplift
Sedimentation (few meters at 1 centimeter/1,000 years)	Thermal subsidence of crust
	Downwarping and/or faulting in tectonically active areas
	Sinking of coastal tract due to compaction of underlying sediment
	Coastal retreat due to active erosion

spots in the mantle seems to support this model because by far the biggest hot spot concentration occurs in Africa. Africa is considered stationary and essentially surrounded by spreading centers that, together with the further cratons beyond, are pushing away toward the Panthalassia convection system centered on the Pacific.

If this model is correct, the Pacific Ocean, unlike the other oceans, has been a permanent ocean since very early in earth history, and this would explain why no geologic evidence has ever indicated collision or juxtaposition of western North America and eastern Asia.

The earth's interior heat, convective movements, and variations in the rate of heat flow, as proposed in the fundamental plate-tectonic model, are accepted as the basic mechanism involved in the cycle. In the Worsley, Nance, and Moody model, however, cratons themselves have some influence on the pattern of convectional movements, rather than being randomly jostled about. In other words, cratons may control the convection cells, rather than the other way around.

Cycles of Sea-Level Change

Changes in the relative level of land and sea result, as discussed in previous chapters, in marine transgressions and regressions. Clearly, both up and down movements of the land and of the ocean level can be involved, and locally, it may be difficult to establish which mechanism is responsible. Typically, the effects of sea-level fluctuations due to local tectonic movements of the crust are superimposed on eustatic sea-level change. In addition, evidence is growing that crustal movements of cratonwide or even global scale also may be involved. The causes of sea-level fluctuations are summarized in Table 9.1. Clearly, only a few of these cause changes of significant magnitude to be reflected in the stratigraphic record.

Long-Term Changes

Certain widespread marine transgressions and regressions extending over many millions of years and approximately simultaneous on a worldwide scale were noted from the earliest days of geology. The great wedges of sediment bounded by regional unconformities known as sequences and discussed in Chapter 5 are evidence of extensive floodings onto all the cratons.

With increasingly accurate biostratigraphic data and, in particular, a wealth of new information from boreholes and seismic studies of the sedimentary wedges along the continental margins, sea-level changes over time can be plotted on a chart. Such graphic plots, or sea-level curves as they are known, are based on local sea-level plots from many different parts of the world. Averaging the values presumably filters out the effects of "noise" produced by local tectonic effects. The end result is a supposedly "pure" eustatic sea-level curve.

The major cycles of sea-level change span tens of millions of years and are believed to be caused by subcrustal changes associated with plate-tectonic mechanisms, particularly by variations in the rate of seafloor spreading. The rate of movement of the lithospheric plates apparently changes over time, and this is particularly manifested in the rate of accretion of new crustal material at the spreading center. When the rate of subcrustal heat flow and the upwelling of mantle material increases, the volume of the midocean ridges also increases. This thermal swelling reduces the total volume of the ocean basin, resulting in a eustatic rise in sea level.

Although the apparently simultaneous worldwide sea-level change can be explained most simply by a eustatic mechanism, some geologists are beginning to believe that this may not be the whole story. Laurence Sloss and

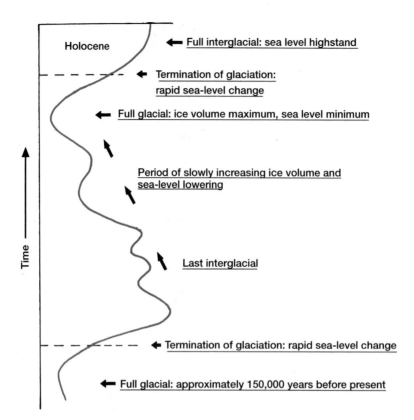

FIGURE 9.4

Late Cenozoic glaciation. A typical glacio-eustatic sea-level curve over a 100,000-year cycle.

Andrew Speed suggested in 1974 that long-distance correlation between local sea-level curves should not automatically be ascribed to eustatic changes and might in some cases be due to crustal movements on a global scale. According to their model, the movement of subcrustal melt in the mantle undergoes periodic change, with consequent effects on processes of solid-melt transformation in the asthenosphere. As heat flow into the asthenosphere increases, the melt fraction becomes thicker, and overlying continental crust is pushed upward. The scale of movement is cratonwide or global, so that a eustatic-like fall in sea level results. Once a critical melt concentration is reached beneath the cratons, there is outward flow of material and the cratons subside. At the same time, the rate of seafloor spreading increases, both of these processes resulting in marine transgression.

Cycles of sea-level change can also be explained in terms of the Worsly, Nance, and Moody model of continental accretion and splitting, discussed earlier in the chapter. The Pangaea stage in the cycle is marked by sea-level fall because ocean floors are at their oldest and maximum degree of cooling and subsidence. At the same time, the continental crust is elevated by thermal doming. On the breakup of Pangaea, continental crust is stretched, and the increase in total continental area reduces the volume of the ocean basins, both of these processes resulting in sea-level rise.

Short-Term Changes

The most obvious short-term eustatic sea-level changes are those caused by fluctuations in the volume of ice caps. As ice caps melt, water is released into the oceans and sea levels rise; conversely, advance of the ice results in sea-level fall. As described earlier in the chapter, ice cap advance and retreat during ice ages likely is controlled largely by the Milankovitch-Köppen effect, but because of complex feedback and nonuniform effects, ice caps do not advance and retreat at the same rate. At least in the case of the 100,000-year cycle seen in the Late Cenozoic ice sheet fluctuations, ice sheets grew slowly over a period of about 90,000 years. Melting of the ice cap is rapid and occurs in 10,000 to 15,000 years, so sea-level rise is correspondingly rapid (Figure 9.4).

Evidence from past ice ages, as well as from the earlier part of the Cenozoic age, suggests that this asymmetrical shape for the cycle of advance and retreat may vary. Much still needs to be learned about the complex interplay of the various cycles involved.

Apart from glacial advance and retreat, the only other known mechanism to account for short-term changes in eustatic sea level is the desiccation of isolated marine basins. As continents and oceans move in the constantly shifting pattern driven by plate-tectonic mechanisms, basins become isolated and eventually lose their water by

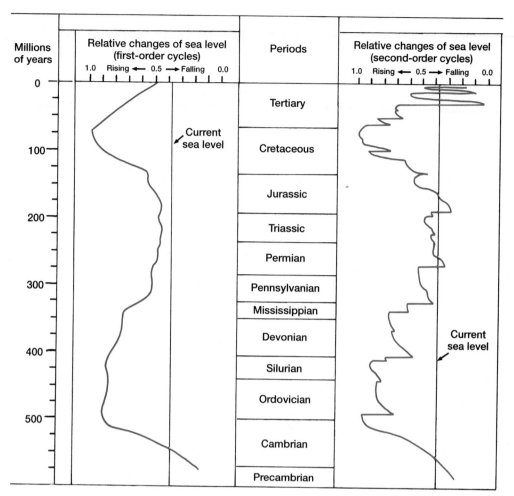

FIGURE 9.5
Original Vail sea-level curve published in 1977. (See also Box 9.2.)

evaporation. The drying up of the Mediterranean in the Late Miocene is an example and is described in Chapter 20. Sea-level fluctuations caused by alternation of isolation and flooding are probably not great and, in any event, are not caused by a mechanism with any marked regularity.

The Vail Curve

The most comprehensive approach to the question of a global sea-level curve was that by Peter Vail and his associates at Exxon Corporation. Their study, first published in 1977, was based on a very large body of data on the subsurface geology of the continental margins derived from thousands of seismic surveys, many with borehole tie-ins. Detected within the thick sedimentary successions beneath the continental shelves were numerous "packages" of seismic reflectors separated by surfaces of discontinuity marked by reflection terminations. These discordant surfaces were interpreted as marking episodes of coastal onlap during marine transgressions (see Box 9.2). The close coincidence in timing of the various episodes at many localities on different continents persuaded Vail that the sea-level changes were eustatic in origin.

The **Vail sea-level curve** compiled from these data showed that sea-level changes have been occurring within three cycles: (1) first-order cycles with a wavelength of 200 to 400 million years, (2) second-order cycles with a wavelength of 10 to 80 million years, and (3) third-order cycles with a wavelength of 1 to 10 million years. The curve as originally published had a rather peculiar "sawtooth" shape, with sea level rising relatively slowly, but falling very rapidly, indeed almost instantaneously (Figure 9.5).

Based as it was on an enormous body of data of the kind unavailable outside of major oil companies, the Vail curve aroused much interest. Not only did it provide much information that was entirely new, but Exxon geologists also used it in a rather novel way—as a primary stratigraphic correlation tool.

Although the Vail curve was generally applauded as an outstanding contribution, there was, not surprisingly, some criticism as well. In particular, the marked asymmetry of the sea-level cycles implied by the sawtooth shape of the curve raised questions with many geologists. They

BOX 9.2

Box Figure 9.2 shows the pattern of sedimentary units that would result from an interpretation of a seismic survey of a shelf margin. The bulk of the sediment does not accumulate in a vertical direction simply by bed piled upon bed. Rather, the sediments are built out largely in a horizontal direction because the shelf is a shallow-water environment. Thus, as fast as sediment settles, it is picked up and moved on by waves and currents. Only off the outer, deeper edge of the shelf is a net accumulation of sediment possible.

During times of low sea level, much of the inner shelf is exposed to subaerial erosion, and earlier deposited sediments are removed. When sea level rises again, new sediments are spread across the eroded surface, which is marked by an unconformity (see part 1 of Box Figure 9.2). On seismic surveys, such unconformities are usually seen as a truncation of this inclined reflecting horizon. Such truncation surfaces divide the total seismic section into a series of reflection packages, each one depicting a cycle of sea-level change.

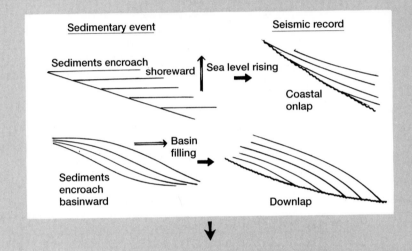

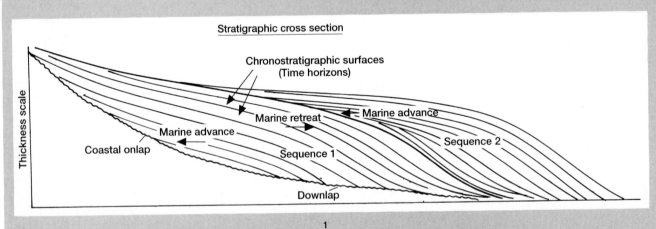

BOX FIGURE 9.2
Typical stratigraphic cross section on a shelf margin.

Seismic surveys do not, of course, contain any intrinsic age indicators, but boreholes at strategic locations provide biostratigraphic data and allow sedimentary horizons to be tied into the seismic picture. Once this is done, the whole succession can be redrawn with the vertical depth scale replaced by a time scale, as shown in part 2 of Box Figure 9.2.

In the third step, shown in part 3 of Box Figure 9.2, a coastal onlap curve can be constructed from the erosional unconformities. Finally, certain corrections are made to account for crustal and sedimentary subsidence and for interpretation of nearshore sedimentary facies. Part 4 of Box Figure 9.2 shows the resultant sea-level curve.

Matching of such sea-level curves from continent to continent strongly

suggests that local tectonic effects ("noise") are eliminated and that the sea-level curve represents an actual eustatic curve. This may not be the whole story, however, because even continental shelves thousands of kilometers apart may experience similar histories of uplift and subsidence, and those appearances of eustatic control may be illusory.

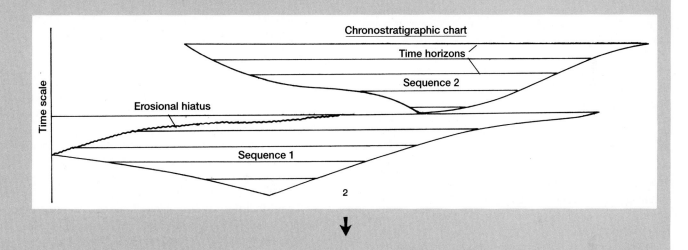

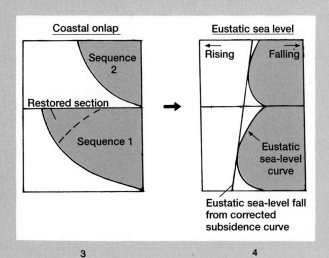

saw the mechanisms responsible for sea-level fluctuations, with the possible exception of glacio-eustatic changes, operating at about the same rate in both directions; in other words, they believed that a curve showing sea-level rise and then fall should be symmetrical.

In later versions of the curve, the sawtooth shape was largely smoothed out. Apparently, limitations of the seismic tool had resulted in misinterpretations of coastal plain and strandline (shoreline) deposits so as to show sea level still rising when, in fact, the transgression had peaked and sea level was already falling again. In the original version of the curve, there had been no room for the regressive phase sediments—hence, the flat, virtually instantaneous sea-level fall.

In addition to the curve's shape, Vail's explanations for the causes of the three cycles of sea-level change also raised many questions. With the long-term (first-order) cycles, there was no problem; variations in the rate of sea-floor spreading or similar plate-tectonic mechanisms could adequately explain them. With third-order cycles, there was no problem either, provided that there was evidence of an ice age. Presumably, the expansion and contraction of ice caps and glacio-eustatic sea-level shifts could account for those cycles. Serious problems over mechanisms did arise, however, when third-order cycles occurred during periods that appeared to have been ice-free. Similarly, plausible mechanisms for the second-order cycles were in markedly short supply. On the other hand, the Worsely, Nance, and Moody model, discussed earlier in the chapter, might provide an answer in suggesting that continent-to-continent collisions occurred frequently enough to cause sea-level fluctuations in a cycle of the right frequency.

The numerous problems with the Vail curve were not helped by the fact that details regarding a critical part of the curve had been left out because they were based on proprietary information that was thus inaccessible to the scientific community at large. Also, only the massive resources available to a major oil company made such studies possible. Thus, opportunities for testing the Vail curve by repeating the study or by acquiring fresh data were clearly out of the question.

More recently, studies, including one based on the same mass of seismic data and borehole logs (this time from British Petroleum), have suggested that major marine transgressions and regressions were caused not only by long-term eustatic changes linked to plate tectonics, but also to changes in the rate of basin subsidence and variations in the amount of sediment supplied to the basin. In addition, coincidence of sea-level curves from either side of an ocean basin may also be simply a consequence of a shared basin history. After all, it would indeed be surprising if the South American and west African margins of the South Atlantic had not had similar tectonic histories since the time of their separation.

Ice Age Cycles

The waxing and waning of ice sheets during an ice age seem to be fairly well understood in terms of the insolation cycles of the Milankovitch-Köppen effect. What is still unknown, however, is the cause of the ice ages themselves.

When Phanerozoic history is reviewed as a whole, there have been three major ice ages: one in the Ordovician, one in the Permo-Carboniferous, and one in the Late Cenozoic, which, of course, we are currently living in (Figure 9.6). Because neither the length of the ice age nor the periodicity seem to be regular, linking the cause of ice ages to other cycles is not easy. Inevitably, speculation has involved extraglactic causes, one of the more imaginative being a connection between the ice ages and variations in strength of the central galactic force (the gravitational field of the galaxy), which is, in turn, related to the cycle of the galactic year. How variations in the gravitational force of the galaxy cause ice ages is not clear. Changes in world climate could also be caused by small changes in the sun's energy output, but again, there is no convincing evidence to support the idea.

One of the more plausible mechanisms suggested to date for causing ice ages is entirely terrestrial and a consequence of continental drift, particularly as it influences oceanic circulation. World climate is and always has been strongly influenced by movement of the oceans on a planetary scale. Together with the atmosphere, the oceans provide an effective heat transfer mechanism and undoubtedly play a leading role in the initiation of an ice age. They do this not only by producing the required cooling of adjacent landmasses, but also by supplying the moisture necessary for the snowfall that obviously must nourish a growing ice cap.

Current models used to explain glacial episodes thus require a continent and/or a relatively small ocean basin to be in **thermal isolation** at one or both of the poles. At the present day, for example, the Antarctic continent is entirely surrounded by the Southern Ocean and thus thermally isolated from the other continental masses. In the same way, the Arctic Ocean has only a limited access to the world ocean between Greenland and Norway, and the narrow, shallow Bering Strait effectively isolates the Arctic Ocean from the Pacific. Recent models to explain the growth of the Late Cenozoic ice caps have also pointed to the need for adequate nourishment by snowfall and emphasize the likely role of changes in oceanic circulation and weather patterns. We return to this topic in Chapters 19 and 20.

In another suggestion, some control of the timing of ice ages has been attributed to the Worsley, Nance, and Moody model of Pangaea formation. A Pangaea-sized continent covers 40 percent of the earth's surface, and a random placement of Pangaea results in a 75 percent chance of at least part of the continent being at a pole.

PLATE 23
A typical sandy beach on a low-energy coast, Bowmans Beach,
Sanibel Island on Florida's west coast.

PLATE 24
A coarse shingle beach on South Georgia. Note the well-
rounded shape of the pebbles and cobbles. (Photo courtesy of
Mary Lemon.)

PLATE 25

A storm ridge at the back of a beach, Grand Cayman, West Indies. Waves only reach this part of the beach during major storms, such as hurricanes.

PLATE 26

A fringing reef, Grand Cayman, West Indies. A shallow lagoon lies between the reef and the shore.

PLATE 27

Closeup view of coarse beach gravel derived from coral reef debris, Grand Cayman.

PLATE 28
Shoal areas on the Bahamas Banks at Sweetings Cay, Grand Bahamas. The water over these shoals is typically less than 1 meter deep, and the bottom sediment is oolitic sand.

PLATE 29
Coastal salt flats at Walvis Bay, Southwest Africa.

PLATE 30
Raised Pleistocene beach at Natural Bridge State Park near Santa Cruz, California. This tectonically active coastal region has experienced intermittent crustal uplift during the recent geologic past.

PLATE 31
Raised beach on the coast of Chile, a tectonically active region.
This example, near Antofagasta, compares closely with the one
near Santa Cruz, California (Plate 30). In this case, however,
wave erosion has isolated a sea stack pierced by an arch.

PLATE 32
Three raised beaches in a staircase-like progression are visible
on this segment of coast south of Antofagasta, Chile.

PLATE 33
Typical scenery on the Canadian Shield. A gently undulating
terrain has many swampy hollows and small lakes. On the
higher ground, the soils are thin or absent, scraped bare by the
Wisconsin ice sheet, as seen in this picture. The vegetation is
largely dwarf spruce and pine, together with birch and alder.

PLATE 34
Rhyolitic dikes intruding greenstones on the Canadian Shield.

PLATE 35
Archean granites and gneisses of the African Shield exposed in
the Namibian desert.

PLATE 36
Stromatolites that are 3,500 million years old, in the Pilbara region of Western Australia. (Photograph courtesy of K. J. McNamara, Western Australia Museum, Perth, Western Australia.)

PLATE 37
Bulbous stromatolites in the intertidal zone at Hamelin Pool, Shark Bay, Western Australia. (Photograph courtesy of K. J. McNamara, Western Australia Museum, Perth, Western Australia.)

PLATE 38
Proterozoic sediments of the Egalulik Group, northern Baffin Island, Northwest Territories, Canada. Here they are discon-formably overlain by Lower Ordovician sandstones that form the upper cliffs in this picture.

PLATE 39
Chilhowee Mountain in eastern Tennessee. The Precambrian-Cambrian boundary occurs in the succession on the left of the picture. The Great Smoky Mountains, underlain by Precambrian rocks, are in the distance.

PLATE 40
Basal Cambrian quartzitic sandstones at Rockville in southwestern Colorado.

PLATE 41
A party from the Royal Ontario Museum excavating the Burgess
Shale at a quarry on Mount Stephen near Field, British Colum-
bia. This site is 8 kilometers south of Walcott's original find.
(Photograph courtesy of Des Collins, Royal Ontario Museum,
Toronto.)

PLATE 42
Ordovician sandstones and shales exposed on the west face of
the Uluksan Peninsula, Baffin Island, Northwest Territories,
Canada.

PLATE 43
Basal beds of the Ordovician Turner Cliffs Formation above the
red sandstones of the Gallery Formation, Baffin Island.

While the Pangaea phase of the Permo-Triassic overlapped in time with the Permo-Carboniferous ice age, the present-day ice age is occurring at a time of maximum continental dispersal.

As the foregoing discussion indicates, opinions are still divided regarding a basic cause of ice ages. For the moment, at least, this issue remains in the "unsolved mysteries" category.

Mass Extinction Cycles

The discussion of mass extinctions in Chapter 4 suggested that such events might have occurred periodically, the interval indicated by one study being 26 million years. Such cyclicity calls for a reexamination of mass extinctions in this chapter on cycles.

High on the list of possible causes of mass extinctions is meteorite (or cometary) impact. Good evidence indicates that such an impact caused the terminal Cretaceous extinction, and of the five other major extinctions recorded during the Phanerozoic, one other and possibly a third may also have been due to similar catastrophes. Among the many and various mechanisms proposed as the cause of mass extinctions, cosmic impacts have a certain appeal because their suddenness cannot be denied. Unfortunately, cosmic impacts are not the only causes of mass extinctions because, despite diligent searching, no unequivocal evidence (iridium anomalies, shocked quartz, and so on) for large body impacts has been found at the other extinction boundaries.

Therefore, mass extinctions must also have been, on occasion, caused by other kinds of events—climatic changes, shifts in oceans chemistry, sea-level drops, anoxic events, and so on. The problem with most of these is that it is difficult to imagine them happening very rapidly without some kind of threshold, or triggering, event. Also, the many and various links among organisms through complex food chains suggest that relatively small changes in one environmental parameter might have a domino effect through a whole spectrum of organisms.

With regard to the question of regular periodicity in mass extinctions, a demonstrated extinction cycle would have an important bearing on the question of causative mechanisms. For one thing, a regular cyclicity would weaken the case for terrestrial causes of mass extinctions and would instead point in the direction of a link with extraterrestrial events.

The whole question of mass extinctions and the mechanisms responsible has, of course, raised a good deal of controversy, and suggestions that they occur at regular intervals have particularly come under fire. Naturally, the validity of the statistical supporting data has been the object of special scrutiny. With this in mind, the proponents of a 26-million-year cycle in mass extinctions—

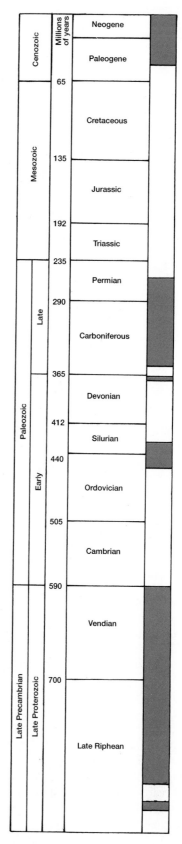

FIGURE 9.6

Ice ages (indicated by shading) through the Late Precambrian and the Phanerozoic.

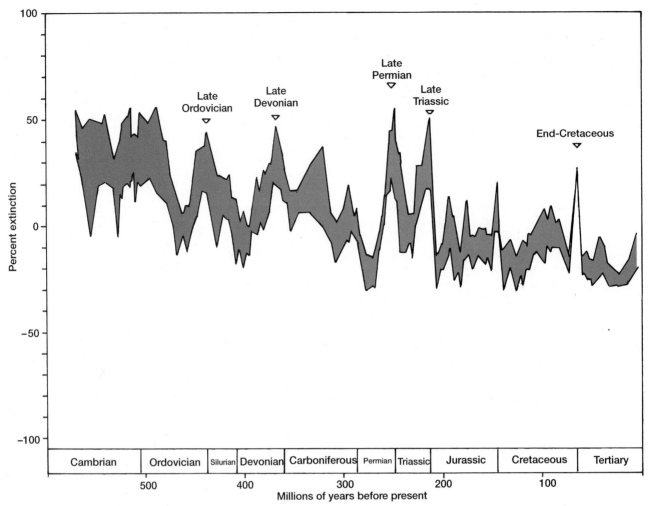

FIGURE 9.7

Extinction profiles from 10 samples of 1,000 genera chosen
at random from a data set of 19,897.

David Raup and John Sepkoski of the University of Chicago—conducted studies based on statistical tests of unusual rigor. One study involved 19,897 fossil genera and
concluded that a pattern of largely congruent rises and
falls in extinction intensity did exist and that the most
likely explanation was a physical and external cause rather
than a biological one (Figure 9.7). On the other hand, Ajoy
Baski of Louisiana State University argues that the 26-
million-year cycle and other suggested periodicities "result
from subjective use of radiometric data," rather than from
real extraterrestrial causes.

Assuming, for the moment, that the cyclicity of mass
extinctions is real, the obvious place to begin a search for
a causative mechanism is, as noted at the beginning of this
chapter, among matching cosmic cycles. The only one that
comes close is a 31- to 33-million-year cycle during which
the solar system, in its rotation around the galactic center,
passes through the galactic plane. At such a time, radiation levels supposedly increase, as does the likelihood of
encounters with interstellar dust and gas.

In 1970, C. Hatfield and M. Camp suggested that the
increased dosages of cosmic radiation might be the cause
of mass extinctions. Possible effects on world climate have
also been suggested as providing the necessary link with
mass extinctions. In yet another scenario, the **Oort Cloud**
of comets might be disturbed, thereby increasing the likelihood of cometary impact with the earth.

In another approach to the question of a cosmic connection, it has been suggested, as mentioned in Chapter
4, that the sun has a dim companion that has been labeled
Nemesis. The Nemesis idea is an entirely artificial one,
and the supposed cyclicity of its orbit is simply made to
match the apparent extinction cyclicity. The lack of any
direct evidence for the presence of Nemesis is, proponents
argue, because it has simply been missed by astronomers.
Comparatively few stars have been studied in detail, so
Nemesis might be a dim star close to the earth that has
been assumed to be a bright star much further away. Barnard's star has recently been mentioned as a possible
Nemesis candidate.

Slightly less artificial is the **Planet X** idea. Certain perturbations observed in the orbits of Neptune, Pluto, and Uranus have been explained by some astronomers as due to the influence of a tenth, as yet undiscovered, planet lying beyond the orbit of Pluto. Again, the link with terrestrial events is through cometary impacts, the eccentric orbit of Planet X disturbing comets not in the Oort Cloud, but in a much smaller swarm beyond the orbit of Neptune.

Clearly, these various cosmic mechanisms are, to say the least, imaginative, and their confirmation or otherwise awaits the acquisition of more hard data. Interestingly, some supporting evidence already exists in a supposedly regular periodicity detected in the timing of cratering events on the earth. Although many craters are difficult to date, among the 120 or so known craters, a 28-million-year periodicity has been discerned. This does not match the 26-million-year periodicity of mass extinction events but is considered significant. An immediate problem is that, over extended periods, the mass extinction cycle and the cratering cycle become increasingly out of sync, but perhaps the tolerances involved in dating both the cratering events and the mass extinctions allow for this.

Conclusion—A Note of Caution

In this chapter, we have discussed some of the newest concepts in geology. Some of the material is highly speculative and may be proven incorrect or in need of modification. This is the way science works. The results of new research and new ideas are described in scientific journals and invariably generate discussion and sometimes heated controversy. It may take several years for a new concept to become generally accepted, and this usually happens only after other similar studies have provided independent evidence.

In writing a textbook, there are obvious dangers in including discussions of recent studies, especially if the studies deal with controversial topics. At the same time, students need to be exposed to "cutting-edge" research. If the reader of any scientific text comes to the last page and is left with the impression that all the scientific facts in the book are cut-and-dried and proven simply because they are in the book, it is most emphatically the wrong impression. Science can be simply defined as the search for knowledge, and that search never ends.

Summary

Uniformitarianism had become the basic philosophy in geology ever since the abandonment of the catastrophist ideas of the early nineteenth century. In recent years, however, it has become increasingly clear that geologic history does not run smoothly and that geologic processes do not operate continuously and uniformly. Instead, many processes are cyclical and subject to interruptions of greater or lesser magnitude.

Natural cycles operate on earth as well as in the solar system and cosmos. Sometimes, the apparent match between terrestrial cycles seen in geological or biological phenomena on earth and extraterrestrial cycles of various kinds has led to a search for connections. Precise cause-and-effect relationships, however, are usually in considerable doubt.

Apart from monthly lunar cycles with their obvious effect on numerous physical and biological earth cycles, and annual cycles that control the seasons, the clearest connection between extraterrestrial cycles and events on earth is seen in the insolation cycles of the Milankovitch-Köppen effect. The cyclical advance and recession of ice sheets during ice ages matches in periodicity the Milankovitch-Köppen effect, as do many other climatic indicators.

Among terrestrial cycles, one of the longest is the Wilson Cycle, lasting about 400 million years, during which a continent is split by subcrustal convective movements and an ocean forms between the pieces. Separation grows as plate movements away from the spreading center continue. Eventually, changes in the mantle movements lead to the formation of a subduction zone between the continents, and the ocean is closed, finally disappearing as the continents collide.

In an expansion of the Wilson cycle concept, Worsley, Nance, and Moody suggested that the world's continents are continually coming together to form a single supercontinent (Pangaea) and then splitting apart again, with the entire process requiring approximately 440 million years. According to this model, an initial global asymmetry in the distribution of continental crust and oceanic crust resulted in one hemisphere being dominated by continent (the Pangaea Hemisphere) and the other by ocean (the Panthalassia Hemisphere). Heat flow through the ocean crust of the Panthalassia Hemisphere is more efficient than through the thick, poorly conducting Pangaea mass, and so the oceanic hemisphere (today's Pacific Ocean) is essentially an area of permanent mantle upwelling and is also a permanent ocean. On the Pangaean side, the thermal expansion consequent of the poor conductivity leads to the rifting of the continental mass, and the fragments drift apart. Currently, the continents are about at their furthest distance from the site of the original Pangaea, with modern Africa being the remnant of the former thermal dome.

Cycles of eustatic sea-level change have also been important in earth history. With increasingly accurate data and new information, sea-level changes over time can be plotted as sea-level curves. The Vail curve has been the most comprehensive attempt so far to construct a global picture of sea-level changes. Long cycles measured in tens of millions of years are probably due to variations in the rate of seafloor spreading and the volume of mid-ocean ridges. Short cycles driven by the Milankovitch-Köppen cycles and their effect on ice volumes are expected during ice ages. At nonglacial times in earth history, short-term cycles of eustatic sea-level change are less easy to explain. Most likely, a noneustatic component is involved.

Opinions are still divided regarding a basic cause of ice ages, but a plausible mechanism involves how continental drift influences oceanic circulation. Current models used to explain glacial episodes require a continent and/or a relatively small ocean basin to be in thermal isolation at one or both of the poles. Some control of the timing of ice ages has been attributed to the Worsley, Nance, and Moody model of Pangaea formation.

Some evidence indicates that mass extinctions occur every 26 million years.

Such a regular cyclicity tends to rule out nearly all the terrestrial mechanisms as causes of mass extinctions and instead focuses speculation on extraterrestrial causes, especially regularly occurring meteorite or cometary impacts. One theory is that the cyclicity is a result of perturbations in the Oort Cloud of comets that are caused by the regular return, on a

highly eccentric 26-million-year orbit, of a dim companion of the sun that has been named Nemesis. This is all highly speculative as no one has ever observed the Oort Cloud or, for that matter, Nemesis. A somewhat similar model involving cometary showers refers to a Planet X, a tenth, as yet undiscovered planet beyond the orbit of Pluto. Again, there are no hard data.

Questions

1. Why is the uniformitarianism envisioned by Charles Lyell been found in need of modification?
2. List as many extraterrestrial cycles as you can.
3. Describe two apparent cycles that have been detected in the behavior of the sun.
4. Describe the insolation cycles of the Milankovitch-Köppen effect.
5. Describe how climatic cycles and various geologic cycles might be linked.
6. What is meant by the Panthalassia Hemisphere?
7. Describe the three orders of cycles present in the Vail curve.
8. Describe some of the reasons why the Vail curve has not been accepted by many geologists as a true picture of eustatic sea-level change.
9. What is the connection between the Worsley, Nance, and Moody model and major cycles of the Vail curve.
10. Describe some of the alternative mechanisms other than eustatic changes that might account for the Vail curve.
11. Describe why ice ages may be cyclical phenomena.
12. Discuss the evidence for and against the concept of a 26-million-year mass extinction cycle.
13. Explain the concept of the Nemesis star and the Oort Cloud as related to mass extinction cycles.
14. Describe the Planet X hypothesis.
15. In your knowledge of geologic processes, list any that you think might be cyclical.

Further Reading

Ager, D. V. 1981. *The nature of the stratigraphical record.* 2d ed. New York: Macmillan.

Byers, C. W. 1982. Stratigraphy—The fall of continuity. *Journal of Geological Education* 30:215–221.

Lemon, R. R. 1990. *Principles of stratigraphy.* Columbus, Ohio: Merrill.

Umbgrove, J. H. F. 1946. *The pulse of the earth.* The Hague, Netherlands: Martinus Nijhoff.

10

THE ARCHEAN

Introduction

As the geologic systems became properly defined and the geologic timetable as we know it today emerged during the nineteenth century, the older rocks beneath the Cambrian System at first received little attention. For one thing, they were believed to be unfossiliferous. They were also typically metamorphosed and heavily intruded by igneous bodies of various kinds, and their structural relationships were usually quite obscure. In short, they were not the easiest rocks to work with.

This Pre-Cambrian (or, as it later became known, **Precambrian**) interval of earth history obviously embraced a long time, at least as long as the time span since the beginning of the Cambrian. No one had any real idea of numbers, but most geologists thought that half a billion years was probably a minimal figure.

In spite of the difficulties inherent in dealing with the Precambrian, many nineteenth-century geologists, particularly in the closing decades of the century, became interested in these ancient basement rocks, for an obvious reason. Much of the world's mineral wealth is found in these Precambrian rocks, and as the demands of industry grew by leaps and bounds, so did the incentives for finding new resources of iron, nickel, copper, zinc, gold, silver, and a host of other economic minerals.

The Precambrian is divided into the **Archean** and the **Proterozoic,** which, as is explained later in the chapter, are divisions that reflect two broad groupings of rocks found in Precambrian exposures. This chapter explores the Archean, the older of the two divisions, while the Proterozoic is the subject of Chapter 11. The chapter begins with a Precambrian overview and progresses to discussions of Archean rocks, models of Archean crustal evolution, and Archean life.

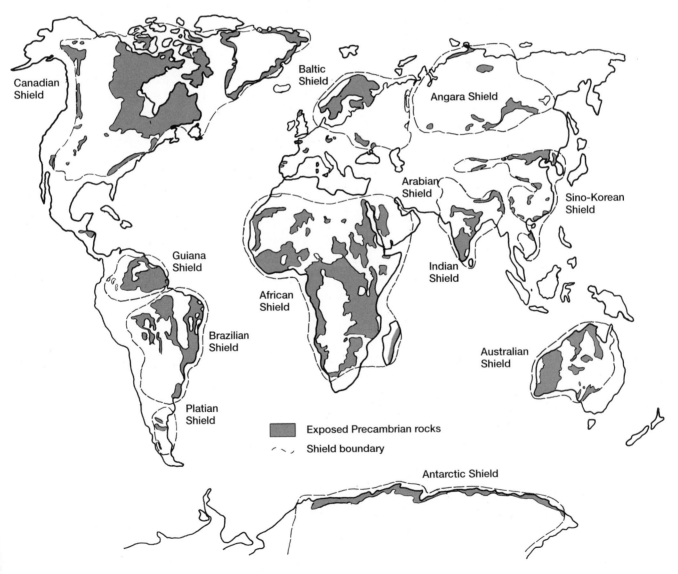

FIGURE 10.1
Precambrian shield areas of the world.

Precambrian Overview

Terminology: Shields and Mobile Belts

Precambrian rocks are best exposed in shield areas. **Shields** are extensive areas of exposed basement rocks of Precambrian age in the central, stable core or nucleus of a continental block. The major shield areas of the world are shown in Figure 10.1. Shields typically are surrounded by extensive areas where the Precambrian basement rocks are covered by veneers of young sedimentary successions. These areas are known as platforms, and together with the shield areas, they constitute the stable **cratons** or **continental nuclei** around which have been added, or accreted, younger portions of the continents.

The accretion process is the result of collision episodes and orogenies, brought about by plate-tectonic mechanisms. The North American continent provides a good example of growth by accretion. The ancient nucleus of the continent is made up of rocks dated at older than 3,000 million years, and they are surrounded by a roughly concentric arrangement of elongated tracts, or **mobile belts,** of younger rocks. As the map in Figure 10.2 shows, the mobile belts become successively younger in moving away from the nucleus. All the continents of the world contain one or more of these ancient nuclei. Africa, for example, is a product of the welding together of several such old cores, or massifs (Figure 10.3).

Three-fourths of the modern continents are believed to have been formed by about 2,500 million years ago, a total area considerably greater than that of exposed shield rocks recognized today. The discrepancy is due to the large areas of Precambrian rocks that are hidden beneath veneers of younger rocks or that are mixed in with younger rocks within the mobile belts that were formed around the shields during the continental accretion process of later time.

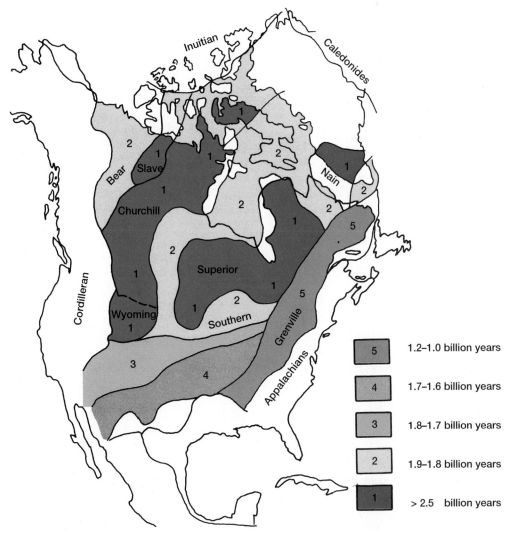

FIGURE 10.2

Distribution of major Precambrian mobile belts and age provinces in North America.

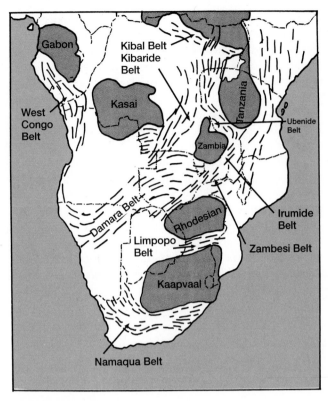

FIGURE 10.3
Late Precambrian mobile belts and cratons of Africa.

Orogenies are marked by regional metamorphism and granite intrusions on a vast scale; thus, the Precambrian rock was altered and overprinted by later metamorphic change. Inevitably, the isotopic clocks started during earlier Precambrian time were reset, and Precambrian rocks are suspected to be present in much younger fold belts formed during the Phanerozoic, although it is difficult to prove their age directly.

Early Precambrian Fieldwork

Much of the pioneering Precambrian fieldwork was done on the **Canadian Shield,** or **Laurentian Shield** as it is sometimes called, the largest single area of exposed Precambrian rocks in the world. Working particularly in the classic areas of the Canadian Shield—north of the Great Lakes and the Saint Lawrence River—geologists of the Geological Survey of Canada were able to map considerable areas and so begin to understand the major Precambrian structural elements, rock associations, and age relationships.

Because all of the Canadian Shield was covered by the Late Cenozoic ice sheets, over large areas, the rock has been scraped bare, the soils are thin, and rock exposures are frequent. In addition, drainage patterns were disrupted by glacial erosion and deposition, the result being

a vast network of rivers and lakes. These became the main travel routes through this enormous wilderness, much of it covered in spruce and pine forest.

Life was not easy for these early geologists: The deep snows of winter brought effective fieldwork to a stop, while in the summer, over often swampy terrain, the hordes of mosquitoes, blackflies, and tiny gnats (or "no see-ums") made life miserable. Some of these geologists' accounts of their remarkable journeys make fascinating reading.

Archean Rocks

From the beginning of the investigations of Canadian Shield rocks, two broad groupings of rocks were recognized: an older basement series dominated by granites and gneisses and, overlying them, usually above a marked unconformity, a younger series of sedimentary and volcanic rocks that were largely unmetamorphosed. The older rocks were called Archean and the younger Proterozoic, and these broad divisions are still recognized today. The generally accepted age for the Archean/Proterozoic boundary is 2,500 million years.

Granulites and Greenstones

Mapping of the Archean rocks showed them to consist of two major kinds of rock associations: Of greatest extent—perhaps underlying 80 to 85 percent of the shield—are granites, granodiorites, and gneisses. These highly metamorphosed rocks are often referred to under the general heading of **granulites** because of their interlocking, evenly granular texture. The second rock assemblage is an association of volcanic rocks, varying in composition from ultrabasic (very low in silica) to andesitic (a moderate amount of silica and sodic plagioclase feldspar), together with poorly sorted clastic sedimentary rocks that, because of their dark color (often a greenish cast due to the presence of minerals like chlorite or actinolite), are collectively known as greenstones. Greenstones typically occur in elongated tracts or **greenstone belts** up to several hundred kilometers long and within which they exhibit a generally synclinal structure that gives them an overall boat-shaped aspect (Figures 10.4 and 10.5). In fact, in their relationship to surrounding rocks, they had been described as "floating in a sea of granite." In marked contrast to the surrounding granulite terrain, the greenstones have undergone much less metamorphic change, and many of the original structures and textures can be easily recognized.

In the classic area of the Canadian Shield north of the Great Lakes, a twofold division of greenstone successions was recognized: A lower succession of basic volcanic

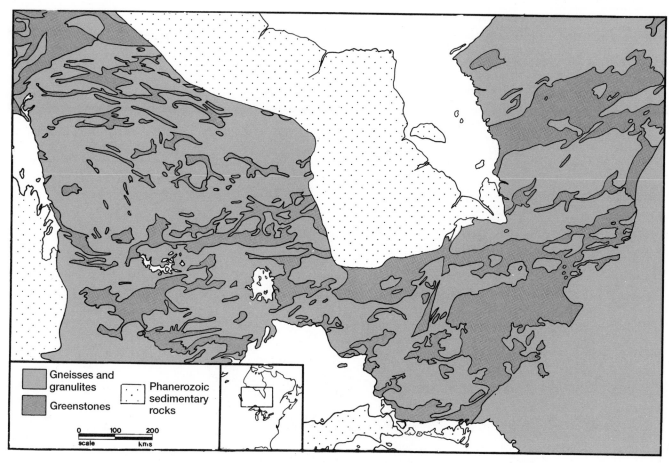

FIGURE 10.4

Part of the Superior Province of the Canadian Shield, showing the distribution of greenstone belts. (Source: Data from Geological Survey of Canada.)

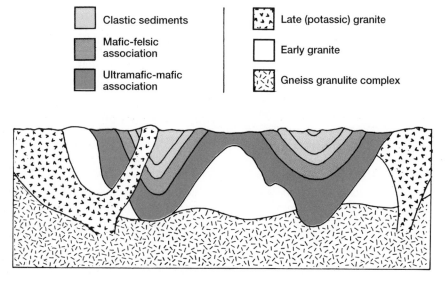

FIGURE 10.5

Typical stratigraphic/structure section through an Archean greenstone belt.

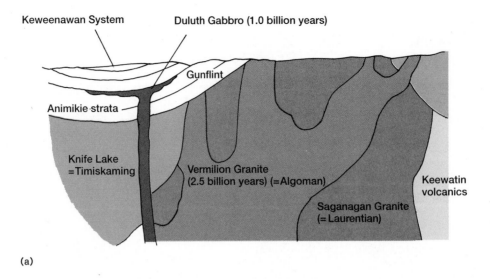

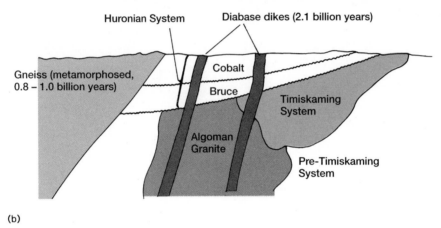

FIGURE 10.6

Field relationships of Archean granites and greenstones, together with Proterozoic successions, in the classic areas of the Great Lakes in (a) western Ontario and Minnesota and (b) eastern Ontario.

rocks was named the **Keewatin Series,** and an upper sedimentary division was labeled the **Timiskaming Series** (Figure 10.6). Greenstone belts discovered in all the other Archean shield areas of the world also show this twofold lithostratigraphic subdivision. Inevitably, the worldwide similarities led geologists to believe that these greenstone successions were all of similar age and could form the basis of a classification scheme with time-stratigraphic significance. After more detailed studies and particularly as isotopic ages began to accumulate, a considerable spread in the ages of the various occurrences became apparent. There had been, in fact, several cycles of greenstone formation.

On the Canadian Shield, the greenstone belts are largely younger in age than those in Africa, with isotopic dating in the Slave Province in Canada giving an age of 2,625 million years and in the Kirkland Lake area of Ontario, Canada (the original "classic" area), 2,370 million years. These younger ages are likely due to an "over-printing" that reset Canadian Shield isotopic clocks during the Kenoran orogeny that culminated about 2,500 million years ago.

Archean Rocks on Other Shields

On the Australian craton, nearly all the Archean rocks are found in Western Australia, where they comprise the Yilgarn and Pilbara massifs. Although separated by a wide belt of supracrustal rocks of largely Proterozoic age that comprise the Hamersley belt, the Yilgarn and Pilbara actually constitute a single tectonic province. (Tectonic provinces are described in Chapter 11.) A third smaller area occurs in the Gawler block in Southern Australia. As in Canada and Africa, the two associations of greenstones and granitic gneisses are present.

Archean rocks in the Indian craton are found mainly in the Dharwar belt of southwest India. Other smaller areas occur in central Sri Lanka and in the Bihan and Orissa regions west of Calcutta.

BOX 10.1

Nomenclature in Igneous Rocks

The igneous rocks are normally classified and given names like granite, basalt, diorite, and so on, based on the mineral associations contained in them and also on the grain size determined by their cooling history. They are also grouped into categories of a more general nature that consider the gross chemical composition. Particularly significant is the amount of silica available in the original magma because this largely controls the gross mineralogy as crystallization proceeds. Box Table 10.1 summarizes the most common terms used in this classification approach.

Rocks formed from magma containing enough silica for quartz to be present are said to be **saturated.** Those with low silica and made of minerals that cannot form in the presence of quartz are said to be undersaturated. Two additional terms used in referring to the crust are **sial** for the upper part of the crust (that is, the granitic crust, rich in silica and alumina) and **sima** for the lower or oceanic crust (rich in silica and magnesia).

BOX TABLE 10.1

Classifications of Igneous Rocks

Category Based on Silica Content	Percentage Silica	Category Based on Light/Dark Minerals
Acid (Silica)	60 % +	Felsic (light minerals)
Intermediate	51–60%	Intermediate
Basic	44–51%	Mafic (one or more dark minerals; *femic* is roughly synonymous)
Ultrabasic	Less than 44%	Ultramafic (chiefly dark minerals, including mono-mineralic types made up of olivine, augite, and so on)

Note: Mnemonic devices for some of these terms are: *felsic* (feldspar + silica), *mafic* (magnesium + ferric), and *femic* (ferric + magnesian).

The South American continent is dominated by two major cratons: the Guyana Shield in the north and the Brazilian Shield. Three small massifs are found in the southwest. Isotopic dates from these shields are still few, but dates slightly older than 2,500 million years have been obtained on the Brazilian Shield. Archean supracrustal rocks have been identified on the Guyana Shield, and even older basement complex rocks underlie them.

On the Baltic Shield, Archean rocks are found in the Lapland and Karelia areas and consist of granites and greenstone belts. They are of Late Archean age and so are comparable with those of the Canadian Shield.

Some of the oldest greenstones dated occur in the Transvaal-Rhodesia massifs of southern Africa, and there a third division of ultramafic volcanic rocks lies beneath the Keewatin-type volcanics. In the African occurrences, as in those in other shield areas, the greenstone successions are often gold-bearing and, therefore, have been mapped in considerable detail. In the Barberton greenstone belt of the Transvaal, the aggregate thickness of what has been named the Swaziland System reaches over 15 kilometers, more than half of which is volcanic rock. These vast outpourings of lava must have continued over long periods. Isotopic age determinations show that the greenstones range from 3,400 million years to 3,000 million years, making them among the oldest anywhere and significantly older than the greenstones of North America.

Detailed stratigraphic studies of the lower part of the Swaziland System, known as the **Onverwacht Group,** show that the volcanic activity was cyclical, each phase of activity beginning with basic lavas followed by more silica-rich lavas higher in the succession. This cyclicity is superimposed on a much larger scale change seen in the Onverwacht as a whole. From bottom to top, the succession demonstrates that, on average, the lavas change from dominantly **mafic** (rich in iron and magnesium) and **ultramafic** (extremely rich in iron and magnesium) to **felsic** (rich in feldspar and silica) in composition; they became progressively richer in silica as time passed (see Box 10.1). A common feature of all the volcanics are pillow structures, indicating that they were erupted in water.

Above the Onverwacht Group are sediments named the **Fig Tree Group,** consisting of fine-grained, poorly sorted, graywacke-type sandstones, many with internal textures that indicate that they were laid down by turbidity currents in fairly deep water. Occasional chert beds within the Fig Tree sediments contain the remains of enigmatic microspheres, together with other rodlike and filamentous structures (Figure 10.7). These have been interpreted as fossil algae and constitute some of the earliest evidence of life. Analysis of the clastic grains in the Fig Tree Group points to their being derived from both volcanic and granitic rocks that must have been exposed to weathering and erosion from nearby land at the time the Fig Tree sediments were being deposited.

At the top of the Swaziland System is a succession of coarse-grained sediments, the Moodies Group. These also consist of volcanic rocks and pyroclastics, together with gravels and conglomerates, some of which contain granitic pebbles. These pebbles are important in showing that granitic rocks were being eroded somewhere very close by.

In the nearby Rhodesian massif, the Archean succession is broadly similar. The lower volcanic series is here labeled the Buluwayo Group, correlated with the Onverwacht. Sediments in the overlying Shamvaian Group contain limestones with stromatolites, among the earliest known.

Greenstones—Older or Younger?

The relationship between the greenstone belts and the surrounding gneissic or granitic terrains has long been debated. This is because the actual contact between greenstones and the surrounding rocks is rarely seen, often being marked by a fault or by cross-cutting younger intrusions, or it simply may be covered by younger sediments or vegetation. Available exposures usually indicate that the contact is an intrusive one, which means that the greenstones are older. Since most of the early work in Canada, Africa, and the other shield areas seemed to indicate this, the idea arose that the greenstones were the oldest of all rocks and might, in fact, represent remnants of the original or primeval crust. This crust was of basaltic composition and marked a time before magmatic differentiation had produced any significant sialic or continental-type crust. Today, this idea has been largely discarded.

That the granites and gneisses that surround greenstone belts are younger is clearly confirmed by the effects of metamorphism, as, for example, in the southern Africa shield area. Here the basal successions of the greenstones (Lower Onverwacht or Lower Buluwayan Groups), where they are exposed around the outer rims of the synclinal greenstone belts, are more highly metamorphosed than are stratigraphically higher levels of the greenstone succession toward the inner part of the syncline and away from the influence of the intrusion. On the other hand, the extensive granitic terrains between the greenstone belts are

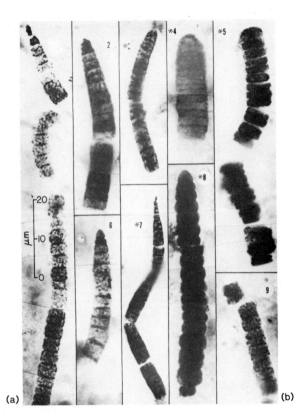

FIGURE 10.7
Similar to the Fig Tree fossils are microfossils from the Bitter Springs formation of the Amadeus Basin, Australia.
(a) *Cephalophytarion constrictum.* (b) *Filiconstrictosus majusculus.*) *(Photos courtesy of J. W. Schopf.)*

not by any means homogeneous. Cross-cutting relationships frequently indicate more than one period of granitic intrusion, while some gneisses have been interpreted as surviving remnants of pre-Swaziland basement rocks. That some sort of early granitic basement existed, albeit only in small areas, is also indicated by the presence in greenstone successions of granitic pebbles and other clastic material derived from terrains adjacent to the greenstone basins.

Perhaps the chief reason why there seems to be conflicting evidence as to the age relationship of greenstones is because there are, in fact, different kinds of greenstones. Particularly in the African, Australian, and Indian shields, some workers have recognized so-called primary greenstones. In the southern African occurrences, typified by the lower part of the Onverwacht and Sabakwayn groups, the composition of the volcanics is typically mafic and ultramafic, and the volcanics apparently predate the oldest granites in the region. They contain no evidence of preexisting sialic crust or nearby sources of clastic material, and so it has been suggested that even older volcanic terrains may exist and that they might even represent remnants of preimpact crust—that is, dating from before the period of heavy meteorite bombardment described in the next section.

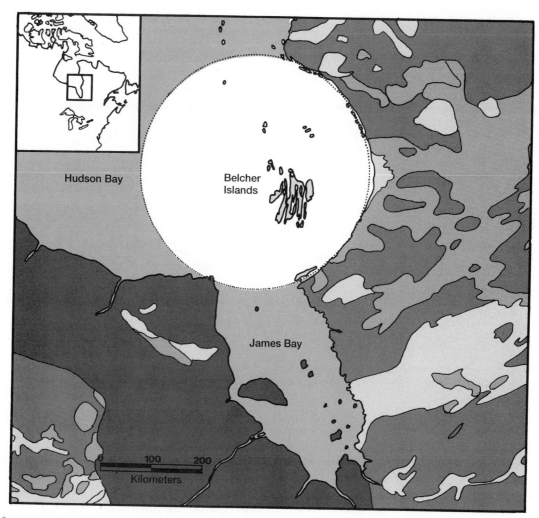

FIGURE 10.8
What may be the world's largest meteorite crater. The almost perfectly circular shape of the shoreline and the fracture patterns may point to an Early Precambrian meteorite impact.

Searching for the Oldest Archean Rocks

The oldest terrestrial rocks dated up to the present time are 3,960-million-year-old rocks from the region north of Great Slave Lake in Canada. Only slightly younger are the greenstones of the Isua region of Greenland, which long held the record for the oldest date. Even older dates have been obtained for several clastic zircon grains discovered in 1983 in Western Australia. These have been dated as 4,300 million years, and they presumably were derived from the erosion of even older rocks in the vicinity, although the actual source rocks remain undiscovered.

As we have seen in earlier chapters, from the evidence of dates from lunar rocks and meteorites and from terrestrial lead ratios, the earth is estimated to be 4,600 million years old (see Figure 6.3a). Is it possible that geologists will eventually find terrestrial rocks that date back to the beginning of the earth? Various lines of evidence suggest that this is unlikely. According to British geologist Donald

Tarling, the projection back in time of terrestrial heat levels generated by radioactive decay indicates an early earth two or three times hotter than at present. The most obvious result of this would have been a considerably accelerated convectional overturn of mantle material. This, in turn, would mean that any early-formed crustal rocks would be "stirred" back into the mantle as vigorous plumes of rising hot material reached the surface, cooled, and descended again. Even if such a scenario is only an approximation of what these early stages were like, it seems unlikely that rocks much older than the ones already found will turn up.

Another factor to be considered is the effect of meteorite impacts. Evidence from the moon indicates that the period from about 4,200 million years to 3,900 million years was one of heavy meteorite bombardment. The earth, with its larger mass and stronger gravity field, certainly received its share of asteroid collisions (Figure 10.8). Some

BOX 10.2

An Archean Landscape Preserved

Although the Archean earth has largely vanished, and little trace of the ancient surface remains today, the Archean moon is still with us. The lunar mountains, craters, and flat plains seen today look essentially the same as they did some 3,000 to 4,000 million years ago. It is a landscape frozen in time!

The geological processes that shaped the moon's surface, unlike those that continue today on earth, came to a stop very early in the moon's history. Observations of how older craters were destroyed by younger impacts or of how they were covered by debris ejected by later events allow a sequential history and even a strati-

graphic succession to be determined for the moon (Box Figure 10.1). Geologists now know, however, that by about 3,000 million years ago, over 95 percent of all the craters had been formed, and since that time, the moon's surface has changed little (Box Figure 10.2).

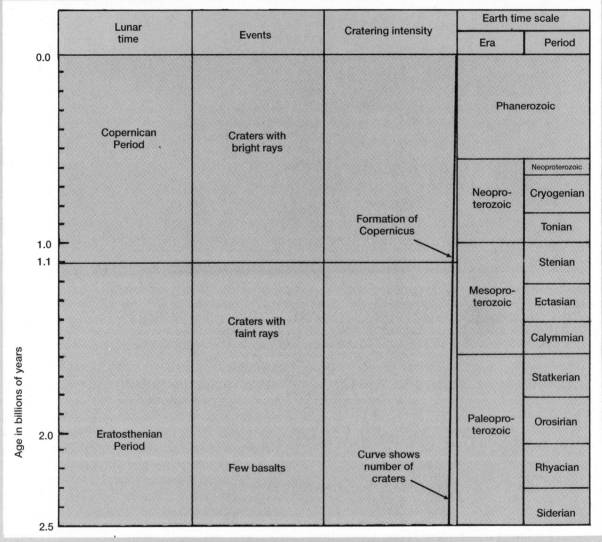

BOX FIGURE 10.1
The major divisions of lunar history compared with the divisions of Precambrian time on earth.

geologists believe that any early crust would have been melted and destroyed by the impacts. The lithosphere was undoubtedly deeply fractured, and enormous outpourings of ultramafic and mafic lavas would have flooded the sur-

face. On the moon, these lava plains are still seen as the dark smooth maria, so called because early astronomers took them to be seas (see Box Figure 10.2). On the earth, certain vestiges of these impact-induced lavas may be rep-

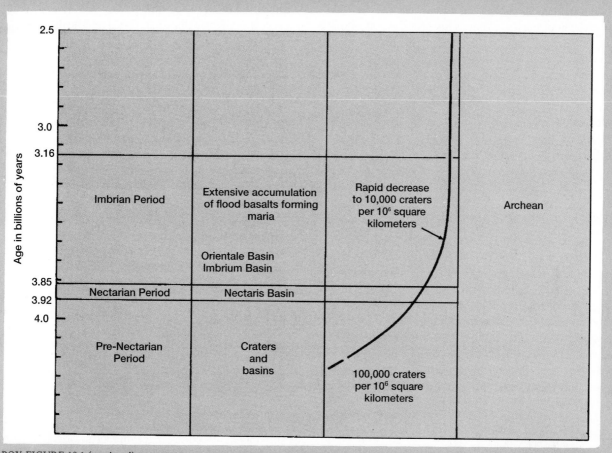

BOX FIGURE 10.1 (continued) Source: Data from W. K. Hamblin and J. D. Howard, *Exploring the Planets*. Copyright © 1990 Macmillan Publishing Company.

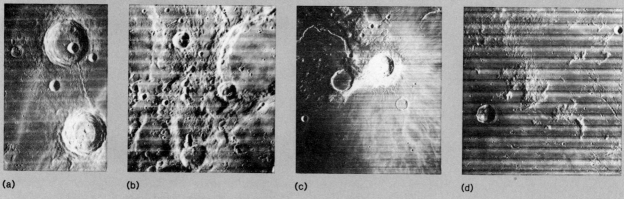

BOX FIGURE 10.2

(a) Slumping of crater walls results in partial filling. (b) Crater rims are partly obliterated by later impacts. (c) The ejecta from the larger crater partly covers older craters. (d) Craters also become partly covered by lava flows. *(Photos by NASA.)*

in scattered enclaves within the oldest greenstone successions. According to Russian geologist Lazarus Salop, some evidence of this period of meteorite impacting can be seen in the striking circular or oval patterns of gneissic foliations found in certain Archean terrains. He does not suggest that they represent impact craters as such, but they may reflect a pattern of locally derived magmas generated at the impact sites.

Clearly, that any direct evidence from this remote time should have survived is highly unlikely, and much of what has been written about the Early Archean is largely conjectural. If only for the sake of convenience, however, this early phase in earth history should be recognized as a distinct division of geologic time. This provides a beginning to the calendar of history, even though the boundaries are somewhat vague. The Early Archean embraces the period from the earth's beginning, dated by several independent lines of evidence as about 4,600 million years, to the time when the first crustal rocks with datable minerals were formed and survived. At the moment, the evidence of the Australian zircon grains puts this date at 4,300 million years. Others might prefer the 3,960-million-year date of the Great Slave Lake rocks.

Models of Archean Crustal Evolution

The various models constructed to explain crustal evolution during the Archean are now quite numerous and, not surprisingly, in many cases contradictory. The major points of difference concern plate-tectonic mechanisms. On one side are proponents of a uniformitarian model with a plate-tectonic mechanism essentially similar to that operating today, and with continental crust appearing early in the Archean. On the other side are those who, while conceding that some kind of plate tectonics was operating, suggest that it was quite different through all the Archean and even well into the Proterozoic.

The common jumping-off place for the various models is a general agreement that the early earth was hotter than it is today. Present-day abundances of radioactive elements in the earth's crust and their known rates of decay allow estimates of their abundance in the geologic past. Calculations show that, in the Archean, the uranium isotopes uranium-235 and uranium-238 were approximately four times as abundant as they are today, while potassium-40 was more than eight times as abundant. Because radioactive decay produces heat, the early earth's internal heat production has been estimated as having been three or four times what it is today.

The Uniformitarian Model

Although an early earth that was considerably hotter is a matter of general agreement, on the subject of how crustal processes were affected, there is considerably less unanimity. Based on studies of some of the most ancient of all rocks exposed in Greenland and elsewhere, British geologist Stephen Moorbath believes that continental crust began to form by chemical differentiation in the upper mantle very early in the earth's history and that the process had already begun before 3,800 million years ago. According to this model, the convectional movements of mantle material were relatively rapid because of the higher heat flow, so the process of crustal creation was also rapid. Once formed, the crust was too buoyant to be subducted or stirred back into the mantle, and the continents grew quite quickly, perhaps in a few hundred million years. Along the margins, continents grew by accretion, and the crust was already thick and rigid from the beginning. This process of continental growth by marginal accretion may not have proceeded continuously but rather in cycles, perhaps linked to an alternation between periods of progressive heat buildup in the earth as a consequence of radioactive decay, and then its release during periods of rapid convection. The possibility of cyclical orogenic activity is discussed further in Chapter 11. One feature of this model that is shared by other suggested scenarios is that early continental crustal massifs were combined into large supercontinents and that they had already grown to Pangaea-like proportions before the close of the Archean.

Alternative Models

Many geologists do not subscribe to this uniformitarian approach. Modeling of the likely effects of higher heat production have suggested to some workers a quite different history—one in which the early crust was thin and did not reach its later thickness and rigidity until the Late Proterozoic. These geologists also believe that Wilson-Cycle plate tectonics did not begin until the Late Proterozoic either and that Archean-type plate tectonics involved a much thicker asthenosphere and a correspondingly thin lithosphere. Higher heat flow required a more efficient heat-dissipating mechanism, and this was presumably achieved in longer midocean ridge systems and/or a higher rate of seafloor spreading. In one calculation involving 64,000 kilometers of midocean ridge (as today), the spreading rate would be 20 to 40 centimeters per year, about two to four times the current rate on the East Pacific Rise.

With a more vigorous convectional system, the Early Archean was presumably characterized by many mantle plumes marking numerous, but small, convection cells, measuring, perhaps, several hundred up to a thousand kilometers across (Figure 10.9). This small-scale plate-tectonic activity was supposedly characteristic of much of the Archean, and in this environment, the earliest small protocratons were produced by a process of magmatic differentiation.

At a later stage, as cratons grew in size, perhaps by collision and marginal accretion, lithosphere and crust were still relatively thin; this would have important consequences in influencing the crust's subsequent history. A weak lithosphere with little mechanical rigidity could still be influenced by subcrustal mantle movements and be prone to the downsagging, rifting, shearing, and other structural distortions required in the various models proposed to explain the observed features of Archean terrains

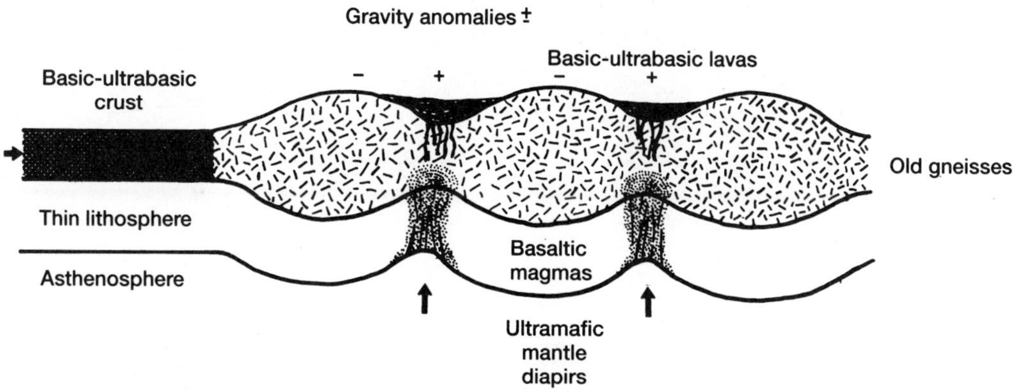

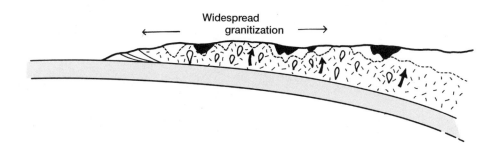

Gravity anomalies ±

Basic-ultrabasic lavas

Basic-ultrabasic crust

Old gneisses

Thin lithosphere

Asthenosphere

Basaltic magmas

Ultramafic mantle diapirs

FIGURE 10.9

Proposed model of semi-mobile Archean tectonics. Compression between thin simatic and sialic lithosphere causes cusp-and-lobe configuration of the asthenosphere-lithosphere boundary. Thinning over cusps causes isostatic sinking to form greenstone belts. Partial melting occurs at depth below the sialic crust, producing high-grade terrains.

Widespread granitization

FIGURE 10.10

A subducted plate passing down at a low angle extends the zone of melting and magma generation over a wide area—in the case of smaller protocratons, likely over the entire extent of continental crust.

(Figure 10.9). Subcrustal mantle movements are, for example, an important factor in one of the various explanations for greenstone belts, as is described shortly.

The widespread granitic/gneissic terrains so typical of the Archean might also be explained by a modified subduction mechanism at plate margins. Along modern continental margins, the descending lithospheric plate plunges at a relatively steep angle so that the magmas generated by melting and that move upward as batholithic masses are confined to a relatively narrow belt along the continental margins. This is a feature, for example, of the Coast Range and other batholiths of the Cenozoic Pacific margin of North America.

With a thin lithosphere, on the other hand, subduction would be at a much lower angle, and the zone of melting and granitic magma generation would be spread over a much wider extent (Figure 10.10). With smaller cratons, this might well mean that the entire craton area would be subjected to massive intrusion by sialic magma, which would certainly provide an explanation for greenstone belts "floating in a sea of granite."

Origin of Greenstone Belts

Models of Early Archean crustal evolution must also explain the origin of greenstone belts. As mentioned earlier in the chapter, some of the early workers in greenstone belts saw them as remnants of an original or primeval crust, a view supported by the upward change from ultramafic composition to rocks with increasing silica content. This pointed to an apparent evolution of the crust as a whole, eventually leading to sialic (that is, granite-type) crust. That there were obvious flaws in this model was indicated by the presence of granitic pebbles in certain greenstone sediments, which pointed to the existence of even more ancient granitic terrains somewhere.

One explanation is that granitic crust was formed as a result of the melting and magmatic differentiation of downsagging areas of early simatic crust. In a model suggested by Australian geologist A. Glickson, linear belts of early simatic crust subsided to great depth. Partial melting of this material produced chemically differentiated magmas of lesser density, which then rose isostatically to

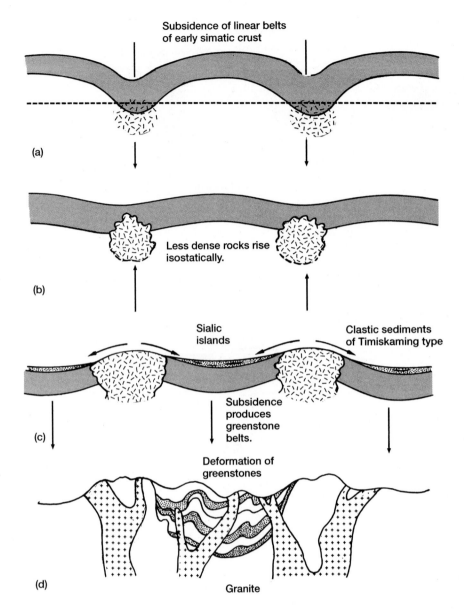

FIGURE 10.11
Glickson's model of Archean tectonic evolution. (a) Partial melting produces chemically differentiated magmas of lesser density. (b) Less dense rocks rise isostatically. (c) Subsidence produces greenstone belts. (d) Later granite intrusion. *(Source: Data from Glikson,* Geological Society of America Bulletin, *fig. 12, p. 3338, 1972.)*

produce sialic islands. Continental subsidence of the regions between the islands produced the greenstone belts, while weathering and erosion of the islands introduced the clastic sediments of Timiskaming type in the upper part of the greenstone successions (Figure 10.11).

In another model, also appealing to downsagging of **intracratonic basins** (basins on a craton surface) by virtue of isostatic causes, the ultramafic and mafic magmas

characteristic of the basal portions of most greenstone successions were derived from contributions of asthenospheric material.

The resemblance of the volcanics and sediments of greenstone belts to certain Phanerozoic basinal successions associated with subduction zones has also been noted. To some geologists, this suggests that greenstone belts originated as infillings of back-arc marginal basins located adjacent to rising orogenic belts generated by plate

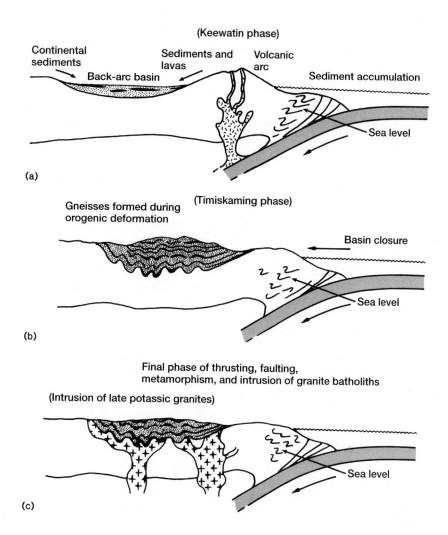

FIGURE 10.12

Model for Archean greenstone belts based on analogues with back-arc marginal basins of Phanerozoic continents. (a) Phase of sediment accumulation. (b) Phase of basin closure and deformation. (c) Final phase of thrusting, faulting, metamorphism, and intrusion of granite batholiths.

(Source: Data from J. Tarney, et al., "Margin Basin Rocas Verdes' Complex from Southern Chile: A Model for Archean Greenstone Belt Formation: in The Early History of the Earth, ed. by B. F. Windley, pp. 131–146. Copyright © 1976 John Wiley & Sons, Inc.)

collision (Figure 10.12). An initial volcanic episode would have been responsible for an early phase of volcanic accumulation (that is, the Keewatin phase). This would have been followed by sediments derived from rising marginal lands as the orogeny reached a climax. These would be the Timiskaming lithologic association. During the final phase, thrusting, faulting, and metamorphism of the basin infilling would have produced the familiar greenstone-belt field relationships. At the same time, the rise of granitic batholiths from the roots of the subduction zone would have intruded and surrounded the linear greenstone belt.

While the presence of pillow lavas, submarine fan-type sediments, and other indicators of deposition in relatively deep water all seem to support a marginal basin origin for greenstones, some serious problems remain. For one thing, if the setting of modern marginal basins is to be considered as at all comparable to those in which greenstones formed, there is the implication that subduction mechanisms were also comparable. On the other hand, the earliest ophiolite suites, generally considered definitive indicators of Wilson-Cycle subduction, did not appear until well into the Proterozoic.

While a cratonic margin setting for some greenstone belts is certainly possible, the size and location of the many discrete greenstone belts and their lens- or pod-shaped bodies within granitic terrains almost certainly preclude it in the majority of cases. Even if large numbers of mini-cratons were involved, the overall field relationships of the granite/greenstone associations at many locations seem to favor some kind of intracratonic origin, either in downsagging folds or tensional rifts.

Archean Life

Although the first direct evidence of life in the form of fossils is seen in rocks that may be as old as 3,400 to 3,500 million years, living organisms undoubtedly existed on the earth long before that. As discussed in Chapter 7, the first living cells had probably evolved about 4,000 million years ago. The first unmetamorphosed sedimentary rocks have been dated at about 3,700 million years, so looking for fossils older than that is probably useless.

One possible model for establishing some sort of timetable for the evolution of early life-forms is found in sediments of the Onverwacht Group in South Africa and involves variations in the proportions of carbon isotopes. The two principal isotopes of carbon-12 and carbon-13 behave somewhat differently in their path through the carbon cycle. Atmospheric carbon dioxide tends to contain a slightly higher proportion of carbon-12 because carbon-12 evaporates more easily from the ocean surface, which means that seawater is slightly enriched in the heavier isotope carbon -13 (that is, the carbon-12/carbon-13 ratio is lower in seawater). According to this model, interchange with the atmosphere causes the cells of photosynthesizing organisms to be richer in carbon-12 because this isotope is more easily taken up. Careful analyses of the Onverwacht sediments show that, in strata dated at about 3,500 million years, there is a sudden increase in the carbon-12 content. One explanation is that the carbon-12 is derived from organic matter produced by some kind of photosynthesis involving carbon dioxide. On the other hand, marine organisms obtain most of their carbon dioxide from that which is dissolved in seawater, not the atmosphere, a factor that appears to be a serious problem with this particular model.

Actual fossils of Archean life-forms are of two kinds: (1) stromatolites and (2) microscopic structures of various shapes and sizes in chert beds. Of these, the cherts provide the best-preserved material, but unfortunately, they are rare. Much more common are stromatolites, which, as discussed in earlier chapters, are organosedimentary structures in which sediment was trapped or precipitated by the action of the cyanobacteria and bacteria that make up so-called algal mats on sediment surfaces in shallow water.

Stromatolites

Most stromatolites are preserved in carbonate rocks, and no traces of the microorganisms responsible for their accumulation usually are found. Occasional silicified examples provide an opportunity to study the actual stromatolite formers, and they are essentially the same cyanobacteria and bacteria forms as those that construct modern living stromatolites. Despite this apparently simple origin, stromatolite assemblages of various ages through the Precambrian apparently demonstrate some progressive changes in gross morphology over time.

From studies of modern stromatolites, geologists know that no single organism is responsible for the encrusting layers that constitute the organosedimentary structures (see Figure 7.5). In fact, a whole colony of different cyanobacteria and bacteria is involved, forming a living mat over the sediment surface. Although extremely thin, each mat or colony consists of different species, whose location within the community is largely controlled by light intensity. On the mat's surface are those species most tolerant to light, while those preferring lower light levels and likely having different oxygen requirements live deeper in the colony.

Stromatolites' external form and also internal texture apparently are controlled both by the biological characteristics of algal mats and by ecologic factors of water depth, tidal regime, wave energy, and so on. Thus, in subtidal environments, stromatolites tend to form in continuous layers across the sediment surface, whereas in intertidal situations, they are produced in discontinuous knobs and pillarlike structures.

Microorganisms in Cherts

As discussed in Chapter 3, the chances that any organism will leave some trace in the rocks are extremely small. In the case of Precambrian organisms, the problems are immensely magnified. Long, slow induration and alteration, with recrystallization and metamorphism likely repeated several times, mean that the odds for even robust animals with hard skeletons being preserved become vanishingly small. Precambrian organisms were microscopic, primitive, and secreted no hard parts, so a combination of rather special conditions would clearly be necessary if any trace of these early life-forms were to be preserved within the sedimentary record. In virtually only one depositional environment are these conditions met: in chert beds.

Chert is a microcrystalline form of silica, and like quartz (the crystalline form of silicon dioxide), it is extremely hard and chemically almost inert (see Box 11.1). Not only in the Precambrian but in rocks of Phanerozoic age as well, chert beds have provided some of the best fossils. The wonderfully preserved brachiopods from the Permian and tree trunks from the Triassic, for example, were apparently fossilized in a molecule-by-molecule replacement of the original tissues by silica. Once the replacement was complete, the durability of the chert ensured fossil preservation to the present day. The physiochemical environment in which many cherts were deposited is not completely understood, and no single set of chemical parameters is likely involved.

Virtually all the microfossils of both Archean and Proterozoic age have been found in cherts. In some cases, the evidence of sedimentary association suggests that the cherts were laid down in shallow water; in other cases, deeper water is indicated. In any event, the depositional environment was a low-energy one because this would be an important factor in the preservation of such delicate structures. In some cases, the cherts replace stromatolites, and the contained microfossils presumably represent the stromatolite formers.

The fossils themselves are not easy to recognize. Apart from their diminutive size (often as small as 2 to 3 microns), their forms are simple and consist of tiny spheres, rods, and threadlike filaments, shapes that are often duplicated in any number of inorganic structures, from gas bubbles to shrinkage cracks. Small wonder that considerable controversy has surrounded some of the more enigmatic structures.

The oldest fossils discovered to date are the microfossils from the Warranwoona Group of Western Australia and the Fig Tree Group of Swaziland (see Figure 10.7). Discovered in the 1960s and described by Elso Barghorn and J. William Schopf at UCLA, the fossils consist of numerous kinds of microspheres, rodlike structures, and filaments that have been interpreted as the remains of cyanobacteria and bacteria. The formations containing these fossils range in age from 2,800 million years to 3,500 million years. From that time on, astonishingly little is known. While stromatolites became increasingly abundant in the Early Proterozoic after about 2,300 million years, the occasional silicified examples contain only prokaryote cells, not unlike those found in living algal mats. The stromatolites forming at the present day are essentially the same as those found in rocks that date back 3,000 million years or more and clearly represent very conservative life-forms.

Summary

Early interest in Precambrian rocks was spurred by the enormous mineral wealth they contain. The major areas of Precambrian exposures are the shield areas of the world. These form the ancient nuclei of the continents, and around them are wrapped successively younger mobile belts in a roughly concentric arrangement.

The Canadian Shield is the largest and best known of the shield areas. Because it was covered by a Late Cenozoic ice cap, much of the rock was scraped clean of superficial deposits and is often well exposed. Geologists of the Geological Survey of Canada did much of the early work on Precambrian terrains here.

Two broad groupings of shield rocks have been identified: an older series of granitic gneisses and greenstone belts, all metamorphosed to a greater or lesser extent, and known as the Archean; and a younger, much less metamorphosed association of sedimentary and volcanic rocks labeled the Proterozoic. The generally accepted age for the Archean/Proterozoic boundary is 2,500 million years.

Early mapping in the classic areas of the Canadian Shield—north of the Saint Lawrence River and the Great Lakes—showed the Archean rocks to be of two kinds: The most widespread rocks, underlying about 85 percent of the Archean areas, are granitic gneisses. Occupying smaller, elongated belts are the greenstones. Described as "floating in a sea of granite," the greenstone belts have a generally synclinal structure and appear, in most cases, to be intruded by the granite and therefore older. That pregreenstone granites existed in some places is indicated by the presence of granitic pebbles in many greenstone successions.

Within the greenstone belts, a broad twofold division was recognized, with a lower volcanic series (Keewatin) overlain by a younger, largely sedimentary succession (Timiskaming). Greenstone belts occur within the Archean terrains of all the shield areas, and the same twofold division into a lower Keewatin-type and an upper Timiskaming-type succession is always found. Greenstone belts are not all the same age, however, because isotopic dating indicates several cycles of greenstone formation, with the oldest cycle occurring in South Africa.

The oldest terrestrial rocks discovered up to the present are 3,960-million-year-old rocks from the region north of Great Slave Lake in Canada. Even older dates have been obtained from individual zircon grains collected in Western Australia. Rocks or minerals much older are unlikely to be discovered because the early earth was two to three times hotter than today, and the crust was very mobile as a consequence of more rapid convectional overturn in the mantle. The heavy meteorite bombardment from 4,200 million years to 3,900 million years may also have destroyed much of the early crust.

Various models to explain early crustal evolution have been proposed. On one side are proponents of a uniformitarian model in which Wilson-Cycle plate tectonics began very early, with the consequence that thick, rigid continental crusts formed quite quickly from chemical differentiation in the upper mantle. On the other side are proponents of models in which the effects of the higher temperatures in the early mantle and crust were reflected in a thick asthenosphere and thin lithosphere. Presumably, a thin crust was relatively weak and easily deformed by subcrustal movements; in particular, downsagging intracratonic troughs and rift basins were a feature of the early protocratons.

Models of early crustal evolution must also explain the origin of greenstone belts. Certain resemblances between volcanic and sedimentary suites in greenstone belts and those in modern marginal basins led to the suggestion that they have a common origin. While this might be true in a few cases, many greenstone belts appear to have an intracratonic rather than marginal origin.

Evidence for Archean life-forms is found in stromatolites and microfossils in chert. Stromatolites are organosedimentary structures made up of layers of sediment precipitated or trapped by algal mats growing on the sediment surface in shallow water. Rare examples preserved in chert show that the layers were built up by the action of cyanobacteria and bacteria.

The microfossils in the chert beds are also the remains of cyanobacteria and bacteria. All are prokaryotic cells, and the formations range in age from 2,800 million years to 3,500 million years.

Questions

1. Much of the pioneer work on Precambrian rocks was done during the latter years of the nineteenth century. What was the reason for the great interest in these rocks?
2. List the major shield areas of the world, and indicate them on a world map.
3. What is the difference between a shield and a platform?
4. In traversing from the center of a central shield area outward across a typical craton, what are the general age relationships of the rocks encountered?
5. What do the mnemonics *felsic* and *mafic* stand for? How are they used in one of the methods of classifying igneous rocks?
6. What are the oldest minerals yet found, what is their age, and where were they found?
7. Why is it extremely unlikely that any direct evidence of the first crustal rocks will ever be discovered?
8. What is the relationship between the lunar surface features observable today and the conditions on the earth in the Early Archean?
9. Several models have been proposed to describe the evolution of the earliest crust. Discuss one of them.
10. What was probably the chief difference between the Early Archean crust and that of the crust since the beginning of the Phaneorozic?
11. Greenstone belts have been described as "floating in a sea of granite." Explain.
12. What feature of greenstone belts seems to suggest that they should not be compared with the marginal basins surrounding modern continents?
13. How are stromatolites formed?
14. Why are the earliest fossils so difficult to identify?
15. Are there any rocks of Archean age in your immediate area? If not, have any been located in deep boreholes or identified with certainty in seismic surveys?

Further Reading

Lowe, D. R. 1980. Archean sedimentation. *Ann. Rev. Earth Planet Sci.* 8:145–67.

Moorbath, S. 1977. The oldest rocks and the growth of continents. *Scientific American* 238:92–104.

Moorbath, S. 1985. The age of the earth and the oldest rocks. *Geology Today:* 75–79.

Schopf, J. W. 1978. The evolution of the earliest cells. *Scientific American* 239:111–38.

Tarling, D. H., ed. 1978. *Evolution of the earth's crust.* New York: Academic Press.

Windley, B. F. 1984. *The evolving continents.* New York: Wiley.

11

THE PROTEROZOIC

Introduction

The geology begins to look a little more understandable in the Proterozoic. Admittedly, usable fossils are not found until the end of the Proterozoic, but at least the rocks are more recognizable. Not only are they much less metamorphosed or not metamorphosed at all, but they contain many familiar features and lithologic associations. Facies changes become discernible, and paleogeographic interpretations begin to make some sense in terms of plate-tectonic mechanisms and more familiar crustal processes. In short, the range of conjecture in the Proterozoic is much more limited than it was in the Archean. This chapter is about the Proterozoic—the familiar yet unfamiliar.

Proterozoic Overview

Up to this point, our discussion has covered the major rock associations found in Archean terrains, but no clear-cut calendar of events has emerged. As mentioned in earlier chapters, radiometric dating does not always provide a definitive answer because isotopic clocks are reset by later episodes of metamorphism. In the Proterozoic, however, a sequence of events and a relative time scale based on stratigraphic succession (superposition) and cross-cutting relationships can usually be determined for any one region. With carefully selected oldest isotopic dates, a real-time calendar eventually may become possible.

In most shield areas, the distinction between Archean and Proterozoic successions is usually seen on a local scale at a marked unconformity where sedimentary rocks, showing little or no metamorphism, lie above granulite/gneiss and/or greenstone basement rocks. While local mapping may be expedited by this contrast between the two rock associations, the actual boundary between Archean and Proterozoic as a time-stratigraphic entity and part of the geologic calendar is less easily defined.

As a segment of earth history, the Archean is usually understood to embrace the period from the origin of the earth up to the time when the crust had "stabilized" and the first granitic cratons or continents had appeared. In North America, the **Kenoran orogeny**, dated at 2,600 to 2,400 million years, is considered to mark this event, and so a more or less arbitrary figure of 2,500 million years was selected by international agreement as marking the Archean/Proterozoic boundary. This boundary, however, has no particular lithologic or historical significance because, in southern Africa, evidence indicates that granitic cratons existed well before 3,000 million years.

Early in the Proterozoic, cratons of continental or probably even of supercontinental size, are believed to have existed (Figure 11.1). Consequently, both over continental interiors and across broad, flooded margins were extensive areas where a wide variety of sediment accumulated. Except in regions involved in later folding/metamorphic episodes these successions have often survived with little or no metamorphism.

The Proterozoic of the Canadian Shield

Proterozoic rocks can be seen in many parts of the Canadian Shield, where they overlie with marked unconformity Archean rocks that were metamorphosed and widely intruded by granites during the Kenoran orogeny. One of the earliest Proterozoic successions to be described was the classic **Huronian System,** studied by William Logan and Sterry Hunt during the 1850s and 1860s. Located in the area north of Lake Huron, the Huronian System is a succession of volcanic lavas and pyroclastics, various clastic sediments, and occasional limestones, totaling some 2 kilometers in thickness. It is divided into the Bruce Series below and the Cobalt Series above (Figure 11.2).

The Cobalt succession is more widespread than the Bruce and, in many places, lies with pronounced unconformity directly on Archean basement rocks. A wide variety of sedimentary environments is represented, including fluvial (river) deposits seen in the thick Mississagi Quartzite. Higher in the Cobalt succession is the **Gowganda Conglomerate,** dated at 2,280 million years and widely considered to be of glacial origin. The individual boulders in the conglomerate do not touch one another and are separated by fine-grained matrix material. This unusual disrupted framework (as opposed to intact, when boulders touch one another) is most commonly found in glacial tills, although it is not exclusive to these deposits. Certain other features of the Gowganda support the glacial origin idea and are discussed later in the chapter.

Traced eastward and southeastward away from the old Archean nucleus of what is called the **Superior Province,** the Huronian succession thickens to over 8 kilometers, although the facies change little as the beds are traced into what is known as the Grenville fold belt (for locations, see Figure 11.3). This suggests that the Grenville belt was a geosyncline—that is, a region of long, continuous downsinking—before it became involved in an orogeny dated at about 1,000 to 900 million years. Within the fold belt itself, the various Huronian formations have typically been metamorphosed, folded, and faulted, and thus are difficult to identify.

FIGURE 11.1
Three interpretations of Proterozoic supercontinent
configuration. (a) Two supercontinents. (b) A Pangaea
configuration. (c) Three continents.

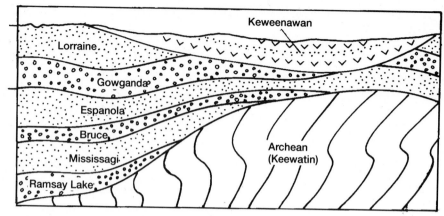

FIGURE 11.2

The Huronian System succession and its relationship to the
Archean in the region north of the Great Lakes.

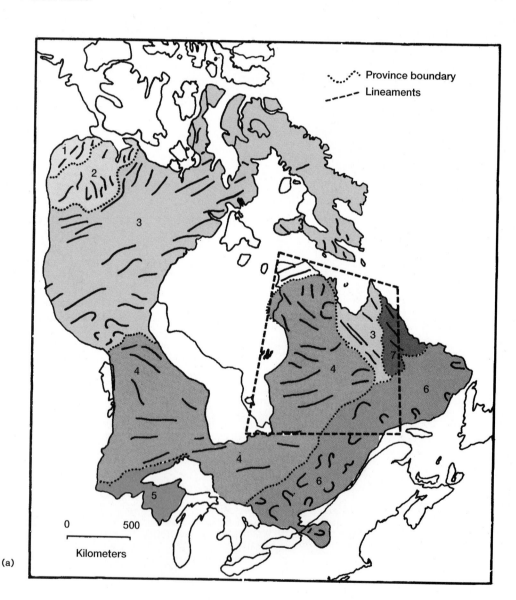

Key

1 Bear Province
2 Slave Province
3 Churchill Province
4 Superior Province
5 Southern Province
6 Grenville Province
7 Nain Province

(a)

FIGURE 11.3

(a) Tectonic provinces of the Canadian Shield.
(b) Enlargement of Quebec region, showing detail of
structural trends and lineaments.

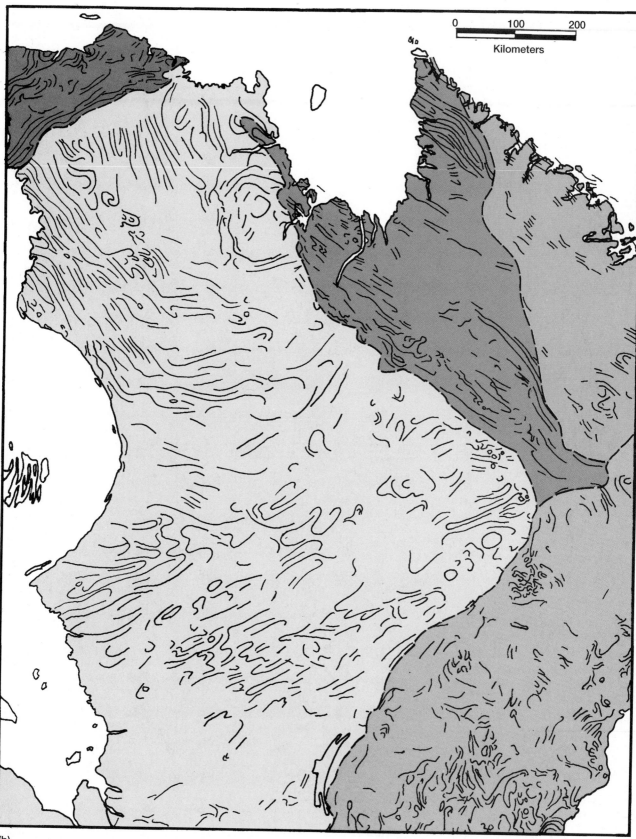

(b)

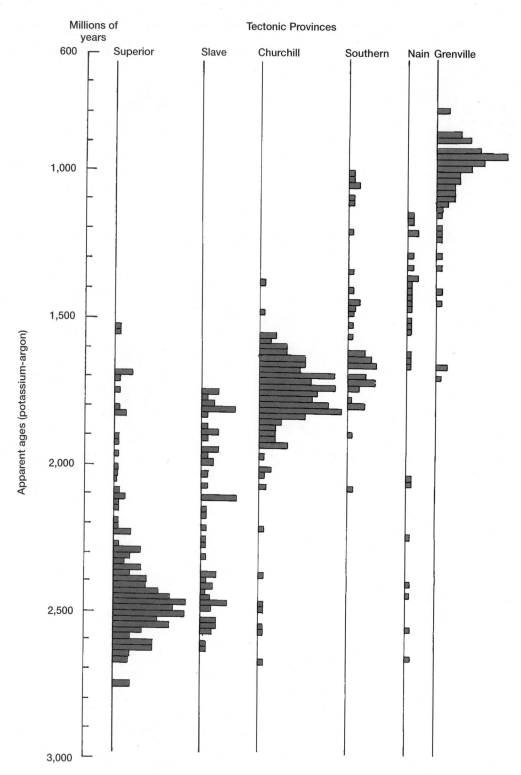

FIGURE 11.4

Histograms of potassium-argon age determinations for
metamorphic and granitic rocks from six tectonic provinces
of the Canadian Shield.

TABLE 11.1

Time-Stratigraphic Classification of the Precambrian of the Canadian Shield

Eon	Era	SubEra	Orogeny (mean potassium-argon mica age, in millions of years ago)
Proterozoic	Hadrynian		
	Helikian	Neohelikian	Grenvillian (955)
		Paleohelikian	Eisonian (1,370)
	Aphebian		Hudsonian (1,735)
Archean			Kenoran (2,480)

A Proterozoic Time Scale

One hundred and fifty years of continuous mapping, mainly by geologists of the Geological Survey of Canada, has made the Canadian Shield the best known of the shield areas. The first real stratigraphic division based upon field relationships was recognized on the Canadian Shield. Not surprisingly, this research has influenced geologists' approach to Precambrian stratigraphy as a whole.

Tectonic Provinces

Quite early in the mapping program, a number of distinct regions, or **tectonic provinces,** each with a certain homogeneity of structural trends—folds and faults, regional foliation, igneous dikes, and mineralized zones—were recognized (Figure 11.3). All tend to follow certain preferred directions, or **lineaments,** that are also often apparent in geomagnetic and gravity surveys. The boundaries of these tectonic provinces are marked discontinuities, where the whole geologic terrain and texture changes within a few kilometers.

Isotopic Dates

The same internal homogeneity in each tectonic province can be seen in isotopic dates. As the number of age determinations from all parts of the shield grew into thousands, they also, when plotted on a map, clustered significantly within each of the tectonic provinces. In a study by R. Dearnley in 1965, 3,200 isotopic ages, plotted in histogram form, showed particular peaks at 2,500 million years, 1,700 million years, and 1,000 million years (Figure 11.4). Clearly, over long intervals, the times of the setting of the radiometric clocks in newly crystallized igneous rocks or in newly metamorphosed rocks were not randomly spread but had occurred during short periods, between which there had apparently been long intervals of crustal quiescence.

Translating this into geologic events, geologists were able to piece together a history of several orogenic or mountain-building movements, separated by periods of sediment accumulation in basins or downwarped troughs. Any given sedimentary succession could be dated by bracketing (that is, it was clearly younger than the granite over which it was deposited and that had been intruded during the previous orogeny and then eroded down). Similarly, a minimum age of the youngest sediments in the succession could be set by dating the granites that intruded them at the time of the next orogenic movement. Obviously, this provided the basis for a time scale of Precambrian events. Four separate orogenic episodes were recognized and used to define a fivefold division of the Precambrian into eons, eras and suberas, as set out in Table 11.1.

Significant clustering of isotopic dates and an apparent cyclicity in crustal activity have also been noted on other shields. Soviet geologists, in particular, were able to subdivide Precambrian time into similar units as those of the Canadian Shield.

Polar-Wandering "Tracks"

In another approach, E. Irving and J. Park noted that the apparent polar-wandering curve for the North American continent had a distinctive shape, consisting of long, relatively straight segments they called tracks, at the end of which the curve took an abrupt turn, almost doubling back on itself (see Box 9.1). They called these sudden kinks in the curve **hairpins** and deduced that they marked changes in the direction of movement of a drifting continental block. Irving and Park used the tracks and hairpins to subdivide Precambrian time into what they called **superintervals.** Five separate superintervals were identified, each separated by a hairpin. The ages of the hairpins in the Precambrian show some measure of agreement with the orogenies used in the Precambrian time division of the Canadian Shield.

Diastrophic Cycles

Russian geologist Lazarus Salop claimed to recognize a roughly 250 million year periodicity in what he called **diastrophic cycles**—that is, cycles of mountain building and shield accretion. Three major cycles, whose timing coincides with the cycles of the Canadian Shield, are interspersed with numerous minor cycles. Salop claimed that diastrophic or orogenic cycles can be recognized worldwide, but not all geologists agree. The Worsley, Nance, and Moody model, described in Chapter 9, proposed a cycle of plate-tectonic activity in which a Pangaea-size continent broke apart and then formed again by accretion. The cycles of orogenic activity may possibly be linked with such long-term movements.

Early Continents

North America

The Proterozoic supracrustal rocks of the large area to the north and northwest of the Superior Province, and between it and the other ancient massif called the **Slave Province,** also include a variety of metasedimentary and sedimentary rocks. Among these are extensive banded iron formations. Similar iron formations are also found at the western end of Lake Superior, as part of what has been called the Animikie Group. Broadly similar to the Hudsonian succession, Animikie sediments lap up northward onto the margins of the old Superior massif and thicken southward into the mobile belt of what has been called the Southern Province. Studies of current bedding and facies changes in the clastic sediments indicate that they were derived from weathering and erosion of the Archean rocks of the Superior Province, which presumably formed a low-lying landmass to the north and northeast.

Along the northeastern flank of the old Superior nucleus is another belt of Proterozoic sediments that occur in two parallel troughs. Facies relationships within this belt are reminiscent of the miogeosyncline/eugeosyncline association of the Appalachian fold belt of Paleozoic age. The sediments of this region, labeled the Kaniapiska System, are interpreted as being laid down on a continental shelf passing along its northeastern edge into continental rise sediments. This clearly marked the northeastern margin of the ancient North American continent. A similar continental margin succession has been described in the so-called Coronation geosyncline that lies to the northwest of the Slave Province which, like the Superior Province, was an Archean nucleus.

Viewed as a whole and summarizing the various Proterozoic successions of the North American continent, the Archean nuclei of the Superior, Slave, Nain, and Greenland provinces were surrounded by extensive platforms and basins, where considerable thicknesses of a variety of sediments accumulated. Traced away from the nuclei centers, all the Proterozoic successions become thicker and, when not metamorphosed beyond recognition, show facies changes that indicate the presence of subsiding basins. Around the northeastern and northwestern margins of the continent, a continental shelf/continental rise couplet was apparently present. A similar margin likely lay along the southeastern edge of the continent at this time, although direct evidence is obscured by the Grenville orogeny that occurred in the Late Proterozoic. Similarly, what the western margin of this Early and Middle Proterozoic North America looked like is also largely unknown because of the later earth movements resulting from plate collision that eventually produced the Cordilleran fold belt.

The Proterozoic terrains of the **Churchill Province** were clearly not marginal to the major mass of ancestral North America but instead seem to have been laid down in an intracratonic basin between the Superior and Slave nuclei. This is supported by the tracts of ancient gneisses dated as of Archean age, the traces of Archean structural trends, and even the greenstone belts that have survived in scattered enclaves throughout the province. Clearly, the Superior and Slave Archean nuclei are part of what once was a much larger craton. This apparently survived as a rigid, probably largely emergent mass, while the region between (that is, the Churchill Province) subsided and was, at least at certain periods, a shallow platform sea.

In any event, both the marginal and intracratonic basins were involved in the **Hudsonian orogeny,** as evidenced by a clustering of isotopic dates, which probably reached a climax over the period 1,800 to 1,650 million years ago. Only those Proterozoic successions and the basin margins where they extended up onto the Archean massifs were unaffected by the folding and metamorphism. In the Churchill Province, the Hudsonian movements involved considerable transcurrent faulting that trended in a northeasterly direction (Figure 11.5).

The close of the Hudsonian orogeny marked the beginning of a long period of comparative quiescence for the North American craton, which had now grown to continental size. Later (post-Hudsonian) Proterozoic sedimentary covers were variable and over extensive areas consisted of relatively thin quartzitic blanket sands. In the area south of Lake Athabaska, for example, the Athabaska Formation consists of well-sorted sands with conglomeratic lenses that were laid down in coastal or shallow offshore environments, associated with dolomitic limestones. Similar blanket sands are mapped as the Sioux Quartzite in Minnesota. In the Lake Superior region, similar shallow-platform deposits, both of marine and nonmarine origin, constitute the Keweenawan Series. Interbedded with the sediments are many thin lava flows of plateau basalt type that have been traced in the subsurface as far as Kansas, some 1,500 kilometers to the south, beneath a cover of Phanerozoic rocks and dated at around 1,100 to 1,200 million years. These basaltic outpourings were apparently part of a major phase of intrusion by basic magmas that affected other cratons as well about this time. This topic is discussed in more detail later in the chapter.

FIGURE 11.5
Aerial view of the McDonald fault scarp, Northwest
Territories, Canada. *(Photograph courtesy of Geological Survey of
Canada. Department of Energy, Mines, and Resources.)*

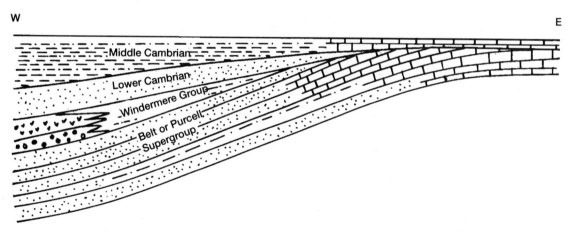

FIGURE 11.6
Stratigraphic succession of the western Canadian margin
from Middle Proterozoic through Middle Cambrian.

Around the margins of the continent, the later Proterozoic presumably saw the accumulation of continental
shelf/continental rise sedimentary prisms. To the southeast and south, these sediments were involved in the Grenville orogeny, which reached a climax at about 900 to 1,000
million years. Along the western side of the continental
margin, sediments of this period are typified by numerous
formations intermittently exposed from northern Canada
to the Mexican border. One of the largest areas of outcrop
is in Idaho, Montana, and up into Canada, where thick

formations, predominantly shallow-water sandstone, comprise the Belt Supergroup (Figure 11.6). Another Proterozoic succession is the Grand Canyon Series, consisting
of sands, shales, and minor limestones exposed in the inner
gorge of the Grand Canyon of the Colorado in Arizona
(Figure 11.7). They are dated as of Middle Proterozoic
age and lie nonconformably on the dark Vishnu and
Brahma schists of Early Proterozoic age that are found at
the bottom of the Grand Canyon and that are intruded by
granitic rocks dated at 1,300 to 1,400 million years old.

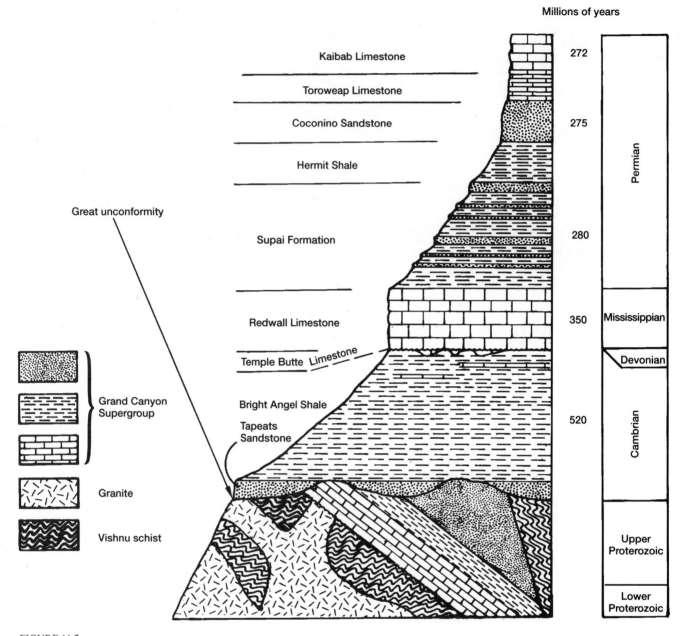

Millions of years

Kaibab Limestone

Toroweap Limestone

Coconino Sandstone

Hermit Shale

Great unconformity

Supai Formation

Grand Canyon
Supergroup

Redwall Limestone

Temple Butte Limestone

Granite

Bright Angel Shale

Tapeats
Sandstone

Vishnu schist

272

275

280

350

520

Permian

Mississippian

Devonian

Cambrian

Upper
Proterozoic

Lower
Proterozoic

FIGURE 11.7
The Middle Proterozoic Grand Canyon Series
nonconformably overlies the Lower Vishnu schists of the
inner gorge of the Grand Canyon. Overlying the Precambrian
succession with marked unconformity are sandstones and
shales of Cambrian age.

Southern Continents: Gondwana

The Proterozoic history of the southern continents is logically discussed as the history of Gondwana. At the center
of this vast land area lay Africa. Probably not coinciden-
tally, craton stabilization began much earlier in southern
Africa than elsewhere. The sediments lying above the
major unconformity that planed off the granulite/gneiss
and greenstone complex in North America and that
marked the Archean/Proterozoic boundary are seen also
in the Transvaal System, but here they are 2,800 million
years old and, therefore, technically of Archean age. The

overlying sediments of the Witwatersrand Supergroup,
consisting of quartzites, shales, and conglomerates, are
reminiscent of the Cobalt and Bruce series of Canada but
are considerably older (Table 11.2). The Witwatersrand
System is itself overlain in many areas by the Ventersdorp
System of sandstones and conglomerates, together with
volcanics dated at 2,300 million years old.

One of the most outstanding features of southern African geology is the so-called **Bushveld Complex,** a massive accumulation consisting of layer upon layer of igneous
rocks that cover 66,000 square kilometers, an area many
times the total area of all the other known basic igneous

TABLE 11.2

Subdivision of the Precambrian in South Africa

Approx. Age (millions of years ago)	Chronostratigraphic Unit — Era	Lithostratigraphic Unit — Group	Supergroup/ Sequence	Thickness	
	Paleozoic	Nama/Malmesbury Gariep. Nosib			
1,080	Namibian		Damara		
	Mogolian	Koras Waterberg/Soutpansberg		6½ km	5 km sediment 1½ km volcanics
2,070	Vaalian	Rooiberg Ollfantshoek Pretoria/Postmasburg Chunlespoort/Campbell/ Griquatown Woikberg	Transvaal/ Griqualand West	11 km	9 km sediment 2 km volcanics
2,630	Randian	Pniel Platberg Kliprlvlersberg	Ventersdorp	5 km	1 km sediment 4 km volcanics
		Central Rand West Rand	Witwatersrand	11 km	9 km sediment 2 km volcanics
2,800		Dominion Limpopo (Belt Bridge)			
2,900	Swazian	Pongola		10 km	5 km sediment 5 km volcanics
3,750		Moodies Fig Tree Onverwacht	Swaziland	21 km	5 km sediment 16 km volcanics

Source: Thickness data from C. R. Anhaeusser, "The Evolution of the Early Precambrian Crust of Southern Africa," *Philosophical Transactions of the Royal Society,* vol. 273, pp. 359–388, 1973.

complexes in the world (Figure 11.8). It was intruded about 2,095 to 1,954 million years ago along planes of weakness in rock of the Pretoria Group, the uppermost division of the Transvaal Supergroup. The igneous activity responsible for the formation of this remarkable rock body was clearly an important event and provides a useful time marker such that Precambrian history in southern Africa falls into three divisions: (1) the ancient granulite/ greenstone basement; (2) the sediments and volcanics of the Witwatersrand, Ventersdorp, and Transvaal systems of pre-Bushveld time; and (3) the Middle to Late Proterozoic sediments—dominantly red and brown sandstones, shales, and conglomerates of the Waterberg and Loskop systems that are post-Bushveld in age (Table 11.2). The Bushveld Complex and other Precambrian mafic intrusives are discussed further in the chapter.

For much of its history, Africa has been a region of positive relief, and it formed the heartland of ancestral Gondwana. Although not surrounded by younger mobile

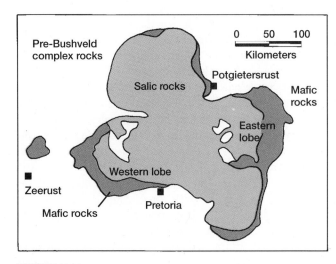

FIGURE 11.8

Sketch map of the Transvaal region, South Africa, showing the Transvaal and Witwatersrand systems intruded by the Bushveld Complex.

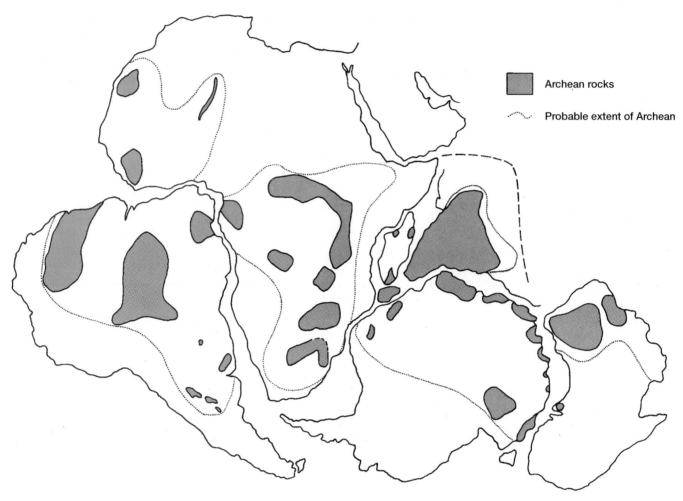

FIGURE 11.9
Archean areas of the southern continents.

belts, as is the North American craton, for example, it obviously has been involved in several continental collision episodes. Apart from the Cape fold belt at its southern tip and the Atlas fold mountains in the far northwest, the post-Archean history of Africa has been virtually free of major orogenic events. Like the African block, peninsula India also formed part of the Gondwana hinterland.

The marginal belts of the Gondwana supercontinent are found beyond Africa. The most continuous margin is that of western South America, although its Proterozoic history has been obscured by several orogenic phases from Late Precambrian time up to the Cenozoic. Elsewhere in South America, and as mentioned in Chapter 10, are two major shield areas—the Guyana Shield in the north and the Brazilian Shield—with three smaller shields in the south (Figure 11.9). The Amazon basin between the Guyana and Brazilian shields has a long history of downsagging and contains a sedimentary fill of both terrestrial material and marine deposits that date back to the Proterozoic. The Amazon may well have the oldest river

course in the world because the major downsag that determines its course already existed during the Proterozoic.

The Yilgarn Shield of southern and central Western Australia and the Pilbara Shield to its north form the Archean shields of Australia. Between the shields lies the Hammersley Basin, underlain by one of the most complete Proterozoic successions anywhere. Included in this succession are extensive and thick banded iron formations.

Australia shares part of the Gondwana continental margin, which is seen in the Adelaide geosynclinal belt. This lies immediately east of another massif of gneisses—the relatively small Gawler Shield of South Australia—parts of which are Archean in age. The Adelaide marginal belt connects with the Andean fold belt of South America via the Transantarctic Mountains of Antarctica, and the Cape fold belt of South Africa, mentioned earlier. Although completely obscured by the much younger Himalayan fold belt, another segment of the Gondwana continental margin presumably lies along the northern edge of the Indian craton.

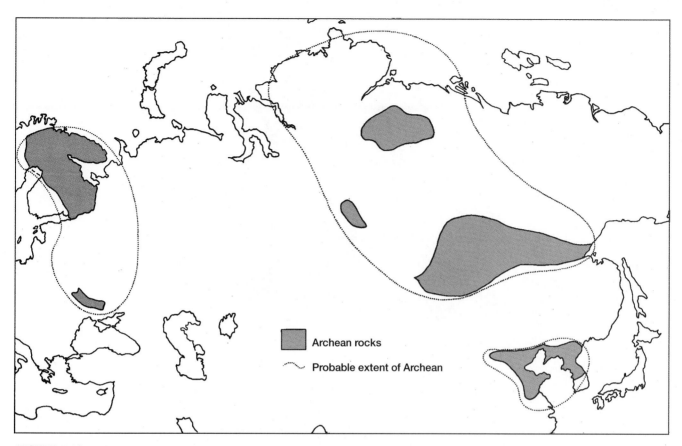

FIGURE 11.10
Archean areas of Eurasia.

Eurasia

Although today the largest contiguous landmass, Eurasia was assembled from smaller continental pieces largely during the Phanerozoic. The two latest additions—the Arabian block and peninsular India—were not joined to Asia until the Cenozoic. The Precambrian history of much of the continent is still only poorly understood because Archean and Proterozoic rocks are exposed only in a few small areas, although they are known to underlie extensive areas of younger rocks. The numerous cratons that are now part of Eurasia east of the Ural Mountains are generally believed to have been separate, small continents whose previous precise geographic locations are unknown (Figure 11.10). One reconstruction has the Siberian platform contiguous with the west coast of North America in Proterozoic time.

The largest shield area in Eurasia is the Baltic Shield and its southern extension—the Ukrainian massif. Three tectonic provinces can be recognized within the Baltic Shield (Figure 11.11). As with the Canadian tectonic provinces, each is characterized by its own structural style and clustering of isotopic dates. The oldest rocks are found in the Suamo-Karelian Province in the northeast, where

isotopic dates include ages of 3,500 million years. The Sveco-Fennid Province, with ages ranging from 2,300 to 1,500 million years, comprises most of Sweden and Finland, while extreme western Sweden and the southern tip of Norway make up the youngest province—the Sveco-Norwegian or Rhipean Province—which underwent mobilization that set the radiometric clocks 1,200 to 900 million years ago. During some of the Proterozoic, the Baltic Shield likely formed part of the North American continent, so that the Sveco-Norwegian Province was, in fact, an extension of the Grenville Province. This would account for their similarity in ages.

Precambrian Crustal Evolution

Any discussion of Precambrian crustal evolution soon becomes divided between uniformitarian and nonuniformitarian views. Some geologists believe that the plate-tectonic mechanism has been operating since early in the earth's history and seek to explain both Archean and Proterozoic geology in terms of settings that have been described from Phanerozoic time. This is almost certainly incorrect.

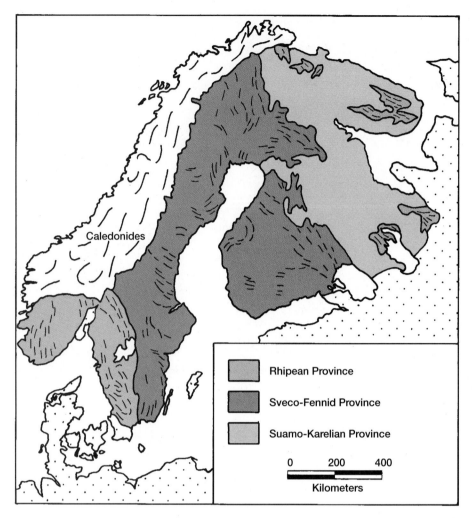

FIGURE 11.11
The three tectonic provinces within the Baltic Shield.

Phases of Crustal Evolution

The single most important control in crustal evolution has been the progressive change in the earth's internal heat budget, as discussed in Chapter 10. Since the Early Archean, when the crustal and subcrustal heat flow was three to four times what it is today, there has been a progressive cooling. Any model constructed to explain the formation of cratons—their size, relative motions, internal deformation, collision, and so on—must consider this cooling trend. The changes may not have been smoothly progressive but initiated threshold effects, resulting in certain discontinuities that, if recognized, clearly constitute important markers in earth history and indicate four major phases of Precambrian crustal evolution. These four major phases can be summarized as follows:

1. Early crustal formational stage, with rapid convectional overturn, from the earth's origin to approximately 4,000 million years ago. Little or no direct evidence of this stage exists.

2. Gradual stabilization and the appearance of the first continental crust as early as 3,500 million years ago in the Swaziland region. Protocontinent formation was spread over the next 1,000 million years. The rocks mapped as Archean date from this period.

3. Early and Middle Proterozoic, with sedimentary successions laid down both in intracratonic basins and in marginal basins around large cratons of continental or supercontinental size. The lithosphere was still relatively thin.

4. Late Proterozoic and the Phanerozoic, with thicker and more rigid lithospheric plates and the beginning of plate-margin subduction and Wilson-Cycle plate-tectonic changes as seen today.

By 3,400 to 3,600 million years ago, crustal differentiation and stabilization had produced the earliest cratonic plates, and the process continued for the next 1,000 million years. During this time, macroplates were assembled, presumably by some kind of collision tectonics, although the precise mechanism is unknown. The earliest well-defined ophiolite suite of ultramafic rocks derived from the upper mantle and deep ocean floor and considered diagnostic of plate suturing along convergent margins was found in Finland and has been dated at 1,990 million years. This occurrence in the Early Proterozoic supports the view that plate movements with margin subduction of Wilson Cycle type did not begin until post-Archean time.

The Supercontinent Hypothesis

The view of many geologists that the Proterozoic continents were large, even of supercontinent size, is supported by paleomagnetic evidence. The apparent polar-wandering paths from the Late Proterozoic to the present show an individuality for each of the continents that demonstrates clearly their movements relative to one another, as described in earlier chapters. The apparent polar-wandering curves for the cratons of Early and Middle Proterozoic time, on the other hand, demonstrate a coherence that suggests that they moved as one mass. Admittedly, the accuracy of dates for the magnetization of these ancient rocks is questionable because of their often complex history of repeated metamorphism and remagnetization. Nevertheless, most geologists agree that a residue of sufficiently accurate magnetic determinations exists to support the Early and Middle Proterozoic supercontinent hypothesis. In one interpretation, all the Precambrian shield area formed part of a single Proterozoic supercontinent of Pangaea size, surrounded by continuous oceanic crust.

The mechanism of assembly of these large continents is, as yet, obscure because the mobile belts (for example, the Limpopo Belt, the Churchill Province, and so on) between the constituent Archean massifs that make up large continental blocks do not seem, in many cases, to have ever been marginal basins or involved in collision episodes. Instead, many seem to have been intracratonic basins and thus postdate the accretionary phase. Presumably, all traces of the actual accretionary process have been destroyed by later events.

Models of Precambrian Crustal Evolution

According to Janet Watson and James Sutton of Imperial College, London, many features of Proterozoic geology, particularly in the Early and Middle Proterozoic, seem to indicate a pattern of crustal evolution that was different from both that in the Archean and the Phanerozoic. In their model, Proterozoic supracrustal successions are of two types: Graywacke/turbidite successions were presumably formed in marginal basins around the periphery of a supercontinent, whereas quartzose/carbonate suites were laid down in intracratonic basins.

One of the important features of this model is that it assumes that the lithospheric plates were still relatively thin and that heat flow although considerably reduced from that of Archean time, was still higher than Phanerozoic values. Unlike the thicker, rigid continental blocks of later time, these Early and Middle Proterozoic continents were supposedly mechanically weak and thus susceptible to considerable internal deformation as, driven by convectional mechanisms, they moved relative to the poles. These internal stresses were largely of a transcurrent rather than compressional nature and were concentrated in those weaker regions where the crust was thinner either due to downsagging and/or necking (a phenomenon best illustrated when stretching a rubber band or pulling apart sticky toffee) consequent on tensional forces. Evidence of this internal deformation is seen in the pronounced lineaments that comprise the tectonic signatures of regions like the Churchill Province (Figure 11.12).

John Rogers of the University of South Carolina and his colleagues also believe that the early cratons were composed of relatively thin crust and that this gradually thickened during a period of "maturing." This process was likely a form of "underplating," as the crust thickened from below.

Proterozoic Basic Intrusions

Twice during the Proterozoic, there were episodes of widespread intrusion by basic magmas. The first occurred at around 2,300 million years ago, the second about 1,200 million years ago. In each case, over a relatively short period of about 200 million years and in virtually every shield area, great clusterings of parallel dikes, or **dike swarms** as they are known, were emplaced. Massive, sill-like (that is, horizontal and conformable to the bedding) bodies, many showing pronounced layering and differentiation effects, were also intruded. These episodes were apparently of global dimensions and so, undoubtedly, of considerable significance in Precambrian crustal evolution. In addition, the rich and often unusual mineralization associated with the intrusions is of great economic importance.

The origin of the magmas and the often complex cooling history of these bodies is still a matter of controversy, and numerous models have been suggested. What is clearly of prime importance, even if not well understood, is the timing of the intrusive episodes. That they appear to come at times of minimal crustal activity and when there was widespread stabilization of the cratons is certainly no coincidence. As can be seen in Figure 11.13, their timing matches those of lows in the histograms of isotopic ages of metamorphism and granitic intrusion episodes (see also Figure 11.4). In other words, the basic intrusions seem to mark the terminal stage of long-term diastrophic or shield-building cycles in crustal evolution.

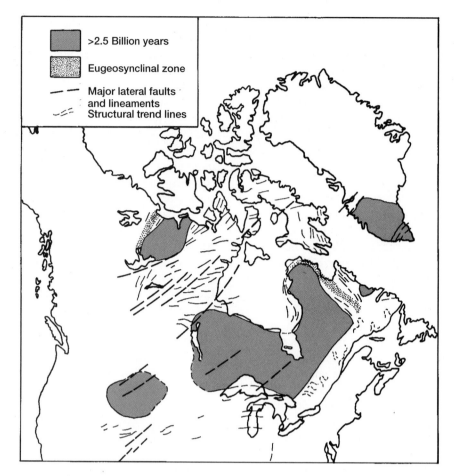

FIGURE 11.12
Structural lineaments in Precambrian rocks of the Canadian Shield.

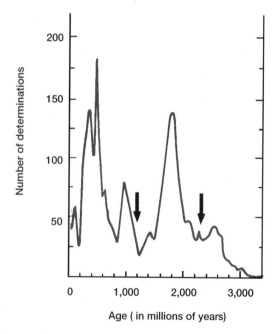

FIGURE 11.13
Timing of basic intrusions in relationship to the frequency curve for age determinations in Archean and Proterozoic terrains. The intrusions clearly coincide with periods of crustal quiescence.

The Bushveld Complex

Undoubtedly, the best known and by far the largest of these intrusive bodies is the Bushveld Complex of the Transvaal in South Africa. Intruded about 2,095 to 1,954 million years ago, the sheer size of this body is almost beyond belief. It covers a total area of 66,000 square kilometers and is larger than the states of New Hampshire, Massachusetts, Connecticut, and Rhode Island combined and more than three times the total area of all the other major mafic complexes in the world put together. Within the Bushveld Complex, rock compositions range from ultramafic types, rich in minerals like olivine, to sialic types containing quartz.

One of the Bushveld Complex's most prominent features is the distinct layering resulting from the segregation of certain minerals during the cooling and crystallization of the magma (Figure 11.14). In some of the layers are rich, concentrated deposits of copper, nickel, chromite, vanadium, platinoid metals, magnetite, magnesite, fluorite, and iron. Of these, chromite has been the most important in terms of production tonnage. Estimated reserves of the minerals are enormous; magnetite iron ore, for example, is estimated at over a billion tons.

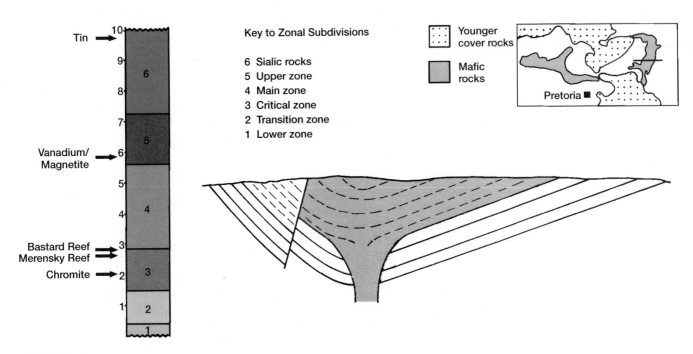

FIGURE 11.14

(a) Stratigraphy of major mineral zones. (b) Structural section through the Bushveld Complex, South Africa. (c) Index map showing line of section.

Explanations for the origin of the Bushveld Complex fall into two broad categories. On the one hand are models with numerous, discrete intrusions arising from an already fractionated magma at depth, and on the other, a single, massive intrusion and then differentiation of the various mineral-rich layers by gravitational settling or other mechanisms.

Great Dyke of Zimbabwe

Another striking basic intrusion in southern Africa is the Great Dyke of Zimbabwe (Figure 11.15a). It can be traced for over 500 kilometers and was intruded about 2,500 million years ago, making it the oldest of the early phase of basic intrusions. It is interpreted as an intrusion into a major tensional rift caused by subcrustal convectional movements.

North American Intrusions

In North America, the largest basic rock body belongs to the younger phase of intrusion dated at about 1,100 million years ago. This is the Duluth Gabbro, with a total area of 4,715 square kilometers. Almost as large and of similar age is the Muskox intrusion in the Northwest Territories of Canada with 3,500 square kilometers (Figure 11.15b). Belonging to the same episode of intrusion is the great Mackenzie dike swarm, probably the world's largest, that extends from Canada's north coast in a great swath south and west down to the Great Lakes. Parts of the swarm are also found far to the northeast on northern Baffin Island.

Precambrian Ice Ages

Over the past 30 years, some of the more interesting geological discoveries have concerned ice ages. Far from being occasional and brief episodes in earth history, data from both continents and ocean floors indicate that ice ages have been more frequent and of longer duration than had previously been suspected. The past 530 million years, for example, have seen three major ice ages, totaling some 160 million years; thus, for nearly one third of the Phanerozoic, continental ice caps existed at one or both poles (see Figure 9.6). Some geologists believe that this is a conservative estimate and that "mini" ice ages were frequent and even regular phenomena, even though they left no direct traces.

Ice Age Indicators

What do geologists look for in identifying an ice age? What kinds of rocks provide glacial clues? Despite their enormous influence and typically great extent, continental ice sheets are largely agents of erosion, and the deposits they leave behind may not be particularly widespread. Nevertheless, certain distinctive glacial features are reliable indicators of glacial activity.

Of particular interest is a group of rocks known as diamictites. These are conglomerates typified by a mixture of poorly sorted or nonsorted boulders or pebbles set in a muddy matrix. Many examples of diamictites are tills, or, as they are also called, boulder clays, and are clearly of glacial origin. Other diamictites had a different origin

Index map

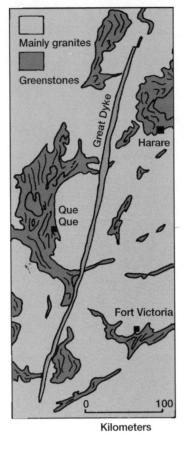

(a)

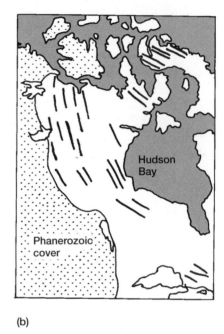

(b)

FIGURE 11.15
Location of basic dike swarms. (a) The Great Dyke of
Zimbabwe. (b) Dike swarms in the Canadian Shield.

and were formed, for example, by submarine slumps or in mudflows. Ancient diamictites—particularly those in the Precambrian, where there may have been considerable alteration and metamorphism—call for cautious analysis. Obviously, not all Precambrian diamictites are indicative of glacial conditions. In practice, additional evidence, such as striations on the boulders, striated rock surfaces below the diamictite, or an association with varved or finely laminated sediments, perhaps containing **dropstones** (pebbles and boulders dropped from floating ice as it melted), greatly strengthens the case for glacial origin (Figure 11.16).

Evidence for Precambrian Glaciations

With evidence for at least three major ice ages during the Phanerozoic, it would be surprising if the earth had not experienced similar episodes during the much longer span of Precambrian time. There is, in fact, considerable evidence from all parts of the world and over considerable time spans for Precambrian ice ages. A compilation of all the available evidence points to at least three and possibly four periods of Precambrian glaciation.

The oldest unequivocal evidence comes from rocks of the Witwatersrand Supergroup of South Africa, which

contain four separate glacial-till horizons metamorphosed into what are termed **tillites.** Isotopic dating gives an age range for these rocks of 2,720 to 2,360 million years, but they are probably older than 2,600 million years and are, in fact, of Late Archean age. In North America, tillite-like conglomerates in the Bruce Series of the Huronian may be as old as 2,700 million years and possibly correlative with the Witwatersrand occurrences. In Montana, also, are some Late Archean diamictites of possibly glacial origin. Of similar age are supposed glacial deposits in the Baikal Mountains of the Karelia area in Russia.

Likely somewhat younger, although with age ranges that partially overlap those of the Witwatersrand glacial deposits, are occurrences of tillites and argillites with dropstones in the area north of Lake Superior. The best known of these formations is the Gowganda, and its glacial origin was recognized even when it was first described by Canadian geologist Arthur Coleman in 1908. Curiously, numerous later workers attempted alternative interpretations, but it is now generally accepted, together with deposits of similar age elsewhere, as evidence of an Early Proterozoic ice cap centered roughly over the present Lake Superior. At least two separate till deposits have been recognized; so, as with the Late Cenozoic ice age, in which, of course, we are still living, glacial advances presumably alternated with retreats, perhaps then, as now, driven by

FIGURE 11.16
Varved sediments of the Gowganda Formation, Early
Proterozoic, dated at about 2 billion years. Note the
dropstone pebble in the varve succession. *(Photo courtesy of
Geological Survey of Canada, Ottawa.)*

TABLE 11.3

Age Relationships of the Proterozoic Glaciations in Australia

				Age (millions of years ago)
Cambrian				
Adelaidean	Proposed Unit	Subunit 1	Egan Glaciation and	570
			Marinoan Glaciation	650
			Moonlight Valley	700
			Glaciation and Sturtian	740 (Late phase)
		Subunit 2	Glaciation	750 (Early phase)
				750 Sturt Marker

the Milankovitch-Köppen insolation mechanism. Early
Proterozoic glacial deposits have also been described in
Australia and South Africa.

Whether the apparent absence of any evidence for
glaciation over the next 800 million years or so is a reliable
indicator is a matter of opinion. For those who favor cyclical recurrences of ice ages, or see them as occurring every
200 or 300 million years in response to changing continental configuration, the long, nonglacial interval is
inexplicable and must be ascribed simply to lack of preserved evidence. In any event, from the Late Proterozoic
comes unequivocal evidence for an ice age of massive proportions, perhaps the biggest in earth history.

Late Proterozoic Glaciations

Evidence for Late Proterozoic ice sheets has been gathered from Africa, Eurasia, Australia, North America,
South America, and, quite recently, from Antarctica also.
In Namibia, Africa, where some of the most complete glacial successions have been studied, evidence points to glacial episodes between 1,000 and 789 million years
(climaxing, perhaps, at 950 to 850 million years) and between 870 and 750 million years. A third phase that may
record only a local mountain glaciation has been dated at
620 to 600 million years. In China, three separate glacial
episodes also have been recognized: the Changan at 800
to 760 million years, the Nantuo at 740 to 700 million
years, and a youngest episode of Vendian (latest Proterozoic) age, which, like the one in Namibia, seems to have
been of more local extent. In Australia, again, there is a
record of several glacial episodes, ranging from 750 mil-

lion years with the so-called Sturtian glaciation, to the
Egan glaciation that ended just before the Cambrian began
(Table 11.3).

A compilation of these and other data hints at a clustering of dates between about 1,000 and 700 million years
that may be separated from a later series of latest Riphean (about 700 million years) and Vendian (670 to 580
million years) occurrences. Alternatively, they may simply
be two phases of the same glaciation. Whether the Late
Proterozoic saw one or several glaciations, the area affected by the ice was undoubtedly very extensive, evidence having been found on all the continents (Figure
11.17).

The apparent size of such an ice cap raises certain
problems that are reminiscent of those posed in the
Chapter 8 discussion of the Permo-Carboniferous glaciation and its apparent enormous extent across a world of
fixed continents. Unfortunately, the movement and relationships of the various continental masses back in the Late
Proterozoic are known with considerably less certainty.
Whether or not one believes in Proterozoic supercont-
nents or even in a single Pangaea continent obviously has
some bearing on the size of the ice cap. If, as paleomagnetic and other evidence seems to indicate, the Late Proterozoic world was one of supercontinents, then the
evidence points to a very large ice cap that, in some areas,
must have reached into low latitudes. If, on the other hand,
a Wilson-Cycle type of plate-tectonic mechanism was already moving the continental pieces around, to assume a
"normal" size ice cap introduces some important constraints on just where those continental pieces were relative to one another. Clearly, many fascinating problems
remain to be solved.

Proterozoic Life

Many Proterozoic successions contain sedimentary rocks
that have suffered little or no metamorphic changes,
thereby considerably improving the opportunities for
finding fossil remains.

FIGURE 11.17
Distribution of evidence for a Late Precambrian ice age.

Progressive But Slow Evolutionary Changes

In passing from the Archean into the Proterozoic, the nature of the fossil record changes little. Just as in the older terrains, the only evidence of life on the earth is the stromatolites and occasional microfossils in cherts (see Box 11.1). The pace of evolution was apparently unchanged, and although at about 2,300 million years, stromatolites became markedly more abundant, the evidence from cherts shows only the prokaryote cells of bacteria and cyano-bacteria (Table 11.4).

Despite the obvious environmental control over stro-matolite morphology, some progressive evolutionary changes in form through the Late Proterozoic have been detected. Pioneer work by Russian paleontologists has shown that stromatolites can be used as biostratigraphic markers, and extending some of the stratigraphic divi-sions recognized in Russia to other continents may become possible (see Box 11.2). Stratigraphic correlation with the Precambrian of Australia is already looking promising.

The first Precambrian microfossils, dated at about 1,900 million years, were discovered in the **Gunflint Chert** in northern Minnesota during the 1950s by Stanley Tyler and Elso Barghoorn. This locality also had turned up stro-matolites preserved in chert, and discerning the nature of the organisms responsible for the stromatolite formation had finally been possible. Even though a billion years younger than the fossils in Fig Tree Group cherts, men-tioned in Chapter 10, the organisms represented still had the most primitive cell structure. Only after another 600 million years were any significant advances seen, in the Beck Springs Formation of southeastern California. Cel-

lular structures in the Beck Springs Formation are con-siderably larger and show internal features interpreted as chloroplasts, mitochondria, and other structures charac-teristic of eukaryotic cells. This marks probably the most significant step forward since the origin of the first prim-itive cells.

In view of the extreme paucity of Precambrian fossils, geologists obviously cannot be sure that the Beck Springs fossils even come close to marking the first appearance of eukaryotes, but they are able, using the dates of the Fig Tree, Gunflint, and Beck Springs formations, to gain some understanding of the extremely slow pace of evolution during these formative years. Assuming that the first true cells appeared, perhaps, some 3,800 million years ago, it took another 2,500 million years to progress to the eu-karyotic level of organization. Why did evolution proceed so slowly? While a definitive answer is not possible at this point, it may have had something to do with the evolution of the atmosphere—in particular, the rate at which the level of oxygen was rising. Most eukaryotes are aerobic and so, presumably, could not have appeared until there was sufficient free oxygen in the atmosphere.

Because eukaryotes have a cell nucleus, they repro-duce by mitosis and meiosis, in contrast to the simple binary fission of unnucleated prokaryotic cells. The advent of sexual reproduction was probably the most significant step of all and is presumed to have occurred approxi-mately 1,000 million years ago. That this date is reason-able is supported by certain remarkable fossils found in the 900-million-year old **Bitter Springs Formation** in Aus-tralia, which show apparent meiotic cell division in prog-ress.

BOX 11.1

Chert, the Preserver

If certain fossils were not preserved in chert, it is doubtful whether there would be any direct evidence of life until 800 to 900 million years ago. As it is, geologists know that life had appeared on earth before 3,500 million years ago, and the evidence of developing organisms in the intervening 2,500 million years is contained almost entirely in chert.

Chert is a microcrystalline or cryptocrystalline form of quartz. Like quartz, it is chemically almost inert, and mechanically, it is very strong, having only vague cleavage and hardness greater than steel. If anything can withstand heating and squeezing and exposure to hydrothermal solutions over millions of years, chert can!

Before the appearance of silica-secreting organisms, such as diatoms, radiolaria, and sponges, the silica content of the oceans was much higher than it is today. Precambrian oceans are believed to have contained perhaps 20 times as much silica as present-day oceans do, so that inorganic precipitation of silica was likely.

In many cases, the silica is thought to have been a product of contemporary volcanic activity.

The microorganisms found in Precambrian cherts were preserved in amorphous silica deposited in a finely divided colloidal state. The silica not only entrapped the microorganisms but also often penetrated the cells. This accounts for the remarkable state of preservation in many cases (Box Figure 11.1).

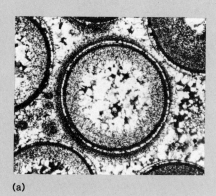

(a)

BOX FIGURE 11.1
(a) Oolith replaced by chert. (b) Algal cells and filaments from the Bitter Springs formation, north-central Australia. *(Photograph by courtesy of J. W. Schopf.)*

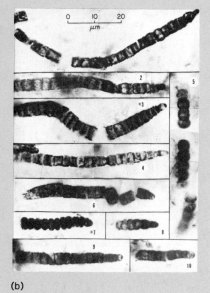

(b)

In addition to stromatolites and the microorganisms in chert, microorganisms of various kinds became increasingly evident also in certain shales and limestones. Collectively called acritarchs, they were clearly unicellular structures. Many were probably phytoplanktonic organisms of some kind, but other organisms of unknown affinities have also been included in this artificial group. Many had a clearly defined central cavity and an external organic wall that was sometimes ornamented with spines and other structures that gave it a sculpted appearance. A large number have been described, and in the Late Proterozoic, some of the "species" are said to have some biostratigraphic significance. Efforts to use them for correlation purposes, however, have not been notably successful to date.

Appearance of Multicellular Organisms

The stage was now set for the appearance of the first multicellular organism. The stratigraphic record contains both direct and indirect evidence of this event. Proterozoic successions at numerous locations and in the 900- to 1,000-million-year age range have revealed unique plantlike carbonaceous impressions. These have sometimes been interpreted as multicellular algae of some kind. In the Little Dal Group of the Mackenzie Mountains in the Yukon, for example, lobate impressions have been compared with those seen in modern sediments and produced by the green algae (*Ulva* spp.), commonly known as sea lettuce.

The earliest evidence of metazoan animals is only indirect and is seen as widespread **bioturbation** of laminated sediments—that is, mixing and disturbance of sediment by organisms, typically burrowing, benthic species. In older successions, undisturbed, finely laminated sediments are a clear indication that no burrowing organisms were present. This changes about 900 to 1,000 million years ago, and from that time on, finely laminated sediments are rare and apparently formed only where bottom conditions were unsuitable (too cold, anoxic, hypersaline, and so on) for benthic organisms. Once this important stage was reached and larger, more robust organisms were appearing, actual body fossils could begin to be preserved. In fact, impressions recently discovered in China and interpreted as primitive wormlike animals date from 700 to 900 million years old.

TABLE 11.4

Development of Life-Forms through the Precambrian

Millions of years ago	Major Biogenic Events	More important Fossiliferous Formations	Lithology and Environment
	First shelly fossils		
	First metazoan fossils	Ediacara	Oxygen content of atmosphere approximately 10 percent of present day
700			
	Origin of sexual reproduction	Bitter Springs (900 million years ago)	Oxidized cratonic sediments (redbeds)
900–1,000			
	First eukaryotes	Beck Springs (1,300 million years ago)	
1,300–2,000			
	Advanced oxygen-mediating enzymes	Gunflint Chert (1,900 million years ago)	End of Superior-type banded iron formations
1,800			
		Transvaal dolomite (2,250 million years ago)	Beginning of free oxygen in atmosphere
2,000			
	Stromatolites becoming abundant	Buluwayan (2,500 million years ago)	Earliest Superior-type banded iron formations
2,500			
	Prokaryotes diversify	Fig Tree (3,000 million years ago)	Mostly unoxidized cratonic sediments
3,000			
	First stromatolites		Potassium-poor granites, greenstones; no free oxygen; earliest metasediments
3,500			
	First autotrophic prokaryotes		
3,800			
	Chemical evolution leading to biogenesis		Earliest lithosphere and hydrosphere
4,200			
	Origin of the earth		Oldest meteorites and terrestrial lead
4,680			

The apparent quickening pace of evolutionary progress is seen in the appearance during the next 100 to 200 million years of the so-called **Ediacaran fauna** containing a variety of metazoans, a few of which may have been ancestral to certain of the great host of Cambrian animals that were to follow. Strictly speaking, we have already crossed the boundary between hidden life and recorded life, between the Cryptozoic and Phanerozoic, and the fact that, technically, we are still in the Precambrian is a point that must be discussed further. The definition of the Precambrian/Cambrian boundary is dealt with at the beginning of the next chapter.

BOX 11.2

Proposed Precambrian Subdivisions

The classification and correlation of Precambrian rocks around the world is receiving much attention both from individual geologists and various international committees. The results of the labor of the many workers appear from time to time in new classification schemes and stratigraphic boundary definitions. The Stratigraphic Commission set up by the International Union of Geological Sciences recently proposed a new set of subdivisions for the Precambrian. These are set out in Box Table 11.1. Greek derivations of the period terms are provided in Box Table 11.2.

BOX TABLE 11.1

Proposed Subdivision of the Precambrian

Eon	Era	Period
PROTEROZOIC	(Base of Cambrian) Neoproterozoic	"Neoproterozoic III" 650 million years ago Cryogenian 850 million years ago Tonian
	——— 1,000 million years ago ———	
	Mesoproterozoic	Stenian 1,200 million years ago Ectasian 1,400 million years ago Calymmian
	——— 1,600 million years ago ———	
	Paleoproterozoic	Statherian 1,800 million years ago Orosirian 2,050 million years ago Rhyacian 2,300 million years ago Siderian
	——— 2,500 million years ago ———	
ARCHEAN		

Source: Stratigraphic Commission of the International Union of Geological Science.

BOX TABLE 11.2

Greek Origins of Period Terms

Cryogenian	Cryos = ice, genesis = birth, in reference to widespread glaciation at this time.
Tonian	Tonos = stretch, referring to crustal extension.
Stenian	Stenos = narrow, referring to narrow belts of deformation and high grade metamorphism.
Ectasian	Ectasis = extension, refers to expansion of platform cover rocks.
Calymmian	Calymma = cover, referring to platform covering rocks.
Statherian	Statheros = stable, solid, referring to craton stabilization at this time.
Orosirian	Orosira = mountain range, refers to orogenic period.
Rhyacian	Rhyax = lava stream, referring to vulcanism and the injection of the Bushveld Complex and other intrusions.
Siderian	Sideros = iron, referring to the Banded Iron Formations characteristic of this period.

Summary

Compared with the Archean, the Proterozoic is more understandable in terms of familiar rocks and processes. At most locations, the boundary between Archean and Proterozoic rocks is marked by an unconformity or nonconformity. In North America, Archean rocks were involved in a widespread orogenic and metamorphic event, the Kenoran orogeny, dated at 2,600 to 2,400 million years. The earliest Proterozoic rocks were those laid down on the erosion surface beveled across the rocks affected by the Kenoran orogeny. This is clearly an important division in the North American Precambrian, and a date of 2,500 million years has been adopted by international agreement as marking the Archean/Proterozoic boundary. This boundary supposedly marks when the earlier crustal unrest of Archean time gave way to a time of crustal stability and the first appearance of true continents. On the other hand, evidence from southern Africa indicates that continental crust had formed and stabilized at least 500 million years earlier.

Pioneer work on Precambrian stratigraphic relationships was carried out on the Canadian Shield. Both Archean and Proterozoic successions were shown to be systematically distributed in terms of geologic characteristics into distinct provinces of varying ages. Including the extensions of the Canadian Shield southward into the United States, the North American Precambrian rocks could be divided into distinct tectonic provinces, each with its own clusters of isotopic dates, structural trends, lithologic associations, and mineralization. Four time divisions were recognized: the Archean and three eras in the Proterozoic. In the other shield areas of the world, Proterozoic successions are, in general, similar to those in North America. In the Baltic area, for example, distinct tectonic provinces are recognized in the Precambrian, just as in North America.

Many geologists believe that, for much of the Proterozoic, the world's continental masses were joined together in a single Pangaea-like continent, or possibly, two continental blocks. Although there are important differences of opinion, Wilson-Cycle type plate tectonics is not thought to have begun until the Late Proterozoic. At that time, the large supercontinents began to break up, and the major components of the Phanerozoic continents came into existence.

The subject of crustal evolution during the Proterozoic, as in the Archean, is controversial and again involves the nature of the crust and the type of plate-tectonic mechanism.

Twice during the Proterozoic—first at about 2,300 million years and then second around 1,200 million years—there were periods of massive intrusion by basic magmas. Dike swarms, some stretching for thousands of kilometers, and other sill-like masses were emplaced at these times. That these intrusive episodes occurred at times when the cratons were stable and not undergoing orogenic movements is probably significant. The mechanisms underlying the basic intrusions, the significance of their timing, and the internal layering of mineral-rich horizons are all mysteries yet to be solved.

From the Late Archean through the Proterozoic, considerable evidence indicates at least three and perhaps four ice ages. Late Proterozoic glaciation, which lasted until just prior to Cambrian time, was the longest and most severe in earth history. The ice cap was present on all the continents and apparently extended almost to the equator.

Proterozoic life-forms at first show little advance over those in the Archean. Stromatolites became more abundant at about 2,300 million years, and by Late Proterozoic time, were showing morphologic variations that Russian geologists in particular have found useful as biostratigraphic indicators. Correlation with the Proterozoic of other continents is possible, the most promising area to date being Australia.

Microfossils in chert found in the Gunflint Formation are of prokaryote type. Only after another 600 million years is there evidence for a marked evolutionary advance: The first known eukaryotic cells were found in the Beck Springs Formation of California. The few pieces of direct evidence of cells show that evolution was proceeding very slowly, this probably being linked to the evolution of the atmosphere and the increase in the oxygen content. In the 900 million-year-old Bitter Springs Formation of Australia is the first evidence of sexual reproduction.

The first evidence for metazoans is seen in widespread bioturbation of laminated sediments about 900 million years ago. The animals responsible are unknown. The first body fossil is that of a supposed worm, dated at between 700 and 900 million years. During this time, the Ediacaran fauna of metazoans also likely appeared.

Questions

1. Compared with the Archean, Proterozoic rocks provide a much more readable account of geologic history. Why?
2. What, if any, is the significance of the 2,500-million-year age of the Archean/Proterozoic boundary?
3. How did the growing number of isotopic age determinations from the Canadian Shield aid in the interpretation of its history?
4. What is the basis for the recognition of the various tectonic provinces of the North American craton?
5. What is meant by bracketing?
6. Discuss the implications of the apparent polar-wandering curve as established for the North American craton.
7. Describe the time scale for the Precambrian used in the Canadian Shield.
8. Describe the episodes of basic intrusion during the Proterozoic.
9. What is the relationship between the Sveco-Norwegian Province of the Baltic Shield and the Grenville Province of the Canadian Shield?
10. Four major phases of crustal evolution can be discerned during the Precambrian. Describe these phases.
11. Describe the Bushveld Complex of Transvaal, South Africa.
12. What evidence is there for glaciations during the Proterozoic?
13. Evidence for a Late Proterozoic ice age is found in locations at all latitudes. What are possible explanations?
14. What direct and indirect evidence supports the appearance of the first multicelled organisms?
15. Draw a rough map of the proposed configuration of supercontinents in the Late Proterozoic.

Further Reading

Glaessner, M. F. 1984. *The dawn of animal life*. Cambridge, England: Cambridge University Press.

Hunter, D. 1978. The Bushveld Complex and its remarkable rocks. *American Scientist* 66:551–60.

Read, H. H., and J. Watson. 1975. *Introduction to geology*. Vol. 2, *Earth history*. New York: Wiley.

Walter, M. R. 1977. Interpreting stromatolites. *American Scientist* 65:563–71.

12

THE CAMBRIAN WORLD AND AN EVOLUTIONARY EXPLOSION

209

Introduction

The calendar of earth history for approximately the past 570 million years is based, as described in earlier chapters, on the fossil remains of an enormous array of organisms. From the very beginning of scientific geology, the Precambrian was usually considered "different," the main reason being that it supposedly contained no fossils. This dichotomy between the Precambrian and the Cambrian was made official by pronouncements like that of a committee of the International Geological Congress of 1954, which set the Precambrian/Cambrian boundary at the base of occurrence of organized fossils. This criterion was essentially reaffirmed in 1972 by the group set up to study the boundary problem. The group proposed that the boundary should be set "as close as practical to the earliest known appearance of diverse shelly fossils."

Even the earliest geologists could see that the base of the Cambrian System marked the sudden appearance of a wide variety of organisms not present in the strata below. As far as these workers were concerned, the Precambrian was unfossiliferous, and the puzzling absence of even traces of forms ancestral to Cambrian species was generally ascribed to their not having hard, fossilizable skeletons.

Darwin also was aware of the sudden appearance of the earliest Cambrian faunas and the apparent absence of ancestral forms. He offered no reason for this phenomenon and stated that it "at present must remain inexplicable." He even admitted that it might well be used as evidence against his theory of evolution.

Early geologists also knew that the Precambrian/Cambrian boundary was, in many parts of the world, marked by a pronounced unconformity. There had apparently been a protracted withdrawal of the seas in latest Precambrian time, and strata dating from that period are uncommon. Many geologists even believed that this hiatus in the stratigraphic record was worldwide in extent, and Charles Walcott—perhaps the greatest of the early students of the Cambrian—named it the **Lipalian interval.** In any event, the unconformity accentuated the lithologic discontinuity of the Precambrian/Cambrian boundary and made the absence of organisms ancestral to Cambrian forms more plausible.

Now that the Precambrian/Cambrian boundary has been somewhat clarified, the chapter goes on to explore the world of the Cambrian and how it differed from the Precambrian. The evolutionary explosion of life-forms during the Cambrian receives special emphasis.

Cambrian Overview

The Shape of the Cambrian World

As discussed in Chapter 11, paleomagnetic data suggest that, for much of the Proterozoic, nearly all the world's landmass formed a single or possibly two large supercontinents. By the beginning of Cambrian time, however, continental breakup had produced at least six separate continents. Again, paleomagnetic observations make it possible to ascertain the paleolatitude of these lands. Instead of finding the ancient pole position, geologists determine the degree of magnetic dip (or inclination), with a steep angle indicating a high latitude, a low or flat dip pointing to a low latitude.

In the Early Cambrian, all the continents were apparently strung out along or close to the equator (Figure 12.1a). Studies of the faunas and other climatic indicators, such as evaporites in various facies patterns, generally confirm this paleogeographic pattern. Longitudinal position is more doubtful, but the cosmopolitan nature of the earliest Cambrian faunas suggests that, at first, the continents were not widely separated, making it possible for shallow-water faunas to migrate readily. Later, as oceans widened, provinciality in various faunas, as for example, in the trilobites, became noticeable (Figure 12.1b).

Cambrian Plate Tectonics

Whether Wilson-Cycle plate tectonics began with the Late Proterozoic continental breakup or had already been operating for a considerable time before that is controversial. The Grenville orogeny that affected the margin of the Laurussia/Baltica continent has been dated at 1,000 to 900 million years, and many geologists believe that it marks the culmination of a Wilson Cycle, during which an ocean opened and then closed as a consequence of plate collision.

The Late Proterozoic sedimentary record, however, makes definitive statements difficult. The continents at this time were largely emergent, an indication of a Pangaea configuration, with only limited areas of platform and shelf deposition. Similar low sea levels and a consequently poor stratigraphic record are also characteristic of the Permo-Triassic, again a time of a large Pangaea-size continent. Such a pattern seems to conform to the Worsley, Nance, and Moody model mentioned in Chapter 9. It is possible also that the tectono-eustatic sea-level low was aggravated at times by glacio-eustatic controls during the severe, Late Proterozoic ice age.

Eustatic Sea-Level Rise and Epeiric Seas

With the breakup of supercontinents and the disappearance of the Late Proterozoic ice caps, the most important feature of latest Proterozoic/earliest Cambrian time was the beginning of a eustatic sea-level rise that continued with minor interruptions for the next 100 million years. Caused largely by the increased production of sea floor along midocean ridges in the newly formed ocean basins, this transgression ultimately resulted in the drowning of enormous continental areas. If a comparable sea-level rise occurred today, 90 percent of the present-day North American continent would, from time to time, be inundated.

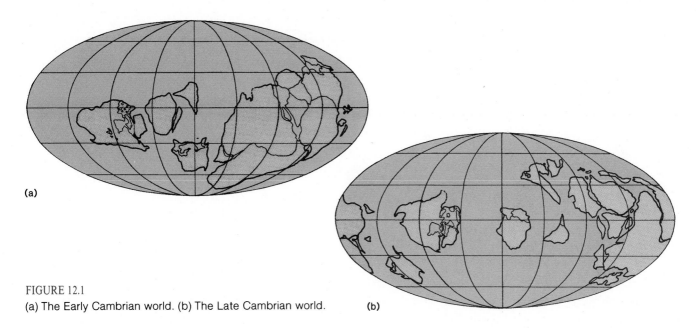

FIGURE 12.1
(a) The Early Cambrian world. (b) The Late Cambrian world.

By the end of the Middle Cambrian, the seas were encroaching further and further onto the North American continent, as indeed they were on several other continents also. As discussed in Chapter 5, **epeiric** (or epicontinental) **seas** were extensive and shallow floodings of the continental interiors. There have been several of these inundations in the last 600 million years. While evidence indicates that the seas made extensive incursions onto Precambrian continents as well, little direct evidence survived the erosion and repeated metamorphism of this earlier time. In addition, the lack of fossils makes it virtually impossible to piece together a sequential story.

A logical approach to reconstructing past landscapes and oceans involves comparisons of the sedimentary record of the past with modern sediments. This is the fundamental "The present is the key to the past" idea discussed in earlier chapters. Unfortunately, this approach does not work with epeiric seas because there are no modern epeiric seas to compare with those of the past. On the other hand, the sedimentary rocks formed in epeiric seas indicate that, while epeiric-sea environments may have been different from currently familiar environments, they clearly were not completely alien.

The first of several major marine transgressions onto the continents during the Paleozoic was the so-called **Sauk transgression.** It began in the late Proterozoic and reached its maximum extent early in the Ordovician. By the Late Cambrian in particular, epeiric seas were extensive, and the sedimentary formations dating from that time are widespread, providing a picture of the various depositional environments.

The Cambrian in North America

What was the North American continent like during the massive Sauk transgression? North America had recently become a separate continent surrounded by passive mar-

gins. With no adjacent orogenic belts and rising mountain chains to supply sediments, the overall distribution of facies across the continent formed a relatively simple pattern. The continental interior was still largely high and dry but probably with no great topographic relief. The continental divide ran along a region of higher ground, known as the **Transcontinental Arch,** that extended from present-day Lake Superior to Arizona. Wide coastal plains on the flanks of the arch extended both to east and west, and they passed, in turn, out onto broad, shallow marine platforms (Figure 12.2). The marked lithologic uniformity of many Cambrian formations suggests that seabottom environments were likewise uniform.

Paleogeographic reconstructions show the Cambrian equator running north-south down the middle of the continent, which was thus aligned at roughly 90 percent from its present orientation. Although the climate was warm, there is some indication that it was not hot. The distribution of the continents along the Cambrian equator has suggested to paleoclimatologists that wind- and ocean-current patterns produced a world climate without the latitudinal extremes of the modern world.

Evidence from central Texas indicates that a semiarid climate existed there in Cambrian time. Sandstones found in this area were apparently laid down in shallow offshore and tidal-flat settings and derived from nearby land areas. They contain grains that exhibit a high degree of rounding, suggesting that they were subjected to continuous mechanical abrasion by the wind in a desert setting. The absence of any land vegetation at that time and the consequent lack of a soil weathering profile might have resulted in such sands, even if the climate were a moist one. On the other hand, there is no evidence in central Texas of the alluvial or deltaic deposits that might otherwise be present in this region.

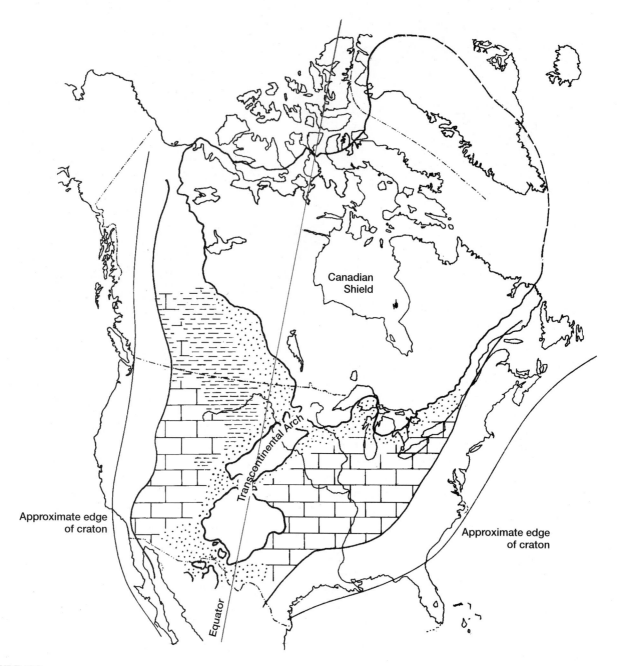

FIGURE 12.2
Paleogeography of the North American craton in the Late Cambrian.

The Inner Clastic Zone: Basal Transgressive Sands

By the Late Cambrian, when large areas of the craton had become covered by shallow seas, a relatively simple pattern of sedimentary facies had developed concentrically around the continent's emergent heartland. Adjacent to the land was an **inner clastic zone** of shallow-water sands derived from the old landmass of the Canadian Shield and its extension, the transcontinental arch. Because such sands represent the initial deposits of an advancing shoreline, they are often referred to in a general way as **basal transgressive sands,** or blanket sands. Typically, they are well-

sorted, quartzose sands described as mature or super-mature, implying that they have undergone several cycles of erosion, transportation, and deposition.

Sands like this are found almost everywhere at the base of Cambrian successions. In a traverse from the continental margin in toward the center of the craton, such sands become progressively younger as successive Cambrian sections are traced toward the craton center (Figure 12.3). Thus, over long distances, the sands can be matched and correlated on the basis of their lithologic characteristics and have even been given the same formation name; however, they are not of the same age and so are said to be **diachronous** (fig 12.4).

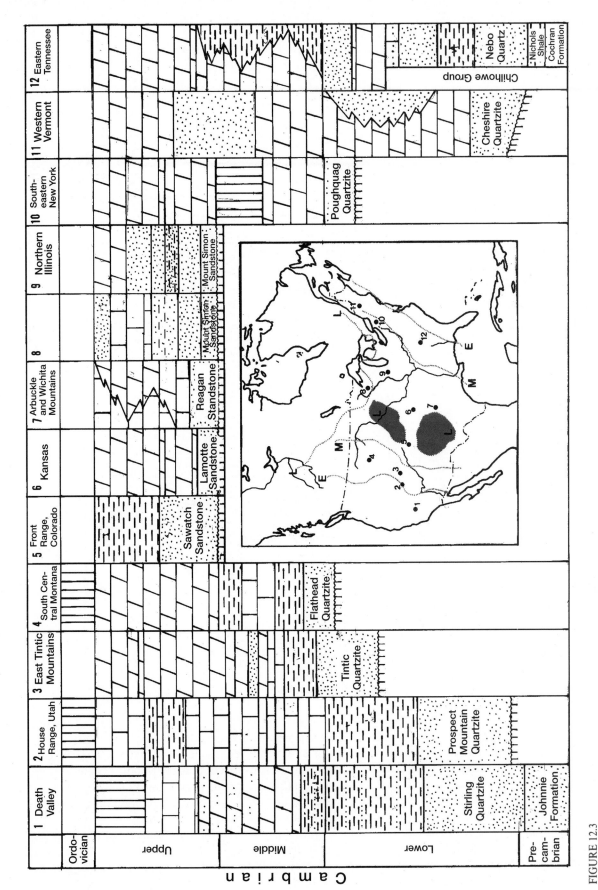

FIGURE 12.3
Key Cambrian stratigraphic sections at U.S. locations. Note the diachronous relationships of the basal Cambrian sands when traced into the craton interior. (E, M, and L on the map signify Early, Middle, and Late Cambrian shorelines, respectively.)

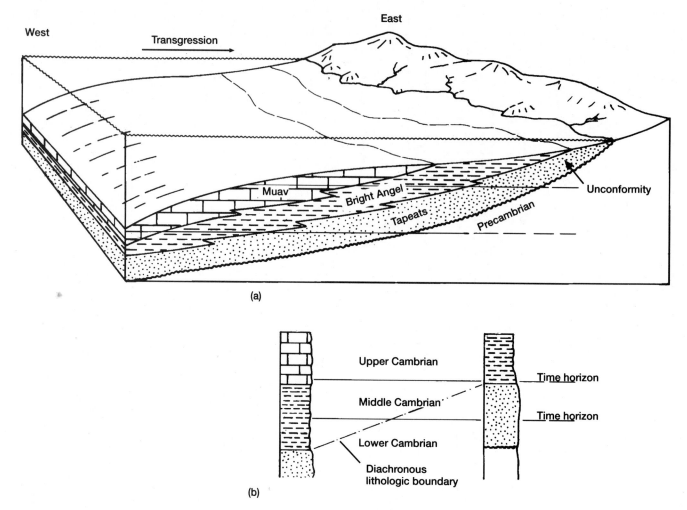

West

East

Transgression

Muav

Bright Angel

Tapeats

Precambrian

Unconformity

(a)

Upper Cambrian

Time horizon

Middle Cambrian

Time horizon

Lower Cambrian

Diachronous
lithologic boundary

(b)

FIGURE 12.4
Diachronism in basal sands of the Sauk transgression.
(a) Block diagram showing facies relationships as seas
transgressed eastward onto the North American craton
during the Cambrian. (b) How time horizons and lithologic
boundaries are related in stratigraphic sections.

In the extreme eastern part of the North American craton, for example, occurrences of these sands form part of the Chilhowee Group exposed just west of the Great Smoky Mountains. Here, the basal beds of the Chilhowee Group are actually of Late Precambrian age, so the critical Precambrian/Cambrian boundary occurs somewhere in the Chilhowee Mountain succession in eastern Tennessee, but it is impossible to locate precisely (Figure 12.5).

The counterpart of these sands on the western margin of the old craton are seen in Death Valley, California, where again the basal beds are of latest Precambrian age. In Utah, the basal sand is known as the Prospect Mountain Quartzite and is of Early Cambrian age. The epeiric seas had reached Montana by the end of the Early Cambrian, so the equivalent sand is the Flathead Quartzite of latest Early Cambrian or possibly Middle Cambrian age. Evidence that the marine transgression finally reached the middle of the continent by Late Cambrian time is seen in the Mount Simon Quartzite of Illinois.

Although these various sandstone formations were long believed to be part of a single sand sheet consisting of coastal sands reworked and spread out before the advancing strandline (a shoreline above the present water level), detailed studies show them to be more complex. In addition to beach sands, shallow, offshore sand environments, tidal-flat environments, and even alluvial environments are all represented in different places.

FIGURE 12.5
The Precambrian/Cambrian boundary occurs within sandstones of the Chilhowee Group that forms the Chilhowee Mountain succession in eastern Tennessee.

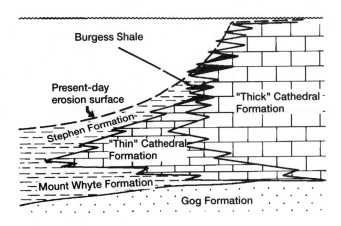

FIGURE 12.6
Stratigraphic relationships of the Burgess Shale. It forms a lens- or wedge-shaped body on the flanks of a massive limestone that presumably was a topographic feature as a Middle Cambrian shelf edge carbonate mass.

The Carbonate Zone

Concentrically, beyond the inner clastic zone, in water that was still relatively shallow but that was largely clear of land-derived suspended sediment, was a zone of carbonate deposits that extended out to the shelf or platform edge. The limestones formed in this **carbonate zone** were made up of lime mud, broken shell sands, and in places, the remains of the reef-building **archaeocyathids** (primitive spongelike organisms) and lime-secreting algae.

By the latest Cambrian, limestones and dolostones were being laid down across a large proportion of the craton. Sands were being deposited only at a few locations, mainly in the vicinity of northern New York, the Great Lakes, and the region to the east, along the trend of what must have been the old margin of the exposed Canadian Shield land area, from which rivers were bringing detritus.

The Outer Detrital Zone

Out beyond the reef zone, the dominant sediment type was silt and mud carried by waves and currents out into the deeper water of the outer shelf and slope. These sediments of what is termed the **outer detrital zone** bypassed the limestone reefs along the shelf edge. The reef edge sometimes may have been abrupt and may even, in places have formed a submarine escarpment.

The famous **Burgess Shale,** discussed later in this chapter, is believed to have been deposited at the foot of such an escarpment. Such shales form lens-shaped bodies within the Stephen Formation and represent small-scale slumps from the platform edge above (Figure 12.6). In the case of the Burgess Shale, one of these slumps apparently carried an assemblage of shallow-water organisms

that were living on the platform down into deeper water to be rapidly buried in anoxic muds. Under such bottom conditions, normal decay processes were inhibited.

Grand Cycles

The Sauk transgression into the North American craton interior was not a continuous marine advance but was interrupted by periods of regression. In Cambrian successions of western North America, eight so-called **Grand Cycles** have been recognized, beginning in the early Middle Cambrian and with the latest in the early Middle Ordovician, each one lasting about 9 million years (Figure 12.7).

In this shelf region, the marine regressions were not marked by actual emergence and erosion but are seen in abrupt changes upward from limestone to silts, indicating the incoming pulses of terriginous sediment presumably derived from erosion of emergent lands to the east in the craton interior. The same Grand Cycles have been detected in the Great Basin (a large region of inland drainage in the area of Nevada and Utah) and also in Newfoundland; they were clearly of eustatic origin, rather than due to local or regional tectonic movements.

The Cambrian Elsewhere

Evidence for the transgression of epeiric seas is seen in Cambrian successions of other continents. In central Europe, northern Africa, South America, and across central Australia are extensive spreads of shallow platform sediments. As on the North American craton, archaeocyathid reefs are common. In the Cambrian type area in

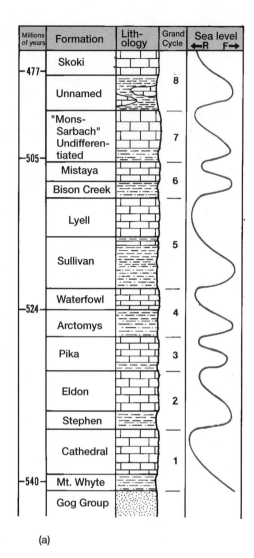

(a)

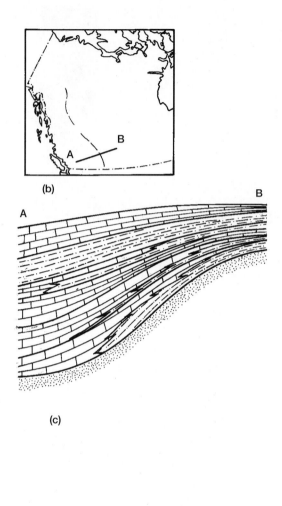

(b)

(c)

FIGURE 12.7

(a) Stratigraphic succession in the southern Rocky Mountains of Canada, showing the Grand Cycles of Middle Cambrian to Middle Ordovician age. (R = rising; F = falling.) (b) Index map. (c) Partial regional cross section.

western Europe, the section contains few limestones, however, and instead is dominated by thick shale and siltstone successions laid down in subsiding marginal troughs. Fossils are scarce or absent in many sections, including, unfortunately, the Cambrian **type section** (the section that supposedly sets a standard for Cambrian successions elsewhere) in the Harlech Dome area of North Wales (see Box 12.1). Any number of Cambrian successions would have made a more satisfactory Cambrian type section.

Less than 200 miles north of the North Wales location, the Cambrian succession in northern Scotland shows a marked contrast. Not only do basal sands pass up into dolomitic limestones, but the fossils are quite different. Trilobites are the dominant elements in the fauna. When

the fauna was first described in the nineteenth century, geologists were surprised to find North American species of trilobites rather than European species. Since continental drift was not yet a proposed theory, explaining how shallow-shelf organisms like trilobites could have crossed a deep ocean was, to put it mildly, somewhat difficult. In these post-plate-tectonic days of enlightenment, the location of such provincial faunas in far-traveled localities is a useful indication of former continent/ocean configurations. Geologists now know that a piece of northwest Scotland originally belonged to the North American continent but was carried eastward during the Triassic/ Jurassic rifting that led to the opening of the modern North Atlantic ocean.

BOX 12.1

The Cambrian Stratotype

The Cambrian System was first described and named in the 1830s by Adam Sedgwick, working in the mountains of North Wales. The main mass of the mountains is formed by a thick series of resistant sandstones and conglomerates that form the center of the Harlech Dome. Around the flanks of the dome, successively younger strata dip outward, with a total measured thickness of over 4,000 meters. (Box Figure 12.1). As a type section, supposedly setting a standard for Cambrian successions elsewhere, the Harlech Dome succession has some serious shortcomings. Not only is the lower third of the succession—the Harlech Series—unfossiliferous, but the base is nowhere exposed. The nature of the Cambrian/Precambrian boundary thus is unknown. In addition, the uppermost portion of the succession—the Tremadoc Beds—contains graptolites and other fossils usually considered typical of the Ordovician.

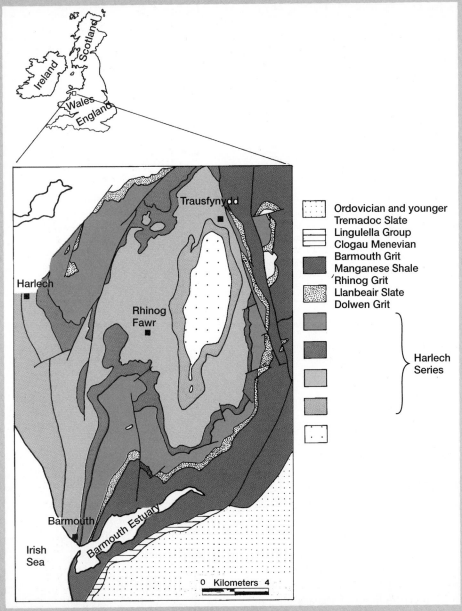

Ordovician and younger
Tremadoc Slate
Lingulella Group
Clogau Menevian
Barmouth Grit
Manganese Shale
Rhinog Grit
Llanbeair Slate
Dolwen Grit

Harlech Series

BOX FIGURE 12.1
Geologic map of the Harlech Dome area of North Wales, the type area for the Cambrian.

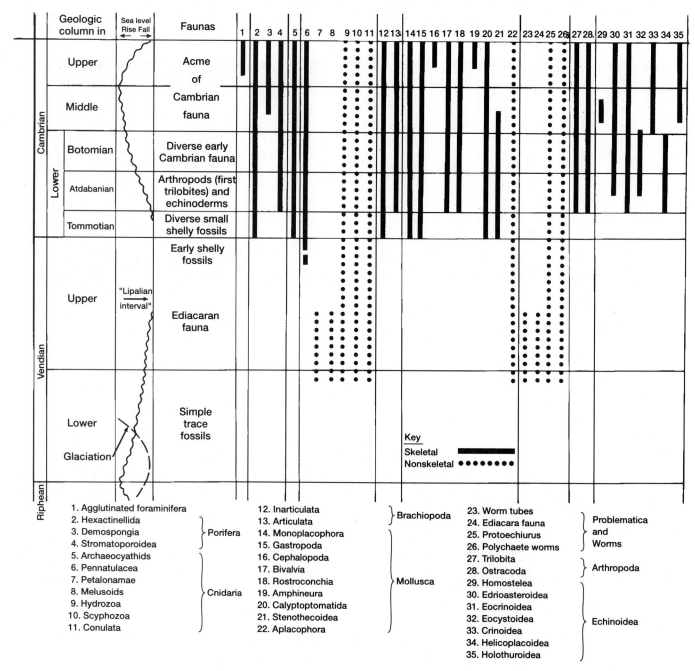

FIGURE 12.8
Major evolutionary events across the Precambrian/Cambrian boundary.

Cambrian Life

Rocks from the very beginning of the Phanerozoic have provided some of the most exciting discoveries in paleontology in recent years. Cambrian faunas are being scrutinized more closely, and new discoveries are revealing much about their possible precursors and the Late Proterozoic fossil record (Figure 12.8). This flood of new information is making it increasingly clear that the sudden appearance of fossils at the beginning of the Cambrian was more apparent than real. This also means that the old Precambrian/Cambrian boundary as a biostratigraphic entity has lost something of its significance. For this reason, a discussion of Late Proterozoic fossils has been postponed to this chapter, so that the important series of evolutionary bursts in the time span between about 700 million years (the latest Riphean, a division of the Proterozoic) and 500 million years (the close of the Cambrian) may be viewed in their entirety.

The Ediacaran Fauna

The first evolutionary radiation began soon after the Late Proterozoic ice age and, according to some workers, may even have been influenced by it as ameliorating climate and rising sea levels provided expanded ecologic niches. Macrofossils from strata below the glacial tillites are very rare and consist only of trails and *Planolites* (possibly a worm) burrows. In postglacial rocks, however, fossils are more abundant and consist mainly of impressions of flat annelid worms and cnidarians, a group that includes jellyfishes.

FIGURE 12.9
Representative fossils of the Ediacaran fauna.
(a) *Mawsonites,* (b) possible echinoderm, (c) *Spriggina,* and
(d) *Charniodiscus. (Photos courtesy W. Wade Queensland
Museum. Brisbane, Queensland.)*

Although the term *Ediacaran fauna* has been loosely applied to these early metazoans (after the discoveries in the late 1950s in the Pound Quartzite of the Ediacara Hills of South Australia), elements of the fauna, which range in age from about 630 to 580 million years, had actually been described much earlier in Southwest Africa (Namibia) in the 1920s. These fossils, together with other occurrences in England, Newfoundland, Australia, and elsewhere, were known as the **Charnian fauna,** named after Charnwood, the classic locality in England. Today, some

geologists believe the Charnian fauna to be somewhat older than the classic Ediacaran fauna found in Australia.

The Pound Quartzite fossils were not the first Precambrian metazoans to be discovered, but they were more abundant and much better preserved than anything encountered previously. As first described, the Ediacaran fauna was shown to be dominated by cnidarians, or at least cnidaria-like animals (67 percent), followed by annelid worms (25 percent), and arthropods (5 percent) (Figure 12.9). Representatives of the Ediacaran fauna have been

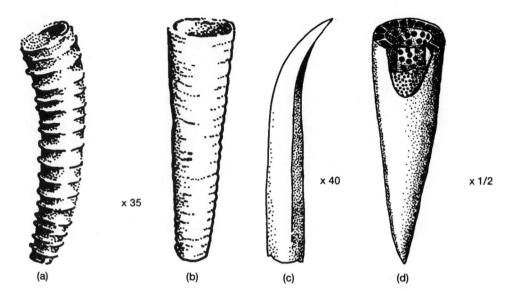

FIGURE 12.10
Fossils from the earliest Cambrian. (a) *Cloudina*.
(b) *Sinotubulites*. (c) *Prothertzina*. (d) *Archaeocyathus*.

found in many parts of the world, and they sometimes even occur in some abundance, which is rather surprising in view of their lack of hard parts. Their survival may have been due to scavengers not yet appearing on the scene.

Although some Ediacaran forms seem to have body plans that are recognizable enough to be classified in known phyla, certain specimens defy classification, or at least have not been identified in younger sediments. On the whole, the fauna does not appear to represent the direct ancestors of the first Cambrian faunas, although trace fossils found in some assemblages seem to be arthropods, possibly ancestral to the trilobites. This is a matter of some controversy, however. In a few cases, what are perhaps the first shelly fossils have been found associated with Ediacaran forms. These shelly fossils include the tube-shaped *Cloudina* from Namibia in Southwest Africa and *Sinotubulites* from southern China, both of which apparently secreted shells of calcium carbonate (Figure 12.10a,b).

The Ediacaran animals are believed to have been, for the most part, filter-feeding and deposit-feeding species, although recent research has suggested that certain jellyfishes may have been predatory in habit. One distinctive feature of the Ediacaran animals is their thin, flattened shape and consequent large surface area relative to volume. This has suggested to paleontologist Mark McMenamin of Mount Holyoke College in Massachusetts that certain species may have used symbiotic photosynthesizing algae within their tissues, just as modern scleractinian coral polyps do. Some species may also have used chemosynthetic bacteria that enabled the animals to take up nutrients from seawater.

As already mentioned, the relationship between the Ediacaran fossils and the first Cambrian fossils is obscure,

and the record shows no clear continuity between the two faunas. Numerous explanations have been put forward. One suggestion is that the disappearance of Ediacaran forms simply reflected preservational factors or might have been due to the appearance of scavengers. Other models have cited changes in ocean chemistry. If many Ediacaran forms were autotrophic, as has been suggested, they may have succumbed to a Late Proterozoic eutrophication (anoxic) or phosphogenic (in which the phosphorous content of the oceans increased markedly) event, for which evidence is apparent in an abundance of sedimentary phosphate deposits around the Precambrian/Cambrian boundary.

Rare shelly fossils are occasionally associated with the more typical soft-bodied Ediacaran species, and small remnants of what appear to be skeletal structures—plates, spines, and spicules, all of unknown origin but clearly derived from larger animals—also are found. In certain Ediacaran species, the body surface is marked by small pits and grooves, which some paleontologists have interpreted as an indication of primitive supportive structures, perhaps marking the beginning of incipient skeletonization.

The obvious peculiarities of the Ediacaran forms have always been something of a mystery and, in the view of Stephen Gould of Harvard, sufficient to set them completely apart. He sees no connection between them, as ancestral forms, and the earliest Cambrian fossils, and this view is supported by recent findings suggesting that the Ediacaran forms may not even have been animals at all! In this latest interpretation of the fossils, the parallel ridges and grooves, previously thought to be body segments, are now seen as growth stages in the tough skin, or periderm, of what were, in fact, forms of algae or fungi. Whatever

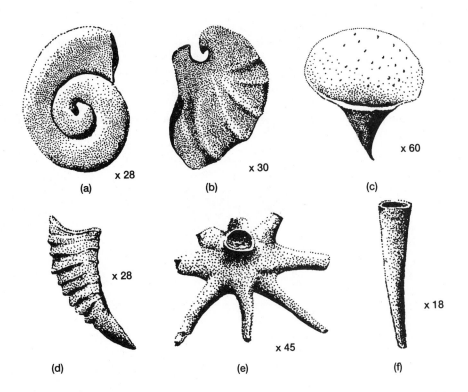

x 28
(a)

x 30
(b)

x 60
(c)

x 28
(d)

x 45
(e)

x 18
(f)

FIGURE 12.11

Representative forms from the Tommotian fauna, collectively known as small shelly fossils. (a) *Aldanella crassa*. (b) *Latouchella* sp. (a) and (b) are probably primitive mollusks. (c) *Fomitchella infundibuliformis,* a possible conodont. (d) *Lapworthella dentata,* of doubtful affinities. (e) *Chancelloria,* a sponge spicule. (f) *Conotheca mammilata,* a worm tube.

these first primitive beginnings in multicelled evolution were, they apparently represented an experiment that failed because they suffered a mass extinction event just prior to the Cambrian.

Small Shelly Fossils

The disappearance of the Ediacaran fauna (or perhaps flora!) was followed closely by the appearance of the first true shelly faunas, dated at about 570 million years, where the base of the Cambrian is usually set. The number of species from this stage is small but included is *Prothertzina,* a particularly significant fossil because it has been interpreted as the grasping spine of an early predator (Figure 12.10c). As the diversity of these early forms increased, important newcomers were the first archaeocyathids, primitive spongelike organisms that secreted skeletons of calcium carbonate and were responsible for the earliest organic reefs (Figure 12.10d).

Some of the best-preserved and most abundant Early Cambrian fossils have been described from sediments of the Tommotian Stage, the lowest stage of the Cambrian, with exposures along the Aldan and Lena rivers of Siberia. Many of these species are extremely small, usually measuring a few millimeters, and thus have come to be called the **small shelly fossils** (Figure 12.11). Although,

traditionally, the biostratigraphy of the Cambrian System was based on trilobites that supposedly arrived at the beginning of the period, trilobites were not contemporaries of the small shelly fossils, so the Tommotian is, in fact, the pretrilobite initial stage of the Cambrian.

First Appearance of Skeletons

Clearly, the event that best marks the beginning of the Cambrian is the development of skeletons. Why, however, was their appearance so sudden? Obviously, within the context of evolutionary improvement, skeletons offer clear advantages. As body structures became more complex and muscular, and respiratory mechanisms became more efficient, a hard, supporting structure was increasingly necessary for muscle attachment. Also, evidence of drilled shells and healed wounds indicates that predators had already arrived on the scene, probably as the Cambrian opened, and so skeletons clearly had great survival value.

Many of the earliest skeletons appear to have consisted of calcium phosphate; only later did calcium carbonate skeletons become more abundant. Some type of phosphogenic event caused by oceanic overturn occurred at about the Precambrian/Cambrian boundary, and some geologists have suggested that the appearance of skeletons was triggered by or was a crisis response to the sudden

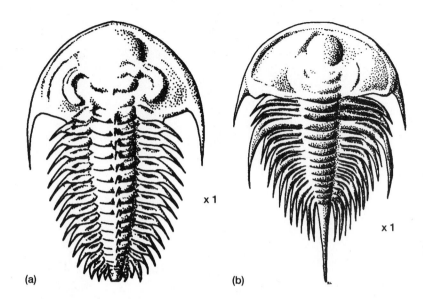

FIGURE 12.12
Trilobites. (a) *Holmia* sp. (b) *Olenellus* sp.

(a)

(b)

increase in phosphorous levels in shallow-shelf seas. By late in the Early Cambrian, calcium carbonate and chitin were the preferred skeletal material, so the phosphorous crisis was clearly over by then.

Trilobites

Over two-thirds of the fossils described within Cambrian faunas are **trilobites,** so trilobites were clearly the dominant animals in Cambrian seas. With their distinctive jointed carapaces and well-developed eyes, they were obviously active benthic organisms and clearly adapted to many different sea-bottom environments (Figure 12.12).

During the Cambrian, trilobites apparently underwent an explosive evolutionary radiation, but most species were relatively short-lived. This means that trilobites are sensitive zonal indicators, and most Cambrian biostratigraphy is based on trilobites. During the Early Cambrian, when the various continents were still close to one another, the trilobites were cosmopolitan in their distribution. Later, as oceanic distances widened and proved too much of a barrier, the trilobites became increasingly provincial.

Although typically associated with the Cambrian, trilobites, as a group, survived right up to the mass extinction that marked the close of the Permian, a span of some 300 million years. Clearly, the trilobites were a success story by any standards. Once the Cambrian was over, they became less important elements in Paleozoic faunas, but they continued to adapt and evolve and even grew to sizes never seen in the Cambrian.

Recent work is beginning to turn up certain trace fossils in the Ediacaran faunas that may have been made by arthropods that were trilobite ancestors, but no definitive body fossils have been found. Some clues as to the early evolution of trilobites emerge, however, when the total phylogeny of the trilobites is reviewed and some of what seem to be certain discernible evolutionary trends are studied.

Comparisons of the earliest trilobites from the Lower Cambrian with those from the later Cambrian and younger strata reveal several potentially significant morphological trends. One of these trends is the degree of segmentation in the animal's tail and head portions. In more "advanced" trilobites, the head shield and pygidium (tailpiece) are smooth or show only vestigial traces of segmentation, whereas in trilobite species ancestral to them, segmentation is apparent down to the tip of the tail, and there are also pronounced furrows on the head shield. According to some taxonomists, a backward projection of this trend produces a hypothetical ancestral form that suggests an annelid worm, and gradualists would argue that trilobites and annelids arose from common ancestral stock.

Brachiopods

After the trilobites, which make up more than half of all Cambrian species, the brachiopods are the most numerous fossils. The earliest species—**inarticulate brachiopods**—constructed chitino-phosphatic shells made up of a complex calcium phosphate linked with chitin, an extremely durable organic compound. The valves were relatively simple and contained no teeth and sockets in the hinge area, as did later brachiopods (Figure 12.13a). A close living relative of the Cambrian brachiopods is *Lingula,* a burrowing brachiopod found in such places as tidal mud flats. Big changes in temperature and salinity are the norm in such tidal environments, so perhaps the Cambrian brachiopods quickly found themselves a suitable niche that required unusual adaptability. Within such a niche, they have apparently remained a conservative group and show little evolutionary change.

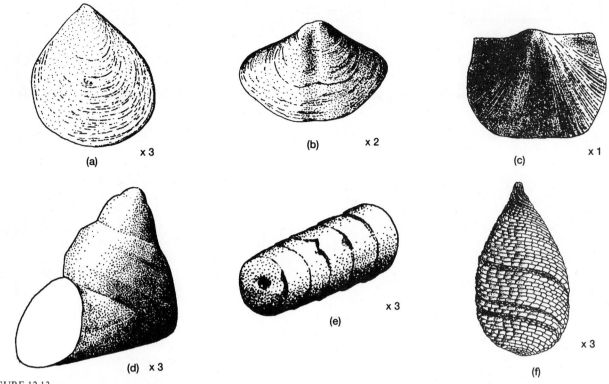

FIGURE 12.13

Cambrian fossils. (a) The inarticulate brachiopod *Linqulella* sp. (b) The articulate brachiopod *Kutorgina* sp. (c) *Diraphora bellica*, another articulate brachiopod. (d) Early gastropod *Matherella* from the Upper Cambrian. (e) An internal cast of a small straight-shelled cephalopod from the Late Cambrian. (f) Early echinoderm. *Helicoplacus.*

Later in the Cambrian, brachiopods with calcareous shells appeared. Some—the **articulate brachiopods**—had the more advanced articulate hinge-line, in which teeth on one valve margin articulate with sockets in the other so that the valves open and close with a more mechanically efficient action (Figure 12.13b,c).

Other Cambrian Life-Forms

Archaeocyathids, primitive spongelike organisms, have already been mentioned and are chiefly interesting because they formed the first organic reefs. Although once thought to be sponges, they are now placed in a phylum of their own. Siliceous sponges of the group Pleospongea were likely also inhabitants of the early reefs.

Among other Cambrian groups that were to become familiar in later time were the mollusks. They were a minor component in Cambrian faunas, but the first ones appeared in the Early Cambrian in the form of cap-shaped monoplacophorans, considered likely ancestors of the gastropods (Figure 12.13d). By Middle Cambrian time, the first bivalves had appeared. These were the forerunners of a great host of species that were to become ever more abundant through the Phanerozoic. This was in marked contrast to certain other molluscan groups that had appeared by the Middle Cambrian but that were short-lived

and destined not to survive past the end of the period. Perhaps the most successful and certainly the most advanced of all the mollusks were the cephalopods. They appeared almost at the end of the Cambrian and are represented by simple, straight-shelled species, none of which was larger than a few centimeters (Figure 12.13e).

The Cambrian faunas as a whole seem to be characterized by an unusual number of short-lived groups, which has led many paleontologists to speak of the Cambrian as a time of experimentation. For example, *Helicoplacus* was an attached echinoderm covered with a large number of small plates of calcium carbonate arranged in spiral rows (Figure 12.13f). Unlike modern echinoderms, the external plates were not fused together, so *Helicoplacus* could expand and contract its body. By Middle Cambrian time, this body plan had apparently been abandoned, and other echinoderms had appeared with fewer large plates, an apparent fundamental shift in structural design.

This obvious fluidity, in which many different designs were tried and then as quickly abandoned, was, as already mentioned, already suspected on the basis of what was known of Cambrian faunas as a whole. Work in recent years on the incredible Middle Cambrian forms preserved in the Burgess Shale has demonstrated beyond doubt the reality of what, in effect, was a Cambrian evolutionary explosion.

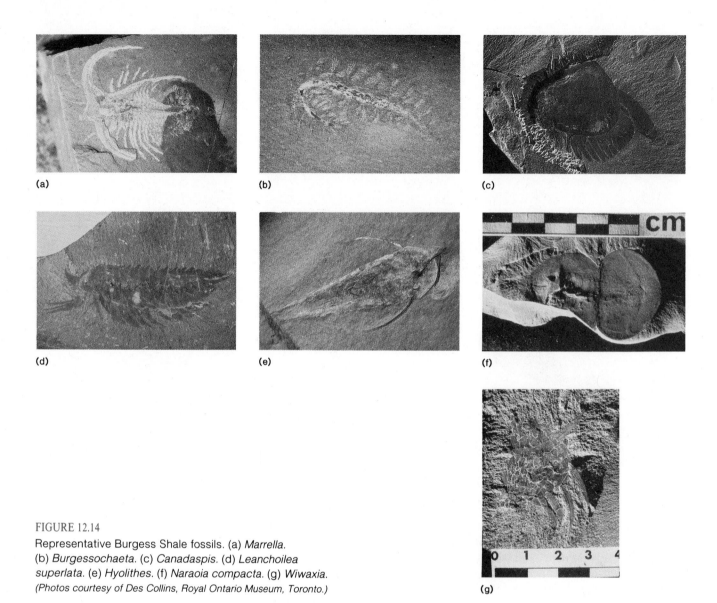

FIGURE 12.14
Representative Burgess Shale fossils. (a) *Marrella*.
(b) *Burgessochaeta*. (c) *Canadaspis*. (d) *Leanchoilea
superlata*. (e) *Hyolithes*. (f) *Naraoia compacta*. (g) *Wiwaxia*.
(Photos courtesy of Des Collins, Royal Ontario Museum, Toronto.)

Burgess Shale Fauna

Of all the many floral and faunal assemblages represented
in the fossil record, none has proven more exciting and
significant than that discovered in the Middle Cambrian
Burgess Shale in 1909 by American geologist Charles D.
Walcott. The special significance of the Burgess Shale fossils is that they were preserved in an unusual depositional
environment that allowed the preservation of traces of the
animals' soft tissues as well as their hard skeletal parts
(Figure 12.14). The Burgess Shale fauna includes many
animals with entirely soft bodies. In a few cases, they are
recognizable as having living descendants, but not a single
additional fossil has ever been found to show the progression in the 500 million years or so of intervening time.

The Burgess Shale fauna was found when Charles
Walcott and his field party were crossing on horseback the
slopes of a ridge near Mount Wapta, just above the town
of Trail in British Columbia. Slabs of rock found along

the trail and clearly derived from higher up the slopes were
seen to contain the flattened carbonized films left behind
by soft organic tissues. The find was made late in the 1909
field season, but the source of the slabs was located and
the first collections made from what Walcott referred to
in his notes as the "Phyllopod Bed." Over the next several
years, the Burgess Shale was excavated for more fossils,
and the carbonized fossils were found to be confined to a
relatively thin, lens-shaped shale bed about 2 meters thick.
Nevertheless, thousands of specimens were quarried out,
described, and monographed (Figure 12.15).

The Burgess Shale fauna, not surprisingly, became
famous, and along with the Solnhofen Limestone fauna of
Jurassic age, is often cited as a prime example of just how
much could be learned about soft tissues in fossils and also
to emphasize the poor state of preservation of all "ordinary" fossils. In other words, the Burgess Shale fauna
provides a tantalizing glimpse of what geologists are
missing!

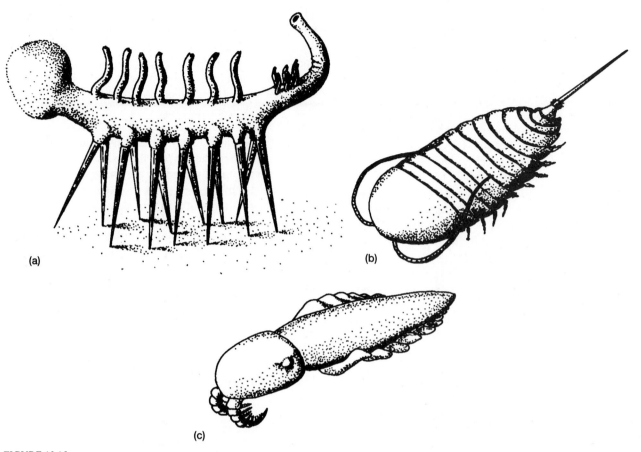

FIGURE 12.15
Organisms from the Burgess Shale. (a) *Halucigenia*.
(b) *Emeraldella*. (c) *Anomalocaris*.

The actual makeup of the Burgess Shale fauna and its possible phylogenetic relationships, as described in the first published descriptions, did not arouse undue comment. The gradualists of the time assumed that the Cambrian faunas had arisen from a long line of Precambrian ancestors that had not had skeletal structures that could be preserved. In this context, the Burgess Shale animals were simply examples of forms that had long ancestral lines and were, in turn, relatively simple ancestors of groups that were to appear later.

Today, paleontologists' view of the Burgess Shale faunas is very different. Beginning in 1971, several workers, including Derek Briggs, Harry Whittington, Simon Conway Morris, and Des Collins, began new studies that by the 1980s were culminating in a complete reinterpretation of the Burgess Shale fossils. The real significance of the Burgess Shale fauna lies in what it tells about the Cambrian evolutionary explosion. The sudden appearance of fossils at the beginning of the Cambrian and the surprisingly late arrival of metazoans in the Proterozoic have already revealed the importance of this explosion. What the Burgess Shale fauna demonstrates is that the explosion was much more extensive than had ever been realized.

The Chengjiang Assemblage

Recently, another Cambrian fauna in a state of preservation equal to and even reportedly better than that of the Burgess Shale assemblage was found in Yunnan Province, China, at a place called Chengjiang. It was discovered in 1984 but only recently brought to the attention of western paleontologists by Swedish paleontologists Jan Bergström and Maurits Lindström of Stockholm. As in the Burgess Shale fauna, among the 70 species described are many soft-bodied forms and a preponderance of arthropods and arthropod-like forms. Some of the species are very similar to Burgess Shale species, even though the **Chengjiang assemblage** predates the Burgess Shale by some 30 million years. The state of preservation of the fossils again points to rapid burial in an anoxic environment. In contrast to the submarine landslide postulated for the Burgess Shale burial event, the Chengjiang assemblage was likely buried by sediment stirred up by a storm. Unlike the Burgess Shale, the containing sediments are found over an extensive area, so many new fossil localities are likely awaiting discovery.

Cambrian Evolution: Selective Experimentation or Pure Chance?

Selective Experimentation

The Precambrian/Late Cambrian interval was apparently a period of rapid diversification and experimentation in morphological design. An astonishing variety of new body plans appeared during this interval and 15 or 20 forms literally defy classification. In some cases, taxonomists are not even sure in which phylum to place them. Taxonomists are sometimes tempted to erect new taxa when a newly described specimen cannot easily be compared with others. This is common at the species level, but in moving up the hierarchy of taxonomic divisions, it becomes increasingly unlikely that the new specimens do not belong to a previously described category.

Yet, the Burgess Shale fauna contains specimens of creatures so completely strange that many taxonomists believe that the only recourse is to erect new phyla to accommodate them. Following this procedure creates the bizarre situation of phyla with a mere handful of species, or even only one.

In the Burgess Shale fauna, the arthropod and arthropod-like animals exhibit the greatest array of body plans, and nearly two dozen of these seem to be unrelated to any other known groups, whether they are extant or belong to extinct fossil groups like the trilobites.

Even without the great flood of information obtained from the Burgess Shale and Chengjiang faunas, the fossil record from the Cambrian as a whole shows numerous groups that did not survive past the end of the Cambrian. Nearly all the phyla contain strange forms that apparently died out with no descendants. Many paleontologists believe that these Cambrian extinctions represented "evolutionary dead ends" or "experiments that failed." Thus, the Cambrian appears to have been a period of experimentation, and only a few apparently better-adapted and therefore more successful forms survived to populate the world during the remainder of the Paleozoic.

"Chance" Evolution and Christmas-Tree Phylogeny

New interpretations stemming from the Burgess Shale studies suggest that this selective experimentation view may not be entirely correct. According to Stephen Gould, the survival of one group or species and the extinction of another may have involved a large element of chance. There was such a plethora of forms, often rather similar and all more or less adapted to a particular environment, that no one group or species may have had a clear advan-

tage. This view implies that evolutionary mechanisms might have been in abeyance and that no constructive selection pressure was operating. That some kind of environmentally controlled selection was going on seems likely, but it may have been operating on a different scale from that seen in later time, when the process of "weeding out" was more advanced and there were fewer basic body plans.

The strangeness of the Burgess Shale fauna inevitably led to speculation and to questions about evolutionary mechanisms, particularly as they seem to be demonstrated by the fossil record. Is the Burgess Shale simply a special case of preservation of soft parts, or does it, in fact, allow a glimpse of a unique period in the history of life—a period when the foundations for future animal dynasties were being laid? If other "Burgess Shales" from other geologic periods were discovered, would they also demonstrate the fragmentary nature of the fossil record as a whole by revealing other bizarre assemblages that would fall outside the established classification?

In Stephen Gould's view, the Burgess Shale was deposited during a Cambrian explosion that represented a vital initial period, when a great array of unusual body plans appeared but which were decimated shortly thereafter, leaving only a limited number of surviving lineages. These few basic forms set the pattern for all later diversity.

This phenomenon of widespread extinction was apparently a random decimation in which, just as in the mass extinctions described elsewhere, chance was perhaps the sole criterion in deciding which groups were eliminated and which ones were not. In the Cambrian world of diversification apparently gone mad, perhaps the odds for and against certain forms were so even that chance as a statistical factor became more important than a selection pressure factor that was so misaligned or diffuse as to be, for all practical purposes, ineffective. As Gould points out, if the Cambrian tape could be rewound and played again, a wholly different assemblage of animals probably would emerge, and life on the present-day earth would be totally unfamiliar, perhaps only imaginable by a science fiction writer!

In discussions of evolution through geologic time, phyletic relationships are generally shown in the form of a "family tree" in which ancestral and descendant species are placed on the twigs and branches of an upwardly spreading bush (Figure 12.16a). According to Stephen Gould, the tree should, in fact, have a Christmas tree shape, with the maximum number of branches appearing early, during an initial period of diversity (Figure 12.16b). This would be quickly followed by decimation of all but a few forms, which would supply a limited number of themes for the later variants in an evolutionary radiation.

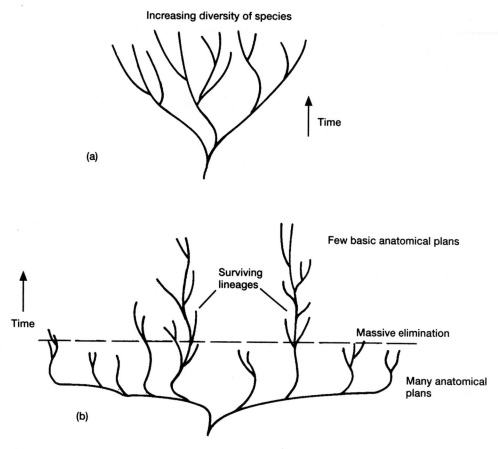

FIGURE 12.16

(a) Cone of increasing diversity. (b) Decimation and diversification. *(Source: Data from J. J. Gould,* Wonderful Life. *Copyright © 1989 W. W. Norton & Company.)*

Summary

The chief feature that distinguishes the Cambrian from the Precambrian is the presence in Cambrian strata of the first good fossils, and this has been the internationally accepted criterion for determining the stratigraphic boundary at the base of the Cambrian. In many parts of the world, the earliest Cambrian strata rest unconformably on Precambrian rocks. This hiatus—named by Charles Walcott the Lipalian interval—was once thought to be worldwide in extent.

As the Proterozoic came to a close, the one or two large supercontinents indicated by paleomagnetic evidence for much of the Proterozoic were beginning to break up, and early in the Cambrian, at least six continents were strung out along or close to the equator. The plate-tectonic movements that caused continental breakup also produced new sea floor along the midocean ridges, which initiated a eustatic rise in sea level as ocean basin volume was reduced.

Rising sea level was marked on the North American continent by the Sauk transgression. It began in the Late Proterozoic and reached its maximum extent early in the Ordovician. The North American craton was surrounded by passive margins, and there were no rising orogenic belts or mountain ranges. The land area consisted of the emergent Canadian Shield and the Transcontinental Arch that extended from Lake Superior to Arizona. It was generally an area of moderate to low relief. Sedimentary facies patterns on the continent as the sea advanced were relatively simple, with an inner clastic zone of shallow-water sands, a zone of carbonates, and an outer detrital zone of silt and mud, all arranged concentrically about the craton interior.

The basal transgressive sand of all Cambrian successions is a mature or supermature sandstone that is given various formation names in different places. In traverses from the continental margins in toward the interior, the basal sands become progressively younger.

The epeiric seas that advanced over North America also extended onto northern Africa, South America, central Europe, and central Australia. At the Cambrian type section in North Wales, the Cambrian sediments were apparently laid down in a subsiding marginal trough and are largely unfossiliferous, at least in the lower part of the section.

The Ediacaran fauna is an assemblage of soft-bodied metazoans that range in age from about 630 to 580 million years. Although dominated by cnidarians or cnidaria-like animals, the Ediacaran fauna contains several forms that do not fit into any existing classification. The Ediacaran fauna does not seem to be ancestral to any of the earliest Cambrian fossils and is believed to have been largely eliminated by a mass extinction before the beginning of the Cambrian.

The earliest Cambrian fossils include tiny calcium phosphate forms from the Tommotian, the lowest stage of the Cambrian. These have been termed the small shelly fossils, and they characterize a pretrilobite stage in the Cambrian. The event that best marks the beginning of the Cambrian is the development of skeletons. Skeletons had great survival value as a supporting structure for increasingly complex body forms and as a deterrent to predators.

The trilobites appeared at the close of the Tommotian. Over two-thirds of the fossils described within Cambrian faunas are trilobites, so they clearly dominated the Early Cambrian ocean floor. They underwent rapid evolution during the Cambrian and also were relatively short-lived, so they make good stratigraphic zonal fossils. Next to trilobites, brachiopods are the most abundant Cambrian fossils. Most species were small. The inarticulate brachiopods constructed chitino-phosphatic shells, while the later brachiopods—the articulate brachiopods—formed calcareous shells. Among other fossils, the spongelike archaeocyathids built skeletons of calcium carbonate and formed the first organic reefs. Primitive mollusks and several bizarre and short-lived echinoderms were also present in the Cambrian.

The Middle Cambrian Burgess Shale was discovered in 1909 by Charles Walcott on a ridge above the town of Trail, British Columbia. Thousands of specimens from this locality show soft tissues preserved on bedding surfaces as thin, carbonized films and reveal an astonishing fauna.

At first glance, the Cambrian appears to have been a period of experimentation, and only a few apparently better-adapted and therefore more successful forms survived to populate the world. According to Stephen Gould, however, the survival of one group or species and the extinction of another may have involved a large element of chance.

In addition, the wide range of different body plans and the presence of many forms that seem not to fit into any known taxonomic division has suggested to Gould that the traditional view of phyletic "trees" be discarded. According to Gould, a Christmas-tree shape would better demonstrate an initial period of rapid diversification followed by widespread decimation. Those few lineages that did survive did so by chance, and their forms and body plans set the pattern for future evolutionary progress.

Questions

1. What stratigraphic features were used to delineate the Precambrian/Cambrian boundary?
2. Explain what is meant by the Lipalian interval.
3. What evidence can be assembled to establish the location of the Cambrian continental pieces after the breakup of the Proterozoic Pangaea?
4. Describe the distribution of sedimentary facies in Cambrian successions across North America.
5. The basal sands of Cambrian successions are described as mature sands. Explain.
6. What features of the Cambrian succession on the North American craton are diachronous?
7. The Sauk transgression onto the North American craton was not a continuous advance. What is the evidence for this?
8. If the Cambrian System had been defined today, its type section would likely not have been in North Wales. Explain.
9. List several examples of exceptionally well-preserved faunas, in addition to the Burgess Shale fauna.
10. Why is the Ediacaran fauna seen as unlikely to be directly ancestral to Cambrian fauna?
11. What advantages did skeletons offer?
12. The chemistry of the skeletal material of Late Cambrian and subsequent fossils was somewhat different from that of the beginning Cambrian. Explain.
13. Why is the biostratigraphic subdivision of the Cambrian based on trilobites?
14. What is special about the mode of preservation of the Burgess Shale fossils?
15. In terms of evolutionary mechanisms, what new ideas have stemmed from studies of the Burgess Shale fauna?

Further Reading

Brasier, M. D. 1985. Evolutionary and geological events across the Precambrian-Cambrian boundary. *Geology Today* 1:141–46.

Conway Morris, S. 1987. The search for the Precambrian-Cambrian boundary. *American Scientist* 75:157–67.

Conway Morris, S. 1989. Burgess Shale faunas and the Cambrian explosion. *Science* 246:339–46.

Cowie, J. W., and M. D. Brasier, eds. 1989. *The Precambrian-Cambrian boundary*. Oxford, England: Clarendon Press.

Gould, S. J. 1989. An asteroid to die for. *Discover* 10:60–65.

Gould, S. J. 1989. *Wonderful life*. New York: Norton.

McMenamin, M. A. S. 1987. The emergence of animals. *Scientific American* 256:94–102.

McMenamin, M.A.S., and D.L.S. McMenamin 1990. *The emergence of animals: The Cambrian breakthrough*. New York: Columbia University Press.

Whittington, H. B. 1985. *The Burgess Shale*. New Haven, Conn.: Yale University Press.

13

THE ORDOVICIAN-SILURIAN: THE WATER PLANET

Outline

Key Terms

Introduction

The Sauk transgression reached its maximum extent early in the Ordovician. The seas then withdrew, leaving much of the continent dry land again. This period of emergence was short-lived, however, because by early Middle Ordovician time, as the cycles of sea-level change continued, the ocean levels were again rising and the seas once more were encroaching to begin the second great transgression. In North America, this is known as the Tippecanoe transgression.

The sea did not recede again until the Early Devonian, and during the intervening time, not only North America but other continental areas were subjected to the greatest inundation in geologic history. Parts of the Eurasian, Brazilian, and West African platforms also show evidence of widespread marine transgression.

During this time, (approximately 350 million years ago), the earth had little dry land. As seas reached their greatest extent, the only landmass of continental size was Gondwana; all the remaining land was represented by half a dozen islands (Figure 13.1). Thus, during the Ordovician/Silurian periods, which are the focus of this chapter, the earth was essentially a water planet.

Ordovician Overview

During the period of emergence prior to the advance of the Tippecanoe Sea, weathering and erosion began stripping away the sedimentary veneers of Cambrian and Early Ordovician age left behind by the Sauk Sea. Limestones formed the land surface over large areas, and they were rapidly removed in solution by chemical weathering. The sandstones, therefore, supplied the bulk of the surface sediment on the emergent land. These older Cambrian sands were reworked by wave action in the shallow seas of the early Tippecanoe transgression.

Ordovician Sedimentary Successions

The majority of all sandstones, as described in Chapter 2, are made up of quartz grains. Quartz can survive many cycles of weathering and erosion, transportation and deposition. Feldspar grains, rock fragments, and other less durable components, on the other hand, are eliminated relatively quickly, usually during a single cycle. Among the quartz grains, polycrystalline grains are weaker than monocrystalline grains, and even the angular shape of the original monocrystalline quartz grains is often worn down until the grains become almost spherical. These various features make a supermature sand easy to recognize.

Over large midcontinent areas, the initial deposits of the Tippecanoe Sea were extremely pure and well-sorted sands. In many places, this **basal transgressive sand,** as discussed in Chapter 12, has been mapped as the St. Peter Sandstone, often cited as one of the best examples of a supermature sand. Because of its extreme purity, the St. Peter Sandstone is widely used in glass manufacturing.

Studies of the St. Peter Sandstone and other basal Tippecanoe sands show them to have been largely derived from the north and northwest, so again, the Precambrian rocks of the exposed Canadian Shield contributed to the advancing shore sands. The shoreline of the Tippecanoe Sea trended in what is now a northeast-southwest direction across the Mississippi valley and extended from the Great Lakes to Oklahoma and Kansas (Figure 13.2).

In a southeasterly direction toward the craton margin, the St. Peter Sandstone passes into a mixed shale, sandstone, and limestone facies, which in the Arbuckle Mountains of Oklahoma, is mapped as the Simpson Group, generally considered a deeper-water offshore facies of the St. Peter. Still further east and southeast and approaching the edge of the North American craton, the basal deposits of the Tippecanoe sequence are limestones, which indicates that the deposits were clearly beyond the influence

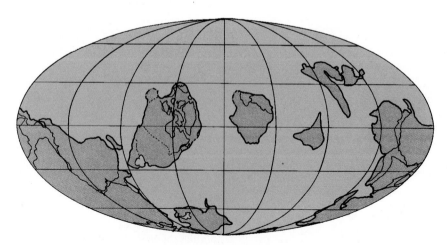

FIGURE 13.1
World paleogeography at the beginning of the Ordovician.

of interior clastic sources. At eastern sections, such as those in Tennessee and Virginia, the post-Sauk unconformity often separates two limestones with broad similarities. This indicates that the carbonate environment of Late Cambrian and Early Ordovician time became reestablished by the early Middle Ordovician. All along the continent's eastern margin, this state of affairs was not to last, however, as events were unfolding in the **Iapetus Ocean** (the ancestral Atlantic Ocean) that were to have a profound influence, as is described later in the chapter.

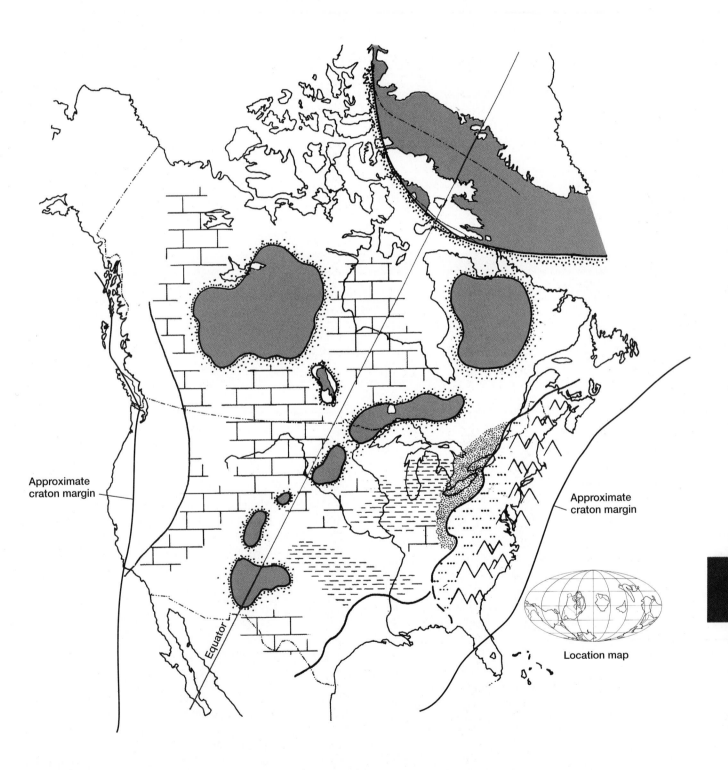

Approximate craton margin

Approximate craton margin

Equator

Location map

FIGURE 13.2
Paleogeography of the North American craton in the Ordovician.

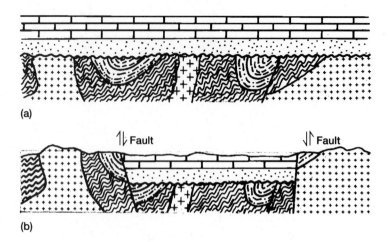

FIGURE 13.3

(a) Epeiric seas flood across rocks of the Precambrian shield, with sandstones, shales, and limestones deposited across the eroded surface. (b) Down-faulted block preserves a small area of epeiric sediments as an outlier. Elsewhere across the shield, the sediments are eroded away.

TABLE 13.1

Carbonate Sediment Accumulation Rates

Location	Total	Rate (per 1,000 years)
Florida reef tract (reef)	25 meters in 7,000 years	3.0+ meters
Florida Bay (lagoon)	3 meters in 3,000 years	1.0 meter
Andros Island, Bahamas (tidal flat)	1.5 meters in 2,200 years	0.7 meter
Faishale, Persian Gulf (sabkha)	4 meters in 4,000 years	1.0 meter
Northeast Yucatan (lagoon)	5 meters in 5,000 years	1.0 meter

The Tippecanoe Transgression

The Tippecanoe Sea eventually covered a larger area than had the Sauk incursion, and even much of the Canadian Shield was finally inundated. Although later erosion stripped away most of the thin veneer of sediments laid down during this transgression, small areas of sediment known as **outliers** occasionally survived in down-faulted blocks (Figure 13.3). Evidence also indicates that the Tippecanoe Sea was somewhat deeper than the Sauk, and the marked, depth-controlled facies belts of the Sauk Sea were replaced by much more uniform bottom conditions.

The most noticeable feature of the Tippecanoe sedimentary cover is the dominance of limestones, many of them richly fossiliferous. Since Cambrian time, the North American craton had moved and rotated in a counterclockwise direction, but it still lay within the equatorial zone, and so the shallow seas were warm. The water was also largely clear of suspended sediment because, apart from a rising orogenic belt far to the east, few potential sources of clastics were still emergent. Under these conditions, the Tippecanoe Sea likely was teeming with life.

Many geologists compare the bottom conditions in epeiric seas with those found on modern carbonate banks, such as the Bahama Banks and the Campeche Bank north of Yucatan, Mexico. Measurements of Pleistocene and Recent corlagal limestones (consisting of coral and lime-secreting algae) and other carbonates in such places show that, in favorable environments, limestones accumulate very rapidly. In fact, and with the possible exception of sediments deposited at the mouths of delta distributaries, accumulation rates are probably equaled nowhere else (Table 13.1).

Depositional Environments: The Epeiric-Sea Mystery

Even though the lithology of many epeiric limestones closely matches that of sediments accumulating on modern carbonate banks, it is by no means certain that depositional environments in epeiric seas were the same. In separate but similar models proposed in 1964 by Martin Irwin and Alan Shaw, it was suggested that the sheer size of epeiric seas and their shallow depth introduced special factors.

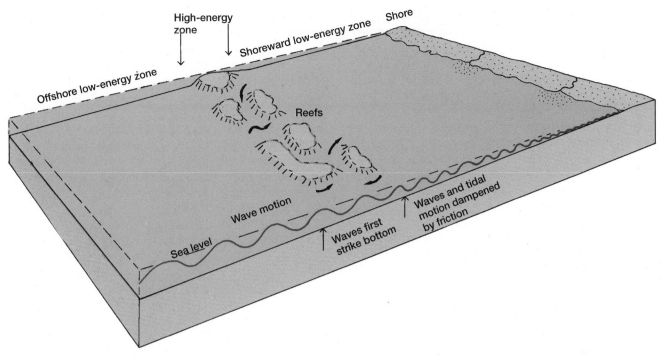

FIGURE 13.4
Zones of sedimentation in an epeiric sea. According to this model, the interiors of epeiric seas are so shallow that frictional drag progressively dampens tidal movement.

Shaw, for example, based his ideas on his observations of Florida Bay, where the water is shallow enough that frictional drag impedes tidal movement to the degree that the bay's interior experiences no diurnal tidal fluctuation. The so-called epeiric clear-water sedimentation model extrapolates this phenomenon into epeiric seas and suggests that the interiors of epeiric seas were similarly tideless because of frictional drag over a shallow bottom (Figure 13.4) and that normal tidal influences were encountered only around craton margins. This model explains the observed abundance of dolostones in craton interior successions, whereas in the outer zones, which presumably were subject to tidal exchange, limestones dominated. In the innermost reaches of epeiric seas, where essentially no overturn of the water column was possible except for wind-driven stirring, evaporites accumulated.

Although an ingenious and plausible explanation for many of the observed facies patterns in Paleozoic epeiric seas, the model has not gained universal acceptance because a considerable body of evidence supports an alternative theory. Many geologists, for example, have difficulty accepting the idea of restricted circulation in the interiors of epeiric seas because, in the Ordovician and Silurian formations of the midcontinent region, the faunas in the outer limestones and those of the inner dolostones appear to differ little. If, indeed, the interior areas of epeiric seas

suffered from restricted circulation, this was not reflected in any diminution in the numbers of fossils.

That tidal circulation was distributing oxygen and nutrients throughout epeiric seas seems to be implied and is supported by direct evidence from the rocks in the form of **tidalites,** sediments containing bedding and textural features indicating regular tidal exchange. In addition, certain modern examples of broad and shallow shelves indicate that, far from tidal effects being dampened by increasing distance in from the shelf edge, tidal ranges actually increase.

That, for the moment at least, is where the epeiric-sea controversy stands; clearly, however, much has yet to be learned about these important events in earth history.

Ordovician Reefs

Although, as stated earlier, limestones dominate many of the Paleozoic epeiric successions, they are not by any means uniform. Early in the Ordovician, several organisms were capable of building up resistant masses of limestone and had replaced the archaeocyathids of Cambrian seas. Apart from the reef limestones themselves, many other kinds of limestones were formed in various bottom environments, where water depth, exposure to stirring by waves, and overall circulation were all controlled by the presence of the reefs.

A typical reef constructed by corals, bryozoans, and stromatoporoids quickly grew almost to the water surface and formed a resistant mass, behind which existed a sheltered lagoon. Conditions in the lagoon contrasted sharply with those on the exposed reef, which was often reflected in a completely different fauna. Lagoon sediment likely consisted of fine-grained lime mud, and many so-called **pellet limestones** formed, the pellets being fecal material produced by mud-ingesting organisms, such as worms and mollusks. The restriction of water flow in and out of the lagoon may have been sufficient to cause salt concentrations to rise in the inner lagoon as a consequence of evaporation. As a result, evaporite deposits of the calcium sulphate mineral gypsum are often found associated with reef structures. Sometimes, water circulation was so restricted that brine concentrations were sufficient to produce the mineral halite (rock salt). On the outside of the reef, where wave action was stronger, pieces of the reef sometimes broke off and tumbled down the submarine slope to form a reef talus deposit.

Clearly, such reefs often had a marked influence on facies distribution in many limestone formations and must have been at least modest topographic features on the sea floor. In some cases, however, limestone masses filled with coral and bryozoan fossils and originally interpreted as topographic reefs may never have formed any particular submarine feature at all. By analogy with modern environments, the bottom organisms, rather than playing the role of frame builders, may have simply caused the trapping and accumulation of mud. Even so, this passive rather than active role was important in influencing the facies patterns in these epeiric seas.

Many reef limestones are typically quite porous because of their complex organic textures and so have frequently acted as reservoirs for oil and gas. Important hydrocarbon reserves have been found in many Silurian and Devonian reefs. Oil exploration requires some understanding of the regional distribution of limestone facies if the reefs themselves are to be located. Many reefs have been located by seismic surveys. One of the first successful reef reservoirs found was the Devonian Leduc field in western Canada, discovered in 1947.

Ordovician Basins and Arches

In addition to the relatively local influence of reef buildups, larger, intracratonic features caused by gentle crustal movements on a regional scale also profoundly influenced sedimentation patterns in Paleozoic epeiric seas. The Michigan Basin, for example, was apparently an area of downsagging that persisted over tens of millions of years,

with successions ranging in age from Ordovician to Mississippian. Its influence is seen in thicker formations and in the location of reef buildups around its margins (Figure 13.5). Further west, the Williston Basin had appeared by Mississippian time and persisted right up into the Neogene. Other basins are shown in Figure 13.6. The cause of such long, continued downsagging is not clear, but geologists assume that deep-seated structures in the old Precambrian basement rocks are responsible. In some cases, old rifts may be involved. Another possibility is that ancient mantle plumes or even large meteorite craters dating from early in the earth's history might still be exerting an influence on geologic history.

In addition to downsagging basins, which structural geologists refer to as tectonically negative areas, are **tectonically positive areas,** which, while rarely emergent as actual islands, are marked by a thinning of various units as formations are traced across them. Sometimes they are dome-shaped—for example, the Nashville Dome—or they may be more linear features, such as the Cincinnati Arch. Again, deep-seated basement rock features are generally believed to be responsible.

Ordovician Tectonics: The Birth of the Appalachians

In a general way and well before the end of the nineteenth century, the Appalachian Mountains had been correctly interpreted as caused by regional compression and crustal shortening. Once the mechanism of plate tectonics was discovered, however, it became clear that plate collision had been the cause and that the North American (Laurentian) and Baltic cratons had been involved. Work in the 1960s and 1970s made it increasingly obvious that this relatively simple picture left many complex problems unanswered.

For one thing, age determinations from many localities up and down the Appalachians often gave apparently conflicting results that were only finally explained when geologists realized that more than one orogeny had occurred. Not only did the time of orogenic climax vary from place to place along the Appalachian ranges, but in some areas, evidence indicated three or even more climactic events. In the Great Smoky Mountains, for instance, are two major thrust faults (the Greenbriar and the Great Smoky faults) separated in age by some 140 million years (Figure 13.7).

Because plate collision, according to the standard plate-tectonic model, continues for as long as a subduction zone is present, the evidence seemed to indicate that two or more subduction zones must have existed. It was also

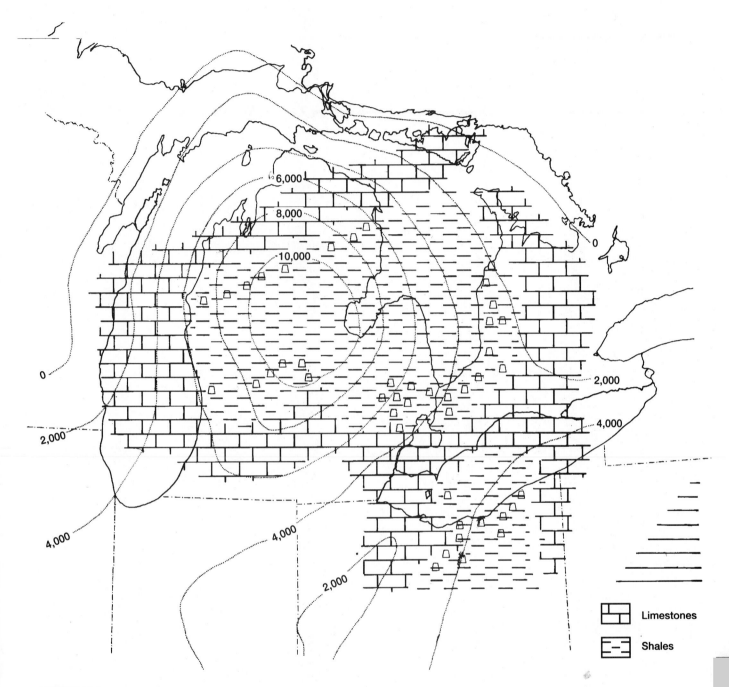

FIGURE 13.5

Map of the Michigan Basin in the Ordovician, showing the distribution of shelf carbonates, barrier reefs, and pinnacle reefs. Contours are for depth to Precambrian basement (in feet). The small rectangles are pinnacle reefs.

clear that the shape of the craton margin was such that the northern region (what is now Newfoundland, the Maritime Provinces, and New England) felt the effects of collision first and that the zone of maximum orogenic movement shifted progressively southwestward along the craton margin.

First Signs of Plate Collision

Although the most obvious effects of plate collision are seen in the evidence for great compressional forces at work, resulting in folding, thrust faults, and metamorphism, very often the first signs that something is happening are many

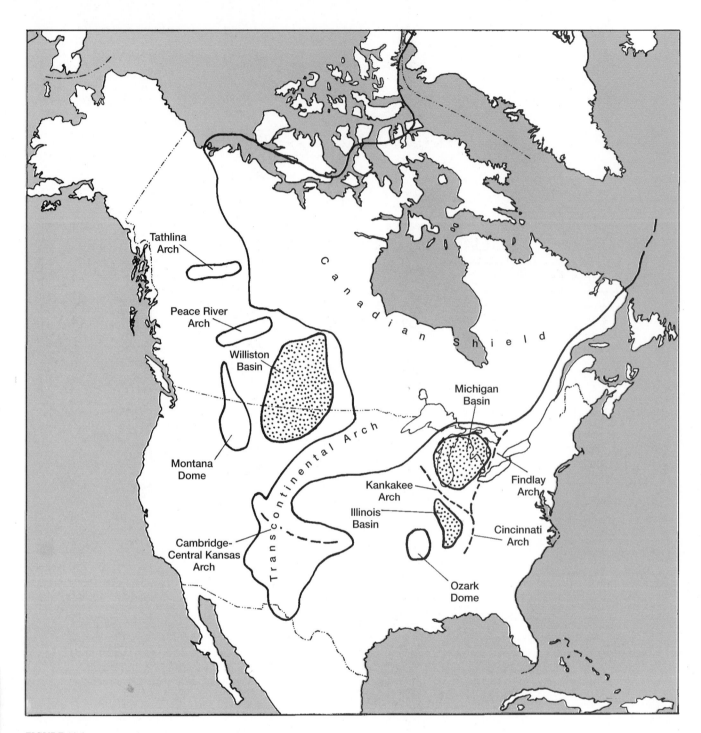

FIGURE 13.6
Major structural features that influenced sedimentary facies
on the North American craton during the Early Paleozoic.

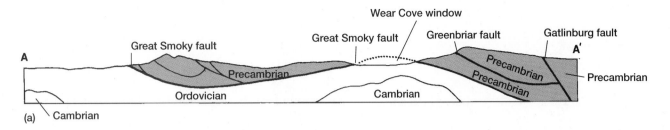

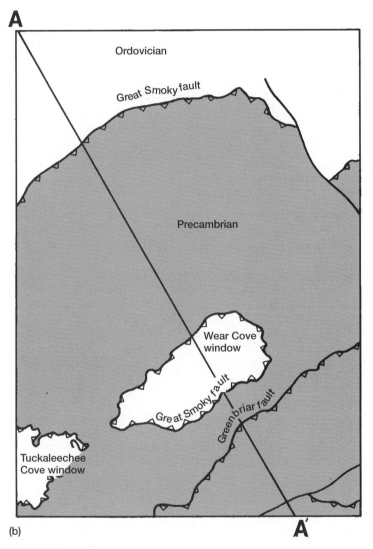

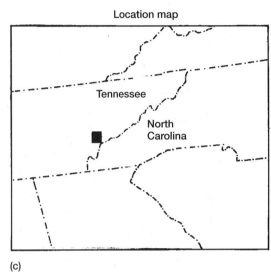

FIGURE 13.7

Evidence of major thrusting in the Great Smoky Mountains.
(a) Two major thrusts—the Great Smoky Mountains and
Greenbriar faults—seen in structural cross section. (b) Map
of tectonic windows through the thrust sheets, revealing the
Ordovician rocks beneath the Precambrian. (c) Location
map.

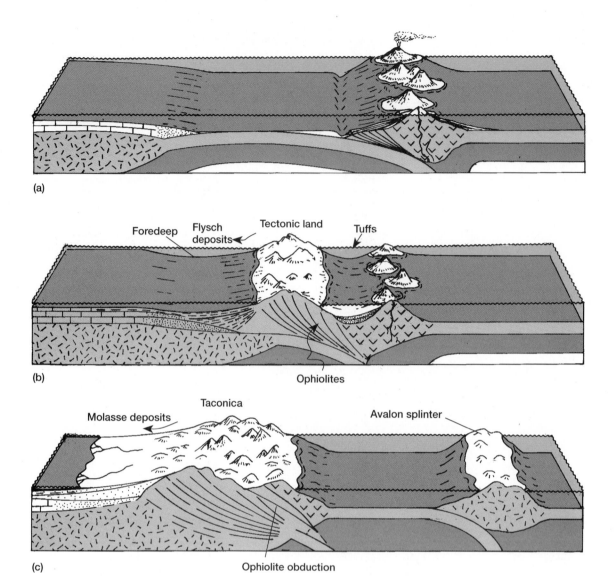

(a)

Foredeep   Flysch   Tectonic land   Tuffs
deposits

(b)   Ophiolites

Molasse deposits   Taconica   Avalon splinter

(c)   Ophiolite obduction

FIGURE 13.8

Plate-tectonic model of the Taconic orogeny. (a) Late Early
Ordovician (465 million years). Subduction zone and island
arc approaches craton. (b) Early Middle Ordovician (450
million years). Emergence of tectonic land terranes.

(c) Taconic orogeny, Middle Ordovician Continent-ocean
collision. Isotopic dates for Taconic orogeny are 480 to 440
million years.

kilometers away from the actual collision boundary, in
areas where no structural deformation is occurring at all.
Instead, the evidence for change is seen in facies changes
in which the carbonates of a shallow shelf environment
give way, often quite suddenly, to sediments of a completely different kind and derived from a new direction.
Such was the case along the eastern margin of the North
American craton in Middle Ordovician time.

All through the Sauk and well into the Tippecanoe
transgressions, the shallow seas of the craton had been
largely the site of carbonate deposition; any clastic sediments—and these were typically mature sands—were derived from the Canadian Shield and exposed areas along

the Transcontinental Arch. Beginning in the Middle Ordovician (and much earlier in some locations—notably, the
Appalachian region), however, clastic sediments began to
arrive from an easterly source. Since Cambrian times, the
Iapetus Ocean had lain in that direction, but now its days
were numbered as it began to close with its margins moving
toward two or more subduction zones (Figure 13.8).

In the cratonic succession, the first indication of
change was seen in the beginnings of a flood of clastics.
In eastern Tennessee, for example, the dolomites of the
Rome Formation change upward quite abruptly into siltstones and shales of the overlying Pumpkin Valley Formation. Fossils indicate an early Middle Cambrian age

for these sediments, which provides a useful means of dating the very earliest manifestation of crustal unrest that was to culminate in the formation of the Appalachian Mountains. Studies of facies changes and paleocurrent directions indicate that the source of these sediments lay in new land areas arising from the sea to the east.

As biostratigraphic data and particularly isotopic dates accumulated, it became clear that the events that led to the Appalachian and Ouachita mountains as a whole were spread over a considerable span of time. Evidence indicates, for example, that, along some segments of the continental margin, crustal unrest began as early as the Middle Cambrian. Although as time passed, there were more or less quiescent periods, one area or another likely experienced some crustal activity along the craton margin until well into the Pennsylvanian.

Appalachian Plate-Tectonic Events

In terms of Ordovician plate tectonics, the North American continental margin lay adjacent to one or more subduction zones with their associated island arcs, and the long history of unrest can be ascribed in a general way to a series of collision episodes. One of these involved the Baltic craton in a full continent-to-continent collision, followed later by the arrival of Gondwana, with effects to be felt along the entire southern margin.

The complexity of the structure and stratigraphy of the Appalachians has inevitably produced numerous models to explain the likely sequence of plate-tectonic events. The most recent interpretation suggests that movement began with an easterly dipping subduction zone beneath a volcanic island arc that eventually collided with the continent. At the collision boundary, segments of oceanic crust adjacent to the volcanic islands, together with parts of the continental rise, were carried up and **obducted** on top of the continental crust. This collision scenario was apparently repeated two or three times, indicating that more than one subduction zone was involved.

The Appalachian chain as a whole is now widely believed to be made up of a collage of small segments of continental crust, together with island arcs and possibly also pieces of oceanic crust, often derived from distant places and carried on moving plate surfaces, eventually to be accreted to the North American continent. This concept of **exotic,** or **suspect, terranes,** as they are known, had earlier been used with considerable success to explain the complicated geologic history of northwestern British Columbia and Alaska. Exotic terranes in that region are believed, in some cases, to have originated as far away as the other side of the Pacific Ocean.

Along the Appalachians, the various terranes are elongated and irregular in shape and are not necessarily continuous, as seen in Figure 13.9. They do, however, exhibit a uniform age relationship to each other, with the oldest on the continental side and successively younger terranes accreted on the ocean side. The origin of some of the terranes is indicated by fossils as well as by lithologic resemblances. The **Avalonian terrane,** named after the Avalon Peninsula of Newfoundland and accreted before or during the Acadian orogeny, is believed to have originated by rifting of the margin of Gondwana. Cambrian fossils in Avalonian terrane rocks are of Euro-African rather than North American species.

Although crustal movements along the Appalachians were spread over some 300 million years, significant clusterings of isotopic dates and the periodicity of folding and faulting have led to the recognition of three major orogenies: (1) the **Taconic orogeny** of Middle Ordovician to Early Silurian age; (2) the **Acadian orogeny,** dated as Middle to End Devonian; and (3) the **Allegheny orogeny** of Carboniferous age.

Orogenic Sedimentary Associations

Quite apart from the structural deformation caused by plate collision, great thicknesses of sediments are produced during an orogeny, and the beginning, the climax, and the waning stages of orogenic activity are all reflected in distinctive sedimentary associations. Many years before plate tectonics had even been recognized, European geologists studying the history of the Alps had distinguished two broad groupings of sediment: What they called **flysch** sediments included shales, siltstones, and sandstones, often of graywacke type, that were derived from erosion of a rising orogenic belt and that were carried down into marine basins subsiding on mountain flanks. As the orogeny reached its climax and structural deformation largely ceased, active erosion produced great wedges of clastic material that spread for considerable distances out from the mountains. The Alpine geologists called these largely nonmarine conglomerates, sandstones, and shales **molasse.**

These same sedimentary associations can be seen in North America. The sedimentary successions of Middle and Upper Ordovician and of Silurian age reflect the profound regional changes that occurred as the Taconic orogeny approached its climax and the volcanic arc along the craton margin was replaced by a rising chain of mountains. Although the ages differ somewhat from one section to another along the entire eastern margin of the continent, the limestones laid down on the broad, shallow shelf—for example, the Beekmantown Formation of Virginia, the Charlesberg Limestone of West Virginia, and so on—pass up into shales of the widespread Martinsburg and Canajoharie formations of Late Ordovician age (Figure 13.10). These are the flysch deposits associated with the rising Taconic Mountains. Still higher in the succession are such sandstones as the Silurian Juniata and Tuscarora formations that pass eastward into nonmarine facies. These are representatives of the molasse facies and are part of a vast wedge that spread westward across the craton platform as far as the area of present Lake Huron.

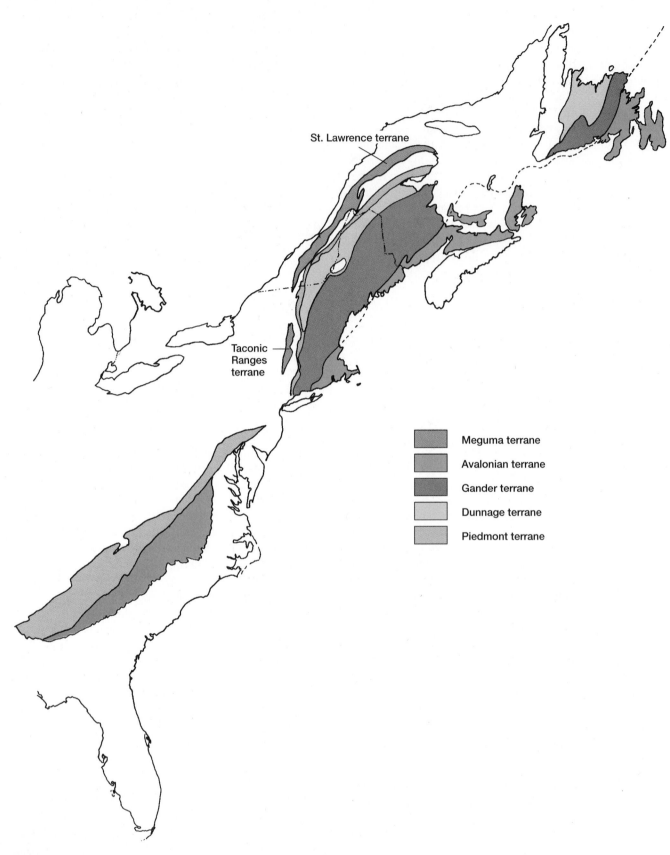

FIGURE 13.9
Exotic terranes in the Appalachian orogenic belt.

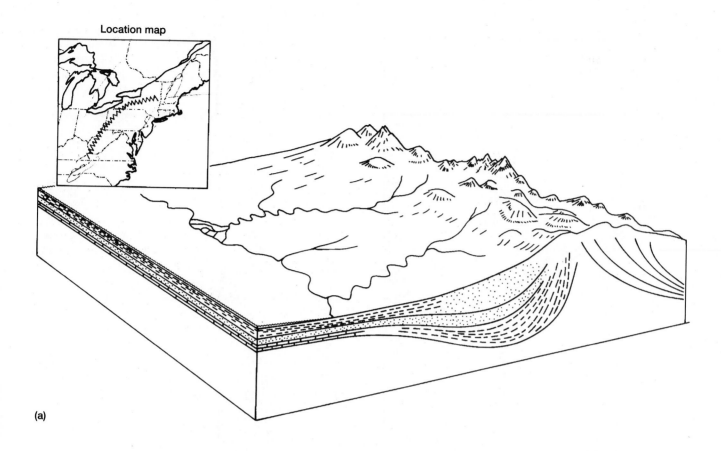

Location map

(a)

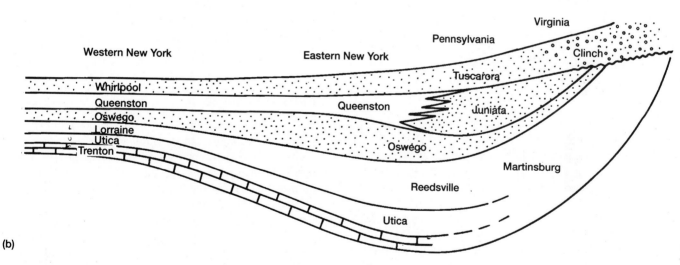

Western New York

Whirlpool
Queenston
Oswego
Lorraine
Utica
Trenton

Eastern New York

Queenston

Oswego

Utica

Virginia
Pennsylvania
Clinch
Tuscarora
Juniata
Martinsburg
Reedsville

(b)

FIGURE 13.10

(a) Block diagram showing location and facies relationships of the sediments derived from the tectonic lands rising during the Taconic orogeny. (b) Diagrammatic cross section through the wedge of flysch and molasse sediments spreading westward from the rising Taconic Mountains.

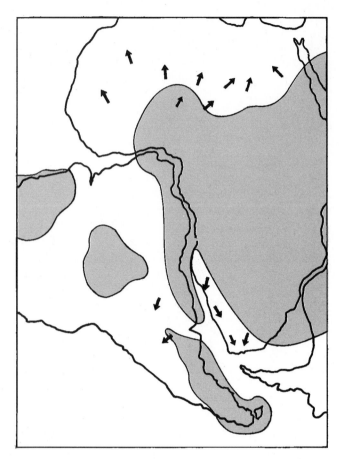

FIGURE 13.11
Location of glacial features in rocks of Ordovician age.
According to some scientists, the Namibian and Brazilian
occurrences may have been due to an ice cap separate from
that in North Africa.

western extremity of the Queenston wedge, the succession
is thinnest, it is, nevertheless, most complete, and in the
Niagara gorge, for example, the red-colored Queenston
Shale of Late Ordovician age is overlain, apparently con-
formably, by the Whirlpool Formation, the basal Silurian
sandstone. Elsewhere and over large areas of the Appalachians, the first Silurian sediments lie unconformably on
an erosion surface that cuts down to varying depths in the
Ordovician succession. One of the key successions, where
the Ordovician/Silurian boundary occurs within an apparently complete succession, is found on Anticosti Island
in the Gulf of St. Lawrence. The dominance of limestone
in this section indicates that it must have lain just beyond
the reach of the Taconic upheaval and clastic influx.

An Ordovician Ice Age

Although this account is largely concerned with events in
North America, events in other parts of the world had far-
reaching effects. While North America in the Ordovician
lay in the equatorial region, Gondwana (which was ultimately destined to collide with North America in Pennsylvanian time) still lay a long way to the south—in fact,
so far south that part of it lay at the South Pole. As discussed in Chapter 11, a continental area located in a polar
position will likely become covered by an ice cap. Gondwana, incidentally, was so large that, despite plate movements, parts of it lay at the pole for long intervals.
Abundant evidence exists in the form of both glacial erosional features and glacial deposits in the Sahara area of
Africa for such an Ordovician ice cap (Figure 13.11).

Even with many local formation names and facies
changes, the sediments of this wedge nevertheless fit into
a broad, regional pattern and explain much about events
that were taking place further east during the Taconic
orogeny. Four general characteristics apply to much of the
succession: First, the clastic units tend to thicken in an
easterly direction. Second, they pass from marine facies
in the west to brackish water and nonmarine facies in the
east. Third, the clastic units generally tend to become
coarser grained to the east. Finally, gaps in the stratigraphic succession tend to increase in number and magnitude in an easterly direction.

The northern Appalachian clastic wedge, often referred to as the Queenston clastic wedge or the Queenston
Delta, is, in fact, a classic example. It is, however, only
one of several such wedges that were shed westward along
the length of the Appalachian trend. All of them have
comparable features and sedimentary associations.

Because the Taconic orogeny lasted from the Middle
Ordovician until well into Silurian time, the Ordovician/
Silurian boundary is often impossible to determine amid
all the facies changes and erosional gaps. Although at the

Ordovician Faunas

The close resemblance between many of the sediments,
particularly carbonates, in the Sauk and Tippecanoe seas
indicates that bottom environments were essentially the
same. The clean-water, warm, and shallow seas of Sauk
time returned during the Tippecanoe transgression. The
same ecologic niches were there, but new organisms appeared to fill them, as if the same roles in a drama were
being played by different actors. The reefs of Cambrian
time were formed by the spongelike archaeocyathids; by
the Ordovician, archaeocyathids were extinct, and the first
reef-building corals had appeared. By the close of the
period, reef masses of corals, bryozoans, stromatoporoids,
and other organisms were important features.

Evolutionary Radiations

An **evolutionary radiation** is a relatively rapid increase in
the number and diversity of particular taxonomic groups.
Typically, the fossil record of ancestors indicates that the
ancestors were without undue prominence, perhaps diminutive in size, few in numbers, or sometimes represented by a single family. The reasons why these few

favored species should become the founders of flourishing dynasties in later time are varied and sometimes obscure. In some cases, the disappearance or extinction of one group makes way for another. This is commonly believed to have been the case with mammals, for example. They had existed side by side with the dinosaurs for over 100 million years, but the great mammalian radiation of the Tertiary began only after the dinosaurs were extinct. In other instances, evolutionary radiations are a response to habitat expansion. A marine transgression, for instance, is followed by a great increase in shallow marine habitats that become occupied by what have been called **opportunistic species.** Sometimes, speciation events and presumably an increase in diversity are triggered by environmental stress brought about by contracting habitats, with the likelihood of increased competition.

Ordovician Invertebrates

Brachiopods

The trilobites that dominated the Cambrian seas were no longer prominent. They suffered at least three extinction events during the Late Cambrian and never really recovered. Instead, the outstanding feature of Ordovician faunas was the great multitude of brachiopods. In particular, many new articulate forms appeared, with shells of calcium carbonate. The "broad-shouldered" shape of the valves and the prominent riblike ornamentation were particularly characteristic of the Ordovician brachiopods (Figure 13.12 a and b). The majority of the animals attached themselves to the substrate by means of a fleshy stalk known as the pedicle that passed out through an opening in the larger of the two valves. (In descriptions of brachiopods, this is known as the pedicle valve; the other is the brachial valve.)

Corals

The evolutionary radiation of the brachiopods was a prominent feature of the Ordovician, but just as important were the corals and crinoids. While representatives of these groups had played a minor role in the Cambrian, they also underwent evolutionary radiation during the Ordovician.

The shallow seas of the Tippecanoe transgression certainly provided ample opportunities for the early corals. The rugose corals—or tetracorals, as they are sometimes called, because the vertical internal septa appear in groups of four—quickly grew to prominence, and both solitary species—the so-called horn corals (Figure 13.12c)—and colonial forms grew profusely on the sea floor. As generation upon generation of polyps left their skeletal remains behind, great masses of limestone formed reefs, or **bioherms.** Such accumulations introduced important modifications to the local seafloor topography, influencing water circulation and sedimentation patterns and providing specialized habitats for other organisms.

Bryozoans

Although some problematic fossils in the Cambrian have been claimed as primitive bryozoans, bryozoans are generally believed to have not appeared until the Ordovician, the last of the major phyla to make a debut. Surprisingly, the closest relatives of the bryozoa are the brachiopods. Although they look very different, they both possess a structure known as a lophophore. No other animal group, with the exception of the phoronids, has a similar feature. Ordovician bryozoans are found associated with corals in many reefs and at times formed small reefs themselves.

Stromatoporoids

By Middle Ordovician time, reefs had become complex associations of organisms, with rugose corals and bryozoans growing alongside tabulate corals (which include the so-called "honeycomb" and "chain" corals) and stromatoporoids. Until recently, stromatoporoids were considered an extinct group that taxonomists, for want of a better place, usually included with the hydrozoans. Work during the 1980s on certain living sponges in the Caribbean, however, has shown the sponges to contain the same internal skeletal structures as stromatoporoids. Thus, what had once been thought a long extinct group is apparently still with us. This discovery was rather unusual because, in paleontology, taxonomies are usually revised as a result of new fossil discoveries, often with the finding of unusually well-preserved material or rare species. In this case, investigations of *living* species solved a problem of taxonomic affinity.

Echinoderms

As mentioned in Chapter 12, the echinoderms were represented in the Cambrian by several short-lived forms. This phylum also became much more important during the Ordovician, both the sessile groups (the crinoids and cystoids) with long, jointed stems attached to the substrate (Figure 13.12d) and the mobile group (the echinoids undergoing their own radiations).

Trilobites

Trilobites were still an important element in Ordovician faunas, and although in the number of genera, the faunas did not recover from the Late Cambrian extinctions, they did undergo a minor radiation with a considerable increase in the number of species. New ecological niches came to be occupied; some species were clearly good swimmers, while others, apparently lacking eyes, became adapted to a burrowing existence. In many species, the thorax became more flexible, and the animal was able to curl up with the head shield touching the tail, thus protecting the soft underside. During the Ordovician, some trilobites reached considerable size, and specimens of *Isotelus gigas,* for example, measuring 60 or 70 centimeters have been found (Figure 13.12e).

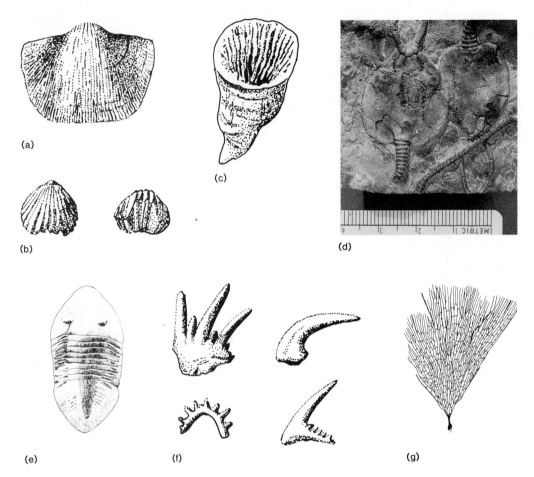

FIGURE 13.12
Typical Ordovician invertebrate fossils. (a) Brachiopod
Hebertella sinuata. (b) Brachiopod *Rhynchotrema.* (c) The
horn coral *Streptelasma.* (d) Cystoid. (e) Trilobite *Isotelus
gigas.* (f) Conodonts. (g) *Dictyonema flabelliforme.*

Cephalopods

Large as many trilobites were, they were dwarfed by giant,
straight-shelled cephalopods, the largest of all Ordovician
animals. Here was another group whose diminutive Late
Cambrian ancestors gave little hint of things to come. From
their earliest beginnings and through a remarkable evolutionary history, up to the cuttlefish, squids, and octopus
of modern seas, the cephalopods have been active predators. In Ordovician seas, where some species grew to an
immense size (massive shells several meters long have been
found), they must have been the lords of creation.

The shells of these cephalopods, just as in the living
Nautilus, were divided into a series of gas-filled chambers
by cross walls, or septa (*see figure 3.20d*). Again, by
analogy with living forms, these animals were presumably
able to control their buoyancy, and there has been much
discussion about their hydraulic stability and swimming
ability, if any. In some groups, massive shelly deposits
within the chambers could only have functioned as bal-
last, suggesting that these species were bottom-dwellers.

Conodonts

The cephalopods may have had some competition because
another group of fossils, the conodonts, suggest that living
among the cephalopods and trilobites was an active eel-
like animal, about which little is known. The conodonts
are tiny, toothlike fossils made of phosphatic rather than
calcareous material, so they are easy to extract from limestone simply by dissolving the rock in dilute hydrochloric
acid (Figure 13.12f). Until recently, the animal from which
these diminutive fossils were derived was entirely unknown. However, this did not prevent taxonomists from
classifying this enormously varied group, many of which
have come to be important zone fossils in stratigraphic
correlation.

The conodonts provide a good example of how different is the approach to taxonomy in dealing with fossils
as compared with living species. Taxonomy is simply a
means whereby different animals and plants are sorted out,
classified, and named. In the case of fossils, paleontologists recognize "morphospecies" (species defined solely by

BOX 13.1

Graptolites

The graptolites were colonial organisms, and the skeletons consist of a series of cuplike *thecae* arranged in series along a branch known as the *stipe*. Inside the stipe was a delicate thread known as the *nema*, which originates at the initial theca of the colony, known as the *sicula*.

What kind of animal occupied each of the thecae is unknown because none has ever been preserved. Because of their delicate structure and small size, graptolites typically are found as flattened, carbonized films on the surface of shales.

Occasionally, however, they have been found preserved in an uncrushed state in limestone and such specimens reveal much about graptolites' internal structure. Pioneer work by Polish paleontologist R. Kozlowski in the 1940s revealed that the skeletal structures were very similar to those

seen in certain hemichordates, and it is now generally agreed that the graptolites belong in that group. Before that, they had been another of the paleontological mysteries and at one time or another were considered by taxonomists as bryozoans, corals, hydrozoa, and even plants.

Detailed studies have shown that not all thecae are similar, and no less than four different types occur in the same colony. Presumably, the tiny animals, or zooids, occupying them were also different, but in what way is unknown. Sexual dimorphism with male and female zooids would account for two of them, whereas the other two may have had respiratory or protective functions.

The graptolites appeared at the beginning of the Ordovician and lasted into the Mississippian. During this time, they underwent rapid evolutionary changes, and because many were also

planktonic or pseudo-planktonic, they became widely distributed across the world oceans. This means, of course, that they have proven to be excellent zone fossils. The short life span of an individual species, typically a little more than a million years, means that quite refined biostratigraphy is possible. The only drawback to graptolites as zone fossils is that they tend to be found only in black-shale successions laid down in quiet, probably deep water often, it is suspected, in an anoxic bottom environment. In shallow-water, high-energy, well-oxygenated environments, the delicate graptolite skeletons were quickly destroyed either mechanically or by scavengers. This means that the sophisticated graptolite zonation established in shale successions cannot be extended into sandstone formations, where brachiopods take over as the zone fossils of choice.

---

external appearance) that hopefully are true species in the genetic sense, but this is only an educated guess. Often, paleontologists are, by necessity, led even further away from reality by having to deal with what are known to be merely fragments of larger animals and plants. What this means is that fossils originally described as separate entities and given generic and species names may eventually turn out to be parts of a single organism. This is particularly true in paleobotany because branches, leaves, seeds, spores, roots, and so on were invariably described separately as they were found, perhaps many years ago. Eventually, a lucky find (and likely a large specimen) may bring two or more of the separate elements together, and they are seen as parts of the same plant or tree.

This was also the case with conodonts, and while the close proximity of many different forms, one to another, pointed to the derivation from a single individual, no one had any idea what the animal looked like. Much of this uncertainty was removed when, finally, in the 1980s, conodonts were found to be intimately associated with the carbonized impression of an eel-like animal.

Graptolites

Characteristic of many Ordovician shale successions are graptolites, diminutive colonial organisms whose flattened remains preserved on bedding planes look like pencil marks—hence, the name from the Greek *graptos* ("Greek written") (Figure 13.12g). Considerable mystery surrounded their taxonomic affinities until studies in the early 1940s by Polish paleontologist R. Kozlowski demonstrated that graptolites were actually hemichordates (invertebrates with a dorsal nerve chord) and so shared a common ancestor with the vertebrates.

The graptolites underwent rapid evolution, and so individual species had short life spans—on average, about 1.2 million years. Various evolutionary "trends" can be discerned in the phylogeny of graptolites, one of which is a progressive reduction in the number of branches, or stipes. This eventually ended with the single stipe of the monograptids that appeared at the beginning of the Silurian. This fascinating and stratigraphically useful group is discussed further in Box 13.1. In addition, the mode of life of many graptolite species was planktonic or pseudoplanktonic, so they became widely disseminated in Ordovician and Silurian seas, with some species eventually coming to have an almost worldwide distribution.

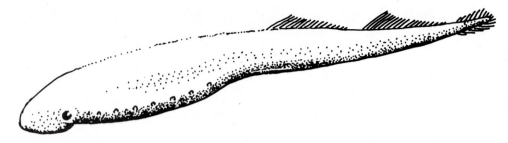

FIGURE 13.13
A lamprey is a living jawless fish that is a parasite of other fish.

The restricted range through time of many species, together with their widespread occurrence, make graptolites the almost ideal zone fossil for use in biostratigraphic correlation. Unfortunately, their fragility means that they are rarely preserved in sandstones and the other shallow-water, high-energy facies that contain the prolific brachiopod/bryozoa/coral faunas. Instead, they are typically found as flattened, carbonized impressions in black shales. Occasionally, graptolites are preserved in pyrite, which suggests that they came to rest in an anoxic bottom environment. Remarkably preserved specimens have also been found in certain limestones in an unflattened condition. With special techniques, they can be extracted and mounted in transparent plastic; otherwise, they collapse under their own weight once the surrounding limestone is gone.

Ordovician Vertebrates

Scattered dermal plates, derived from what were presumably fishes, have been found in rocks as old as Late Cambrian. Such fossils have been found at numerous horizons in the Ordovician also, together with the first rather poorly preserved remains of whole fish. That these first fishes were marine species is indicated by their association with brachiopods, bryozoans, and corals.

All of these early fishes are classified as belonging to the Agnatha, the jawless fishes. Their mouths were openings surrounded by a circlet of small plates, and they presumably fed by sucking up small particles of food from the sea floor by a sort of vacuum-cleaner suction mechanism. Most were bottom feeders and probably sucked up mud as well.

One group of jawless fishes—the lampreys and hagfish—are still with us today (Figure 13.13). At some point in their history, they adopted a parasitic life mode. Significantly, however, in the early stages of development, immature lampreys are bottom dwellers and feed from food particles on the mud surface.

The Agnatha are classified on the basis of whether they have one or two nostrils. Those with two nostrils appear first in the record, but although the more primitive, they gave rise to higher vertebrates. The single-nostril group, on the other hand, gave rise to the modern cyclostomes that include the lampreys.

All the Paleozoic agnathid fishes are classified as *ostracoderms,* which means "bony skin," and many are characterized by a heavy, bony armor, particularly in the head region, although the internal skeleton was cartilaginous. Many ostracoderms had a flattened body shape and, being bottom dwellers, were probably not very good swimmers.

Late Ordovician Extinction Event

The Late Ordovician ice age and the consequent effect on world climate is generally held accountable for a mass extinction event at the close of the Ordovician. These extinctions were widespread, involving approximately 50 percent of Ordovician species, and particularly decimated the coral, bryozoan, and brachiopod communities of the shallow epeiric seas. Some workers have suggested that lowered sea levels during glacial advances and contraction of shallow marine habitats were responsible for the terminal Ordovician extinctions. Although these might have had a minor influence, climatic change seems to be the favorite when assessing the possible causes. Naturally, the extinctions may have been caused by something else altogether; there are no clear indicators.

One of the problems in studying mass extinction events is the possibility of circular thinking. If a stratigraphic horizon is defined on the basis of extinctions, then inevitably, all the species involved will have become extinct at that horizon. Equally puzzling is the question of the suddenness of a mass extinction. Whatever caused the demise of so many species was certainly not an overnight event and may even have been spaced over thousands of years. This is hardly "sudden" by human standards, but within the context of the millions of years of geologic time, it is a short time span.

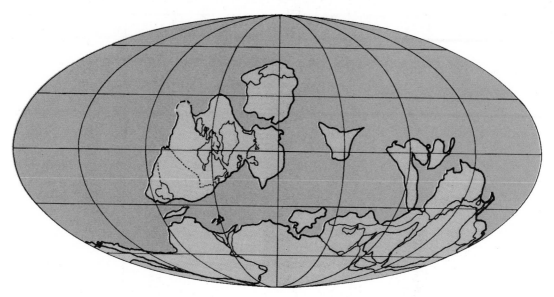

FIGURE 13.14
World paleogeography in the Middle Silurian.

Silurian Overview

The Ordovician/Silurian Boundary

The close of the Ordovician was not marked by any major changes in the distribution of land and sea or in any major mountain building in North America (Figure 13.14). Along the eastern margin of the continent, earth movements associated with the Taconic orogeny resulted in erosional breaks in latest Ordovician time so that, in many areas, an unconformity is chosen as the Ordovician/Silurian boundary. Westward onto the North American craton, the Tippecanoe transgression was still in full swing and had barely passed its greatest advance. In some areas, there were erosional discontinuities, but this was likely due to a glacio-eustatic drop in sea level associated with the Late Ordovician ice age. The Ordovician/Silurian boundary also is marked by a pronounced biostratigraphic discontinuity, since, as mentioned earlier, about 50 percent of Ordovician species are estimated to have become extinct.

The Eastern North American Craton during the Silurian

At the beginning of the Silurian, along the eastern margin of the North American craton, the highlands formed during the Taconic orogeny were rapidly becoming lowered by erosional forces. Much of geologic history concerns the balance between deposition and erosion, and these processes operate at largely different rates. Sediment accumulation in terms of what is actually preserved (in other words, net accumulation) is typically slow when compared with the rate at which erosion can destroy sediments once they become exposed to subaerial processes.

For example, the mountains produced by the Taconic orogeny likely were reduced to sea level in a far shorter span of time than it had taken to form them, even though the buoyancy effect of isostatic rebound was always at work to counter the erosional beveling process as it "unloaded" the crust.

Thus, most of the early Silurian formations of the eastern craton are of clastics derived from the Taconic highlands further east. Up and down the Appalachians, various local names, such as the Whirlpool Sandstone of the Niagara area, the Shawangunk Conglomerate in Pennsylvania and New York, the Tuscarora Sandstone in Virginia, and the Clinch Sandstone in Tennessee, have been applied to these molasse-type deposits.

Traced westward onto the craton, these generally coarse-grained clastic formations predictably become thinner and pass into shales and eventually into limestones as the influence of the Taconic belt is left behind. Although widespread in their distribution, the Silurian-age limestones of the Tippecanoe Sea were generally quite thin and indicate relatively shallow water conditions. The small outliers preserved in down-faulted blocks on the Canadian Shield indicate that much of that region was also covered at times, making the Tippecanoe Sea the most extensive of any epeiric sea in history.

Silurian Intracratonic Structures

By Late Silurian time, intracratonic warping was beginning to affect sedimentation. Subsidence in localized areas, such as in the Michigan, Illinois, and Williston basins and in the Hudson Bay area, is reflected in greater thicknesses of sediments and in the distribution of reef limestones and evaporites.

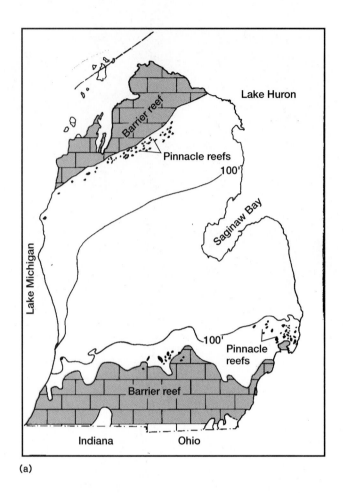

(a)

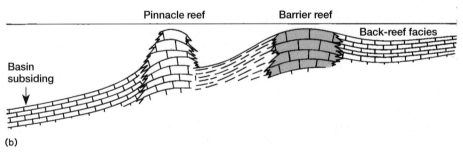

(b)

FIGURE 13.15

(a) Silurian reef buildups in the Michigan Basin. (b) The
trends of barrier reefs and pinnacle reefs.

Silurian Reefs

Around the Michigan Basin, a massive barrier reef developed, with a steep inner face to the presumably deeper
water of the basin and extensive "back-reef" carbonate in
the areas behind (Figure 13.15). Inside the basin, the response to somewhat deeper water and the progressive subsidence of the basin is seen in the occurrence of a second
type of reef known as a **pinnacle reef.** Superficially, pinnacle reefs resemble the familiar small and localized patch
reefs of modern carbonate banks and may indeed have
been initiated in the same way. Their narrow pinnacle

shape is surely a reflection of relatively rapid subsistence
of the substrate, with the reefs growing actively upward
to remain in the photic zone. Many of these reefs, later
buried in impermeable sediments, have proven to be traps
for oil and gas. Extensive drilling has naturally resulted
in extremely detailed maps of the reef tracts, and voluminous literature on the subject exists.

Silurian Evaporite Deposits

Also characteristic of Late Silurian sedimentation on the
craton interior are extensive evaporite deposits, typically
the Salina Group succession of the Michigan Basin (Figure

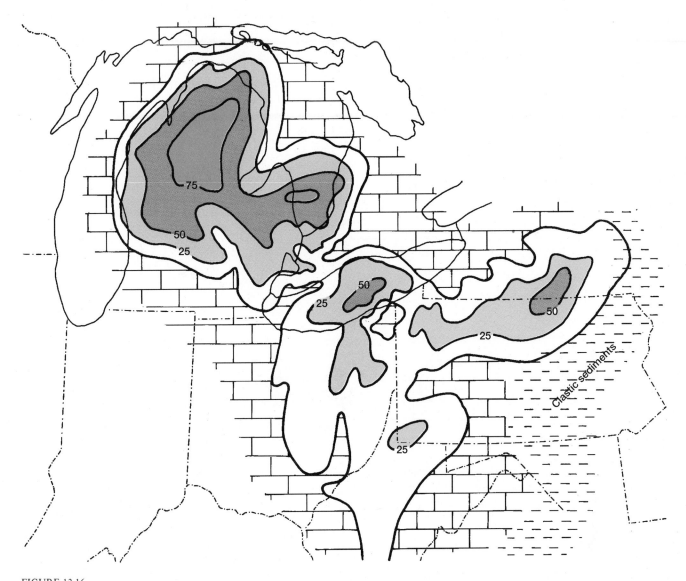

FIGURE 13.16

Evaporite facies of the Upper Silurian Series in the Great Lakes area. Note the increasing percentages of halite in moving from the periphery into the center of each basin.

Surrounding the basins are shelf carbonates. The shales and siltstones on the eastern side of the area are derived from the Taconic tectonic highlands to the east.

13.16). As with the distribution of reefs mentioned earlier, the Salina Group is a well-documented example of control by regional tectonics in which a pattern of evaporite facies is influenced by basin subsidence. The Late Silurian climate of the region was hot and dry, so at least one requirement for evaporite formation was met.

Detailed analyses of Salina Group stratigraphy show that the evaporites formed during three major depositional cycles in which salinity fluctuated between normal marine conditions, during which limestones were deposited, and high concentrations, resulting in the precipitation of halite. While the Michigan Basin had the highest concentrations and thickest deposits of salts, other basins in the Great Lakes area—notably one centered in Lake Erie and another in the area of northern Pennsylvania and

western New York—also were the sites of thick deposits, although evaporating conditions were less extreme.

The age relationship between the enormously thick deposits of halite, anhydrite, gypsum, and sylvite in the central basin areas and the adjacent reefs around the margins is difficult to determine. Because the evaporites are completely unfossiliferous, their precise age is unknown. Field relationships at some localities indicate that they were at least partially contemporaneous with the reefs, which may have been a factor in restricting water circulation. If this were the case, however, it is difficult to see how the reef-building organisms could have survived in the highly saline water that must have occupied the basin. In an alternative model, the salts are assumed to have formed only after the reefs had ceased to grow—

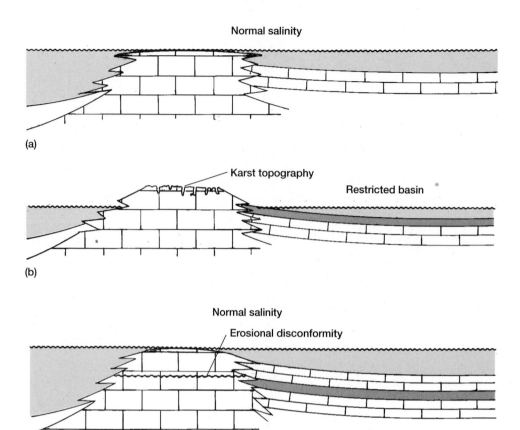

Normal salinity

(a)

Karst topography

Restricted basin

(b)

Normal salinity
Erosional disconformity

(c)

FIGURE 13.17

Model of evaporite/reef facies relationships. (a) Marginal reef with back-reef facies in shallow water behind. (b) Sea-level fall results in emergence and subaerial erosion of limestone.

Evaporites form in back-reef area. (c) Sea-level rise results in reefs becoming reestablished on older reef trends.

indeed, the increasing salinity may well have killed the reefs. A third model is a combination of the first two (Figure 13.17): Perhaps, periods of reef growth alternated with times when evaporites formed. This is the most plausible explanation, although hard to prove. Small-scale erosional gaps, or diastems, are difficult to demonstrate in reef limestones for the simple reason that, because they form so close to sea level, they contain many such depositional breaks in response to minor sea-level fluctuations. The same also applies to evaporites.

Silurian Iron Ores

During the Early Silurian, the Taconic Mountains were still high enough to supply large amounts of sediment to westerly flowing streams. By Middle Silurian time, however, epeiric limestones began encroaching eastward once more, an indication that the supply of sediment from the east was dwindling as the highlands were reduced by erosion.

Residues from deep weathering of the Appalachian belt to the east were probably the source of the extensive Clinton iron-ore deposits, named after the Clinton area of

western New York. The iron occurs mainly in the mineral hematite (Fe_2O_3) in the form of sand-sized pellets and ooliths. Their similarity in form to those found in limestones, and an overall similarity between bedded iron deposits and limestones, has suggested to many geologists that hematite is simply a replacement of an original made of calcite. Other workers, however, believe that the iron oxide was a primary precipitate—if not of hematite, then perhaps of the iron silicate mineral chamosite—and that this was later changed to hematite by **halmyrolysis** (submarine weathering) on the sea floor.

In New York, the iron ores were mined from early colonial times, but the ore beds were rarely thicker than 1.5 to 2 meters, so they were worked out many years ago. Further south, in the vicinity of Birmingham, Alabama, the beds are at least four times as thick and still support a big steel industry in that area.

For the remainder of the Silurian and into Early Devonian time, the Taconic Mountains continued to dwindle, and as the Silurian drew to a close, limestones once more extended far to the east. In many areas, they lay with a marked unconformity across the worn-down roots of the Taconic Mountains.

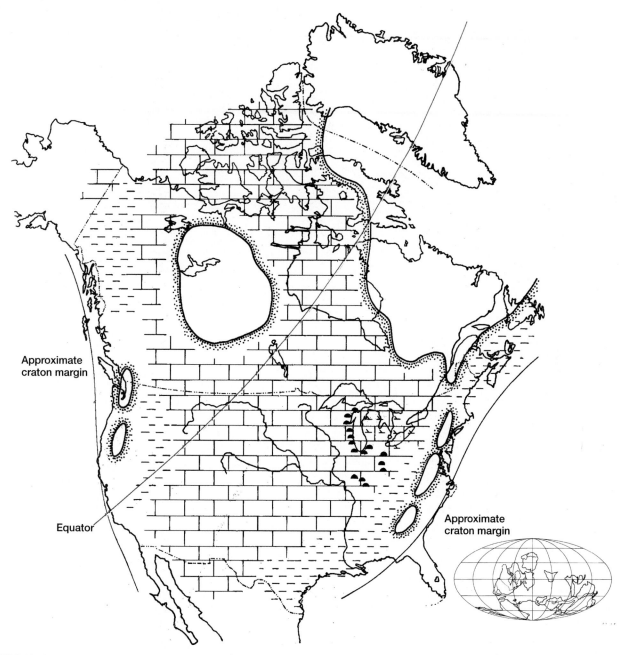

FIGURE 13.18
Paleogeography of the North American craton in the Silurian.

The Western North American Craton during the Silurian

Silurian deposits on the western craton are dominated by carbonates, the easternmost areas toward the craton interior being largely dolomitic. Traced westward, these pass into deeper shelf-slope environments with limestones and clastics. Still further out onto what was presumably the continental slope are shales and siltstones, together with volcanics. Boundary determination between these various facies and a detailed reconstruction of the Silurian paleogeography are greatly hindered by the regional thrusting that occurred during the Antler orogeny in Late Devonian to Mississippian time.

Across the Great Basin, the desert region centered on Nevada, Lower Silurian shelf carbonates were laid down, essentially as a continuation of formations that are primarily of Ordovician age (Figure 13.18). Over large areas, there was apparently a period of emergence during the latter part of the Early Silurian, but above the hiatus are the same shallow, shelf-type limestones of Middle and Late Silurian age. These same conditions apparently continued into Early Devonian time.

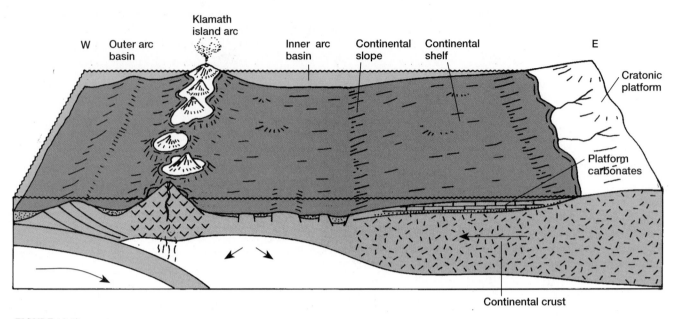

FIGURE 13.19
Diagrammatic section showing the relationship of the
Klamath Island arc and the North American cratonic platform
during the Silurian. Long arrows show direction of plate
movement.

Along the Cordilleran margin of the craton, the Silurian was a time of considerable tectonic and volcanic activity. One or more island arcs, perhaps together with
continental slivers, apparently became incorporated into
the main mass of the craton during one or more subduc-
tion/collision events (Figure 13.19). Numerous rock units
along the entire western borderland from Alaska to Mexico
are distinguished as exotic terranes, each of which typically contains a melange of a variety of siliciclastic sediments, shales, and volcanics. In some cases, these suites
of rocks are claimed to have been derived from midocean
ridge locales; others are said to be of pelagic origin. Frequently, back-arc basin and deep-sea slope deposits can be
recognized. Ages generally range from Middle or Late
Ordovician to Early Devonian. Palinspastic restoration
(see Chapter 8) to provide a coherent paleogeographic
picture is hampered by post-Tippecanoe faulting and
overthrusting.

Silurian Faunas and Floras

No fossil evidence indicates when life first emerged onto
the land. Plant life is assumed to have preceded animals,
however, and the first land plants likely were primitive
algae and lichenlike forms coating the rock surfaces. But
when did they first appear on land?

First Land Life

Cyanobacteria, or blue-green algae, have a considerable
tolerance for ultraviolet radiation and, not requiring soil,
they can draw their sustenance from the weathering residues on exposed rocks. Such plants may have entered the
subaerial environment in the Late Precambrian, but in the
absence of fossils, the time is unknown. On the other hand,
the timing may have been linked to the evolution of the
atmosphere—in particular, the buildup of ozone, which is
an effective ultraviolet shield. From another angle, some
sedimentary evidence has been interpreted to indicate an
absence of appreciable soils for most of the Early Paleozoic.

These various clues, together with increasingly reliable fossil evidence, point to the Middle Silurian as the
likely time of appearance of the first vascular plants—that
is, plants with definite conducting tissues for carrying
water and mineral nutrients from the soil. Certain cuticle
and spore fossils of Ordovician age have been interpreted
by some workers as vascular plants, but they may be of
freshwater aquatic forms rather than true land plants.

Recovery from Late Ordovician Extinction Event

As discussed earlier in the chapter, the cause of the mass
extinction in marine faunas that marked the close of the
Ordovician is still a matter for speculation. Lowered sea

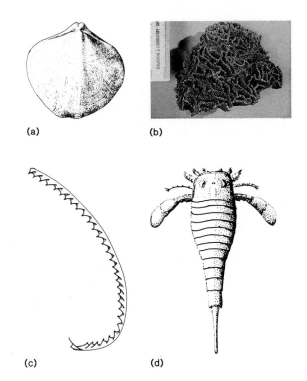

FIGURE 13.20
Typical Silurian invertebrate fossils. (a) Brachiopod *Eospirifer radiatus.* (b) Chain coral *Halysites.* (c) Graptolite *Monograptus.* (d) Eurypterid.

levels have been cited by some workers, while others attribute the extinctions to global cooling from a major ice age during the Late Ordovician. Perhaps the answer lies in a combination of both. In any event, the rich marine life of Ordovician seas was decimated, leaving many ecologic niches vacant. With ameliorating temperatures, the postglacial rise of sea level, and the expansion of shallow marine habitats, however, the potential for another evolutionary radiation was considerable, and many new forms rapidly appeared in the Silurian.

The brachiopods that had been so important in Ordovician seas resumed their former dominance and continued to be well represented in Silurian time. Of the five orders of brachiopods present in the Ordovician, all survived, with the strophomenids, rhynchonellids, and spiriferids all showing diversification and increases in the number of species (Figure 13.20a). By the Late Silurian, the terebratulid brachiopods had appeared, although they tended to remain a minor element right through to the close of the Paleozoic. The terebratulids were to have their heyday in the Jurassic and Cretaceous, after nearly succumbing at the close of the Permian.

Bivalves and gastropods likewise returned with new vigor, as did the corals and stromatoporoids, which were again prominent reef builders through all the Silurian. The

distinctive genera *Halysites* (chain coral) and *Favosites* (honeycomb coral) are particularly characteristic of the Silurian, although they actually first appeared in the Late Ordovician (Figure 13.20b).

Among the hardest hit of Ordovician groups was the graptolites, and their renewal and adaptive radiation during the Silurian was spectacular. The new arrivals included graptolites with a single stipe—the monograptids—and in graptolitic shale successions, their appearance provides a useful Ordovician/Silurian boundary marker (Figure 13.20c).

During the Ordovician, the chief predators, particularly in terms of size, were the cephalopods. In the Silurian, they were replaced by the arthropods, which with their segmented exoskeletons and many jointed limbs were among the most active animals. In brackish and freshwater deposits of Late Silurian age, the remains of immense scorpion-like eurypterids, some up to 3 meters long, have been found, making them the largest arthropods ever known (Figure 13.20d). Although spectacular fossils, such giants were not typical of the group as a whole, the majority being no more than a few centimeters in length. They had six pairs of jointed limbs attached to the front part (the prosoma) of a segmented body, and in most species, these served as swimming paddles. Analogies with living phyllopods and immature horseshoe crabs suggest that eurypterids swam on their backs. In a few species, the limbs may have been walking legs, although probably not very efficient ones. From the Ordovician through the Permian, the eurypterid fossil record is generally poor, likely a consequence of the brackish water or possibly hypersaline environments in which the eurypterids apparently lived.

Fishes

The Early Stages

Among the most noteworthy fossils in rocks of Silurian age are the first articulated skeletons of fishes. As mentioned earlier, scattered dermal plates indicate that the fishes had first appeared in the Late Cambrian, and although, beginning in rocks of Early Ordovician age, far more complete fish fossils have been found in places like Australia and southern Bolivia, they are still only molds and provide little information about the skeletal structure. The evidence from the lithology of the containing sediments and the associated invertebrate fossils suggests a shallow marine habitat for the Cambrian and Ordovician fishes, but the Silurian fossils have been found in freshwater sediments, so the fishes clearly were already undergoing a vigorous expansion into new habitats.

The armor of many of these early fishes suggests that they were preyed upon by other creatures. The eurypterids were probably the biggest menace to the Silurian

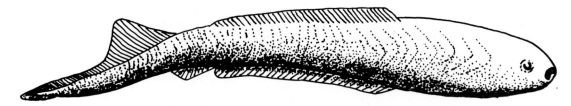

FIGURE 13.21

The Silurian fish *Jamoytius.*

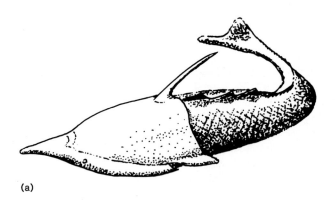

(a)

FIGURE 13.22

(a) The later Silurian fish *Pteraspis.* (b) *Cyclaspis,* a Silurian fish with heavy armor. Its flattened shape indicates that it was a bottom dweller and probably not a very good swimmer.

(b)

fish species. Speed and agility were probably fishes' best defense against the eurypterids' formidable forelimbs with their huge, pincerlike claws. By Middle Silurian time, many agnathids were adapting to a more free-swimming mode and consequently were more lightly armored. *Jamoytius,* for example, looked quite similar to a modern lamprey (Figure 13.21). By the close of the Silurian, early species of *Cyclaspis* had appeared as forerunners of a host of Devonian forms (Figure 13.22).

The Evolution of Jaws

Evolution does not progress as steady and continuous change but rather moves in a series of steps, some being major steps and of profound importance, whereas others have less obvious significance. In the latter part of the Silurian, a series of immensely important transformations in certain fishes led to the evolution of jaws. This example shows how certain organs that filled one particular function came, over the course of time and through a series of relatively small changes, to have a quite different function.

At the very front of a fish head, behind the mouth, are a series of small bones whose function is to support the gill openings—clearly, an important role in the animal's vital system. In the agnathids, each of these **gill arches,** as they are called, is a group of bones arranged in the shape of a *V* on its side with the open end directed forward (Figure 13.23). In the course of an early evolutionary trend, the first (front) and second cycles of gill-arch bones disappeared, the third being changed into a pair of jaws hinged at the point of the *V.* This transformation undoubtedly took place quite quickly within a series of punctuated equilibrium speciation events (see Chapter 4).

No direct fossil evidence of the various intermediate steps exists, but, as is so often the case in such evolutionary progressions, careful studies of embryological development provide vital input. Certain modern fishes have been particularly instructive in this regard. In addition, the anatomy of certain soft tissues provide other useful clues. For example, in the sharks, the arrangement of the nerves in the head region show the jaws and the gill structure to be in series. In particular, the trigeminal, or fifth, cranial nerve branches, with one branch running forward to the upper jaw and the other down to the lower jaw. This is exactly the same way that the nerves branch and run in front of and behind each gill opening.

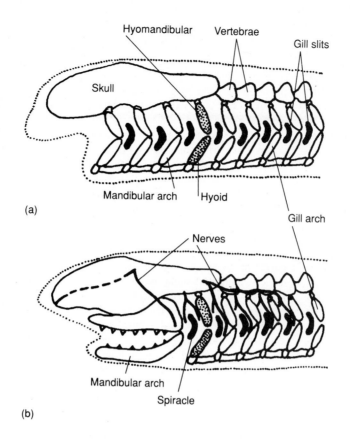

FIGURE 13.23

Evolution of jaws. The third row of gill-arch bones in a jawless fish was converted into a jointed jaw. Teeth originated as modified scales. (a) Diagrammatic section through head region of jawless fish. (b) Section through head region of early jawed fish.

Summary

The Sauk transgression ended early in the Ordovician and was followed by the next marine incursion—the Tippecanoe—the greatest inundation of all geologic history and seen on all the continents. Pre-Tippecanoe weathering and erosion left little but sands on the old land surface, and these were reworked by the oncoming sea. Such basal transgressive sands typically are pure quartz sands and have textural characteristics that distinguish them as supermature. The St. Peter sandstone of the midcontinent region is one such sand, and it and correlative sands originated to the north and northwest, largely from the Canadian Shield.

Toward the periphery of the craton, the sands pass into limestones laid down in broad shelf seas, and these gradually came to cover most of the craton as the Tippecanoe marine advance continued. During this time, the first coral/bryozoan reefs appeared, and this development influenced the distribution of sedimentary facies.

Sediment distribution and accumulation was also influenced by regional tectonic features, such as intracratonic basins and arches. The Michigan Basin, for example, was an area of downsagging from very early times and accumulated sediments of much greater thickness than on the surrounding craton surface.

Along the eastern margin of the North American craton, the Appalachian Mountains were formed during a long history of plate-tectonic movement. This involved several subduction zones, the accreting of numerous island arc/exotic terrane masses, and eventually, the full continent-to-continent collision between the Laurentian and Baltic cratons. In places, there are indications of crustal unrest as early as the Middle Cambrian, but the main episode of the Taconic orogeny affecting the northern Appalachians is dated from early Middle to Late Ordovician. The overall geology of the Appalachian chain shows it to be made up of a collage of different terranes accreted onto the main mass of the craton at different times. Some of these exotic terranes were derived from the North African portion of Gondwana. As the Taconic orogeny reached its climax, great thicknesses of coarse, molasse-type sediments were spread westward onto the craton.

Outside of North America, the continent of Gondwana was moving across the South Pole, and an ice cap formed. Particularly in the Sahara region of North Africa is widespread evidence of glacial activity in the form of glacial erosional features and glacial deposits.

The transition from Ordovician to Silurian time was not marked in North America by any particular event. The Taconic Mountains in the east were becoming worn down, and by the close of the Silurian, shallow shelf seas were once

again covering some areas where the mountains had been.

On the craton interior, the Tippecanoe Sea was still widespread but, toward the close of the Silurian, was withdrawing. Over large areas of the midcontinent region, there were reefs and associated evaporites. In the west, the craton was also submerged by shallow shelf seas, and the limestones deposited there passed westward into deeper-water, outer shelf and slope deposits. Offshore apparently lay an island arc tract, and volcanic sediments are found in some areas.

Although an extinction event occurred at the end of the Ordovician, Ordovician and Silurian marine invertebrate faunas exhibit an overall continuity. Particularly important were the brachiopods, corals (both rugose and tabulate), the bryozoans, and stromatoporoids. All of these were associated in the widespread reef developments. In deeper-water shales,

the graptolites are important fossils from this time. They underwent rapid evolutionary change and are important biostratigraphic zone fossils. The monograptids appeared at the beginning of the Silurian and provide an important marker horizon.

Giant, straight-shelled cephalopods were the most important marine predators in the Ordovician, whereas in the Silurian, large, scorpion-like eurypterids were undoubtedly the dominant predators in fresh and brackish water. Fish fossils showing complete skeletons, rather than scattered dermal plates, are found in Ordovician rocks, but the first well-preserved, articulated fish skeletons do not appear until the Silurian. Before the end of the period, an important step forward was the evolution of the first jawed fishes.

On land, there is evidence that the first vascular plants might have appeared as early as the Ordovician, but the first moderately well-preserved land plants are of Silurian age.

Questions

1. Compare and contrast the paleogeography of the North American craton during the advance of the Sauk Sea with that during the advance of the Tippecanoe Sea.
2. Describe the St. Peter Sandstone—its textural characteristics, its likely history, and its significance in Ordovician paleogeography.
3. Describe the clear-water sedimentation model for epeiric seas.
4. Describe some of the intracratonic structures that influenced sedimentation across the North American craton during the Early Paleozoic.

5. Why do reef limestones often make good oil and gas reservoirs?
6. Describe the kinds of reef buildups that were associated with the Michigan Basin during the Silurian.
7. What is the significance of the exotic terranes of the eastern margin of the North American craton in the geologic history of the region?
8. What is the difference between flysch and molasse?
9. Describe how the Ordovician succession of the northern Appalachians and the area to the west reflects events during the Taconic orogeny.
10. What creatures likely dominated Ordovician and Silurian seas?

11. What is an evolutionary radiation? Describe some of the ways in which changing environments play a role.
12. In what way were trilobites adapted to a variety of habitats?
13. What is meant by "morphospecies," and how do they point up one of the important differences in paleontologists' approach to taxonomy compared with biologists'?
14. Describe events on the western half of the North American craton during the Silurian.
15. Describe how jaws likely evolved and some of the evidence that supports this theory.

Further Reading

Bassett, M.G., ed. 1974. *The Ordovician System: Proceedings of the Paleontological Association Symposium, Birmingham 1974.* Cardiff, Wales: University of Wales Press.

Bird, J.M., and J.F. Deasey. 1970. Lithosphere plate-continental margin tectonics and the evolution of the Appalachian orogeny. *Bulletin of Geological Society of America* 81: 1031–60.

Fairbridge, R.W. 1970. Ice age in the Sahara. *Geotimes* 15: 18.
Lane, N.A. 1978. *Life of the past.* Columbus, Ohio: Merrill.
Rodgers, J.R. 1987. The Appalachian-Ouachita orogenic belt. *Episodes* 10: 259–66.

PLATE 44

The Cades Cove window through the Great Smoky thrust sheet in the Great Smoky Mountains, eastern Tennessee. The flat floor of the valley is underlain by relatively soft and undisturbed Ordovician shales and limestones. The surrounding hills are formed by massive quartzites of Precambrian age lying above the Great Smoky thrust fault.

PLATE 45

Flat-lying Ordovician limestones near Kingston, Ontario. Thin, shaly partings represent periods of minor turbidity in an otherwise clear-water depositional environment.

PLATE 46

Flat-lying Ordovician and Silurian limestones exposed in the walls of the Niagara gorge, Ontario.

PLATE 47
Iron-rich sediments of the Silurian Clinton Group, Birmingham, Alabama.

PLATE 48
Devonian limestones exposed in one of the thrust fault blocks that make up the Front Ranges of the Rocky Mountains, Alberta, Canada.

PLATE 49
Devonian siltstones and shales exposed on the north coast of Devon, England. This is the type area of the Devonian system.

PLATE 50
Limestones with thin coal beds (seen as the soft, recessive units) in the Pennsylvanian of southwestern Colorado.

PLATE 51
The lobe-finned fish *Eusthenopteron* copes with drought
conditions. (From a painting by John Gurche.)

PLATE 52
Hylonomus, an early reptile of the Pennsylvanian. (From a
painting by John Gurche.)

PLATE 53
View from the south rim of the Grand Canyon, Arizona. In the
foreground is the Coconino Sandstone of Permian age.

PLATE 54
The Permo-Triassic boundary occurs near the base of this
succession in the Animas River Valley near Hermosa, Colorado.

PLATE 55
The Cutler Formation of Late Permian age exposed along the
Uncompahgre River near Ouray, Colorado.

PLATE 56
The Canyon de Chelly sandstone member of the Cutler
Formation, exposed in the Canyon de Chelly, Arizona, the type
section.

PLATE 57
The iron oxide mineral hematite colors the sandstones of
northwestern Arizona. These are typical "redbeds."

PLATE 58
The Shinarump Conglomerate, basal member of the Upper
Triassic Chinle Formation.

PLATE 59
The Painted Desert, Arizona. The varicolored shales and
siltstones of the Chinle Formation are exposed over large areas.
In this view, the dark-colored rock bluff in the foreground is
formed by a capping of Tertiary lava.

PLATE 60
Logs replaced by silica weathering out of the Chinle Formation
in the Petrified Forest National Park. The flora is dominated by
the conifer *Araucarioxylon*, but ferns and cycads are also
present.

PLATE 61
Sandstones of the Jurassic Navajo Formation in Zion
National Park, Utah. The prominent cross-bedding of these
sands indicates that they were deposited as desert dunes.

PLATE 62
Sandstones, shales, and coals of the Cretaceous Mesa Verde Group at
Mesa Verde, Colorado.

14

THE DEVONIAN: THE GREAT INVASION

Introduction

On a world scale, the Devonian is considered one of the more fossiliferous systems, during which numerous new facies appeared and new ecologic niches were filled. Figure 14.1 shows world paleogeography in the Devonian. By the end of the Devonian, the world was a markedly different place from that of the beginning Devonian. Perhaps the most outstanding features were an evolutionary explosion among the fishes and the great invasion of the land with the first true forests and the appearance of the first primitive amphibians.

The First "Golden Spike"

Although the geologic time scale has been in use for some 150 years, determination of the precise boundaries between the periods and their magnitude in terms of real time (that is, in years) presents problems that are still in the process of being solved. Because geologic systems and the periods they represent are recognized worldwide, stratigraphic correlation involves setting standards that are acceptable to geologists in all parts of the world.

The Silurian-Devonian boundary is special in this regard because it was the first systemic boundary to be tied to a single geologic section and locality. The Devonian contains some of the most fossiliferous rocks, and its biostratigraphy has been studied in considerable detail. An international committee of geologists finally decided that they could define virtually the instant in time when the Devonian period began. It was not, as British geologist Derek Ager put it, that a great bell in heaven tolled to mark the beginning of Devonian time, but simply a question of establishing a reference stratigraphic horizon. This reference horizon occurs in a single bed of sedimentary rock that contains particular index species—in this case, graptolites—that can be used to establish the beginning of the Devonian in other places around the world.

This official world type section, known as a **Global Boundary Stratotype Section and Point (GBSSP),** is at a place called Klonk near Suchamasty in Czechoslovakia. Here, in "bed number 20," the Devonian began with the sudden appearance of the graptolite species *Monograptus uniformis* and *M. uniformis angustidens.*

Such a boundary is not a natural phenomenon waiting to be discovered but is an entirely human-made artifact established only as a matter of convenience. In fact, several other locations probably would have been just as suitable, but Klonk won on a vote by committee members. Thus, the first of what became popularly referred to as "golden spikes" was metaphorically hammered into the stratigraphic succession.

The Devonian lasted for more than 40 million years, and concern about the instant in time when it began may seem slightly ridiculous. However, the Devonian Period itself is only a theoretical abstract and, therefore, there must have been theoretical moments when it began and when it ended. Global time correlations provide the framework on which historical geology is built and are becoming so finely tuned that the stratigraphic successions formed at these instants in time, or at least as close in time as possible to them, must be discovered, described, and used as standards of comparison.

North America during the Devonian

On the North American craton, now part of Laurussia (see Figure 14.1), no particular events mark the closing of the Early Paleozoic and the opening of the Devonian. The Tippecanoe Sea was ebbing away, and extensive areas of the continent were emerging as dry land. What seas there were, were becoming restricted, and evaporites were laid down over extensive areas. The Taconic highlands of the craton's eastern margin were by this time greatly reduced by erosion or even, in places, submerged beneath shallow shelf seas. As the craton became emergent, weathering

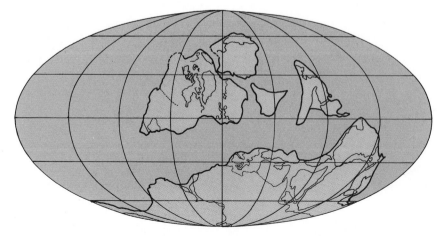

FIGURE 14.1
World paleogeography in the Devonian.

and erosional processes began to strip away the rocks that had formed in the Tippecanoe Sea. Erosion bit deepest in the rising, tectonically positive areas; in some places, such as along the Transcontinental Arch, even rocks of the old Precambrian basement became exposed. Because the Tippecanoe Sea was retreating by earliest Devonian time, only around the craton margins, where the sea lingered longest, are there complete stratigraphic successions through the Silurian and into the Devonian.

The Kaskaskia Transgression

By late in the Early Devonian, the third great marine transgression was underway, and the continent was to be largely covered again—this time by what has been called the **Kaskaskia Sea.** As with the earlier transgressions, the basal beds were again blanket sands occurring as thin spreads over large areas and with various local formational names: in the Appalachian region, the Oriskany Sandstone; in Virginia and West Virginia, the Ridgeley Sandstone; far to the west, in the Illinois Basin, the Dutch Creek Sandstone.

The irregular distribution of the earliest Kaskaskia sediments suggests that the sea was advancing across a continent with some relief, so that the initial Kaskaskia carbonates were laid down largely in basinal areas, whereas areas of positive tendency persisted as islands. By the end of the Early Devonian, however, much of the eastern half of the craton was submerged, and an arm of the sea in the far northwest had also begun a southward advance, with shales and evaporite deposits being laid down over much of central Alberta (Figure 14.2). Much of the central and western part of the craton remained dry land until the very end of the Middle Devonian.

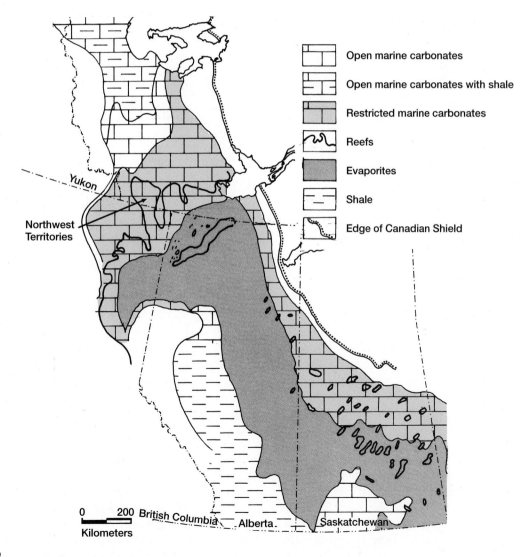

Open marine carbonates

Open marine carbonates with shale

Restricted marine carbonates

Reefs

Evaporites

Shale

Edge of Canadian Shield

FIGURE 14.2

Devonian paleogeography of western North America, showing the major reef buildups and back-reef facies on shallow platforms behind the reefs.

FIGURE 14.3
Upper Devonian limestones exposed in the Big Horn Range of the Rocky Mountains, Alberta.

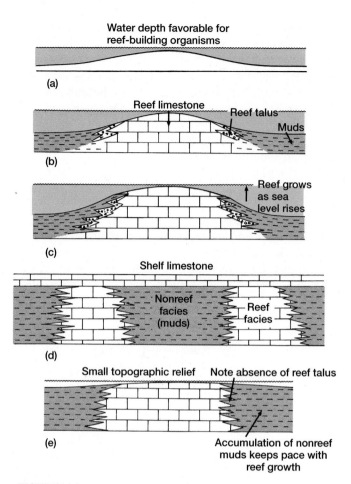

FIGURE 14.4
(a and b) Reef-building organisms, such as corals and stromatoporoids, prefer slightly shallower habitats. (c) As sea level rises (or the substrate subsides), reef building keeps pace to maintain shallow-water depth over the area of reef growth. Areas that were originally slightly deeper become ever deeper as the process continues. (d) Muds are the characteristic facies in nonreef areas. (e) Limestones form preferentially in areas with very small topographic relief originally.

In the Late Devonian, the Kaskaskia Sea encroached further onto the continent, and the western regions also became inundated. The most striking features of the Upper Devonian successions of western North America are the extensive and thick reef limestones. In the Canadian Rockies, such reefs are often prominently displayed in mountainside outcrops (Figure 14.3). The reefs also extend under the adjacent prairies to the east, where they are buried beneath Cretaceous and younger sediments. As seen in Figure 14.2, the reefs extended for some 600 kilometers and were probably similar in many ways to the modern Great Barrier Reef that lies off the eastern coast of Australia.

Devonian Reefs and Oil

The Devonian reef buildups were constructed largely by frame-building rugose and tabulate corals, together with stromatoporoids (Figure 14.4). Modern coralgal reefs, with their relatively open texture and resistance to wave action, are believed to be similar to the Devonian reefs. The host of other organisms that find modern reefs a congenial habitat have their counterparts in Devonian reefs also.

Exploratory drilling in the 1940s resulted in the discovery of vast reserves of oil and gas in the porous reef limestones. Seismic surveys could determine the location, shape, and trends of the reef masses because of the marked acoustic velocity contrast between reef limestone and the surrounding shale (Figure 14.5). As mentioned in Chapter 13, in 1947, the Leduc field in Alberta became the first big discovery based on seismic stratigraphy, as opposed to purely structural studies.

Although the reef limestone reservoir rocks contain the oil and gas, the hydrocarbons did not originate in the limestones but instead migrated from elsewhere. Thus, the explanation of how oil and gas accumulates must also involve the relationship between reef limestones and the surrounding nonreef sediments.

(A) ORIGINAL DATA

2 MILES

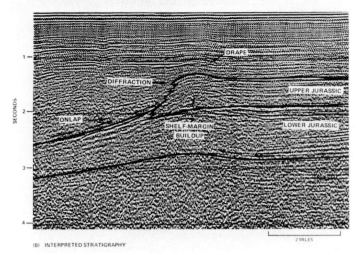

(B) INTERPRETED STRATIGRAPHY

2 MILES

FIGURE 14.5
Seismic record of Carbonate reef. (a) Original data.
(b) Interpreted stratigraphy. *(Photos courtesy of American Association of Petroleum Geologists.)*

Reef Characteristics

The reef masses themselves are relatively restricted in their distribution, and they undoubtedly formed considerable features on the Devonian sea floor. The reef-building organisms—especially the corals—were typically quite sensitive to changing conditions of light, water depth, and so on. For example, the initiation of a reef at a particular place may have been controlled by the presence of a minor topographic rise on the sea floor; even the difference of a few meters may have provided a more suitable habitat than the surrounding, slightly deeper sea floor. Once active reef growth began, and under conditions of slowly subsiding sea floor, or rising sea level, or both, the sequence of events is not difficult to visualize. Upward growth of the reef was concentrated in the shallower areas, while what had been areas of only slightly deeper water accumulated sediments of nonreef facies.

Many of the Devonian reef masses had considerable vertical development and probably were large topographic features rising from the sea floor. In places, accumulations of reef talus around their flanks confirm this. In other cases, certain reefs may have had little original relief, and the initial small difference in character between the areas of sea floor where reefs were growing, as compared with areas where nonreef muds were accumulating, remained relatively small. In other words, the hollows between the reef mounds were continuously filled with mud swept into the quieter water between the reefs. In this second category might be placed those carbonate reef buildups in which the constructional mechanisms involved the passive trapping of lime mud as the sediment-carrying currents sweeping over the ocean floor were slowed down by the interference of thickets of lime-secreting algae, crinoids, and so on. The presence of scattered corals in these limestones should not be interpreted as indicative of a cor-algal frame-building community.

Characteristics of Surrounding Nonreef Sediments

With the abundance of life so evident in the reefs, the muds deposited in the deeper water around the reefs undoubtedly trapped considerable amounts of organic material, derived from a variety of organic contributors in the water column above. In particular, geochemists have found that certain porphyrins in petroleum indicate that phytoplankton was probably the principal contributor. Typically, the pore space waters in such muds were deficient in oxygen, and the complex chemical reactions that eventually result in the production of hydrocarbons require such reducing conditions.

Model of Hydrocarbon Accumulation

From the reef/nonreef associations, a picture of the classic model of petroleum generation and accumulation can be derived (see Figure 14.6). As every petroleum geologist knows and at a most fundamental level, an oil field requires that three conditions be met: There must be (1) source beds for the petroleum, (2) a reservoir rock, and (3) a suitable structural setting and a cap rock to "trap" the petroleum. These physical parameters must be supported by an appropriate geologic history in which subsequent tectonic movements and major folding and faulting are conspicuously absent. Naturally, many other factors also are involved, but if any one of the previous conditions is not met, there will be no oil field.

An important difference between the reef limestones on the one hand and the adjacent nonreef muds on the other is the sediment compressibility. Although geologists commonly speak of "coral reefs," the corals may occupy only a small percentage of the total reef volume. Sometimes, the reef may consist of as little as 10 percent corals, the remaining 90 percent being made up of stromatoporoids, bryozoans, lime-secreting algae, and many other reef

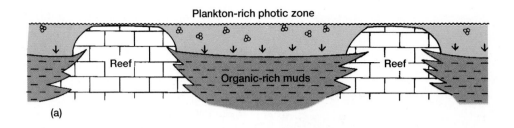

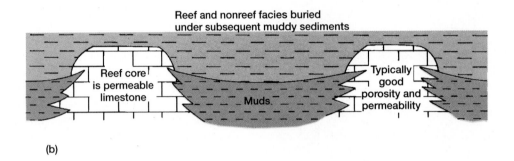

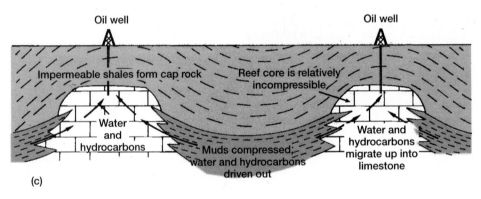

FIGURE 14.6
Hydrocarbons formed in organic-rich muds (a) migrate into porous reef limestones (b), which then become reservoirs for oil and gas (c).

FIGURE 14.7
Drill core of porous reef limestone.

dwellers, together with reef debris and other sediment that sift down into the reef interstices. On the other hand, the corals usually play the key role as frame builders, and their presence as rigid structural elements within the reef mass gives the reef considerable mechanical integrity. It follows that, when buried under thousands of meters of overlying sediments, reef limestones are relatively incompressible, in marked contrast to adjacent nonreef muds. The initial porosity of the muds is such that 60 to 70 percent or even more of their original volume can be water. With increasing pressure from the superincumbent sedimentary load, this water is progressively squeezed out, and the muds become mudrocks.

The fluids squeezed out of the muds then migrate up into and fill all the open pore spaces of the reef limestones (Figure 14.7). The hydrocarbons formed in the muds travel along with the water, and as the fluids fill the reef, the hydrocarbons, being lighter, migrate to the top of the reservoir.

BOX 14.1

The Dolomite Problem

The geologic succession from Precambrian to present indicates that, whereas younger carbonate rocks are dominantly limestones, made of the mineral calcite or aragonite ($CaCO_3$), with increasing age, carbonates progressively tend to be dolostones, dominantly of the mineral dolomite CaMg (CO_3)$_2$. Close examination reveals that this progressive swing from limestones to a preponderance of dolostones occurs because, in virtually all cases, the dolostones were once limestones, and at some time in the past, the calcite was recrystallized and transformed into dolomite during a so-called dolomitization process. In most cases, this changeover can be clearly documented by examples in which the alteration is incomplete.

Although the dolomitization process has been studied for many years, no single model has yet provided a general explanation. Linked to the dolomitization problem is the question also of primary dolomite. Although most dolostones are unquestionably altered limestones, rare examples are known of what appear to be microcrystals of

original dolomite formed as primary precipitates. Although evidence indicates that they, too, may have been initiated as calcite and then charged by ionic diffusion, many questions remain.

Seawater is almost saturated with respect to dolomite, but direct dolomite precipitation does not occur because, at normal temperatures, nucleation of dolomite is much slower than that of calcite. This means that, in competition for calcium and carbonate ions, the calcite is preferentially precipitated. Although in the laboratory, at temperatures of several hundred degrees celsius, dolomite is easily precipitated, within the temperature range in normal sediments, dolomite can only form when concentrations of magnesium ions are high. Solving the dolomitization puzzle, therefore, must involve finding a mechanism to provide high concentrations of magnesium ions.

One such mechanism is the so-called evaporative reflux model, based on observations made in Bonaire, Netherlands Antilles. Here, in a shallow, evaporating lagoon behind a porous

beach ridge of coral rubble, evaporation of seawater that seeps through the ridge produces gypsum ($CaSO_4$). The extraction of calcium ions in this process changes the calcium/magnesium ratio of the remaining seawater, resulting in a dense, magnesium-rich brine that seeps downward into the porous underlying limestones. Clearly, this is an ongoing process so that the limestone substrate is continually being flushed with magnesium-rich brines and as a consequence is altered to dolomite.

The observed association of modern dolomite and supratidal flats and evaporating basins clearly ties this particular mechanism to an appropriate sea level. The projection of this model to dolostones of all ages and through great thicknesses of strata can presumably be explained by sea-level fluctuation. At times of rising sea level, the dolomitizing process moves progressively inland. Dolomitization is an irreversible process because, at times of falling sea level, dolostones are not converted (that is, dedolomitized) back to limestone.

Dolomitization

The open, textured character of the typical reef limestone is a result not only of the way the reef is constructed by the various reef-building organisms, but also of the boring activities of numerous other reef dwellers. Together, these produce what is termed the primary porosity of the reef limestone. Circulating fluids that introduce minerals such as calcite in solution often result in a reduction, or occlusion, of the pore spaces as the pore spaces become filled with secondary minerals precipitated in them.

On the other hand, porosity and permeability may be greatly improved by a diagenetic process known as **dolomitization.** This is a complex recrystallization process whereby the original calcium carbonate mineral calcite ($CaCo_3$) is changed, by the introduction of magnesium ions, into the double carbonate dolomite (CaMg (Co_3)$_2$). How this happens is not precisely known, although numerous models have been proposed. While discussing this topic in detail is beyond the scope of this text, a brief summary is presented in Box 14.1. In the present context, dolomitization is important because the process involves a 12

to 13 percent volume reduction. In other words, a given volume of limestone takes up 12 to 13 percent less space when it is changed to dolostone, and so its porosity is improved.

Devonian Reefs and Evaporites

Reef growth around the margins of the western Canadian basin at times restricted water circulation, and by Middle Devonian time, a huge basin at the southeastern extremity of the western seaway was more or less cut off by a line of reefs across what is now northern Alberta. With increasingly restricted circulation and ever higher salinities, the patch reefs and pinnacle reefs of the inner lagoons were presumably killed off, and limestones gave way to **evaporites.** At first, gypsum and halite deposits were formed, but as evaporating conditions intensified, various **bittern salts** began to accumulate. Bittern salts, which include magnesium salts, such as epsomite, together with various bromide, iodide, and potassic salts, are the most

FIGURE 14.8
Potash mining in Saskatchewan. These large, four-rotor,
continuous-boring machines can excavate 720 tons per hour.
(Photo courtesy of Potash Corporation of Saskatchewan, Inc.)

soluble salts in the ocean and are only precipitated when more than 90 percent of the original water has evaporated. In southern Saskatchewan, the Middle Devonian Prairie Formation is estimated to contain over 50 million tons of potassium salts, which are mined and processed chiefly for use in fertilizers (Figure 14.8). Recent calculations indicate that southern Saskatchewan alone holds nearly half of the world's reserves of potassium salts.

By Late Devonian time, the configuration of the reefs and conditions in the basin had changed somewhat, and the main reef barriers had migrated southward to the central Alberta area, where a succession of reefs, such as the Swan Hills and Leduc reefs, flourished. Behind the reefs, conditions in the basin are believed to have resembled those existing in the present-day Persian Gulf, with a shallow lagoon passing shoreward into broad coastal **sabkhas,** extensive supratidal flats in arid regions and on which accumulates a variety of evaporite minerals.

Reef development had largely ceased by middle Late Devonian time, perhaps as a consequence of a brief fall in sea level. When sea level rose once more, formations like the massive cliff-forming Palliser Limestone and the Wabamun Formation of Alberta were laid down as shallow platform carbonates. Traced eastward, they pass into evaporites in the Williston Basin area of Montana and then eventually into sandy shoreline deposits at the limits of the basin.

The Black-Shale Mystery

Over large areas of the western North American continent are indications of a brief emergence near the end of Devonian time. In some successions, this hiatus is, as a matter of convenience, used as the Devonian/Mississippian boundary. In fact, the boundary typically occurs within a black shale that is widespread not only in western North America but also in the east.

Black shales are common in stratigraphic successions of all ages and in many places. The Devonian black shale is mysterious, however, in its widespread extent (Figure 14.9) and in the indications that it was laid down during a brief interval of unusual sea-bottom conditions. This is another case where the uniformitarian approach seems to break down because there are no modern analogs.

One of the better-known formation names for this latest Devonian/Mississippian black shale is the Chattanooga Shale; in other areas, its equivalent is known by such names as the New Albany, Antrim, and Exshaw shales.

The restricted fauna, the common presence of pyrite, and a relatively high content of uranium all point to black-shale deposition under reducing bottom conditions. The simplest explanation, based purely on the lithology of the rock, is to assume that the shales were laid down in deep water. This hardly seems likely, however, since only a brief time earlier, the craton had been widely emergent. The

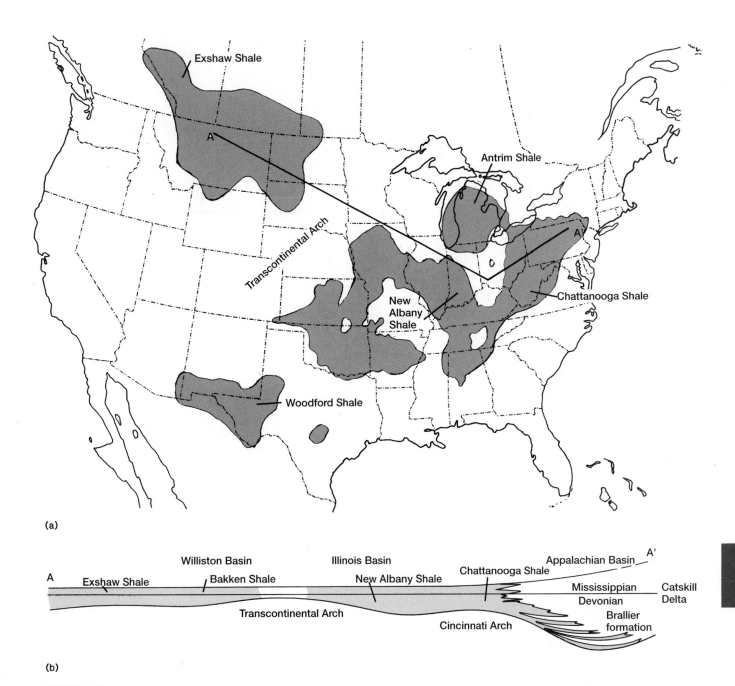

(a)

(b)

FIGURE 14.9

(a) North American distribution of black shales in the
uppermost Devonian. (b) Diagrammatic cross section,
showing black-shale facies.

black shale's extensive distribution also would seem to
preclude a deep-water origin, and in any event, many formations immediately overlying the shale are clearly of
shallow-water type.

An alternative model suggests that high salinity led
to marked density stratification, thereby inhibiting mixing
and oxygenation of the water column. This explains the
anoxic bottom conditions, but the absence of any associated evaporites presents a problem.

Yet another model assumes that ocean temperatures
were relatively warm and that this might result in anoxic
seafloor conditions because gases are less soluble in warm
water and so less oxygen is taken up. Higher global temperatures would also inhibit the deep thermohaline circulation of ocean waters characteristic of today's well-
mixed oceans. On the other hand, there is evidence from

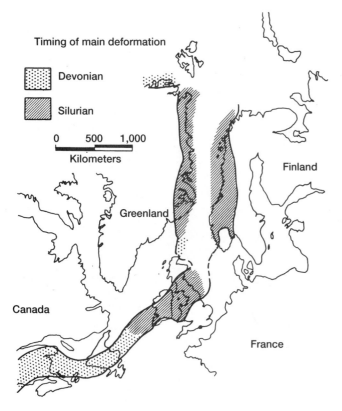

FIGURE 14.10

The collision of the Baltic and Laurentian cratons resulted in the disappearance of the Iapetus Ocean, the formation of the supercontinent of Laurussia, and the production of the Caledonide fold mountain chain.

South America of a glacial episode at the end of the Devonian with at least two separate ice advances. The preceding discussion clearly demonstrates that the black-shale mystery remains a fruitful field for speculation and future work.

The Eastern Craton Margin

Just as the geologic history of the North American craton interior has seemed somewhat repetitive, with three major marine transgressions and regressions since the late Precambrian, so also is there some repetition of events along the eastern North American continental margin. The Late Devonian saw another orogenic/collision episode and the facies associations and structures resulting from the Acadian upheaval are similar to those of the earlier Taconic upheaval. As is becoming convincingly clear, much of geologic history is repetitive and cyclical. That the same kinds of events produce the same results demonstrates that the basic interpretative model is correct.

The chief difference between the Taconic and Acadian orogenies was that the **Acadian orogeny** represented a full continent-to-continent collision. As far as the northern Appalachians was concerned, the Acadian

FIGURE 14.11

Siltstones of the Devonian Ilfracombe beds exposed on the coast in North Devon, England.

marked the last collision event because, with the suturing of the North American (Laurentian) and Baltic cratons, the Iapetus Ocean was no more. There were no more subduction zones, island arcs, or microcontinental slivers to be accreted, and so the Acadian orogeny marked the end of a cycle. It produced a new entity in the form of what has been named Laurussia, the emergent portion of which is referred to as the Old Red Sandstone Continent, which is discussed shortly.

Although the Acadian orogeny of Late Devonian time generally marks the welding together of the Laurentian and Baltic cratons, contact between them had been made earlier in the far north, where Greenland, together with what is now northern Scotland, had collided with the Baltic craton as early as Silurian time. This event was marked by the **Caledonian orogeny** (named after the Caledonian Mountains of Scotland) of Greenland, northern Britain, and Scandinavia (Figure 14.10). In the sense that Greenland was actually part of Laurentia, the joining of the North American and Baltic blocks was spread over a protracted interval of time. During a period of over 100 million years, the zone of maximum crustal involvement, in terms of metamorphism, regional structural deformation, and igneous activity, moved progressively southward along the line of the Appalachians.

The Old Red Sandstone Continent

When William Smith (as discussed in Chapter 5) was piecing together his geologic time scale and arranging the various rock formations of England in proper order, he named the lowest division of his succession the **Old Red Sandstone.** It made a suitably distinctive unit because, unlike most of Smith's stratigraphic column, it contained fossils that were clearly of nonmarine origin. Chief among

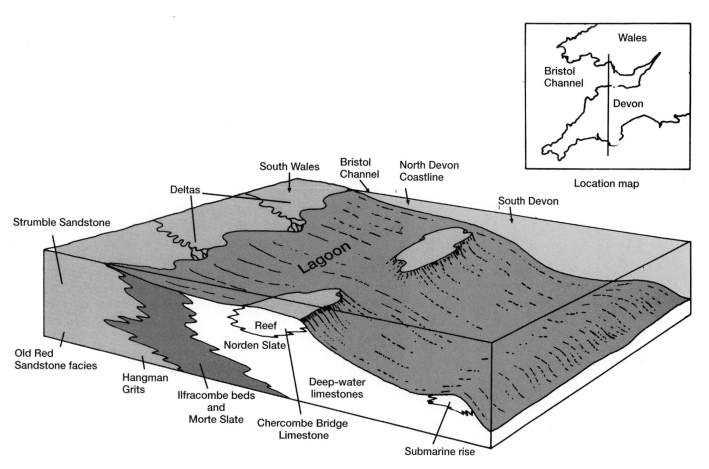

FIGURE 14.12

Relationship between terrestrial facies of the Old Red Sandstone continent and marine facies to the south across the Devonian type area in the county of Devon, England.

these was a variety of fishes—often strikingly well preserved—together with many plant remains. Interest in what affectionately become known as the "Old Red" was further enhanced by the publication in 1841 of *The Old Red Sandstone* by Hugh Miller, which described the fossils. Remarkably, the book became a best-seller! Miller was a self-educated man of outstanding talent who had begun his working life as a humble rock-quarry worker and stone mason but who became a poet, editor, and quite prolific writer and philosopher of some renown.

Eventually, marine facies of the Old Red Sandstone were found to be widespread, the first description coming from the county of Devon in southwest England. In this classic type area of the Devonian System, the marine succession is dominated by poorly fossiliferous coarse sandstones and siltstones that interfinger northward into the nonmarine Old Red Sandstone facies (Figure 14.11). To the south, limestone and deeper-water facies tend to be more fossiliferous, but, unfortunately, they are also increasingly metamorphosed so that the fossils are poorly preserved and often only identifiable with some difficulty

(Figure 14.12). Small wonder that the successions in the county of Devon have made little contribution to an understanding of marine Devonian biostratigraphy.

The distinctive Old Red Sandstone facies was mapped across a wide area of central and northern Europe. The Caledonian orogeny of Silurian time clearly had produced an extensive area of continental size and with indications of rugged relief (Figure 14.13). Indeed, the time relationship between the orogeny, as seen in folded and faulted Silurian rocks, and subsequent events, with Devonian sediment lying across the erosionally beveled edges of folded strata, was noted by James Hutton. At one such locality in Scotland, Hutton began to come to grips with the immensity of geologic time.

Old Red Sandstone facies also began to be recognized at many localities in North America (Figure 14.14), and in the days before plate tectonics and an understanding of continental drift, paleogeographic maps showed the Old Redstone Sandstone continent to have had huge proportions. What had happened to the area of continent now occupied by the North Atlantic, however, was not easily

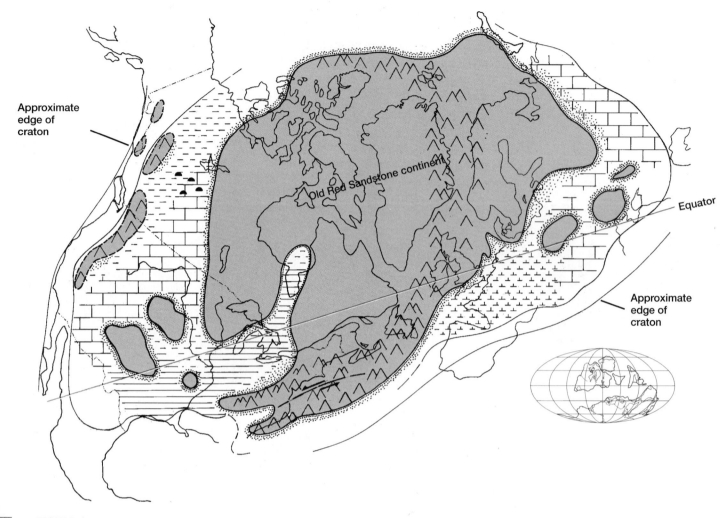

FIGURE 14.13
Paleogeography of the Old Red Sandstone continent.

explained. Today, most of the pieces of the puzzle have dropped into place, and a reasonably complete paleogeographic picture of the Old Red Sandstone continent constructed.

The Western Craton

The southwestern part of the North American craton was largely emergent through the Middle Devonian, but early in Late Devonian time, a eustatic sea-level rise resulted in widespread carbonate deposition from the area that is now central Utah down to northern Mexico. In places, there was extensive reef development.

The Chafee Formation of northern and northwestern Arizona records a cyclic repetition of shales and sandstones that may have been of glacio-eustatic origin. This is particularly likely in view of evidence for continental glaciation in the Upper Devonian of South America. This presumably marks the beginning of the great **Permo-Carboniferous ice age.**

Toward the end of the Devonian, a protracted regression of the Tippecanoe Sea was underway, but the many local erosional breaks are more likely indicators of the beginning of the crustal unrest that culminated in the Antler orogeny during the Mississippian.

Life in the Devonian

Range charts of the major fossil groups show few changes across the Silurian–Devonian boundary, and the general features of faunas and floras display an essential continuity. Among the important evolutionary advances of the Devonian, however, were the development of leaves, seeds, and forests; considerable progress among the fishes; and the appearance of the first amphibians.

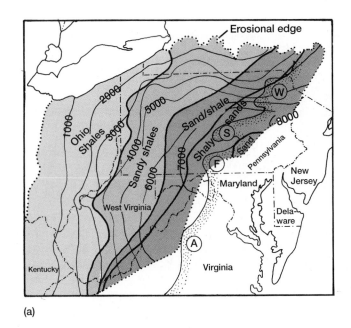

(a)

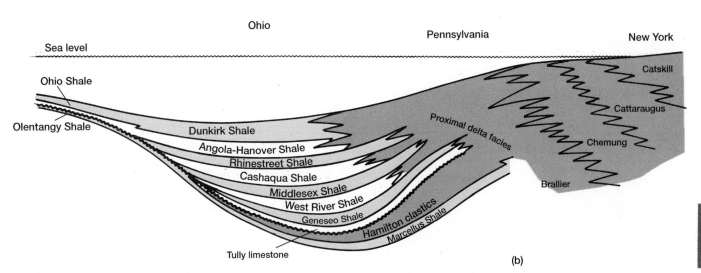

(b)

FIGURE 14.14

(a) Map and (b) section showing the distribution of the
principal clastic wedge deposits of different ages in the
Appalachian belt.

Devonian Flora: Leaves, Seeds, and the First Forests

The earliest vascular plants appeared in the Silurian or
possibly even earlier, but the fossil record is fragmentary.
The improved fossil record in rocks of Lower Devonian
age, however, shows a relatively rapid and worldwide proliferation of land plants (Figure 14.15). The simple, spiny,
and leafless psilophyte-type plants of earlier times were
joined by a second group with sporangia located along the
stems rather than at the extremities. *Zosterophyllum* and
Cooksonia, together with the lycopods (club mosses) *Drepanophycus* and *Psilophyton*, are examples (Figure
14.16). The majority of these plants are seen as flattened,
carbonized impressions on bedding planes, and preservation often leaves much to be desired. On the other hand,
plant tissues, although obviously softer than shells or bony
skeletons, are sometimes more resistant to chemical
breakdown. Plant cuticle, for instance, is almost inert
under certain conditions and may be preserved unaltered.
One example is seen in the Lower Devonian flora of the
Sextant Formation of northern Ontario (*see Figure 3.11*).

FIGURE 14.15

Reconstruction of a Devonian landscape as the first forests spread over the land.

FIGURE 14.16

Drepanophycus spinaeformis from the Lower Devonian Sextant Formation of northern Ontario.

One particular flora in an excellent state of preservation is the **Rhynie flora** from the Rhynie Chert in Aberdeenshire, Scotland. Just like the primitive life-forms in Precambrian rocks, these plants are preserved in silica; some even occur in their position of growth, a rarity for plant fossils. The special attributes of silicification and molecule-by-molecule replacement by a virtually inert substance again provides the rare glimpse that is invaluable in reconstructing these ancient life-forms. The Rhynie flora, dominated by the primitive genus *Rhynia* (Figure 14.17), was discovered and described in the early twentieth century by Robert Kidston and William Lang. For a long time, the precise location where the collection had been made was kept a secret, since any new locality with an unusual or exciting fossil discovery naturally attracts much attention and overenthusiastic amateurs.

Lower Devonian plants are distinctive in their relatively simple structures and a lack of leaves and true roots. Water and nutrients were transported by underground stems, or **rhizomes,** which, in the Rhynie Chert specimens, were covered by minute, hairlike structures. The psilopsids were typical of these early leafless plants, and many of the better-preserved examples reveal that the stems also often bore abundant hairlike spines. These spines eventually evolved into leaves, as branches of the vascular system extended into them (Figure 14.18a). Stems with scalelike coverings of leaves became a feature of many later Devonian species and were particularly characteristic of the large arboreal species in the Mississippian and Pennsylvanian forests described in Chapter 15.

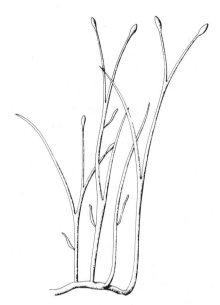

FIGURE 14.17

Rhynia, a primitive plant from the Devonian.

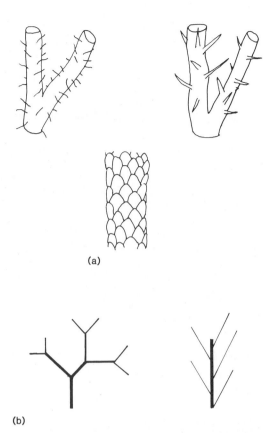

(a)

(b)

FIGURE 14.18

(a) Evolution of scale leaves from spines. (b) Evolution of branching, from the primitive dichotomous patterns (left) to the more advanced arrangement with small branches leaving the main stem.

Another feature of Late Devonian floras was the increasing importance of fernlike species with the complex multilobed leaf outline so familiar today. These evolved, it is believed, from the flattened extremities of repeatedly branched stems that divided dichotomously. Dichotomous branching—that is, equal splitting—is the more primitive pattern, while the arrangement whereby small branches split from a main stem is the more advanced type of plant architecture (Figure 14.18b). Leaves, abundantly served by a complex vascular system, became the chief centers for chlorophyll development and so for the plant's food manufacture.

In Middle and Upper Devonian rocks, the fossil record improves considerably. The largely diminutive and shrubby plants of Early Devonian time were being joined by true arboreal species with woody stems, as forests of trees appeared on the earth for the first time. True leaves had now become important, and in the tree-sized lycopods, appeared in spiral rows on the main stem; hence, the name **scale trees** is often applied to them. Genera like *Sigillaria* and *Lepidodendron* (Figure 14.19) were to become especially prominent in Mississippian and Pennsylvanian floras. Lycopsid (spore-bearing plants with leaves typically in spiral rows on the stems) representatives still can be seen in the relatively common creeping "ground pine" *Lycopodium,* also referred to as "club moss," although these plants are, of course, neither pines nor mosses.

Another so-called living fossil is the common horsetail *Equisetum.* Belonging to the sphenopsids (plants with long, unbranched, ribbed stems), this single genus, with some half-dozen species, is all that remains of what were once important and widespread plants. Today, *Equisetum,* with its distinctive jointed and longitudinally ribbed

FIGURE 14.19

Typical Pennsylvanian plant fossils, at left is a portion of a stem of *Calamites* sp., and on the right is *Lepidodendron.*

FIGURE 14.20
Devonian reefs in the Napier Range of the Canning Basin,
Western Australia. *(Photograph courtesy of Dr. Phil Playford,
Geological Survey of Western Australia.)*

stems and tufts of leaves at each joint, is a diminutive plant
found in swampy and shady places. It rarely exceeds a
meter in height, but in Middle Devonian and later floras,
some sphenopsid species of *Calamites* (Figure 14.19) were
sizable trees.

By the close of the Devonian, both the *Zosterophyllum* and *Rhynia*-type psilopsids had disappeared. The
psilophytons had also become extinct, although not before
giving rise to the **progymnosperms,** forerunners of the
gymnosperms (the naked seed plants whose seeds are
commonly borne on a cone). The earliest true ferns had
also appeared, so the stage was set for a great evolutionary
radiation during the Mississippian and Pennsylvanian,
perhaps the greatest in all of plant history.

Despite the emergence of plants onto land during the
Silurian, nearly 50 million years passed before land floras
became widespread, the chief reason being these early
plants' mode of reproduction. A moist environment was
necessary so that the sperm could swim through surface
water films to find the egg; thus, such plants could survive
only in low-lying and swampy areas. By Late Devonian
time, tree-size plants with secondary wood growth, complex vascular systems, and leaves had evolved. The appearance of seeds, however, was the most important step
forward since they allowed plants to move into drier areas.
The first forests soon expanded into all but the most inhospitable corners of the continent and provided a vast
habitat with enormous potential for the expansion of animals of all kinds.

Invertebrate Life

The extensive limestone formations of Devonian age on
several continents are among the most fossiliferous in the
entire geologic column. On the North American and Australian cratons, in particular, reefs grew prolifically (Figure
14.20). Both the rugose and tabulate corals that had flourished during the Silurian continued to dominate the reef
tracts. Stromatoporoids and bryozoans also were important contributors.

The brachiopods proliferated both in numbers and
variety during the Silurian, and during the Devonian, they
seemed to reach their zenith. Perhaps the most characteristic of all Devonian brachiopods belonged to the family
Spiriferidae. Spirifers, with their straight hinge lines and
peculiar winglike extensions, have been collected widely,
and throughout the Midwest, they are popularly called
"butterfly stones." The spirifer valves' peculiar shape reflects a special internal anatomy characterized by a complex spiral brachidium (spiridium), shaped like a coiled
spring, that supported the lophophore or respiratory apparatus.

Cephalopods also continued to be important elements
in the marine faunas (Figure 14.21), and the first representatives of the ammonoids, a group that was to prove of
enormous stratigraphic significance, appeared in the Early
Devonian. They arose from earlier straight-shelled cephalopods, and during the group's long life span that extended to the terminal Cretaceous extinction, their

FIGURE 14.21
A typical Devonian cephalopod, *Manticoceras,* sp. from the Upper Devonian.

evolution was amazing. Many paleontologists and bio-stratigraphers consider ammonoids the ideal index fossils since they have generally short species life spans and are widely disseminated through the world's oceans.

Trilobites continued to flourish during the Devonian, and some of the best-preserved specimens are from Devonian limestones. *Phacops rana,* for example, with its remarkable multifaceted eyes and curled-up posture, is an attractive feature of virtually every fossil collection. The graptoloid graptolites, with often only a single stipe, were in decline as the Devonian opened and had become extinct by the middle of the period. On the other hand, the dendroid group, with multiple branching stipes, survived into the Mississippian.

The Age of Fishes

The Devonian Period has often been described as the "Age of Fishes," but this is somewhat misleading. Fishes had actually first appeared some 100 million years earlier, in the Late Cambrian, although fossil remains consist only of scattered dermal plates. The first skeletal outlines have been found in rocks of Ordovician age, but skeletal material preserved well enough for detailed anatomical studies does not appear until the Silurian.

What made the Devonian a unique interval in the evolutionary history of fishes was an evolutionary radiation that saw the appearance of all seven of the major taxonomic divisions. Of the original seven divisions, only two—the acanthodians and placoderms—have disappeared, both becoming extinct at the close of the Permian, when so many other groups also became extinct. During the Devonian, the fishes also expanded from their original marine habitat into freshwater lakes and streams, and by the end of the Devonian, were giving rise to the first amphibians.

As the Devonian opened, the Agnatha, the jawless fishes of Silurian time had, as discussed in Chapter 13,

been joined by fishes with jaws, and two distinct divisions were already recognizable. The primary difference was in overall body shape, and this, in turn, indicated two different habitats and life modes.

Placoderms

On the one hand were the placoderms, whose most distinctive feature was a body covered by heavy armor, particularly in the head region. Some placoderm species, such as the antiarch *Pterichthyodes,* were flattened in shape, suggesting that they were largely bottom dwellers and probably not very good swimmers. Other placoderms, including the largest of them all, *Dunkelosteus,* which sometimes grew to 10 meters in length, were clearly good swimmers and active predators. Geologists believe that, when placoderms first appeared in the Early Devonian, they occupied freshwater habitats and only later expanded into marine environments.

Acanthodians

The second group of jawed fishes were the acanthodians. Unlike placoderms, their general body plan was rather similar to that of many modern fishes. Although as a group they became extinct at the end of the Permian, they possessed advanced features, such as paired fins and a body covered by scales rather than bony plates. Their overall shape was more streamlined than the placoderms, and the acanthodians probably were much more active. Although small in size, most acanthodians were predators. *Euthocanthus* from the Middle Devonian was about 20 centimeters long and is fairly typical of the group.

Ostracoderms

Although the jawed fishes were eminently successful and expanded into many niches, the agnathid ostracoderms remained a prominent element in Devonian faunas. They were generally small: *Pteraspis,* for example, was 5 or 6 centimeters long, whereas *Hemicyclaspis* was about 20 centimeters long. Their survival may have been related to their being inconspicuous.

The close of the Devonian saw a disastrous decline in their fortunes, however, and the ostracoderms became extinct early in the Mississippian. Only one small group of unarmored jawless fishes has survived to the present day and is represented by the lamprey and hagfish, both of which are parasitic on other fish. Interestingly, young lampreys, before taking up a parasitic mode of existence, begin life as bottom feeders, reminiscent of their remote ancestry of Devonian times.

Lobe-Finned Fishes

Currently, the fundamental and obvious division in fishes as a whole is between the bony fishes, the Osteichthys, and the cartilaginous fishes, the sharks and rays grouped in

FIGURE 14.22
The Devonian shark *Cladoselache*.

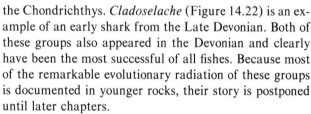

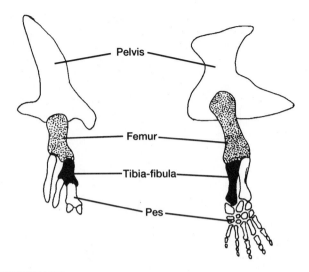

FIGURE 14.23
Comparison of the bones in the pelvic region and hind limb in the Devonian crossopterygian fish *Eusthenopteron* (left) and the Permian labyrinthodont amphibian *Trematops* (right).

the Chondrichthys. *Cladoselache* (Figure 14.22) is an example of an early shark from the Late Devonian. Both of these groups also appeared in the Devonian and clearly have been the most successful of all fishes. Because most of the remarkable evolutionary radiation of these groups is documented in younger rocks, their story is postponed until later chapters.

Of the many and varied Devonian fishes, those groups that ultimately succeeded (as opposed to those destined for extinction) had the anatomical features that made them better fishes. These features, such as gills as opposed to lungs, and in one group, the flexible, light, and eminently efficient ray fins, set them along an evolutionary pathway that restricted them to a purely aquatic existence.

It is to a second group of bony fishes—the so-called lobe-finned fishes—that we must now turn. This is because it was in this group that evolutionary changes eventually resulted in the appearance of the **tetrapods,** the animals that eventually conquered the earth and even began to expand into space! In contrast to ray fins, lobe fins are supported by a series of articulated bones that are attached to shoulder and pelvic bones and moved by muscles that extend out from the body into a stumpy, lobelike limb.

Two groups of lobe-finned fishes were important elements in Devonian faunas: the lungfishes and the crossopterygians. Fossil evidence indicates that they lived in freshwater lakes and rivers, many of which, on occasion, became stagnant or even dried up entirely. Although the consequence would ordinarily be disastrous to most fishes, the lobe-finned fishes possessed two features that allowed them to often survive such episodes. First, studies of living lungfishes and of Devonian fossils indicate that lobe-finned fishes could extract oxygen from the air rather than the water with the enlargement of two saclike structures below

the esophagus. Well supplied with blood vessels, these structures gradually evolved into lungs. A second important anatomical feature was the lobe fin, particularly the strong muscles that moved it. While a lobe fin is probably no more efficient than a ray fin in its primary locomotory function as a paddle, it unquestionably provides a distinct advantage to a fish desperately slithering over the mud in search of another water hole.

Lungs and lobe fins are called **preadaptations.** They did not evolve to provide certain groups of fishes with a means of achieving their ultimate destiny as land dwellers, but rather to enable such creatures to better survive *as fishes*. That lungs and lobe fins should eventually ensure the means for existence on dry land was entirely fortuitous!

Both lungfishes and crossopterygians still exist, although in markedly different habitats. The lungfishes, with one genus in each of the three southern continents, possess gills, and when the water is well oxygenated, live essentially as do other fish. If the streams and lakes where lungfishes live dry up, the lungfishes survive by relying on their lungs.

While the lungfishes presumably remained a relatively conservative freshwater group, the crossopterygians gave rise to two separate branches, one leading to the coelacanths, a group that eventually moved into the marine environment, and the other to the amphibians (Figure 14.23), as discussed in the next section. A modest fossil record apparently ended with the close of the Cretaceous, when the coelacanths were thought to have become extinct. In 1938, however, a living coelacanth was caught in deep water off South Africa, and since that time and thanks to generous cash incentives offered to fishermen, numerous other specimens of what was named *Latimeria* have become available for study (Figure 14.24a).

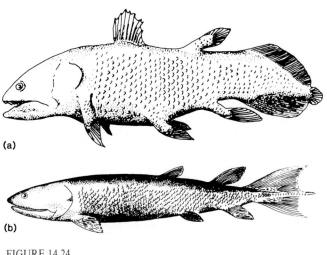

FIGURE 14.24
(a) *Latimeria.* (b) *Eusthenopteron.*

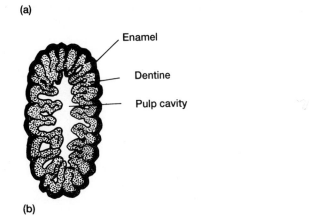

FIGURE 14.25

(a) The earliest known amphibian, *Icthyostega,* from the Upper Devonian of Greenland. (b) A cross section through a labyrinthodont tooth, showing the complex infolding of the enamel.

The Origin of Amphibians

Amphibians are cold-blooded vertebrates that use gills in the early stages of development, but lungs as adults, and require water in which to reproduce. The amphibian line of descent began with a group of crossopterygians known as rhipidistians, which were still very fishlike in appearance. *Eusthenopteron,* for example, was relatively small, measuring less than 30 centimeters in length, and had an elongated body, two pairs of lobed fins, two dorsal fins, a further ventral fin, and a fish's tail (Figure 14.24b). The skull and lower jaw, however, compare bone for bone with those of a land-dwelling amphibian called *Icthyostega* found in the early twentieth century in Greenland in rocks of latest Devonian age (Figure 14.25a). Apart from the skull bones, the bones in *Icthyostega's* legs resemble those in the lobe fins of *Eusthenopteron* and similar species. *Icthyostega* is further tied to its lobe-finned ancestors through its fishlike tail, which was vestigial in the sense that it clearly played no role in assisting locomotion, at least on land.

One other anatomical feature of considerable significance is the internal structure of the teeth. A cross section through a tooth of *Icthyostega* shows the enamel to be deeply infolded in a labyrinth-like pattern (Figure 14.25b). This distinctive feature is characteristic of a whole group of amphibians, known as the **labyrinthodonts,** that evolved during the later Paleozoic and persisted into the Early Mesozoic. That their ancestry began with the crossopterygian fishes is clearly indicated by the same distinctive architecture in the teeth of *Eusthenopteron* and related species.

The Amphibian Ancestry Controversy

As previously discussed, in the Devonian, the three major groups of lobe-finned fishes were: the lungfishes, the coelacanths, and the rhipidistians, with the latter two often grouped together as crossopterygians. Which one of these three groups was ancestral to the amphibians has been a matter of some controversy and depends upon which of the anatomical features supposedly diagnostic of a tetrapod are selected.

Some paleontologists believe that the third nostril, or **choana,** is an especially important feature, and at one time, all three of the lobe-finned groups were thought to have had it—hence, they were classified as Choanicthyes. Later work seemed to show that the lungfishes did not possess a true choana, so they were eliminated. In the case of the coelacanths, the living *Latimeria* does not possess a choana, but this may be of little significance if, as many experts believe, it was simply lost as a consequence of the fish adapting to a deep-sea environment in its later evolutionary history. At first, a choana supposedly was detected in *Latimeria's* Devonian ancestors, but this was later shown to be incorrect. Only the rhipidistian branch of the crossopterygian fishes appears to be left in the running, and the family Osteolepidae comes closest to the link between fishes and amphibians.

Although this is the most generally accepted view, some questions have been raised in recent works by Brian Gardner of London University. Gardner believes that the lungfishes do, in fact, possess a choana and that there are many other anatomical resemblances between living lungfishes and tetrapods. If Gardner is correct, then the line of tetrapod descent will have to be shifted over onto the lungfish rather than crossopterygian side.

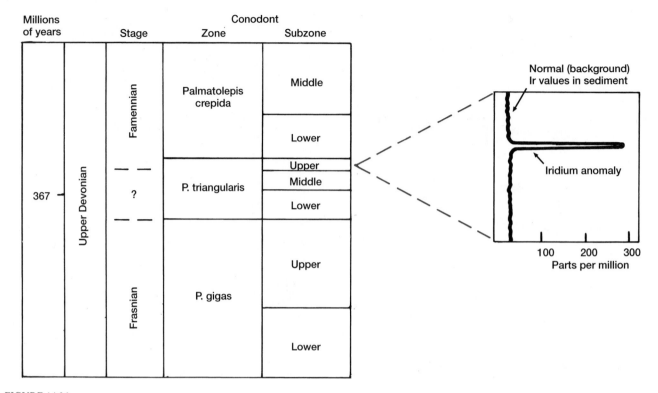

FIGURE 14.26

The iridium anomaly at the Late Devonian Frasnian-Famennian boundary has been interpreted as evidence of a major meteorite impact.

The Late Devonian Extinction

A mass extinction event occurred just before the close of the Devonian, near the boundary of the Frasnian-Famennian stages. This extinction decimated the reef communities in particular, and the corals, stromatoporoids, and bryozoans suffered severely. The trilobites, crinoids (the sessile echinoderms known as sea lilies), and cephalopods also showed a marked decline, as did the brachiopods, which, according to some authorities, experienced an 80 percent reduction in the number of species. The freshwater fishes were also affected, although land plants seemed to survive unscathed.

Numerous explanations have been advanced regarding the cause of the extinction. According to one scenario, the extinction was caused by a marked drop in world temperatures, perhaps associated with the Late Devonian glaciation. A cooler climate certainly would affect a wide spectrum of life-forms and is consistent in this particular mass extinction event with declines in tropical species, whereas boreal groups show few changes. That land plants could survive such changes is puzzling, however, since they are normally extremely sensitive climatic indicators. In addition, most Devonian floras were of generally tropical or subtropical type, which would intensify their risk. Thus, the idea of climatic deterioration as a cause of the Late Devonian extinction is seriously flawed.

An alternative hypothesis for the Late Devonian mass extinction suggests a large meteorite impact into the ocean that produced a huge tsunami (a seismic sea wave) that stirred up sediment and flooded the clear epeiric seas with mud. Studies of modern reef communities show that this would have had the necessary effect, and many geologists support this idea, especially in view of the wide agreement that a similar catastrophe caused the terminal Cretaceous extinction. Supporting evidence is provided by Australian geologist John Playfair and Canadian geologist Digby McClaren, who located an iridium anomaly, generally considered an indication of meteorite impact, in Australia in stratigraphic successions at about the Frasnian-Famennian boundary (Figure 14.26).

In assessing the possible causes of mass extinctions, geologists must consider many complex relationships because an abrupt change in one environmental parameter likely has a domino effect on others. Likewise, the disappearance of a particular group of animals or plants can profoundly influence the food chain. All forms of life on this planet are in a state of delicate balance with the environment. It follows that some of the mass extinctions of the past were simply a result of a momentary disturbance of that balance. We have only to look around at our modern world to realize that it may be happening again.

Summary

The Devonian System contains some very fossiliferous rocks, and its biostratigraphy has been studied in considerable detail. This is one of the reasons why its lower boundary with the Silurian was the first to be established in terms of a Global Boundary Stratotype Section and Point, or "golden spike."

During the Devonian on the North American craton, the Tippecanoe Sea was retreating and becoming restricted, which resulted in extensive evaporite deposits in many areas. Along arches and in other tectonically positive areas, post-Tippecanoe erosion cut down, deeply exposing older rocks. Only around the craton margins, where the sea lingered longest, are there complete stratigraphic successions through the Silurian and into the Devonian.

By late in the Early Devonian, the third great marine invasion of the continent began, involving the Kaskaskia Sea. As with earlier transgressions, the basal beds were again blanket sands, with the succession passing up into widespread limestone.

In the western region, a great arm of the sea extended progressively south and southeast across what is now western Canada. Extensive coral reefs were later to become the habitat for oil, and several major oil fields produce from these Devonian reefs. Behind the reefs, restricted circulation resulted in evaporite deposition, and in south Saskatchewan, for example, such deposits are estimated to comprise nearly half of the world's potash reserves. By the middle of Late Devonian time, reef development largely ceased, probably due to a brief eustatic sea-level drop.

At the end of the Devonian, large areas of the North American craton became covered by a thin, black shale. Several models have been proposed to explain the vast extent of the shale and the brief time interval it represents.

The eastern margin of the North American craton was involved in the Acadian orogeny caused by the collision between the North American and Baltic cratons, which resulted in the final closing of the Iapetus Ocean. This collision welded together the North American and Baltic landmasses, producing the Old Red Sandstone Continent.

Along the western margin of the North American craton, Devonian deposits are largely of Late Devonian age, the area being extensively emergent during earlier Devonian time.

The Silurian/Devonian boundary shows no marked faunal break. The shallow epeiric seas that covered large areas were clearly favorable for an abundance of organisms.

Although land plants had appeared much earlier, the Devonian saw a great proliferation of many forms. Among the most important evolutionary advances were leaves and seeds. By Late Devonian time, plants had reached tree size, and once seeds had evolved, plants were no longer confined to swampy areas. Forests quickly spread over all but the driest and coldest land areas.

The flourishing invertebrate marine faunas of Silurian time continued into the Devonian. During the period, the rugose and tabulate corals, together with the brachiopods, probably reached their zenith. An important first appearance was that of the ammonoid cephalopods, destined for an interesting evolutionary history.

Fishes had appeared in the Late Cambrian and undergone considerable advances during the Ordovician and Silurian, although the fossil record is poor. Beginning in the Devonian, fossils became much more abundant, and during the period, all seven of the major taxonomic divisions appeared, with fishes increasing rapidly in numbers in both marine and freshwater habitats.

A group of bony fishes—the lobe-finned fishes—eventually gave rise to the first amphibians. In the latest Devonian rocks appear fossils of *Icthyostega*, which although clearly a land-dwelling amphibian, had skull bones, limb bones, and tooth structures that compared closely with those of the rhipidistian fishes. Most experts believe that amphibians descended from the rhipidistian branch of the crossopterygian fishes, although recent research is questioning this view.

A mass extinction event occurred late in the Devonian, approximately at the boundary between the Frasnian and Famennian stages. The shallow-water marine faunas suffered a marked decline, while land plants were apparently unaffected. The exact cause of the extinction is unknown, but a cooling of the world climate and a meteorite impact are among the mechanisms suggested.

Questions

1. What is meant by a Global Boundary Stratotype Section and Point?
2. Where would one most likely find stratigraphic successions containing the Silurian/Devonian boundary? Explain the distribution of such locations.
3. What is the significance of the scattered distribution of the basal Kaskaskia sandstone formations on the North American continent?
4. Explain why some of the biggest oil reserves in North America are in reef limestones.
5. Describe how reef growth over extended periods is controlled by changes in relative sea level.
6. What are the most important requirements for the accumulation of oil and gas in economic quantities?
7. Explain why reef limestones and evaporite deposits are frequently found in close association.

8. In what way does the Middle and Upper Ordovician succession of the north central Appalachians compare with the Devonian succession in that region?
9. Describe the geography of the Old Red Sandstone Continent. Locate your own area relative to it.
10. The Devonian was a critical period in the evolution of plants. Explain.

11. Contrast Devonian invertebrate faunas with those of the Silurian.
12. Why is the Devonian often described as the "Age of Fishes"?
13. What is meant by preadaptation? Cite an example from the Devonian.

14. In the Devonian, there were three major groups of lobe-finned fishes. What were they, and what anatomical feature is considered important in establishing the line of descent to the amphibians?
15. Explain why marine invertebrate faunas of the latest Devonian were considerably different from Middle Devonian faunas.

Further Reading

Colbert, E.H. 1969. *Evolution of the vertebrates.* 2d ed. New York: Wiley.

Dineley, D.L. 1984. *Aspects of a stratigraphic system: The Devonian.* New York: Wiley.
Halstead, L.B. 1968. *The pattern of vertebrate evolution.* San Francisco: W.H. Freeman.

Levin, H.L. 1975. *Life through time.* Dubuque, Iowa: Wm. C. Brown.

15

THE CARBONIFEROUS: AN END AND A BEGINNING

Introduction

The Mississippian and Pennsylvanian systems are not recognized as such outside of North America; elsewhere, they are lumped together as the Carboniferous. North American usage is, in many ways, preferred because it recognizes a fundamental division that had been clearly apparent to William Smith in his original stratigraphic table when he described the Mountain Limestone and the Coal Measures. In 1822, British geologists W. D. Conybeare and William Phillips combined Smith's two units, partly because they were sandwiched between the Old Red Sandstone (Devonian) below and what Smith had called the New Red Sandstone (Permian) above.

In any event, the contrast between the dominantly marine carbonates of the Mississippian (Lower Carboniferous) and the largely nonmarine clastic sediments of the Pennsylvanian (Upper Carboniferous) is marked both in North America and Europe. Many parts of the world show both stratigraphic and paleontologic evidence for a major eustatic fall in sea level at about 330 million years ago. The widespread unconformity that resulted, which is seen in North America as the Mississippian/Pennsylvanian boundary, has its counterparts in places as far apart as Europe, North Africa, central Russia, China, and Japan.

The changes that occurred at the Mississippian/ Pennsylvanian boundary are, as we will see in this chapter, in large measure due to events of worldwide significance involving not only a continental collision that was to result in the formation of Pangaea but the onset of a major ice age. The close of the Mississippian marked the end of the Paleozoic epeiric seas with their vast carbonate banks and the beginning of new environments heralding the formation of Pangaea.

Mississippian Overview

North America during the Mississippian

As discussed in Chapter 14, on the North American craton, the Devonian closed under conditions that left many unanswered questions, and attempts to explain the paleogeography that produced the widespread black shale of the Chattanooga and other formations have not been entirely successful. Even though the black shale is relatively thin in many places, it apparently embraces the Devonian/Mississippian boundary. Devonian fossils, although not common, have been found in the lower part of the formation, and Mississippian species occur in the upper, although between them is no apparent sign of any erosional break.

Mississippian Limestone Deposition

In any event, the widespread carbonate-forming conditions that had abruptly ended when the shale was deposited apparently soon returned because, over large areas of the North American craton, the main mass of Mississip-

pian strata is dominated by limestone. Over the central and western part of the craton, the shallow marine conditions that prevailed were a consequence of yet another cycle of sea-level change. This was the last of the great limestone-producing cycles, and it heralded a significant change in a cratonic geography that had prevailed more or less since the late Precambrian.

Within the world picture, North America was during the Mississippian part of the larger continental mass of Laurussia formed by the Acadian collision event. The heartland of this continent was the Old Red Sandstone Continent, and it was more or less surrounded by shallow, submerged platforms (Figure 15.1). On the European segments of the platform, the limestones that were being laid down were similar in many respects to those forming on the North American portion of the craton and included, in fact, the Mountain Limestone of William Smith's original table of strata. Across an ocean known as the **Tethys,** the continent of Gondwana was still some distance away, although moving closer (Figure 15.2).

In the semiarid southwestern United States, many of the more massive Mississippian limestones, such as the Redwall Limestone of the Grand Canyon (*see Figure 11.7*), are important cliff formers. In the type region of the Mississippian in the Mississippi Valley and other areas of the Midwest, the succession is also dominated by limestones, and many formations, such as the Salem and Burlington limestones, contain facies widely utilized as building stones. The famous Indiana Oolite, for example, is extensively quarried around Bloomington, Bedford, and other locations in Indiana and is highly valued because of its uniform texture and pleasing appearance (Figure 15.3). As with the Devonian limestones, many Mississippian limestones have been extensively dolomitized and, consequently, have good secondary porosity and permeability. The Mission Canyon Limestone of Montana, for example, is an important reservoir rock and oil producer.

As mentioned earlier, these carbonate platforms fringed the Old Red Sandstone Continent, so that, in North America, a traverse in an easterly or northeasterly direction shows the limestone passing into the clastic facies of a broad coastal plain. With a shallow offshore region and low relief of the land, small sea-level fluctuations during the Mississippian caused shoreline migration. In general, the volumes of detrital clastics derived from easterly sources, however, tended to decrease. As the Mississippian drew to a close, the Kaskaskia Sea began its final withdrawal, perhaps a response to the growth of an ice cap on distant Gondwana, and later Mississippian sediments are typically regressive sands prograding out into the sea's dwindling remnants.

New Faunas and Ecologic Niches

Although limestone deposition was again widespread across much of the North American craton, the formations of Mississippian time had unique characteristics due

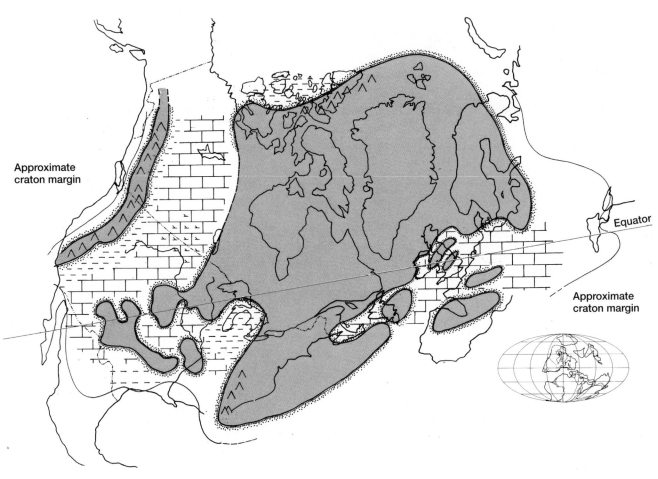

FIGURE 15.1
Paleogeography of Laurussia in the Mississippian.

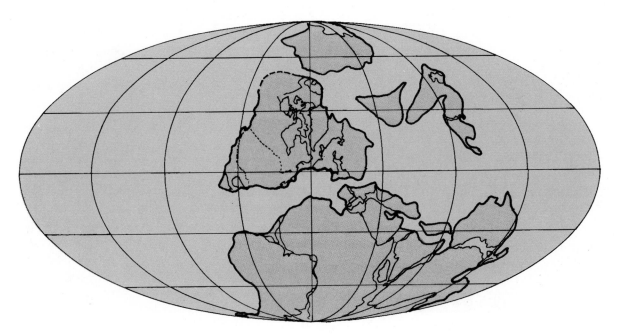

FIGURE 15.2
World paleogeography in the Mississippian.

(a)

(b)

FIGURE 15.3

Quarrying of the Salem Limestone (known as Indiana
Limestone in the industry). (a) A ''cut'' is being turned by
airbags filled with compressed air. Note the absence of
horizontal bedding planes in contrast to the overburden
rocks. (b) The limestones are being cut by a quarry belt saw
(the white machine at center). The height of the resulting cut
will be about 11 feet—average for the Indiana Limestone.
*(Photograph by courtesy of the Indiana Limestone Institute of
America, Inc.)*

FIGURE 15.4

Diorama of a Mississippian echinoderm community on a mud
sea floor. *(Photograph by courtesy of the Field Museum of Natural
History, Chicago.)*

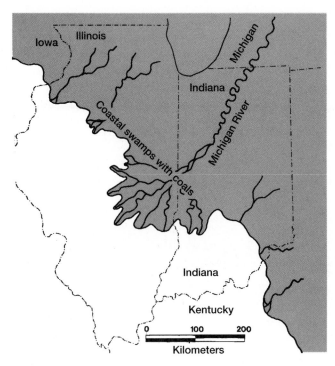

FIGURE 15.5

Paleogeographic map of the Michigan River in the Mississippian.

largely and inevitably to new faunas and shifts in the importance of particular ecologic niches. Corals and bryozoans were still abundant, but the great coral-stromatoporoid reef tracts of the Devonian never returned, likely a consequence of the Late Devonian mass extinction event. Instead, the crinoids and blastoids, which are described in more detail later in the chapter, provided the most spectacular biogenic contribution to the sediments. Given the enormous masses of limestone that are made up almost entirely of crinoid and blastoid stem ossicles and calyx plates, these animals must have formed veritable forests on the shallow sea floor (Figure 15.4).

Water movement across Mississippian platforms apparently was less restricted than during Devonian time, as suggested by the absence of reef barriers, and the much more limited occurrences of evaporites in the Mississippian. Similarly, the abundance of oolitic limestones and cross-bedded crinoidal limestones all attest to vigorous stirring of the water column. Lacy bryozoans were also abundant and, as sediment traps, were often responsible for reeflike mounds. Spiny brachiopods, such as the productids, were becoming abundant, and living in dense clusters with intertwined spines, they also formed small limestone buildups. For the first time, the Foraminifera were important biogenic contributors to the bottom sediment. In particular, the fusulinids had appeared and were to become even more important in the Permian. All of these are discussed in more detail later in the chapter.

The First Mississippi River

Quite early in the Mississippian, rivers draining the Old Red Sandstone Continent were bringing floods of sands south and southwest into the shelf seas of the eastern interior region. At the end of the Kinderhookian, the earliest of the Mississippian stages, there was a eustatic sea-level drop, and with rejuvenation of streams, many deltas began to prograde rapidly westward and southwestward. Typical of these sedimentary associations are sands and delta muds mapped as the Borden Group in Indiana and Kentucky. Further south over much of the Mississippian type region and beyond the reach of the clastic influx, carbonate shelf conditions persisted for much of the period, but by the Chester Stage that closed the Mississippian, the Kaskaskia Sea was disappearing (Figure 15.5).

In southern Illinois, Kentucky, and adjacent areas, the Chester Stage is represented by sandstones, many of which were laid down in river channels. Detailed mapping of the sandstone distribution and of the cross-bedding directions showing which way the streams flowed has enabled assembly of a comprehensive paleogeographic map. Several major rivers draining the continental area of the Canadian Shield and the Acadian highlands to the north and northeast terminated in an extensive delta complex that was prograding across a broad shelf area to the south and southwest. The most important of the rivers draining this ancient land has been called the **Michigan River,** and because from this time on, the midcontinent region was to remain dry land, the Michigan River can be considered a direct ancestor of the modern Mississippi.

Mississippian Craton Margins

A southward traverse from the North American craton platform shows shallow-water carbonates passing into deep-water shales in what was shortly to become the **Ouachita mobile belt.** A volcanic arc associated with Gondwana was already believed to be close enough to begin affecting this region, and during the Mississippian, deep-water, flysch-type sediments were encroaching northward and westward. Unfortunately, the picture is not clear. Not only was this region heavily involved in the collision of Gondwana and Laurussia, but the Ozark-Ouachita fold belt that extends through Arkansas, southern Oklahoma, and parts of Texas is today only poorly exposed and much less is known of its orogenic history than the main Appalachian ranges.

Along the North American craton's western margin, the Antler uplift had been a source of clastic sediment that spread eastward to the platform in latest Devonian time. This continued into the earliest Mississippian, and then the activity apparently ceased. Further offshore lay the Klamath volcanic island arc, and a deep basin lay between it and the craton margin (Figure 15.6). The closure of this basin and an eastward movement of crust along what is known as the Roberts Mountain thrust had, in fact,

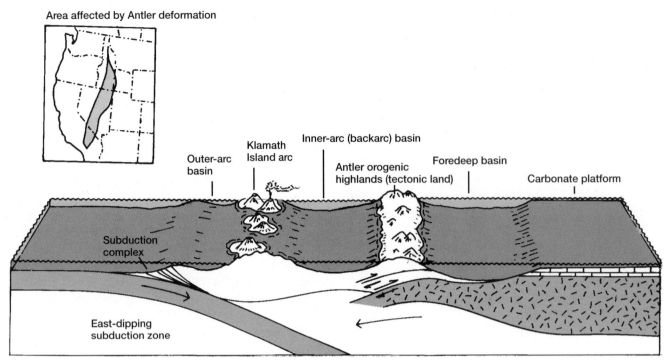

FIGURE 15.6

Subduction model for the Klamath island arc in the Mississippian.

produced the Antler orogeny. The effects of these movements extended for considerable distances along the craton margin because, even as far north as Alaska and the Yukon Territory, latest Devonian and Early Mississippian clastics were being shed from uplifted source areas to the west.

Finally, the Ellesmere orogeny of Devonian time had stabilized and uplifted the region along the craton's northern margin, so no Mississippian sediments are present in northern Canada. Further west, in the Brooks Range of Alaska, however, Mississippian shales and limestones transgress southward over a surface eroded across Devonian sediment folded in the Ellesmere orogeny.

Life in the Mississippian

Mississippian Floras

The relatively simple plants of Early and Middle Devonian time had declined by the Late Devonian, and the opening of the Mississippian saw a new aspect to the forests. The psilopsids, so typical of the Devonian, were dwindling rapidly, and other groups—the **lycopsids, sphenopsids,** and filicales (the true ferns)—which had all appeared at various times during the later Devonian, were now quickly spreading and coming to dominate the landscape.

During the Mississippian, another group—namely, the **Pteridospermaphyta,** the seed ferns—also appeared. Representing a considerable evolutionary advance over the true ferns, which reproduce by spores, the pteridosperms nevertheless looked like ferns in virtually every other an-

atomical detail. Indeed, nineteenth-century paleobotanists attempting to sort out the taxonomy found it confusing. To make matters worse, even some of the lycopsid and sphenopsid species had fernlike leaves. The problem is that paleobotanists must use "form genera," in which the various parts of the plant are classified as they are found without necessarily knowing the interconnections between stems, roots, leaves, and other parts of the plant anatomy.

As a whole, the fossil record leaves no doubt that the Mississippian landscape, especially the lower-lying areas, was covered by a lush carpet of vegetation. Dominant among the forest trees were *Lepidodendron* (Figure 15.7), *Lepidodendropsis,* and *Cyclostigma,* these names being applied to impressions of bark from what were clearly large trees 15 to 20 or more meters tall. Rootlike structures believed to be associated with these forms are usually placed in the form genus *Stigmaria. Calamites,* a giant tree-size horsetail, was another prominent component of the flora.

Notable new arrivals in the Mississippian were the first true gymnosperms, represented by the conifers, along with the Cordaitales (primitive conifera). Both of these groups would reach their heyday in the Mesozoic, by which time the character of the world's forests would have changed completely.

Mississippian Invertebrate Faunas

As discussed in Chapter 14, in the mass extinction near the end of the Devonian, the shallow-water marine organisms, such as the corals, stromatoporoids, and bryozoans, were particularly hard hit. The brachiopods also were

FIGURE 15.7
Reconstruction of the scale tree *Lepidodendron.*

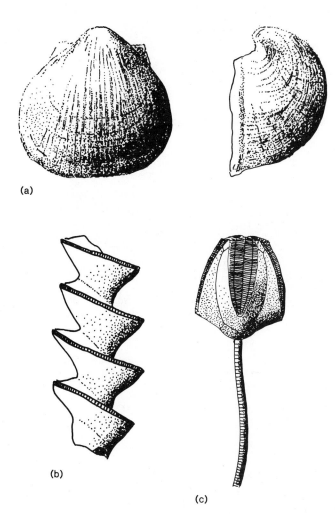

FIGURE 15.8
Representative Mississippian invertebrate fossils.
(a) Productid brachiopod *Marginicinctus marginicinctus.*
(b) Bryozoan *Archimedes wortheni.* (c) Blastoid
Pentremites sp.

decimated. The corals and stromatoporoids never recovered their former importance, while the whole aspect of brachiopod faunas changed.

Almost as though they were moving to fill ecologic niches left by the reduction in the corals and other reef builders, certain brachiopod species began to show a tendency to grow in dense clumps. The **productids,** the most characteristic of later Paleozoic brachiopods, included many species with long spines that intertwined with those of other individuals to form brachiopod communities (Figure 15.8a). One productid does not bud from another, however, so they are in no way true colonies. By the Permian, one group of productids, including *Prorichthofenia,* even grew quite coral-like in their appearance with a long, cone-shaped pedicle valve that bore a marked resemblance to a rugose "horn" coral. The much smaller brachial valve formed a sort of lid.

Lacy bryozoans were abundant, and one form with a distinctive spire-shaped axial region and named *Archimedes* is so common in some Mississippian limestones that so-called **Archimedes limestones** were mapped over large midcontinent areas by nineteenth-century geologists (Figure 15.8b).

Of all the invertebrates in Mississippian seas, the echinoderms dominated the faunas. Both blastoids and crinoids were important sediment producers. The tulip-shaped calyx, or body, of the blastoids and the cuplike crinoid calyx were relatively small, measuring a centimeter or two in diameter (Figure 15.8c). Typically, these animals were attached to the sea floor by jointed, flexible

stems often several meters long (Figure 15.9). Each stem was made up of hundreds of disc or drum-shaped columnal ossicles which, like the calyces, consisted of coarsely crystalline calcite. Connecting the columnals was flexible cartilaginous tissue which, on the death of the animal, naturally decayed quite quickly, releasing the ossicle to contribute to the sea-bottom sediment. Crinoid and blastoid ossicles (in many cases, they are indistinguishable from one another) are by far the most common fossils in Mississippian limestone, and some limestones are made up almost entirely of them. Sometimes, the crinoid fragments make up a sort of bioclastic "gravel" that shows cross-bedding and other sedimentary features. Vast communities, or "meadows," of these so-called "sea lilies" must have covered hundreds of square kilometers of sea floor to produce such volumes of sediment.

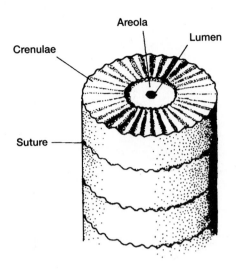

Areola

Crenulae

Lumen

Suture

FIGURE 15.9
Cystoids, blastoids, and most crinoids were attached to the substrate by a long, jointed, and flexible stem made up of circular or sometimes pentameral calcite discs called columnals. The central lumen carries the coelome and nervous system. Disarticulated columnals are the most common of all crinoid fossils. This illustration is a columnal of *Isocrinus,* showing interior structures.

FIGURE 15.10
A Mississippian ammonoid *Goniatites kentuckiensis.*

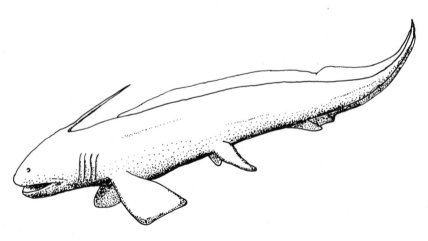

FIGURE 15.11
The Mississippian shark *Xenacanthus.*

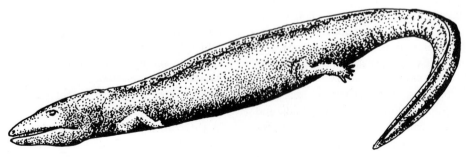

FIGURE 15.12
A typical Carboniferous amphibian, *Eogyrinus.*

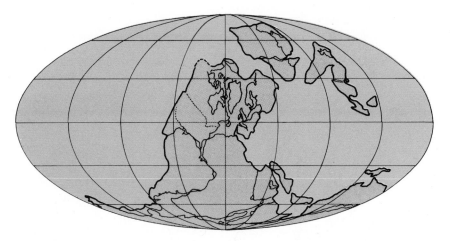

FIGURE 15.13
World paleogeography in the Pennsylvanian.

Ammonoids, although suffering a decline during the Late Devonian extinction event, apparently recovered quickly. During the Mississippian, one group known as goniatites flourished and evolved rapidly. The short life of many species make ammonoids good biostratigraphic indicators (Figure 15.10).

Mississippian Vertebrate Faunas

Fish faunas from the Mississippian show an essential continuity from the more advanced forms that had appeared during the Late Devonian. At the same time, some of the more archaic forms were beginning to drop out of the picture. The placoderms, for example, became extinct.

The sharks had appeared during the Devonian, but having a cartilaginous rather than bony skeleton, their fossil record is almost nonexistent. Sharks flourished during the Mississippian, and even before the close of the Devonian, one group—the xenacanths (Figure 15.11)—had moved into a freshwater habitat. Sharks, however, have always been predominantly marine predators.

The most interesting changes during the Mississippian occurred among the amphibians. From the first amphibians—animals such as *Icthyostega,* which, as discussed in Chapter 14, had appeared just at the close of the Devonian—arose a whole range of new forms. Even though the land was becoming covered with forests by this time, larger animals apparently had not yet evolved to exploit them. The amphibians, for example, were required to stay close to water for reproductive purposes, and, in any event, their teeth show them to have been carnivores rather than herbivores (Figure 15.12). Some species likely were scavengers.

Although, as is described later in the chapter, the amphibians gave rise to the reptiles and were eventually displaced as the leading terrestrial vertebrates, they were remarkably successful. From their first appearance for well over 50 million years (into the Early Permian), they were the dominant land animals, apparently competing successfully with the early reptiles after they appeared in the Late Mississippian or Early Pennsylvanian.

The great variety of forms seen in Mississippian and Pennsylvanian amphibians has suggested to some paleontologists that, rather than selection pressure within a relatively hostile environment providing the "trigger" for evolutionary variation, quite the reverse may have been the case. Perhaps, the widespread tropical lowlands and swamps provided an equable habitat in which virtually any new variant was able to succeed. In other words, the *lack* of selection pressure may have allowed any morphological type, however odd, to survive.

Pennsylvanian Overview

Early Pennsylvanian time saw the final closing of the Tethys Ocean and the collision of Gondwana with Laurussia (Figures 15.13 and 15.14). The assembly of Pangaea, embracing all the continental areas of the earth, was approaching completion, although some remaining pieces—notably the Siberian and Chinese cratons—would not be finally joined until the Triassic.

North America during the Pennsylvanian

On the North-American craton, the effects of the collision between Gondwana and Laurussia are seen in what has been termed the **Allegheny orogeny** in the southern Appalachians. This is where what is now the western bulge of North Africa was finally sutured to North America. The northern margin of Africa, in collision with southern Europe, produced what is variously known as the **Hercynian,**[1] Variscan,[2] or Armorican[3] orogeny (Figure 15.15).

---

1. Named after the Harz massif in central Germany.
2. Named after the Variscan Mountains of central Europe.
3. Named after the Armorican massif of Britanny, France.

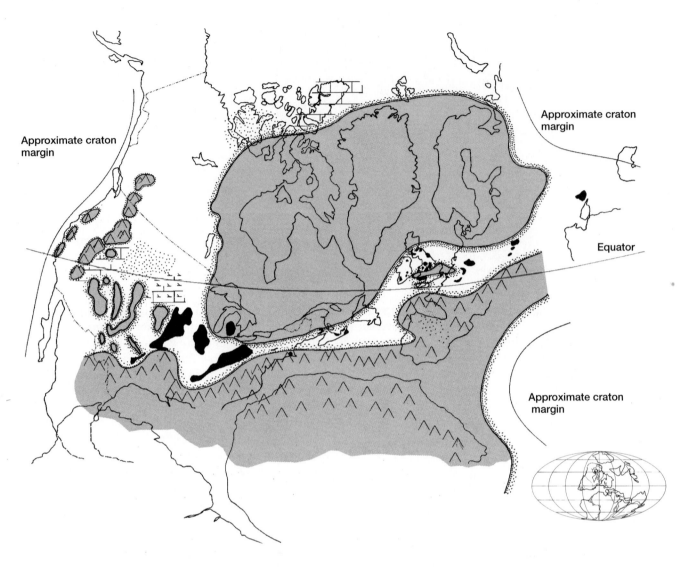

ÙRE 15.14

Paleogeography of Laurussia in the Pennsylvanian. (major
coal basins in black)

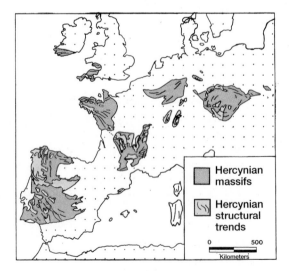

FIGURE 15.15

Structural trends and igneous intrusions associated with the
Hercynian orogeny in Europe.

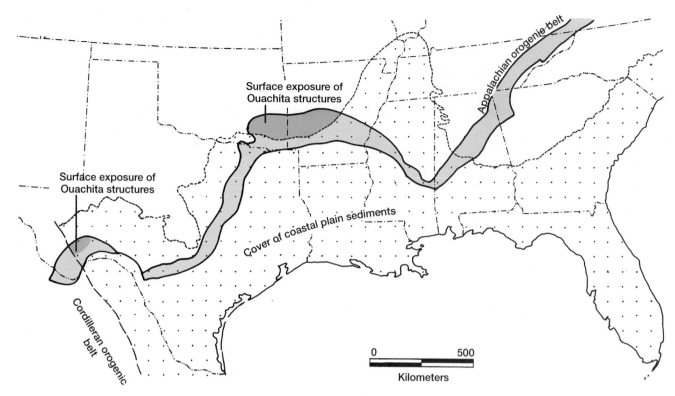

FIGURE 15.16

The Ouachita fold belt and its relationship to the
Appalachian fold belt.

The collision of the South American portion of Gondwana, moving northward against the southern margin of the North American craton, produced, as mentioned earlier in the chapter, the Ouachita fold belt (Figure 15.16).

In the southern Appalachians, the effects of the orogeny are seen in the presence of great thrust sheets in which rocks as old as Late Precambrian and part of the old craton margin have been moved for great distances westward. In one of these thrusts—the Great Smoky fault—the rocks are estimated to have been moved at least 50 kilometers from their place of origin. This estimate, however, is conservative, and some geologists believe that the distance traveled might amount to hundreds of kilometers.

The nature of these movements has only become understood since evidence from deep seismic surveys has been used to construct a whole new model to explain Appalachian structures. The model proposes what is called **thin-skin tectonics,** in which relatively thin thrust slices or slabs of older rocks traveled over a more or less flat decollement surface, below which much younger rocks remained relatively undisturbed. At Cades Cove in the Great Smoky Mountains, for example, Precambrian rocks overly limestones of Ordovician age that are exposed in a "window" eroded down through the overlying thrust sheet (*see Figure 13.7*).

Seismic surveys, supplemented by deep boreholes, also finally began to throw light upon the Ouachita mobile belt. Although a continuation of the southern Appalachian mobile belt as it swings abruptly in a westerly direction, the Ouachita mobile belt is largely buried by younger sediments of the coastal plain of the southern United States and the Mississippi embayment. Outcrops occur mainly in two sections: the Ouachita Mountains of southern Oklahoma and Arkansas, and the Marathon uplift of West Texas. The trend continues on into north central Mexico, but outcrops are small.

Even though poorly exposed, the essential outlines of the orogenic history of the Ouachita mobile belt are becoming fairly well understood. Unlike the Appalachians, the Ouachita mobile belt was not involved in several collision/subduction events and so is not made up of a collage of suspect terranes; consequently, it is much narrower. The Ouachita mobile belt is discussed in more detail later in the chapter.

In Colorado and northern New Mexico, the Uncompahgre and Front Range uplifted blocks trended roughly along the site of what was to later become the Rocky Mountains, and so they are sometimes referred to as the Ancestral Rocky Mountains (Figure 15.17). This is rather misleading, however, because they had long since been eroded flat before the Rocky Mountains proper appeared over 100 million years later.

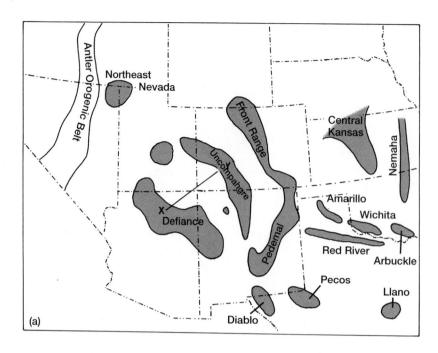

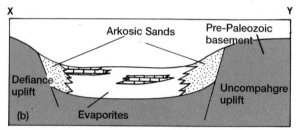

FIGURE 15.17

Major structural features of the southwestern North American craton during the Pennsylvanian. (a) General distribution of the major uplifted areas that supplied sediment to the adjacent basins. (b) Diagrammatic cross section across a typical "yoked basin." The climate was likely arid or semiarid so that evaporites are prominent in many of the basin-filling successions.

The Absaroka Sequence

Over a large area of the North America craton is a marked erosional break between Mississippian and Pennsylvanian sediments. This is one of the original sequence-boundary unconformities and separates the Kaskaskia sequence from the Absaroka. The **Absaroka sequence,** as a major sedimentary envelope laid down during a continent-wide inundation, is in several ways quite different from earlier sequences.

For one thing, the craton's interior was not nearly as isolated from clastic sources as had been the case during earlier inundations. Therefore, although limestones were deposited in many areas, they no longer dominated the sedimentary record. In the west, the site of the Antler orogeny was an uplifted clastic source (*see Figure 15.14*). Across the southern margin, a major highland area uplifted along the Ouachita fold belt was shedding sediments

northward. To the east were large, mature river systems with their various deltas spreading sands and silts over the craton interior.

A further contrast is seen in the geography of the craton heartland. The old Transcontinental Arch, with its northeast-southwest trend across the continent, seemed to have disappeared for good; instead, intracratonic structures, consisting of numerous uplifts with basins between, showed a general alignment in a northwest-southeast direction (Figure 15.17). These uplifted areas were often emergent and so provided local sources of clastics that accumulated in the adjacent basins. No major folding was involved in these intracratonic structures. Instead, the movement was predominantly along steep-angled faults. Movement along the faults continued over long periods so that, as the basins subsided, enormous thicknesses of infilling sediments accumulated. Some of these **yoked basins,** as they are called, were so active that subsidence along the boundary faults amounted to 3 or 4 kilometers and still they were kept filled (Figure 15.17). Many, despite their depth, were not always invaded by the sea, and instead, much of the sediment is of nonmarine type, typically arkoses and conglomerates derived in place from ancient Precambrian granites exposed in the uplifted areas. In some of the basins, evaporites were a characteristic feature.

Surprisingly, the influence of the Ouachita mobile belt as a source of clastic sediment did not extend far northward onto the craton. The widespread Atoka Formation of the midcontinent region, for example, is generally thought to have been derived largely from northerly and northeasterly sources, even as far away as the Canadian Shield and the Old Red Sandstone continent. This is, perhaps, easier to understand when some comparison is made with the modern Mississippi because, clearly, the northern Gulf of Mexico is today also receiving sediment from far distance sources. Also, by Pennsylvanian time, there was, as described earlier in the chapter, already at least one large river, labeled on paleogeographic maps as the Michigan River, flowing from an extensive hinterland to the northeast (see Figure 15.5). As in so many cases where geologic data seem to give conflicting results, the various proponents of different sourcelands for Pennsylvanian midcontinent sediments may all be right. Many different terranes may have been the ultimate source of the sediments.

The Gondwana/Laurussia Collision

Pennsylvanian through Permian stratigraphic successions provide some record of the events leading up to and including the Gondwana/Laurussia collision.

What is called the Arkansas or Caballos Novaculite of Devonian age was laid down in the deep water beyond the southern craton margin when Gondwana was still a considerable distance away, even though a volcanic arc associated with Gondwana may have been making itself felt. **Novaculite** is a distinctive white variety of the siliceous mineral chert. Bedded cherts in marine sedimentary successions have always presented something of a problem in terms of the source of the silica. Ocean waters are undersaturated in silica, and such organisms as diatoms, radiolaria, and siliceous sponges do not seem abundant enough to solve the problem. Instead, geologists generally agree that submarine vulcanicity and/or ash falls into the ocean provide the necessary silica. Direct evidence is not always available, but alternative explanations are lacking. No lava flows are found associated with the Arkansas Novaculite, although ash beds are present. Into Mississippian time, the overlying Stanley Group contains graywackes, fine sands, and shales interpreted as flysch deposits. Paleocurrent measurements and studies of the detrital minerals suggest that the major source of these deposits was a rising magmatic arc to the south.

The general pattern of Gondwana/Laurussia collision was now beginning to emerge, and most geologists agree that the convergent boundary involved a south-dipping subduction zone and a north-trending volcanic arc (Figure 15.18 a–c). Flysch deposition by turbidity currents sweeping down into the basin continued into Pennsylvanian times, unaffected by the events on the craton to the north. The Jackfork Formation above the Stanley Group was long dated as Mississippian, but later research found that the fossils had actually been derived by reworking from Mississippian rocks exposed on a shallow shelf somewhere and carried in by turbidity currents.

By now, the basin between the approaching mass of Gondwana and the North American craton to the north was apparently closing, zipper-fashion, from east to west because paleocurrent data indicate that sediment was being transported westward rather than northward. Just as in the Lower Paleozoic of the northern Appalachians, the zone of orogenic climax apparently shifted laterally. In the Ouachita Mountains of Arkansas, for example, activity had largely ceased by mid-Pennsylvanian time, whereas crustal unrest in the Marathon region to the west continued well into Permian time.

Direct evidence of earthquakes associated with the tectonic activity is seen in the John's Valley Formation of western Arkansas. Certain shaly units contain huge blocks of older rocks of all kinds piled together in a jumbled mass as they slumped and tumbled down the continental slope in a submarine landslide. Such deposits are termed **olistostromes** or *wild flysch*.

Many questions remain concerning the Gondwana/Laurussia collision, and numerous models have been proposed to explain some of the obvious contrasts in Ouachita mobile belt geology compared with that in the Appalachians. According to some workers, the movement of the Gondwana plate stopped before the remnants of the Tethys Ocean had completely closed. This was due, perhaps, to the irregular shape of the two cratons concerned. They obviously did not fit together like pieces of a jigsaw puzzle, so portions of ocean floor or volcanic arc likely remained within reentrants along the cratonic front. This would explain why evidence indicates that the deeper-water successions and continental rise deposits beyond the continental slope seem to have suffered the most deformation before being thrust northward against carbonates of the shallow continental shelf (Figure 15.18).

Also involved in attempts to reconstruct this segment of the Gondwana collision are possible microplates that were caught up between the two major craton masses. Today, they are considered the likely origin of portions of the Central American crust (Yucatan, Guatemala, and so on). These Central American crust portions had to come from somewhere, and projected movements and reconstructions during the Pangaea breakup place the microplates approximately in the area that is now the Gulf of Mexico.

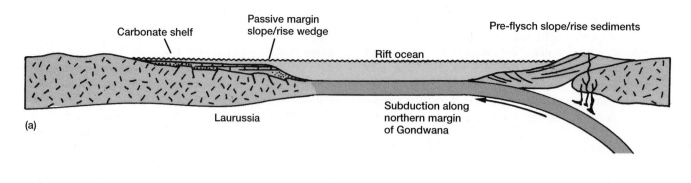

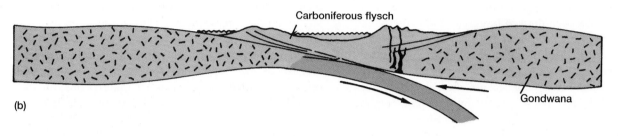

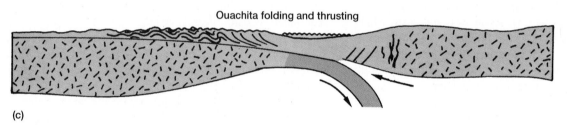

FIGURE 15.18

A reconstruction of events during the collision of Gondwana and Laurussia during the Ouachita orogeny. (a) 500 to 340 million years before present (Ordovician-Mississippian).

(b) 340 to 305 million years before present (Mississippian-Pennsylvanian). (c) 305 to 290 million years before present (Pennsylvanian).

Gondwana Glaciations

Before Pennsylvanian coal-bed successions of the midcontinent region can be discussed, the climatic controls that influenced much of this region's sedimentary history must be described.

As discussed in Chapter 8, the first evidence for pre-Pleistocene glaciations came from rocks of Permo-Pennsylvanian age in Africa. The enormous thicknesses of what could only be glacial till, the striated rock pavements, polished and grooved by ice, and many other unequivocal indicators of an ice age provided irrefutable evidence for the reality of continental drift. As Gondwana moved northward toward its rendezvous with Laurussia, the apparent path of the South Pole moved progressively across the huge landmass.

Evidence of the first continental ice sheets came from South America and central Africa in rocks as old as Mississippian or even latest Devonian age. With the movement of Gondwana, the ice centers shifted across the continent, and some of the latest glacial sediments are found in Australia and are dated as Permian in age (Figure 15.19).

North America lay in the tropics, so all of this was very remote. Nevertheless, the Permo-Pennsylvanian ice age, as it is usually labeled, lasted for some 100 million years and profoundly influenced sedimentary regimes in many parts of the world. Just as during the Late Cenozoic ice age, in which we are currently living, the Milankovitch-Köppen insolation cycles undoubtedly controlled the cycle of ice sheet advance and retreat, and this, in turn, inevitably drove the mechanism of glacio-eustatic sea-level fluctuation. If the magnitude of sea-level swings was similar to that recorded for the Late Cenozoic glaciation, which seems reasonable, sea-level fluctuations of 70 or 80 meters are indicated.

The effects of a given rise or fall of sea level vary, depending upon the particular geologic or geographic setting. Along a coastline of low relief and with a broad and shallow offshore shelf, even a small shift in sea level may cause the shoreline to migrate over a considerable distance.

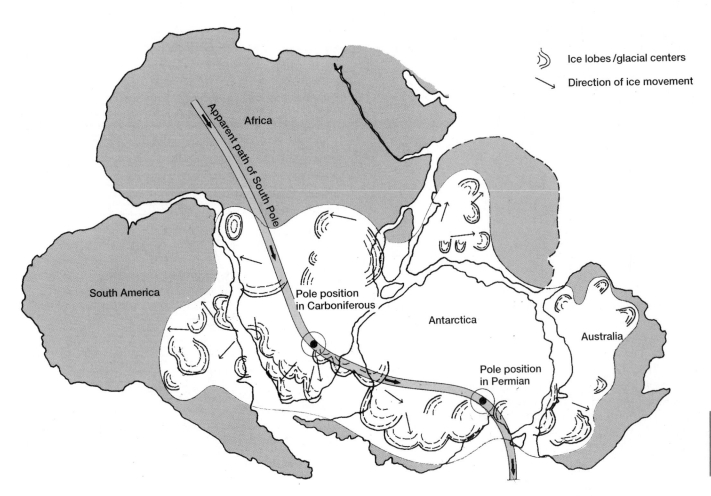

FIGURE 15.19
Movement of the Gondwana continent across the South Pole from Devonian through Permian time.

Pennsylvanian Coals and Cyclothems

Lithologic Associations of Coal Beds

One of the most striking features of Pennsylvanian successions in many parts of the world is the prevalence of coal beds that tend to be interbedded within distinctive sedimentary associations in which sandstones, shales, and limestones occur in regular and repetitive succession (Figure 15.20). In the Pennsylvanian of Illinois, for example, where some of the classic studies were conducted in the 1920s and 1930s, nearly all of the many different coal beds occur within groupings of 10 distinct members that always occur in the same order (Table 15.1). The repetition of these lithologic associations clearly indicates that some kind of cyclical mechanism controlled their deposition. The ordering of the different sediment types and their contained fossils indicate that sea-level changes were responsible.

Each cycle begins with a massive, cross-bedded sandstone, which is overlain by a sandy shale. Then comes a limestone with freshwater fossils, which is followed, in turn, by a clay. This is usually referred to as the **underclay**

FIGURE 15.20
Marine limestone overlying coal in the Pennsylvanian of southwest Colorado.

TABLE 15.1

The "Ideal" Cyclothem

Member	Sediment Type
10	Shale with ironstone concretions
9	Marine limestone
8	Black shale with black limestone concretions
7	Impure lenticular marine limestone
6	Shale
5	Coal
4	Underclay
3	"Freshwater" limestone
2	Sandy shale
1	Sandstone (unconformable on underlying beds)

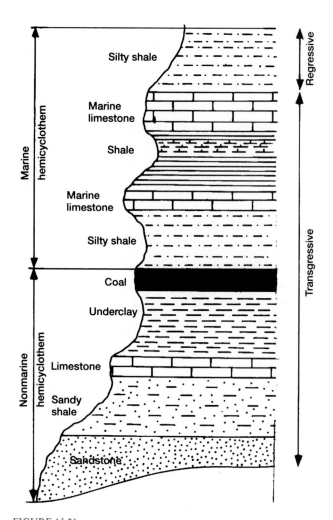

FIGURE 15.21

Typical coal cyclothem with all 10 sedimentary units described in the "classic" studies. The lower nonmarine and upper marine successions are grouped into hemicyclothems.

because it lies directly beneath the coal bed. The underclay often contains fossils of tree roots and, because chemical analyses show that it typically has been extensively leached of its more soluble components, it is considered to represent the soil in which the coal-forming vegetation grew. Immediately above the coal begins a succession of shale and limestone with fossils indicating marine conditions, and the forests of the coastal swamps in which the coals were formed clearly were killed off as the sea flooded in.

Cyclothems

Each coal, with its associated shales and limestones, forms part of what is termed a **cyclothem**, the succession of sediments deposited through one cycle of sea-level rise and fall. The paleogeographic setting for the coal beds of Illinois and the entire region along the western margin of the Appalachian landmass was a broad and low-lying coastal plain that passed out into a shallow offshore shelf of equally low relief. Even a small shift in sea level resulted in a dramatic and widespread change in the sedimentary environments. Although studies of many coal beds have shown that the "ideal" cyclothem consists of about 10 members (Table 15.1), as shown in Figure 15.21, cyclothems are often incomplete, with certain members missing, presumably because sea-level rise or fall was too rapid or because it was interrupted before the cycle was complete.

The top of a cyclothem is marked by an erosion surface produced after sea level had fallen again and the coastal plain was once more emergent. In some cases, therefore, missing members of a cyclothem may simply be due to loss by erosion prior to the next cycle of sea-level rise. Overlying the erosion surface is the basal cross-bedded sand of the succeeding cyclothem, marking the beginning of the next cycle of sea-level rise.

Cyclothem Causes   While the underlying cause of cyclothems seems clearly related to sea-level fluctuation, there has been considerable discussion as to the precise

mechanism responsible. That individual coals have sometimes been traced for hundreds of kilometers is strongly suggestive of a eustatic rather than a local tectonic cause of sea-level change. This is supported by the sheer number of cyclothems; over 100 have been counted in some areas. Their regularity in thickness, suggesting a similar regularity in the timing of the sea-level cycles, also points to an external cyclical mechanism. In view of the major ice age occurring at this time, with its probable Milankovitch-Köppen cycles of advance and retreat, most geologists accept a glacio-eustatic mechanism as playing the major role in the formation of Pennsylvanian coal cyclothems.

On the other hand, many intriguing questions remain, and certain other factors must be considered. For example, local tectonic or epeirogenic warping likely occurred from time to time. Sometimes, local subsidence was due to sediment compaction. There is also the question of the lateral migration of deltaic depocenters (localized areas of maximum deposition). Much of the coastal plain on which the coals were formed was probably deltaic in character, with the constantly shifting distributary channels characteristic of such environments. Indeed, lens- or pod-shaped channel sands are a common feature of all coal-bearing successions (Figures 15.22a,b). The effects of these various mechanisms would naturally be superimposed upon the glacio-eustatic cycles and introduce local or even regional variations. They could, for example, be responsible for the many cyclothems with missing members.

Cyclothem Symmetry   One further question concerns the rate at which sea level rose and fell during a typical glacio-eustatic cycle, more particularly with the symmetry of the cycle. Detailed studies by British coal geologist William Ramsbottom suggest that European cyclothems were asymmetrical in that sea level rose relatively slowly but then retreated rapidly. Curiously, in the midcontinent region of North America, the cyclothems seem to exhibit asymmetry in the opposite direction, with rapid sea-level rise, followed by slow fall. Clearly, both theories cannot be correct, so it presumably is a question of the interpretation of the various sedimentary facies.

Because the same Milankovitch-Köppen mechanism drove the Pennsylvanian ice sheet fluctuations just as it does the Late Cenozoic ones we are still experiencing, it seems logical to look at the most recent glacio-eustatic cycle of sea-level change. This unequivocally points to a fast-rise/slow-fall asymmetry. Unfortunately, even this may not settle the argument because the cycle involved runs only about 100,000 years, as opposed to the Pennsylvanian cycles, which are three to four times as long.

Life in the Pennsylvanian

Pennsylvanian Floras

Because of the prevalence of coal deposits of Pennsylvanian age, a great deal of attention has naturally been paid to the plants that formed the coal, and consequently, more is known about the floras from the Pennsylvanian than from any other geologic period. Although coals are made up entirely of plant remains, containing no true minerals as such, the coal beds themselves yield surprisingly poor plant fossils. The complex coalification process that transforms dead and partially decayed vegetation into peat and then into coals of increasing rank largely destroys the plant material and often obliterates all traces of the plant's cellular structure (see Box 15.1). Only in so-called **coal balls** (concretions found in the coals) is any direct evidence of the coal-forming plants preserved.

In general, the finest plant fossils have been found in the shales associated with the coals. Preservation as carbonized impressions on bedding surfaces is often remarkably good, and sometimes, pyritized and silicified remains provide details of internal features and cell structures. Ironstone nodules in sandstones associated with coals are also often a fruitful source of good fossils.

Pennsylvanian floras were, in general, similar to those of the Mississippian, the chief differences being, perhaps, an altered balance of genera and species and the fact that certain groups grew to a much greater size than they ever had in the past. *Lepidodendron,* for example, is known to have attained heights of over 30 meters with a trunk over a meter in diameter (Figure 15.7). *Sigillaria,* another lycopod, was also an extremely important element in the coal swamp forests (Figure 15.22a,b). The herbaceous plants that formed the undergrowth were dominated by ferns.

Although in Pennsylvanian floras as a whole, moisture-loving, low-ground species were very important, higher and drier land areas were also covered by forests, and sphenopsids, such as *Calamites,* flourished (Figure 15.22c,d,e). As a spore plant, *Calamites* still required plenty of moisture. The seed plants needed much less moisture and probably dominated the high ground, although, naturally, their fossil record is considerably poorer. In particular, the seed ferns (Figure 15.22f,g,h) and other gymnosperms, such as *Cordaites* (Figure 15.22i,j), were important forest trees, often rivaling the *Lepidodendron* species in stature.

The various North American Pennsylvanian plant species are familiar to Northern Hemisphere geologists, but much less familiar are those plants of the Southern Hemisphere continents that once formed Gondwana. At this time, the continent lay close to the South Pole, and so parts of it were experiencing an ice age. Clearly, the cool-temperate climate in regions surrounding the ice cap produced a different set of floral associations than those in the moist tropics, where the coals were forming. Particularly characteristic of and widespread in Gondwana terrestrial Carboniferous deposits was the seed fern *Glossopteris,* with its distinctive tongue-shaped leaf.

Pennsylvanian Invertebrate Faunas

The coals and associated strata not only provide a record of plant life, but also of a group of animals whose fossil record is, in general, extremely poor: the insects and other land-dwelling arthropods. Over 400 species of insects have been described from Pennsylvanian rocks. The discovery of a few extremely large examples, such as dragonflies with 70-centimeter wingspans and 10-centimeter long cockroaches, led to the erroneous impression that this was an age of giants. Most of the insects and members of other groups, such as spiders, scorpions and centipedes, were, by modern standards, unremarkable in size.

The marine faunas contained many groups that had flourished in the Mississippian. The bryozoan *Archimedes* and the productid brachiopods were still plentiful. Particularly noteworthy in the Pennsylvanian was the rapid growth in importance of large foraminiferans of the family Fusulinidae. Fusulinids had appeared in the Mississippian, but in the Pennsylvanian and Permian, they underwent an evolutionary radiation. Short species life and wide

BOX 15.1

The Origin of Coal

Coal is produced as a result of the burial, compression, and alteration of dead plant debris that accumulates in freshwater and brackish-water swamps, where anoxic bottom conditions inhibit the decay of the plant material by aerobic bacteria. The first stage in the coal-forming process is the accumulation of **peat,** a material that is friable (fragile) and in which the plant remains are still identifiable. With further burial, the process of **coalification** begins, during which increasing pressure and, more importantly, increasing heat drive out the moisture. The different stages in coal-

ification are recognized in terms of increasing rank. Thus, peat turns into the low-rank coal lignite (brown coal). The further changes in rock as the coalification process continues are summarized in Box Table 15.1.

Another approach to the classification of coal recognizes the various botanical origins of the coal constituents, based largely on microscopic examination. Coal is unique in that it is not composed of minerals in the normal sense of the word. It originates as plant material that, after the coalification process, turns into rock-forming constituents termed macerals.

The differences between the macerals reflect coal's botanical origin. Thus, of the 10 or so macerals recognized, cutinite is derived from plant cuticles, fusinite is composed of cellular material, resinite originates as plant resin and waxes, alginite is composed of algal bodies, and so on.

The macerals, in turn, are arranged in groups, and these correlate with a practical classification of coal types based on appearance in hand specimen. For example, the banded appearance of typical bituminous coal is due to the alternation of several kinds of coal defined on the basis of texture, as shown in Box Table 15.2.

BOX TABLE 15.1

Typical Chemical Composition (percentage) of Different Stages in the Coalification Process

Coal Rank	Carbon	Hydrogen	Oxygen and Nitrogen	Ash
Lignite	57.28%	6.03%	36.16%	0.59%
Subbituminous coal				
Bituminous	83.47	6.68	9.54	0.20
Semibituminous coal				
Semianthracite				
Anthracite	91.44	3.36	2.79	1.52

BOX TABLE 15.2

Coal Types

Coal Type	Maceral Group	Appearance
Fusain	Inertinite	Charcoal appearance
Vitrain	Vitrinite	Bright, jetlike (glistening)
Durain	Liptinite	Dull matt
Clarain		Satin luster

distribution in marine successions make them important stratigraphic zone fossils for this time period.

Pennsylvanian Vertebrate Faunas: The First Reptiles

That the general evolutionary progress of early vertebrates was from fishes to amphibians, and from amphibians to reptiles, is axiomatic. That steps in this increasing sophistication of physical organization and anatomy would be clearly defined in the fossil record also would seem logical. Unfortunately, however, this is not the case.

At first, the fossils seem to provide the proper documentation: The links between the fishes and the first amphibian in the form of *Icthyostega,* as described in Chapter 14, are clear-cut. The next step, however, from amphibians to reptiles, is more ambiguous. In general bodily organization and skeletal structure, the amphibians and reptiles have many features in common. The more advanced amphibians look much like primitive reptiles, and from skeletal remains alone, no single criterion can be selected as clearly separating the two groups. Even among

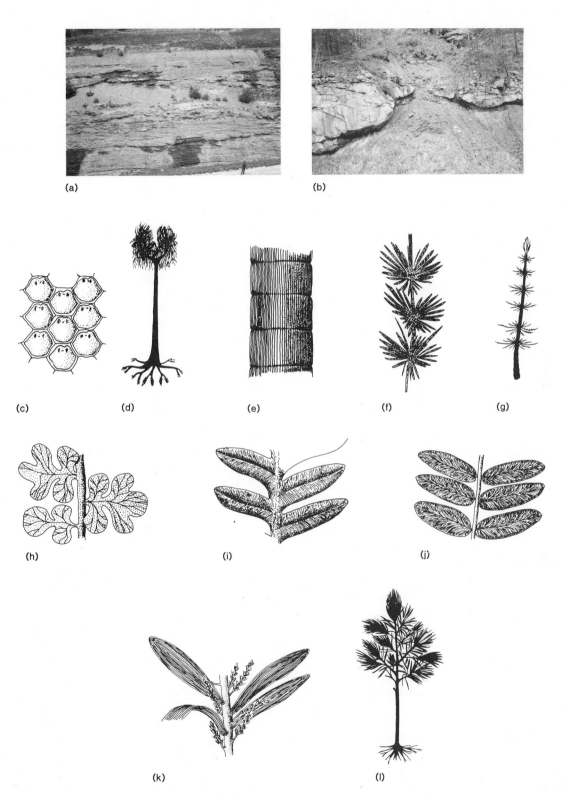

FIGURE 15.22

Pennsylvanian plants. These, together with *Lepidodendron* (see Figure 15.7), are the most common forms associated with coals. (a) Sandstone lenses in Pennsylvanian coal-bearing succession, eastern Kentucky. (b) Close-up of channel-filling sandstone in coal beds. (c) Leaf cushions of the *Sigillaria elegans* type. (d) Restoration of *Sigillaria* sp. (e) *Calamites* sp. pith cast from ribbed stem. (f) *Annularia radiatus,* the name assigned to leaves of *Calamites.* (g) Restoration of *Calamites.* (h) Pinnules of *Sphenopteris,* a seed fern. (i) Pinnules of *Alethopteris,* a seed fern. (j) Pinnules of *Neuropteris,* a seed fern. (k) Branch of *Cordaites* with leaves and fertile shoots. (l) Reconstruction of *Cordaites.*

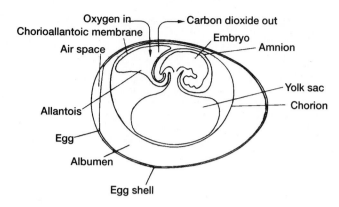

FIGURE 15.23
The amniotic egg.

FIGURE 15.24
Hylonomus, one of the first true reptiles.

the experts, opinions are divided. The one obvious difference between amphibians and reptiles involves the mode of reproduction, which is not reflected in the skeletal structures and therefore leaves no fossil record.

Amphibians, although land dwellers, require an aquatic environment for reproduction. Amphibian eggs are fertilized externally and laid in large numbers, usually in water, or at least in very moist environments. Only a tiny percentage of amphibian eggs ever hatch, let alone develop into mature animals. The remainder provide a free food supply for countless creatures living in the water.

With the appearance of the **amniotic** or **cleidoic egg,** with its yolk to provide a food supply for the developing embryo and a shell to protect it and yet allow oxygen intake, every egg had its own "private puddle" (Figure 15.23). Amniotic eggs are fertilized internally, and at birth, the hatchling is a miniature of the full-grown animal. There is no tadpole stage as with the amphibians. Clearly, this is a far more efficient mode of reproduction: Not only can eggs be laid on dry land, but far fewer eggs are necessary. This important step forward in evolutionary development is believed to have taken place during the Pennsylvanian, although no fossil eggs dating from that time have yet been found. The oldest fossil eggs, in fact, date from the Permian.

The majority of amphibians during the Mississippian and Pennsylvanian possessed a body form in which the head and torso were relatively flat and the limbs extended from the sides of the body, as though the animal were doing push-ups. The limbs still were not strong for walking on dry land, and in the vast swamps of Pennsylvanian time in particular, amphibians probably spent as much of their time in the water as out of it.

Although certain skeletal fragments considered by some paleontologists to be the earliest reptiles have been found in rocks of Mississippian age, it is more generally agreed that the first true reptiles appeared in the Pennsylvanian. Because reptiles were ranging much farther

afield and into habitats remote from the water, the chances of finding well-preserved fossil reptiles begins, on a purely statistical basis, to drop.

Fortunately, in one location near Joggins, Nova Scotia, Lower Pennsylvanian sediments contain well-preserved stumps of tree-size lycopods. Inside some of the stumps were found the remains of small, lizardlike reptiles about 50 centimeters long and named *Hylonomus* (Figure 15.24). How these animals came to be inside the stumps is not hard to guess. When the trees died and fell over, the soft, pithy part inside the stumps quickly decayed, leaving the more resistant bark on the outside. Some of the animals clambering over the trees in search of insects may have fallen inside the hollow stumps and could not get out again. Or, perhaps, the stumps had become buried, and the rotting out of the interiors had left holes in the ground that acted as pitfalls to trap the unwary. In any event, the stumps and their contents were eventually buried beneath subsequent increments of sand.

Hylonomus, lacking any fenestration in the skull and so classified as an anapsid, belonged to a group known as captorhinomorph cotylosaurs (see Box 15.2). These cotylosaurs were generally quite small and, like *Hylonomus,* were all lightly built and undoubtedly led a relatively active existence preying on small amphibians, reptiles, and probably also large insects. In later time, particularly during the Permian, this group of relatively unspecialized reptiles evolved in several directions.

At another locality in Nova Scotia, this time near Florence, other tree stump traps of a slightly younger date contain a reptile that, although similar to *Hylonomus,* shows some important new features. The most obvious of these is a temporal fenestrum behind the orbit and between the postorbital squamosal bones above and the jugal bone below; the reptile is, therefore, classified as a synapsid (see Box 15.2). Named *Archaeothyris,* it is considered a pelycosaur and the earliest of the so-called mammal-like reptiles. Even at this early date, a reptilian evolutionary radiation was beginning, and already discernible were the first steps along the pathway toward the mammals.

BOX 15.2

Holes in the Head—A Classification of Reptiles

The classification of reptiles has been a subject of some controversy for many years, and no system has yet found universal reception. The main problem centers on the question of the evolution of reptiles—specifically, their phylogeny. On the one hand is the view that all reptiles arose from a single ancestral amphibian and that, after reaching the reptilian level of organization with the appearance of the amniotic egg, a rapid evolutionary radiation then produced all the many and varied reptilian groups. An alternative view holds that reptiles are polyphyletic in origin—that is, that different groups arose independently from various lines of advanced amphibians and that the evolutionary step from amphibian to reptile was achieved on a broad front.

Since these arguments may never be decisively settled, the lack of consensus on reptile classification is hardly surprising. In the meantime, an empirical approach has produced a work-

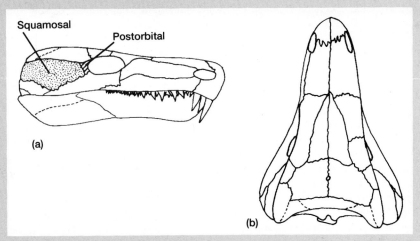

BOX FIGURE 15.1
Skull of *Limnoscelis,* an anapsid reptile from the Permian, showing the location of the squamosal and postorbital bones. (a) Side view. (b) View from above.

able system based on variations in the temporal region of the skull. The most obvious differences in reptiles involve the number and position of the open-

ings in the skull—the temporal fenestrae. Accordingly, five groups are recognized, as shown in Box Table 15.3 and Box Figure 15.1.

BOX TABLE 15.3

Reptile Classification Based on Temporal Fenestrae

Subclass Anapsida		No temporal openings in the skull behind the orbit
Subclass Synapsida		A single, lateral, temporal opening bounded above by the squamosal and postorbital bones
Subclass Euryapsida		A single, superior, temporal opening bounded below by the squamosal and postorbital bones
Subclass Parapsida	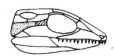	A single, highly placed, temporal opening bounded by the supratemporal and postfrontal bones
Subclass Diapsida	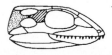	Two temporal openings, separated by the squamosal and postorbital bones

Summary

The Mississippian and Pennsylvanian systems in North America are recognized elsewhere in the world as lower and upper divisions of the Carboniferous System. The Carboniferous System as a whole is not a particularly natural unit and almost worldwide contains a marked unconformity approximately in the middle.

During the Mississippian in North America, the craton was covered in many areas by the Kaskaskia Sea, and the widespread Mississippian limestones were formed in the last of the great clear-water epeiric cycles. The shallow marine platforms in which these carbonates formed extended as broad shelves around the emergent heartland of what had been the Old Red Sandstone Continent of earlier time. The most prominent biogenic contributors to the Mississippian limestones were the crinoids and blastoids. Along the western side of the continent, clastic sediment spread westward in broad alluvial plains and deltas. Delivered by rivers flowing from the Old Red Sandstone Continent, these sediments encroached progressively across the craton as the Kaskaskia Sea began its withdrawal in Late Mississippian time. The most important of these rivers has been called the Michigan River, which is considered a direct ancestor of the modern Mississippi River. To the south, Mississippian successions contain deep-water, flysch-type deposits, indicating the approaching influence of the Gondwana continent as it moved northward. Along the craton's western margin, the Antler orogeny had produced clastic sources that spread eastward. The Ellesmere orogeny of Devonian time had stabilized and uplifted the craton's northern margin, so no Mississippian sediments are present in northern Canada.

Mississippian plant fossils show that forests were becoming widespread on the land, and many of the trees that were to be important coal-formers during the Pennsylvanian had appeared. In the seas, invertebrate faunas were dominated by crinoids and blastoids. The brachiopods, although decimated by the Late Devonian mass extinction, moved to fill empty ecologic niches; particularly characteristic were the productids. The most distinctive Mississippian bryozoan was *Archimedes*. Among the vertebrates, the fish faunas began to take on a more modern aspect as many of the archaic, heavily armored Devonian forms became extinct. The most interesting changes during the Mississippian occurred among the amphibians, with a wide variety of forms flourishing in the extensive coastal swamps of the time.

Early in the Pennsylvanian, Gondwana collided with Laurussia and completed the closing of the Tethys Ocean that had lain between them. The continental collision was marked by the Allegheny orogeny in the southern Appalachians and by the Hercynian orogeny in southern Europe. A continuation of the southern Appalachian fold belt is seen in the Ouachita fold belt, although the Ouachita belt is poorly exposed. Sections can be seen in the Ouachita Mountains of southern Oklahoma and Arkansas and in the Marathon uplift of west Texas.

The major sedimentary envelope of Pennsylvanian time forms part of what is known as the Absaroka sequence. Unlike earlier inundations, there were no widespread carbonate-forming epeiric seas. Instead, deposition was concentrated in relatively localized basins that often became filled by clastic sediment derived from adjacent highland areas.

Pennsylvanian through Permian stratigraphic successions provide some record of the events leading up to and including the Gondwana/Laurussia collision. Most geologists agree that the convergent boundary involved a south-dipping subduction zone and an associated volcanic arc.

During the Pennsylvanian on Gondwana, an ice cap formed, and advances and retreats of the ice, driven by the Milankovitch-Köppen insolation cycle mechanism, caused many glacio-eustatic sea-level fluctuations. More than 100 cyclothems have been counted in some places. Associated with the cyclothems were widespread coal deposits that formed in vast coastal swamps and deltas.

Pennsylvanian coals were formed in lush forests containing species of *Lepidodendron* and *Sigillaria,* some of which grew to over 30 meters tall. Insects and other fossils from the sediments associated with the coals show that a rich fauna flourished in the forests, including some unusually large species of dragonflies and cockroaches. Invertebrate life in the seas was largely a continuation of the same groups that had flourished in the Mississippian, although a marked evolutionary radiation among the fusulinid foraminiferans was noteworthy. Living in the swamps was a wide variety of amphibians. Evidence indicates that the first reptiles evolved quite early in the Pennsylvanian. With the development of the amniotic egg, animals were free to move away from the immediate vicinity of water and so were able to rapidly expand into all kinds of habitats during the Pennsylvanian. Before the end of the period, the first mammal-like reptiles had appeared.

Questions

1. The subtitle of this chapter is "An end and a beginning." Discuss the significance of this.
2. What is unusual about the stratigraphic record of the Devonian/Mississippian boundary over much of the North American craton?
3. Limestone deposition across the North American craton was widespread during the Mississippian, just as it had been in the Devonian. How did the Mississippian limestone differ from the Devonian? What do these differences tell about the sedimentary environment and marine faunas of the time?
4. What was the significance of the Old Red Sandstone Continent during the Mississippian and Pennsylvanian? Give some account of the climate.
5. Describe some of the distinctive features of Mississippian marine invertebrate faunas.
6. One particular group of vertebrates can be said to have reached their heyday by the Late Mississippian. Explain.
7. What were the most immediate obvious effects of the collision of Gondwana with Laurussia?
8. Describe the likely link between Carboniferous cyclothems and Gondwana glaciations.
9. List in order the major sedimentary units in a typical coal-containing cyclothem.
10. What is the significance of the distribution of the major Pennsylvanian coal basins in North America and Europe?
11. If coals are made up entirely of organic material, why are fossils in them typically poorly preserved or nonexistent?
12. Describe Pennsylvanian floras.
13. Why is the transition from amphibians to reptiles virtually impossible to detect in the fossil record?
14. Describe the internal structures and discuss the significance of the amniotic egg.
15. Explain the basis for a classification of reptiles based on temporal fenestrae.

Further Reading

Kemp, T. S. 1982. *Mammal-like reptiles and the origin of mammals.* London: Academic Press.

Rodgers, J. R. 1987. The Appalachian-Ouachita orogenic belt. *Episodes* 10: 259–66.

Taylor, T. N. 1981. *Paleobotany: An introduction to fossil plant biology.* New York: McGraw Hill.

16

THE PERMIAN

Introduction

Of all the geologic systems, the Permian is the only one with a type region outside of western Europe. Although it was described and named by British geologist Roderick Murchison who, as discussed in Chapter 5, had earlier established the Silurian System, Czar Nicholas I of Russia was also involved. In 1841 during his second visit to Russia, Murchison met and apparently became well acquainted with the czar. This, not surprisingly, greatly expedited his subsequent geologic travels through Russia.

Murchison and his companion, French paleontologist Eduard de Vermeil, traveled from Moscow eastward to the Urals and then south to the Sea of Azov. Over a period of five months, they mapped a considerable area and made important collections of fossils and rocks (Figure 16.1). Perhaps, Murchison's most significant discovery was thick, fossiliferous sections in the southern Urals (Figure 16.2). Paleontological evidence indicated that these rocks were younger than the Carboniferous and correlated with formations in Britain that William Smith had labeled the New Red Sandstone, which is typically only sparsely fossiliferous. To recognize this fossiliferous succession in the Urals, Murchison erected a new system which, in honor of his royal patron and as a gesture of thanks to his Russian hosts, he named after the district of Perm. Much of Murchison's original Permian section later proved to be of Carboniferous age, although subsequent studies in the area did find a true Permian succession.

As the chapter discussion traces the changing continental configurations, the distribution of land and sea, and climatic change through the Permian, it will become clear that the world was undergoing profound changes. In particular, the repetitive nature of many eustatic and tectonic events during the Paleozoic came to an end with the construction of a continental mass of Pangaea proportions, something that had not existed since the Precambrian.

The close of the Permian was marked by what most scientists regard as the greatest crisis in the history of life on this planet, with perhaps as many as 90 percent of all animal species becoming extinct. While the cause of this mass extinction is as yet unknown, many theories have been suggested. Although an extraterrestrial event seems a likely explanation in the case of at least one other mass extinction, the Permian event, at least up to the present, has offered no evidence pointing in this direction. Instead, it may well provide an example of a catastrophe wrought here upon earth and caused by the interaction of several terrestrial, climatic, and geologic phenomena, perhaps culminating in a runaway effect.

In this, there may be a lesson to be learned in our modern world as we continue to tinker with the environment without any real understanding of what lies ahead. We should not forget that environmental catastrophes are part of world history!

Permian Overview

Thus far in this book, the focus has been on the geologic history of North America. Events on other continents have been mentioned, but doing more is clearly impossible within a book of manageable proportions. On the other hand, and as was apparent in the previous two chapters, dealing with North American history as a distinct entity

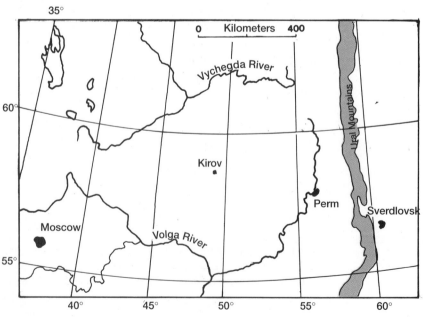

FIGURE 16.1

Location of the Permian type area.

is becoming increasingly difficult simply because North America was not a separate continent any more.

On a planetwide scale, the Permian had four unique features:

1. By the close of the Permian, virtually all the continental areas were merged in Pangaea.
2. A major ice age was in progress.
3. World sea levels were considerably lowered due to the Gondwana ice caps, combined with the effect of a high-standing Pangaea continent uplifted by thermal expansion above the mantle, as described in Chapter 9.
4. The Permian closed with a mass extinction event, the likes of which the earth had not experienced before.

FIGURE 16.2

Old photograph dating from the 1920s of the country around Perm. *(By courtesy of Anton E. Oleinik, Russian Academy of Sciences.)*

Permian Continental Configuration: Pangaea Again

As the Permian opened, and as Figure 16.3 shows, Gondwana had collided with Laurussia to form a vast landmass that extended across the equator and far to the south to the pole itself. Only a portion of China, a relatively small cratonic block whose geographic position is still uncertain, remained unattached.

By the close of the Permian, virtually all the major continental masses had been assembled into a supercontinent of Pangaea proportions. Not since the Proterozoic had there been such a configuration. During the intervening 400 million years, this earlier Pangaea had broken apart, and now it was reassembled. The Worsley, Nance, and Moody cycle described in Chapter 9 provides a plausible explanation of the mechanism involved.

Permian Stratigraphy—Pangaea-Style

Permian sedimentary patterns across equatorial Pangaea indicate that relatively local structures exerted considerable control. No orogenic belts were active, and the structural style almost everywhere was one of tensional block faulting. This, together with the generally emergent nature of the cratons, was a consequence of thermal expansion; therefore, the uniqueness of Permian stratigraphy likely owes much to a mechanism controlled by a 400-million-year cycle of crustal change.

The sheer size of Pangaea also means that the Permian world climatic pattern was also inevitable. A landmass of Pangaea proportions must inevitably extend to at least one pole, so that at these "Pangaea times" in earth history, an ice age was similarly inevitable.

In summary, Permian-style stratigraphy seems to go with Pangaea-style continental distribution. Confirmation of this model is naturally difficult because of the length of the cycle implied. The first time that a Pangaea type of continent had formed had been in the Late Proterozoic, and the overall sedimentary record from that period of history is poor. Nevertheless, the evidence for a Pangaea continent at that time and also for a major ice age is overwhelming, so a causal relationship apparently exists. Obviously, however, this does not explain all ice ages. The Ordovician ice age, as well as the current late Cenozoic ice age, however, clearly occurred without a Pangaea continental configuration.

The Permian in North America (Western Pangaea)

What is now North America lay in the tropics, with the equator, as shown in the most up-to-date reconstructions, running through the northern United States and southeastern Canada (Figure 16.4). Europe lay to the east, also in the tropics; thus, many Permian facies of successions now separated by the Atlantic Ocean show an essential continuity.

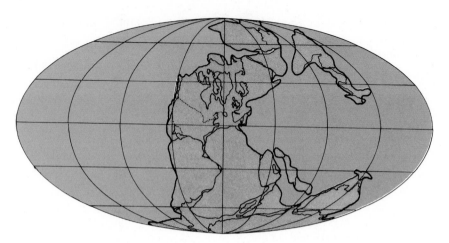

FIGURE 16.3
World paleogeography in the Permian.

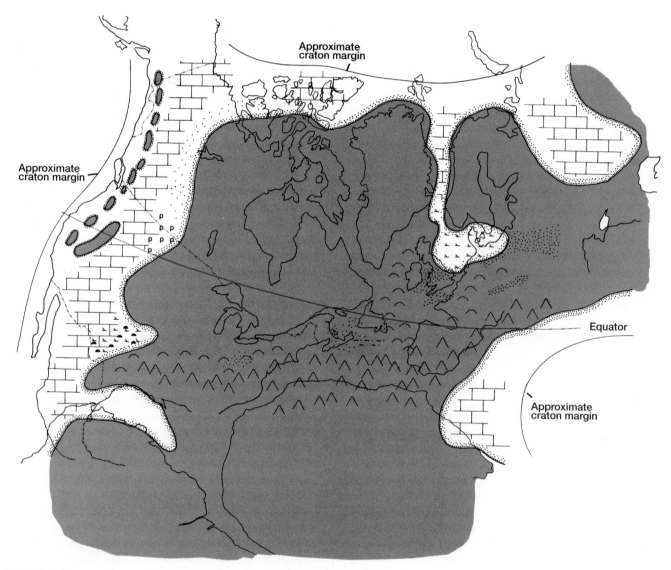

FIGURE 16.4
Paleogeography of Laurussia in the Permian.

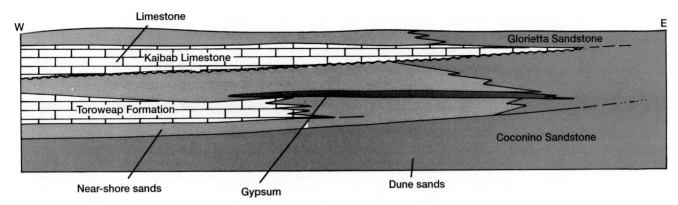

FIGURE 16.5

Diagrammatic cross section in the southwestern North American craton, showing the relationship of the Kaibab Limestone to nonmarine redbeds as the Absaroka Sea retreated.

During the Pennsylvanian, the shallow epicontinental sea that covered much of western and central North America advanced eastward and retreated many times, in response to eustatic changes in sea level caused by fluctuations in the size of the distant Gondwana ice cap. By the close of the period, however, there had been a net withdrawal of the sea, and large midcontinent regions were becoming dry land. The yoked basins of Pennsylvanian time in the area of the so-called Ancestral Rockies were now becoming filled with terrestrial deposits, including thick arkoses derived from granites exposed in the cores of uplifted areas. By the earliest Permian, connections with the open sea were disappearing, and the limestones alternating with shales, together with deltaic sediments, point to marginal marine swamps in many areas. Marine conditions persisted only in the west, where shallow shelf carbonates, together with phosphate deposits, were laid down. In what is now the Texas panhandle area, extensive reefs developed around a series of subsiding basins.

Although much of the Permian succession of the midcontinent and western region is characterized by redbeds, over large areas of the central craton, the earliest Permian sediments are similar to those of the preceding Pennsylvanian, and the Permian/Pennsylvanian boundary is difficult to place. Local uplift in some areas brought marine sedimentation to a close, and the boundary in such places is delineated at an unconformity where the overlying redbeds are markedly distinct from the Pennsylvanian sediments below. This relationship is seen in southwestern South Dakota and adjacent Wyoming.

In other areas of local uplift, the adjacent basins filled with redbed formations, such as the **Cutler Formation** of southwestern Colorado and the Four Corners area (where Utah, Colorado, New Mexico, and Arizona meet). The lithology is typically variable, with red sandstones and conglomerates together with mudstones. Because such sediments generally grade west and northward into limestones, the sea clearly lay in that direction. By Late Permian time, however, the sea was losing the battle, and for the remainder of the period, terrestrial redbeds predominated over large areas. Only in a narrow belt along the western side of the continent did marine conditions linger, and at the close of the Wolfcampian (earliest Permian) Stage, the Absaroka Sea made its last stand here (Figure 16.5). Restricted circulation of the shallow water led to the formation of gypsum and other evaporite salts.

Given the easterly source of the terrestrial redbeds, both the Cutler and Supai formations consist of red-colored silts, sands, and muds that were deposited in sluggish streams that flowed from the Ancestral Rockies and other uplifts. In many areas, dune sands were accumulating, and the Canyon de Chelly sandstone member of the Cutler Formation is a well-exposed example in the canyon of the same name. Further north, in Wyoming and Idaho, thick phosphate deposits of the famous Phosphoria Formation date from this time. They were laid down in a deeper-water, outer-shelf environment, and they pass westward into the volcanic island arc belt that marked the craton's western margin.

The Permian Basin Area of West Texas

Across the southern margin of the North American craton, and marking the line of collision with Gondwana, lay the **Ouachita-Marathon orogenic belt**—in Permian time, a range of mountains supplying sediment to a foredeep basin to the north. A **foredeep** is a downwarped trench adjacent to an island arc or orogenic belt. In the area that is now New Mexico and West Texas, the foredeep was apparently influenced by a series of deep-seated structures that

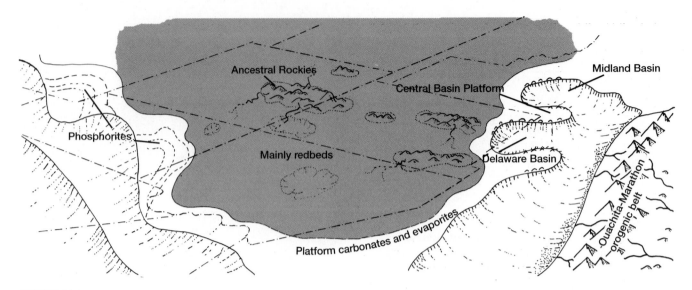

FIGURE 16.6

The regional setting of the Permian Basin area of West Texas.

trended northwest-southeast, probably related to the uplifts, mentioned earlier, that had controlled Permian sedimentary patterns across the craton to the north (Figure 16.6).

Permian sedimentation in large areas of the western and southwestern craton had occurred over carbonate platforms and also had been markedly influenced by intermittently active uplifts with various small basins between. Stratigraphic successions in such basins tend to be autonomous and of only local significance. Not surprisingly, correlation between them is far from easy, a problem made worse by the intermittent nature of the exposures in many separate fault blocks.

The situation is different in the West Texas area. Here, Permian sedimentation was again strongly influenced by structural elements, but a wealth of data is available from the thousands of boreholes drilled in the exploration for oil in this region, while countless seismic sections add further information. This so-called **Permian Basin** area has proven to be one of the most important oil- and gas-producing regions in North America. Figure 16.6 shows the regional and structural setting of the Permian Basin.

At the beginning of the Permian, the Permian Basin area was essentially a southward continuation of the broad carbonate-shelf area that lay to the north, and, in fact, it represented the shelf margin. Early in Wolfcampian (earliest Permian) time, downsagging in two major basinal areas—the Midland Basin on the east and the **Delaware Basin** on the west—separated by the **Central Basin uplift,** became increasingly evident and facies differences more marked. Fossiliferous bioclastic limestones are characteristic of the Wolfcampian of the shelf areas, whereas organically rich shales and dark limestones accumulated in the basins.

By Leonardian (mid-Permian) time, carbonate bank deposits began to form around the margin of the basins, and, in places, the presence of small reefs heralded the massive reef limestones that formed somewhat later. Guadalupian (late Middle Permian) sediments of the Permian Basin include some of the most spectacular reef limestones known anywhere, and this area has become a classic example of reef/basin facies relationships (Figure 16.7). By this time, the Midland Basin had ceased to be active, but the adjacent Delaware Basin continued to subside even more markedly. Eventually, the Midland Basin filled with sediment and became, in effect, part of the shallow-water carbonate platform.

The most prominent reef carbonates are seen in the so-called Goat Seep and overlying **Capitan** limestones, both of which are massive, richly fossiliferous formations. Particularly prominent fossils are the chief frame-building organisms—the sponges, algae, and bryozoans. Fusulinid foraminifera, brachiopods (particularly spiny productids), rugose corals, and echinoderms were also prolific reef inhabitants and contributed to the limestone mass.

There has been considerable argument as to the real nature of these Permian reefs. The presence of corals led early workers to assume that the Capitan and other reef limestones were formed in a manner directly analogous to the spectacular coralgal reefs of modern seas—the reefs in the Bahama Islands and the Great Barrier Reef of Australia, for example. The Permian reefs were, however, somewhat different. In the first place, corals, although present, were not frame builders, that role being filled largely by sponges and even in places by spiny brachiopods. On the other hand, the reefs undoubtedly formed considerable submarine topographic features because, on

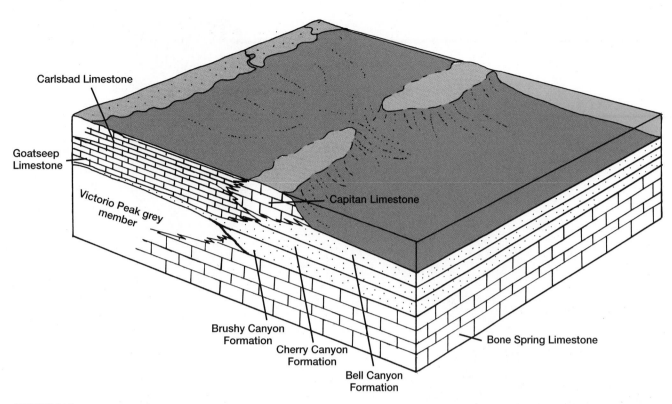

Carlsbad Limestone

Goatseep Limestone

Victorio Peak grey member

Capitan Limestone

Brushy Canyon Formation

Cherry Canyon Formation

Bell Canyon Formation

Bone Spring Limestone

FIGURE 16.7
Facies relationships of the Capitan and other reef limestones in the Delaware Basin, West Texas.

their steep basinal inward sides, reef talus deposits accumulated. For example, some of these can be seen forming the roof rock in parts of the Carlsbad Caverns in New Mexico. The reefs also undoubtedly restricted water circulation because, by Late Guadalupian (late Middle Permian) time, they had become so extensive on adjacent shelves that normal carbonates were giving way to dolostones, mapped as the San Andreas Formation, and these graded westward into evaporitic facies.

Inside the ring of reefs around the rim of the Permian Basin, equivalent basinal sediments are relatively thin and include limestones of the Delaware Mountain Group overlain by the Cherry Canyon (basinal equivalent of the reefal Goat Seep Limestone) and the Bell Canyon (equivalent in age to the Capitan Limestone). Both of these basinal formations seem to have been deposited under quiet water conditions. Although often referred to as a "starved basin" environment, some sands, derived from the shallow platforms above, apparently bypassed the surrounding reefs and were swept down into the basin.

The basinal sediments were typically rich in organic matter and have proven to be the source beds of the hydrocarbons that have migrated up into the reef masses and platform deposits around the basins. The same reef/basin facies association with relationships to hydrocarbons was described in Chapter 14 with regard to the Devonian reefs of western Canada.

Permian Basin sediments indicate that, by the close of the Guadalupian, changes were imminent. The growing importance of evaporites indicates increasing restriction of the shelf seas, while to the north and east, redbeds were encroaching, marking the sea's final withdrawal from the region. Only the continued subsidence of the Delaware Basin prevented the rapid disappearance of the entire Permian Basin beneath a flood of terrestrial sediments.

The thick evaporite succession mapped as the Castille, Salida, and Rustler formations marks the final drying up of the sea, but precise dating of when this happened is difficult because, naturally, the evaporites contain no fossils. Moreover, the first redbeds seen in the Dewey Lake Formation above are similarly unfossiliferous, and some workers consider them of earliest Triassic age. In any event, a period of emergence followed because the overlying Dockum Group is of Late Triassic age.

The Permian in Europe (Eastern Pangaea)

Eastward of the shallow shelf seas of the North American midcontinent region, a land area persisted that probably by now was of only moderate relief. What had once been the Old Red Sandstone Continent had been an emergent stable region for some 100 million years. Uplift associated with the Allegheny orogeny had now ceased, and the only sediments of Permian age still preserved are dominantly

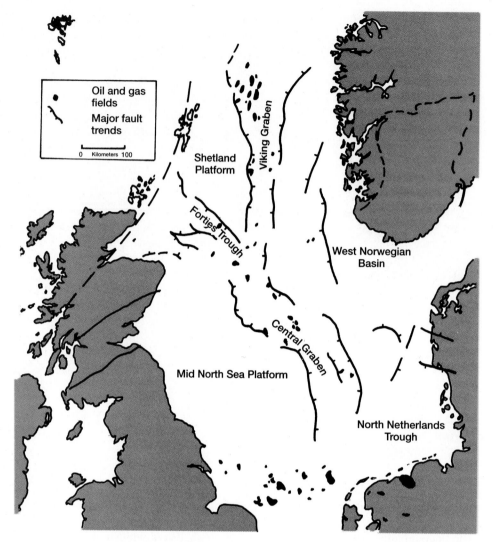

FIGURE 16.8
Sketch map of the North Sea Basin, showing the major structural trends that influenced Permian sedimentation. The dominant structural style was a horst-and-graben pattern, with sediments filling down-faulted basins.

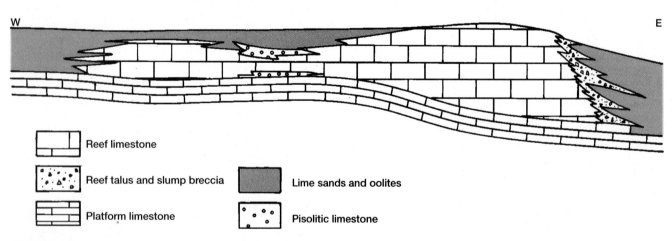

Reef limestone

Reef talus and slump breccia

Platform limestone

Lime sands and oolites

Pisolitic limestone

FIGURE 16.9
Diagrammatic cross section through reef margin limestones in eastern England on the western edge of the Zechstein Sea.

of alluvial origin. Named the Dunkard Group, they represent only the Wolfcampian (earliest Permian). Thereafter, the area was apparently undergoing erosion—at least, if any sediments did accumulate, they have long since gone. The general lack of fossils in the Dunkard Group has made age assignments difficult, and some geologists have suggested that the sediments may, in fact, be slightly older and date from the latest Carboniferous.

Further eastward, into the area of what is now western Europe, a record of Permian sedimentation again appears. Comparisons of the Permian succession of the North American area with that in Europe reveal some striking resemblances, but also important contrasts. Taken as a whole, the Permian System is particularly characterized by evaporites and redbeds, and in both North American and European successions, they figure prominently. When details of the structural setting and particularly of the timing of events are compared, however, the history of the two regions differs significantly.

Over much of western Europe, Permian rocks are typically only poorly fossiliferous. In England, the yellow sands that William Smith labeled the **New Red Sandstone** are pure, well-sorted sands with large-scale festoon bedding, indicating deposition as aeolian dunes in a desert environment. Their good porosity and permeability make them important aquifers in many areas in northern England. Evidently, the climate here in Permian time, just as further west in the North American area, was arid with prevailing winds, as indicated by dune bedding, blowing from the east. The European and North American regions were at approximately the same latitude and in the region of the trade winds. The Permian sands of northern England vary considerably in thickness and fill in irregularities in an ancient pre-Permian land surface.

The information gleaned from Permian outcrops in England and elsewhere in Europe represents only a small part of what is known about Permian history. The discovery of gas in the giant Groningen field of northern Holland in 1970 triggered active exploration for oil in the North Sea Basin. Since that time, the subsurface data from thousands of wells, together with a vast body of seismic data, have made the history of this whole region much more understandable (Figure 16.8).

Just as with the Paradox Basin, the Uncompahgre uplift, and other structures that had persisted since the Pennsylvanian in the midcontinent region of North America (see Figure 15.18), European sedimentary basins have, from time to time, been strongly influenced by intermittent movements. Many of the areas of typical Old Red Sandstone deposits, for example, had been laid down in so-called **cuvettes,** or intermontane basins that were largely fault-controlled. North American geologists refer to these as yoked basins. Just as in the Paradox and other North American basins, the Central Graben and other downfaulted blocks of the North Sea region received thick deposits of sediments derived from surrounding highland regions. In the subsurface of the North Sea, the Permian **Rothliegende Sandstone,** for example, is an important source of gas and is equivalent, in part, to the yellow sands of the New Red Sandstone of the Durham area of England.

At about the end of what in European stratigraphy is called the Kungurian Stage (approximately the Middle Guadalupian in the North American scheme), there was a marine invasion into the North Sea Basin area. It is marked in English successions by a thin black shale characterized by an abundance of ganoid (rhomboid-shaped and massive) fish scales (Figure 16.9). This so-called Marl Slate has been correlated with the Kupferschiefe, a copper-rich shale in many German Permian successions. Bottom conditions in this sea were apparently anoxic, and the environment has been compared with that on the floor of the modern Black Sea. Above the slate in the English succession is the Magnesian Limestone, in which are fossil reefs that evidently lay around the western margin of an arm of the sea that was invading from the north. In Thuringia, Germany, reef talus deposits mark the southern shore of the sea, and steeply dipping limestone conglomerates in other places suggest that the reefs faced onto a deep marine basin to the east.

This marine invasion of the North Sea Basin was apparently quite rapid, and the so-called **Zechstein Sea** eventually covered some million square kilometers over what is now the North Sea and much of Germany (Figure 16.10a). Water circulation in the sea was sluggish, and the sea may have been tideless. In any event, the most characteristic deposits of this sea were evaporites. As the salinity increased, the reef-forming organisms at the margins were eventually killed off, just as they were in the Capitan Reef of West Texas.

Soon after the initial flooding, the sea receded, but there were three further marine advances before the close of the Permian. Labeled the First, Second, Third, and Fourth Evaporites, each advance was represented by a distinct cyclothem (Figure 16.10b). Given the presence of a distant ice cap at the Permian South Pole, it is tempting to see these cycles as glacio-eustatically controlled. On the other hand, in the latest Guadalupian and the Ochoan (latest Permian) of the North American Permian, although marine advances and retreats in the shelf areas were ongoing, no cycles to match those of the Zechstein Sea have, as yet, been identified. As in all cases of relative sea-level change, the interplay of eustatic mechanisms and regional crustal movements is a problem. If the Zechstein cycles were simply a response to intermittent basin downwarping, then clearly, there would be no corresponding North American cycles. By the same token, however, crustal warping in North America may have obscured eustatic cycles that might otherwise have left a record.

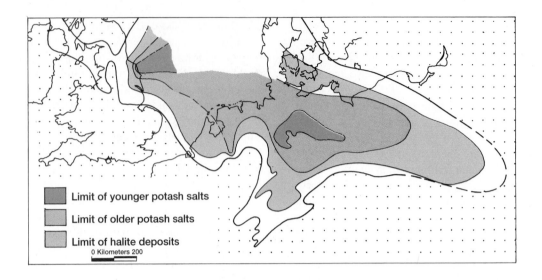

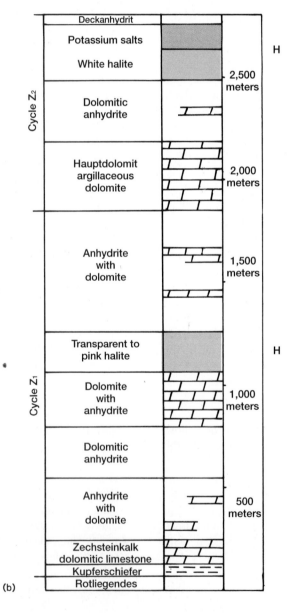

(b)

FIGURE 16.10

(a) Distribution of evaporite salts in the Zechstein Sea.
(b) Stratigraphic succession during two of the four major

evaporite cycles recorded in the Zechstein Permian.

The Permian in Russia

Still further to the east—into Russia and approaching the eastern margin of the craton—Permian successions are characterized by normal marine sediments, many of them fossiliferous limestones. It was here, in the district of Perm, that Roderick Murchison established the Permian System. The sediments in this area were laid down in a subsiding marginal basin that was shortly thereafter involved in an orogenic episode that marked the collision of the Siberian craton and resulted in the Ural mountain chain.

This added yet another piece to the growing Pangaea supercontinent, and only the craton that is now part of China remained unattached. Although the exact position of the Chinese block and its direction of movement are as yet poorly understood, the distinctive flora of the region is a clear indication that an ocean still separated it from the rest of the Pangaea landmass.

Permian Ice Age

The Gondwana ice cap that had first appeared in Late Devonian time in South America persisted until nearly the close of the Permian, with the ice center moving progressively across the African continent into Australia. Here, glacial conditions reached their climax in the Early Permian and persisted into the Late Permian. Scattered tillites also indicate that glacial conditions continued in South America until Middle Permian time. Glacial advances and retreats inevitably caused glacio-eustatic sea-level swings, as evidenced by the cyclothemic successions of Permo-Carboniferous age in many parts of the world. In Victoria, Australia, as many as 51 separate glacial tillites have been counted, and assuming a Milankovitch-Köppen mechanism with a 100,000-year cycle, glacial conditions must have persisted in that region for over 5 million years.

In the Northern Hemisphere, Permian successions that were formed in high latitudes also show evidence of glacial conditions. No tillites have been found, but there are numerous reports of conglomerates with dropstones delivered by icebergs. This interpretation indicates the presence of valley glaciers or even a small ice cap somewhere.

A characteristic feature of many Gondwana glacial successions is an alternation of tillites and coals. This has suggested to some geologists that, during the Gondwana glaciation, temperatures fluctuated more widely than they did during the Late Cenozoic glaciation. Coals are, of course, common in successions of Permo-Carboniferous age formed in tropical regions, but in higher-latitude Gondwana successions, the coals formed from trees of temperate species, such as *Glossopteris* and *Gangamopteris*. Considerable forests of these trees apparently grew close to the ice margin, and annual growth rings seen in fossil tree trunks indicate a marked seasonal regime.

Life in the Permian

Permian Invertebrate Faunas

The Permian was a time of widespread continental emergence, and extensive shallow seas were in short supply. Particularly lacking were clear-water carbonate platforms. In North America, for example, the shallow shelves were often offshore from large drainage systems, and the presence of fine, suspended sediment had a pronounced influence on the marine biota and resulted in distinctive Late Paleozoic faunas.

Corals, for example, were still present but not nearly as important as before. Tabulate corals were clearly in a marked decline and are missing or few in numbers in many Permian sections. The rugose corals also were past their prime and were no longer important reef builders. The bryozoans became important reefal elements, and colonies of the lacy fenestrellids are the dominant forms in many Permian reef limestones (Figure 16.11a). Prominent also were the spiny productid brachiopods.

As discussed in Chapter 15, the **fusulinid foraminifera** appeared early in the Pennsylvanian and underwent a marked evolutionary radiation that continued right through the Permian (Figure 16.11b). The vast majority of foraminifera are microfossils, the calcareous skeletons, or tests, as they are called, measured in microns. The fusulinids were unusual in being "giant" microfossils. Many were about the size of rice grains, and some species even reached 3 centimeters or more in length (Figure 16.11b). The spindle-shaped test of aragonite was surrounded in life by a layer of cytoplasm, and the animal floated in the surface water as part of the zooplankton.

Fusulinids occurred in vast numbers in Late Paleozoic seas and came to have a worldwide distribution. Because they evolved rapidly, each particular species had a relatively short life span, so that, as a group, the fusulinids are remarkably good stratigraphic zone fossils. They also are readily identified in drill cuttings and can be used to correlate subsurface successions. Like so many groups, the fusulinids became extinct at the end of the Permian.

Permian Vertebrate Faunas

Much of what is known about Permian vertebrate faunas is based on fossils from north central Texas, where the succession ranges in age from the earliest Permian (Wolfcampian) to the early part of the Late Permian (Guadalupian). The sediments are mostly redbeds laid down across an extensive deltaic floodplain where southwardly flowing rivers reached the coast. The climate was warm and humid, with evenly distributed rainfall. The Lower Permian sediments indicate the presence of numerous lakes and swamps, and an important element in the fauna likely was at least semiaquatic in its life mode.

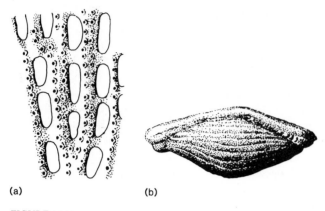

FIGURE 16.11
(a) Permian bryozoan *Fenestrellina*. (b) Fusulinid foraminiferan *Triticites*.

By the opening of Permian time, terrestrial **tetrapods** (vertebrates with four legs) were already important and widespread. As early as the Middle Pennsylvanian, the synapsid pelycosaurs, among the oldest known reptiles, dominated the terrestrial faunas. In the Pennsylvanian, more than 50 percent of known reptile genera were pelycosaurs, and by the Early Permian, this figure had risen to 70 percent.

Ophiacodon, a fish-eating pelycosaur, probably spent much of its time in the water (Figure 16.12a). Semiaquatic amphibians such as *Trimerorhachus* and *Archera* were also abundant. *Dimetrodon,* a carnivorous pelycosaur, also probably ate fish as part of its diet (Figure 16.12b). Among numerous fish fossils in the Texas sediments was the freshwater shark *Xenocanthus* and the lungfish *Sagenodus.*

Higher in the succession are indications that the climate was becoming drier, probably with a markedly seasonal rainfall pattern. Significantly, the lungfish *Crathorhiza,* capable of aestivating in the mud of dried-up lake bottoms, is a fairly common fossil. The balance among the tetrapods changed in this drier environment. The fish-eating pelycosaur *Ophiacodon* became extinct, as also did *Edaphosaurus,* a large, herbivorous pelycosaur, which suggests that it was largely a swamp dweller. Only *Dimetrodon,* the carnivorous pelycosaur, survived, presumably because it was less dependent on water.

Essentially, the same faunal association has been found at widely scattered locations in other parts of North America and also in Europe, suggesting that the faunas occurred throughout the Permian tropical zone. The richness of the Texas reptilian fauna is due to the dominance of largely lowland forms. Mixed in, however, are occasional fossils derived from a different fauna. Found typically in nodules and fissure infillings, the fossils were preserved under conditions very different from those of the contemporaneous lowland forms, which suggests that they represent the rare preservation of material derived from a different ecosystem, most likely drier uplands far distant from the coastal deltas. Significantly, in Upper Permian sediments, these drier-climate/upland forms become more abundant, and clearly, they simply replaced the lowland forms as the climate became drier.

We now look more closely at the two divisions of synapsids that were common during the Permian: the pelycosaurs and the therapsids.

Pelycosaurs

Perhaps the most characteristic of Permian reptiles were the **pelycosaurs,** the earliest and most primitive of the mammal-like reptiles. The ancestral stock from which they arose is obscure but was presumably the same eureptilian group of Early Pennsylvanian age that also gave rise to the captorhinomorphs.

During the Permian, the pelycosaurs underwent a considerable evolutionary radiation and came to fill many ecologic niches. Some pelycosaurs were small insectivores, others grew to a considerable size and included herbivores, fish-eating species, and carnivores. Of particular interest is the so-called fin-backed pelycosaur, *Dimetrodon* (see Figure 16.12b), a large carnivorous form with greatly elongated neural spines along the vertebrae that projected up from the animal's back in a sort of comblike arrangement. A membrane is assumed to have connected the spines to form a large sail-like fin.

Like all typical reptiles, the pelycosaurs were **ectothermic**—that is, they could maintain a more or less constant body temperature only by absorption of heat from the ambient environment or by radiating it into the surrounding air. The large dorsal fin most likely served as a heat-regulating mechanism. When turned to face the sun, its large surface area probably was extremely efficient in raising the animal's temperature. With its edge to the sun, the fin likely could effectively radiate surplus heat. That pelycosaurs were ectothermic is also indicated in a separate line of evidence seen in serial-growth, ringlike structures in the bone tissue, a feature characteristic of modern ectothermic reptiles.

Interestingly, the dimetrodonts were not the only fin-backed pelycosaurs. The modification also arose independently in one of the herbivorous groups represented by edaphosaurs, some of which grew to 3 meters in length. A distinctive feature of the neural spines in this group was the presence of small cross "spars," or tubercles, whose function, if any, is unknown (Figure 16.13).

Therapsids

The other division of synapsid reptiles belongs to the order Therapsida, a group clearly derived from a pelycosaur ancestry. **Therapsids** first appeared quite abruptly in the lower part of the Guadalupian (early Late Permian), where they are associated with the later pelycosaurs, such as *Dimetrodon,* together with the dryland/upland elements already mentioned. They are neither common nor very well preserved, but fortunately, in sediments of about the same

(a)

(b)

FIGURE 16.12
Permian reptiles. (a) *Ophiacodon.* (b) *Dimetrodon.*

age in Russia, a well-preserved and abundant fauna of similar forms has been described, which has helped to clarify the therapsid story. Therapsid fossils also are found in higher and younger horizons than those containing the last remnants of the North American fauna, but they finally peter out with the incoming of evaporites and unfossiliferous desert sediments.

Reptilian Evolutionary Pathways

As described in Chapter 15, the first reptiles had appeared by the close of the Pennsylvanian. Although the amphibians remained an important element in the vertebrate faunas through the Permian, they faced competition from the many and varied reptilian forms that appeared during a significant Permian evolutionary radiation.

The fossil record of the earliest reptiles begins in rocks of Late Pennsylvanian age, but the state of preservation is not good. By Permian time, the fossil record is greatly

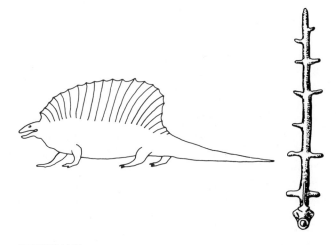

FIGURE 16.13
Neural spine of *Edaphosaurus.*

(a)

(b)

(c)

FIGURE 16.14

(a) *Seymouria.* (b) *Eryops.* (c) *Diadectes.*

improved, and a variety of forms is found, some of which are undoubtedly reptiles, and others that exhibit both reptilian and amphibian features and whose exact status is in doubt. One of the best-documented forms that exhibits both primitive (amphibian) and advanced (reptilian) features is *Seymouria* (Figure 16.14a). Originally described as a primitive reptile, *Seymouria* is now generally acknowledged as an amphibian. As seen in Figure 16.14a, *Seymouria* differed little in its gross features from *Eryops* (Figure 16.14b), a large amphibian that was *Seymouria's* Permian contemporary.

As discussed in Chapter 15, the appearance of the amniotic egg marked the most significant step to the reptilian level. The first direct evidence in the form of fossil eggs was found in Permian rocks, although no eggs have been associated directly with the skeletal remains of any particular species.

Temporal Fenestrae

Features diagnostic of the reptilian level of organization are revealed in details of the skeleton, particularly the skull. The size and relative positions of the various bones in the skull form the basis for most classifications; of especial interest are the various openings, or **temporal fenestrae,** in the skull.

As described in Box 15.2, the temporal fenestrae provide a widely used, relatively simple way of classifying the reptiles. The lack of any temporal fenestrae, as seen in the subclass Anapsida, is considered the most primitive state; the living turtles belong in this group. The mesosaurs, a group of marine reptiles, are, on the basis of admittedly ambiguous evidence, also placed in this subclass. Another order, the Cotylosauria, are also anapsids, but whether cotylosaurs are really reptiles is now doubtful, as described in the next section.

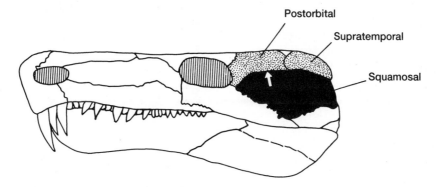

FIGURE 16.15
Skull of *Limnoscoelis*. Arrow indicates the suture between postorbital/supratemporal bones and the squamosal bone.

The generally accepted purpose of the temporal fenestrae has been to accommodate the bulging jaw muscles as body and particularly skull size increased and elaborate jaws evolved, particularly in response to more specialized dietary trends. Recent work has suggested, however, that the real significance of the fenestrae lies in the opportunity for an increased area for muscle attachment.

The size, shape, and position of the temporal fenestrae are all closely studied in the tracing of evolutionary lineages in the reptiles. Some interesting (and sometimes confusing) relationships emerge. The synapsid reptiles, according to a recent study, arose from the limnoscelids, a group that had previously been assigned to the captorhinomorph reptiles but is now considered amphibious. This suggested link with an amphibian ancestor is based on the open suture, or line of weakness, between the supratemporal and postorbital bones on the one side and the squamosal on the other. The synapsid type of temporal opening was, according to this hypothesis, simply derived by enlargement of this "slot."

If this interpretation is correct, it provides a direct link to even more remote ancestors. According to A. L. Panchen, the suture is a remnant of the special kind of hinge in the crossopterygian jaw and is still seen in several living amphibians.

The Reptile That Never Was

The transition from the amphibian to the reptilian level of organization has been a subject of considerable controversy, particularly because there is only skeletal material to work with. Depending upon which anatomical features are selected, there is inevitably considerable overlap, and an advanced amphibian to one worker is considered a primitive reptile by another. One of the strangest stories in this rather murky corner of tetrapod taxonomy concerns the **cotylosaurs.**

The order Cotylosauria, erected in 1883 by Edward Drinker Cope, is based on the genus *Diadectes* (Figure 16.14c). Cope's interpretation of the occipital region showed two cup-shaped condyles, and the name *cotylosaur* was derived from the Greek word *kotyle,* meaning a "cup-shaped hollow." Cope later realized that his interpretation of admittedly poorly preserved material was incorrect, and he published a new description. In the meantime, however, the Greek origin of the name led to further confusion because *kotyle* was also taken to mean "plant" or "stem," and so the term *stem reptile* was coined. The popular fallacy then arose that the cotylosaurs were the "stem reptiles" from which all other reptiles arose. This inevitably led to the broadest definition of the so-called Cotylosauria, and the order became a sort of taxonomic garbage can containing many diverse groups.

Despite these misconceptions, vertebrate paleontologist Alfred Romer later decided that *Diadectes,* the type genus of Cotylosauria, was not really a reptile at all and instead was actually an amphibian, specifically in subclass Anthracosauria. Taxonomists were then faced with two alternatives: either to (1) continue to recognize the cotylosaurs as a class of reptiles but, rather awkwardly without their type genus, or (2) simply consider the cotylosaurs as an amphibian rather than reptilian order. The second of these two options is now widely followed, although many textbooks still refer to the cotylosaurs as "stem reptiles."

The relationship of the cotylosaurs to the reptiles can be described in terms of a parallel line of descent from a batrachosaur amphibian ancestor (the group to which *Seymouria,* mentioned earlier, belongs). Along the other line of descent from the batrachosaurs are the captorhinomorphs, animals that have close similarities to the cotylosaurs and indeed were once included with them but that are unquestionably reptiles.

This whole controversy on amphibian/reptile relationships only arose because drawing the line is admittedly difficult and because many cotylosaurs possess markedly reptilian features. *Limnoscelis,* for example, looks very "reptilian" (Figure 16.15). This suggests that the reptilian level of development may have been reached on a broad front with several amphibian ancestral lineages rather than one. The question of where in the fossil record the boundary between amphibians and reptiles lies may never be resolved.

The End-Permian Extinction

The **end-Permian extinction** saw the disappearance of so many groups of organisms that it undoubtedly ranks as the biggest mass extinction of all time. Small wonder that it was selected by nineteenth-century geologists to mark the era boundary between the Paleozoic and the Mesozoic.

A True Mass Extinction?

What actually happened at the close of the Permian? The answer is, unfortunately, still shrouded in mystery and may never be known. There is even considerable debate as to whether the end-Permian event was a true mass extinction. To some workers, there was no sudden catastrophe. The extinctions of the various groups were real enough, but, it is argued, they were spread over several million years, which hardly qualifies as "sudden," even within the context of geologic time.

As in earlier chapters, the "circular thinking" factor must be taken into consideration. If the end of a geologic period is defined on the basis of extinction of certain species, given the fragmentary nature of the fossil record, the species concerned obviously appear to become extinct at the same time.

The Permian/Triassic stratigraphic boundary is also a problem. Because the continents were widely emergent with few shelf seas, stratigraphic successions within which the Permian/Triassic boundary is recorded in marine strata are extremely rare. In North America, as in most other Permian terrains, the boundary is seen either as a stratigraphic discontinuity or else it apparently occurs within redbeds or desert sands containing no fossils. Only along the margin of the Tethys Ocean, in places like Indonesia and the Salt Range of western Pakistan, are more or less continuous Permo-Triassic marine successions found. Even in some of these key sections, however, detailed paleontologic studies have shown that the biostratigraphic succession has gaps.

The Victims

Putting aside the controversy regarding the suddenness of the end-Permian extinction, there is no question that, across a wide spectrum of ecologic niches, many animals and plants did not survive into the Triassic. Among the invertebrates were many groups that had been important elements of marine faunas throughout the entire Paleozoic: The trilobites; the rugose and tabulate corals; the orthid and productid brachiopods; the cryptostome, fenestrate, trepostome, and cystoporate bryozoa; the inadunate, flexible, and camerate crinoids; the blastoids; the eurypterids; and the fusulinid foraminifera all disappeared forever. In addition, other groups suffered marked reductions. For example, eight families of ostracods disappeared, as did 10 superfamilies of ammonoids, one whole suborder of echinoids, five families of sharks, and eight families of bony fishes.

Although all these groups were gone by the end of the Permian, they did not by any means all disappear at once. Some of the groups began to drop out of the picture during Late Permian time. In some cases—as, for example, with the trilobites—numbers had been declining since the Pennsylvanian and earlier, so that, in their case, as certainly was the case with groups such as the tabulate corals, their days were apparently numbered and whatever happened at the close of the Permian had, possibly, a "last straw" effect.

Possible Causes of the End-Permian Extinction

Mass extinctions seem to be an integral part of the story of life on this planet, a fact that must, of course, be considered when discussing causes. The simplest and what could be called the "uniformitarian" approach is to assume that these periodic disasters were all caused by the same thing. Since the revelations of the 1980s on the terminal Cretaceous event, everyone has naturally been looking for giant meteorite impacts as the cause of all mass extinctions, and, of course, such extraterrestrial happenings may be responsible. Unfortunately, however, the evidence, at least as gathered to date, is far from convincing. Despite a diligent search, no key boundary horizon containing a geochemical signal has yet been found; neither for that matter has there been any sedimentary—that is, non-paleontological—evidence, either chemical or physical, of any kind of unusual happening. The Cretaceous/Paleocene event is much closer to us in time and is recorded in many stratigraphic sections; thus, the lack of similar evidence for the Permian/Triassic event may not be all that surprising.

Assessments of possible causes of a mass extinction, should, perhaps, look not so much at the groups that disappeared but rather at those that survived. In the end-Permian extinction, the terrestrial animals, with the notable exception of the therapsid reptiles, which suffered a decline of 20 or so families, came through the crisis quite well. The terrestrial floras similarly show a general continuity across the boundary, although, again, there was an exception with the disappearance of the cordaites. Certain of the large tree-size forms, such as sphenopsids and lycopsids, survived, but only as nonarboral, shrublike plants.

Whatever happened at the end of the Permian, its effect apparently was felt mainly in the marine environment. Ocean factors might have included changes in (1) ocean chemistry, (2) ocean temperature, and (3) physical character (depth, shape, and size) of the ocean basins. With regard to the first, the great abundance of evaporites in Permian successions may have led to an impoverishment of salts in the ocean so that, in effect, the ocean became "fresher." Calculations of the volumes of salts locked up in Permian rocks, however, show that they fall far short of the quantities required. A lack of oxygen has also been suggested as a cause, although there is no direct evidence that anoxic bottom environments were more common than usual in the Permian. With regard to possible ocean temperature changes, fluctuations in world climate would be involved, and here there is some supporting evidence. Changes in Permian floral distributions suggest that the close of the Permian saw a global warming trend. This is supported by indications that cooler-water marine species suffered more than did those in warmer latitudes.

While little or no direct evidence supports either variation in ocean chemistry or temperature, some obvious conclusions can be drawn regarding Permian continental configuration. The vast shelf seas that had seen such prolific marine faunas during the Paleozoic had largely disappeared, and this was an important factor. Shrinking shelf areas would increase enormously the environmental stress, and all but the most adaptable forms would likely disappear. Also a Pangaea phase of continental accretion would markedly reduce the barriers to the dispersal of benthic organisms and this, in turn, would reduce the potential for allopatric speciation, with a consequent lowering of organic diversity.

Summary

At the beginning of the Permian, Laurussia collided with Gondwana to form a supercontinent. Only a small cratonic block that is now part of China remained unattached. By the close of the Permian, this had also collided so that, apart from a few microcontinental pieces, all the main continental masses had been brought together into Pangaea.

Other features of the Permian include a major ice age and the fact that the continents were largely emergent, partly due to a glacio-eustatic sea-level drop and partly because of thermal expansion in the mantle beneath the supercontinent crust. Also, the Permian closed with a mass extinction event, the likes of which the earth had not experienced before.

Permian-style stratigraphy seems to go with Pangaea-style continental distribution although confirmation of this model is difficult. The sheer size of Pangaea also means that the Permian world climatic pattern was also inevitable.

Both the North American and European portions of Pangaea lay in the tropics, and the climate was, for the most part, warm and dry. Terrestrial sediments were deposited over large areas in downfaulted basins, with arkoses and sands derived from the adjacent highlands. In many places, the remains of shallow seas on the continents were marked by extensive evaporite deposits, but by the close of the period, much of the area that is now North America had become dry land.

Typical of sedimentary patterns over large areas are the Cutler and Supai formations seen, for example, in the Four Corners area. They are typically red-colored silts, sands, and muds carried by streams westward from highlands called the Ancestral Rocky Mountains. To the north and west, pushing onto the continental shelf, these formations grade into phosphate deposits mapped as the Phosphoria Formation.

In the continental interior, the sea took its last stand in the panhandle region of West Texas. Here, a series of subsiding basins, including the Midland Basin on the east and the Delaware Basin on the west, were separated by the Central Basin uplift. As the basins subsided, extensive reef limestones formed around their margins. The best known of these reefs is the Capitan Reef. Because of their good porosity and their relationship to the organically rich sediments laid down in the basins, the Capitan and other reef limestones are important oil and gas reservoirs.

Comparisons of the Permian succession of the North American area with that in Europe reveal some striking resemblances, such as evaporites and redbeds, but details of the structural setting and the timing of events differ significantly. As in North America, Permian rocks are also important sources of gas and oil in Europe, and sands such as the Rothliegende Sandstone are found in faulted basins in the subsurface of the North Sea region. Permian successions in the Urals region of Russia are characterized by normal marine sediments, and the Permian type region, as defined by Murchison, is located here.

During the Permian, an ice sheet at the South Pole covered large areas of Gondwana. As the plates moved across the pole, the ice cap moved progressively from Africa into Australia, where glacial conditions reached a climax in the Early Permian.

Probably due to the shrinking of shallow shelf seas as the continents became increasingly emergent, there were some important changes among marine invertebrate faunas during the Permian. The rugose and tabulate corals were declining markedly, and their place as reef builders was taken by bryozoans, sponges, and even spiny productid brachiopods, particularly characteristic of the Permian.

The fusulinid foraminifera underwent a pronounced evolutionary radiation during the Permian and are important zone fossils in sorting out Permian biostratigraphy.

Permian tetrapod faunas were at first dominated by the synapsid pelycosaurs that had been so important in Pennsylvanian time. Among the most typical of the pelycosaurs was *Dimetrodon*, the fin-backed reptile. Associated with the pelycosaurs were the therapsids.

During the Permian, both amphibians and reptiles were important elements in tetrapod faunas, and from the fossils it is often difficult to tell whether the animals produced amniotic eggs and were reptiles or whether they were advanced, reptilian-looking amphibians. The cotylosaurs, for example, were long considered reptiles, and because they were thought to be ancestral to later reptilian lineages, were incorrectly termed "stem reptiles." They now are considered advanced amphibians rather than reptiles.

The temporal fenestrae in the skull have provided a relatively simple way of classifying the reptiles. The Permian closed with a mass extinction event generally considered the most disastrous in all geologic history with, according to some paleontologists, 90 percent of animal species becoming extinct. The cause of the mass extinction is unknown, although many models have been proposed. One of the problems in seeking a cause is that, because of the general emergence of the continents during Permo-Triassic time, few places have a continuous succession of sediments that might record the boundary event. Where studies have been made, there are, apparently, no indications of a giant meteorite impact or other catastrophic event. There is some suggestion of a warming trend at the close of the Permian, but whether this had anything to do with the extinction is unknown. The unusually emergent continents and the lack of shelf seas may have caused enough environmental stress to result in the extinctions and currently are the most likely explanations.

Questions

1. Give some account of how the Permian System was first established and named.
2. How can many features of Permian paleogeography and geology be explained in terms of the Worsley, Nance, and Moody cycle?
3. Describe the major features of the paleogeography of the Permian world.
4. Compare and contrast the major features of Permian successions in North America and those in Europe.
5. Many of the Permian successions of western North America are of nonmarine type. Discuss the general character of such sediments and their local tectonic setting.
6. Describe briefly the history and setting of the Permian Basin of West Texas.
7. A major ice age occurred during the Permo-Carboniferous. Describe the evidence for it in various locations. Account for the fact that the time of maximum glaciation varies from place to place.
8. How did Permian marine invertebrate faunas differ from those of the preceding Mississippian/Pennsylvanian faunas?
9. Describe the pelycosaurs, and make a rough sketch of a typical pelycosaur.
10. Discuss the significance of the genus *Seymouria*.
11. Describe the problems associated with the taxonomy of the cotylosaurs, the so-called "stem reptiles."
12. What happened at the close of the Permian? Describe why the Permian/Triassic boundary is also the Paleozoic/Mesozoic boundary.
13. What explanation is there for the shortage of good stratigraphic successions that straddle the Permian/Triassic boundary?
14. Describe the magnitude of the end-Permian mass extinction event.
15. What are some of the mechanisms proposed to explain the mass extinction event at the close of the Permian?

Further Reading

Hutton, D. H. W., and D. J. Sanderson, eds. 1984. *Variscan tectonics of the North Atlantic region.* Geological Society of London Publication. Oxford, England: Blackwell.

Larwood, G. P., ed. 1988. *Extinction and survival in the fossil record.* Special volume no. 34. Oxford, England: Systematics Association.

Nitecki, M. H., ed. 1984. *Extinctions,* Chicago: University of Chicago Press.

Thomas, B. A., and R. A. Spicer. *The evolution and paleobiology of land plants.* London: Groom Helm.

West Texas Geological Society. 1975. *Permian exploration, boundaries and stratigraphy.* Publication no. 75–65. West Texas Geological Survey/S.E.P.M. Midland, Texas.

17

THE TRIASSIC AND JURASSIC

Introduction

The Triassic and Jurassic periods are a natural pair to look at together in this one chapter because there is an essential continuity from Triassic up into Jurassic sedimentary successions in most places. In addition, during this interval, Pangaea finally became fully assembled and then began to break apart again (Figure 17.1). The worldwide distribution of Triassic tetrapods shows that only during that period were all the land areas connected. Even before the close of Triassic time, however, Pangaea began to rift apart. No actual separation took place until the Jurassic, but many Late Triassic terrestrial successions accumulated in down-faulted rift basins, some of which were later to widen and become full-fledged oceans (Figure 17.2). In terms of major global cycles, the Triassic and Jurassic marked the end of one Worsley, Nance, and Moody cycle and the beginning of another—the one, in fact, in which we now find ourselves, with the continental masses still dispersing.

The Triassic

The Triassic System was established in 1834 by Fredrich A. von Alberti, based upon the marked threefold formations of sediments in Germany: the Bunter, Muschelkalk, and Keuper. The Bunter and Keuper are rather similar nonmarine, redbed successions, whereas the Muschelkalk (literally, mussel limestone) is a distinctive marine unit sandwiched in the middle.

The Bunter and Keuper redbeds are far more extensive than the Muschelkalk and, when seen in the context of Triassic successions on a global scale, are unquestionably typical of the Triassic. The color of the redbeds is due to the presence of the mineral hematite, an iron oxide. Even a small amount of this mineral imparts a strong color to rocks, and shales, being made up of clay minerals, are especially susceptible (see Box 17.1). Even quartz sand grains acquire a coating of hematite staining when they are immersed in iron-rich groundwater in the zone of weathering. The depositional environment of redbeds was typically a terrestrial one, with many of the sediments laid down in playa lakes, streams, deltas, and mud flats in a semiarid to monsoonal, warm to hot climate. They are often associated with evaporite sediments.

During the Triassic, Pangaea stood at its highest elevation. The ice caps of the Gondwana region were gone, and over large areas of the world, the climate was warm. In general, this was a continuation of conditions that had existed in the Late Permian, and with the withdrawal of the sea from shelf areas, few localities had continuous marine sediment accumulation from Permian into Triassic time. In terrestrial successions, the Permian/Triassic boundary is generally difficult to find because the sediments are typically unfossiliferous.

The Triassic in Western North America

The Moenkopi Formation

Over large portions of Nevada, Utah, Arizona, and New Mexico—a vast area of impressive scenery, semiarid climate, and an abundance of rock exposures—the most striking feature of the landscape is the color of the rocks. Everywhere is an abundance of redbeds. Sandstones, conglomerates, siltstones, and shales have colors ranging from pale pinks and terra cotta to deep reds and purples. In many areas, such sediments are mapped as the **Moenkopi Formation,** which ranges in age from Early into Middle Triassic. At many horizons are beds with dessication cracks, raindrop impressions, and the casts of salt crystals. Such features, together with the all-pervading red coloration, all point to deposition on shallow-water deltaic mud flats or in playa lakes periodically exposed to the air. The tracks of tetrapods, both amphibian and reptile, are not uncommon.

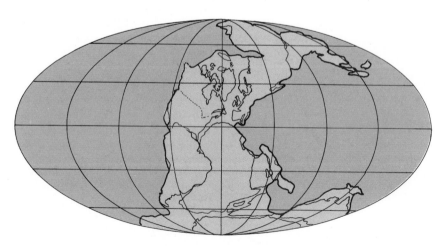

FIGURE 17.1
World paleogeography in the Triassic.

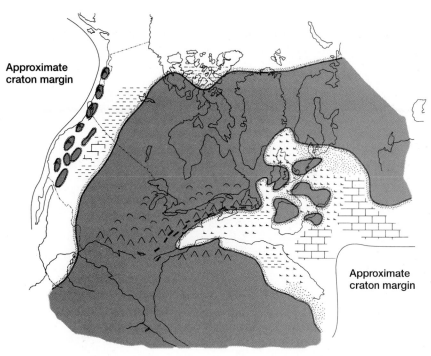

FIGURE 17.2

Paleogeography of Laurussia in the Triassic.

BOX 17.1

Riddle of the Redbeds

In successions of many different ages are clastic sediments stained to a deep brick red, terra cotta, or even purple color by the presence of the mineral hematite (Fe_2O_3). Such sediments are generally referred to as redbeds and seem to be almost entirely of nonmarine origin.

In modern terrestrial settings, red clastic materials are commonly found in the red soils typical of tropical regions. Such so-called lateritic soils are today distributed in a belt roughly within 30° north and south of the equator. Climate appears to strongly influence the formation of laterites, and optimum conditions seem to be a monsoonal climate with a marked alternation of wet and dry seasons.

This view of modern red coloration of sediment has strongly influenced the broader interpretation of ancient redbeds. On the whole, the geological settings of most redbed successions, if not unequivocally corroborating such a climatic interpreta-tion, do not indicate anything markedly to the contrary.

Many questions about redbeds remain, however, and, for example, considerable controversy still exists regarding how the red color gets into the sediment in the first place. The numerous suggested models fall into two or three broad categories.

One model suggests that the hematite was formed in lateritic soils under moist tropical conditions in which ferrous iron derived from the weathering of such iron-rich minerals as hornblende (average of 15 percent iron oxide), biotite (22 percent), chlorite (21 percent), limonite (46 percent), and magnetite (95 percent) was oxidized and in a ferric state was washed down into lowland situations and redeposited in its present state.

In an alternative model, the hematite formed only after deposition and originated by alteration of iron transported to the site of deposition in a ferrous state. In this case, the chemical model points to derivation of the iron from oxidation of iron-rich minerals in a hot, arid rather than humid climate. In other words, the sediment was originally laid down as nonred alluvial sediment, and the oxidation to the red ferric state occurred late in the diagenetic process.

A third model—which is, in effect, a blend of the other two—suggests a moist, warm climate in which the hematite is the product of an aging of brown and yellow hydrated ferric oxides (limonite) in a moist, tropical climate. Some geologists believe that this process marked the end stage of an in situ alteration of iron-rich mineral grains that were part of the original sediment. Others argue that a soil-forming stage is necessary and that transportation of the iron to its present site was in the form of soil residues rather than original fresh mineral grains.

Again, as in many other geological situations, the evidence is unequivocal, and no one model stands out from the other. Perhaps, as is often the case, all of them may be correct, depending upon site-specific factors.

The Moenkopi rests unconformably on Permian beds that in many places are represented by the Kaibab Limestone laid down in the final vestiges of the Absaroka Sea. No Permian-Triassic transition beds have been found, and as the Permian passed into the Triassic, this region probably was an emergent land undergoing erosion. A time traveler to this region would likely have seen far to the south the peaks of the mountain range that marked the collision suture of Laurussia and Gondwana. Running from the Marathon region of Texas, through the Ouachita area and then eastward into what is now the Hercynian (Variscan) fold belt of southern Europe, this mountain range was undoubtedly the main continental divide of Pangaea (Figure 17.3).

The bulk of Moenkopi sediments were transported by streams in a westerly and northwesterly direction from an extensive area of low relief. In the midcontinent region, the streams were sluggish as they flowed across a broad plain, and from their lithology, reconstruction on a local scale of the depositional environment is not difficult. Fossil remains add a further dimension. Large amphibians and reptiles browsed and wallowed in the streams and delta distributaries. Preying on these herbivores were numerous carnivores, and both the hunters and the hunted left their tracks in the soft mud.

To the west and northwest, the Moenkopi passes into marine strata, mapped in Montana and Wyoming as the Chugwater and in northern Utah as the Dinwoody and Woodside formations (Figure 17.4). Above the Woodside in Utah is the Thaynes Limestone, with ammonites that date it as Early to Middle Triassic.

During most of Middle Triassic time, western North America was emergent, and there is no sedimentary record; instead, erosion produced an extensive and, in many areas, a conspicuous unconformity. In some places, the old, eroded land surface can be seen with stream channels filled with coarse conglomerate beds that are sometimes nearly 40 meters thick. The sediments were apparently derived from highland areas to the east, where renewed uplift and erosion had resulted in extensive floods of gravels across a piedmont area to the west. Being much more resistant than the underlying shales of the Moenkopi Formation, this conglomerate, mapped as the Shinarump Conglomerate, often forms a cap rock on many mesa tops.

The Chinle Formation

As the easterly source areas were reduced by erosion, the conglomerates gave way to sands and silts, many of which show remarkable color variations, ranging from blues and grays through pink, red, and purple. These are mapped as the **Chinle Formation,** with the Shinarump Conglomerate as the basal member. The Chinle has attained considerable fame and is well known to thousands of visitors to the Painted Desert of Arizona. It also contains the Petrified Forest, with fossils of various species of conifers (dominantly *Araucarioxylon*), cycads, and ferns. Many tree

FIGURE 17.3

Continental divide of Gondwana. (*Map drawn on a Lambert equal-area projection.*)

trunks, some over 3 meters in diameter, litter the ground as they have weathered out of the streambed sediments in which they were buried as driftwood. After burial, the tree trunks were exposed to circulating groundwater charged with dissolved silica. As a result, the woody tissues were gradually replaced molecule by molecule and are now remarkably preserved as agate and jasper, which are forms of chert.

At some horizons in the Chinle are thin limestones and marls, likely laid down in floodplain lakes. The presence of gypsum suggests at least a semiarid climate and the existence of playa lakes that periodically dried up. Another feature of Chinle successions are volcanic ash horizons, sometimes altered to bentonite clays. The source of the ash was likely island arc volcanoes to the west where, as is described later, tectonic activity had been increasing since the Permian. Marine conditions returned briefly in the Late Triassic, but this was to be the last of the Absaroka Sea.

Toward the close of Chinle time, there are indications that the climate was becoming progressively more arid, and in some places, the uppermost Chinle contains sandstones that some workers have interpreted as aeolian. The top of the Chinle is marked by an unconformity that, as a matter of convenience, is often designated the Triassic/

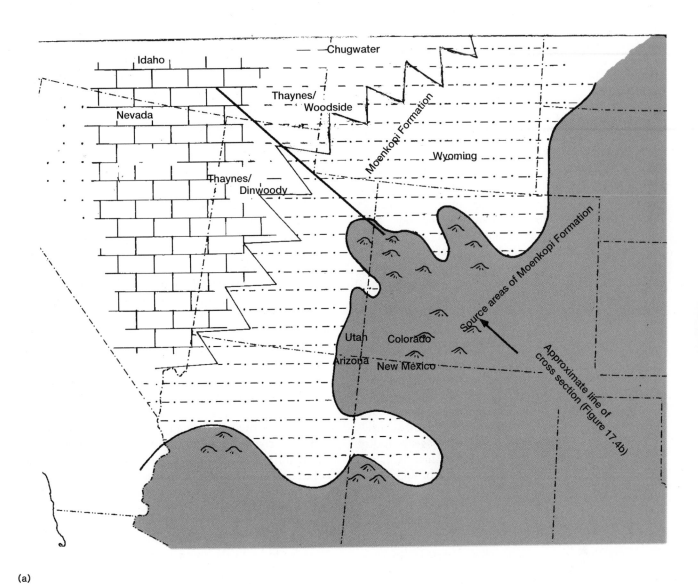

(a)

(b)

FIGURE 17.4

Moenkopi Formation. (a) The formation has a wide distribution, with sediments derived dominantly from the region to the east and southeast. To the northwest, it passes into a marine succession with limestones. (b) Regional cross section showing facies changes and the chief formations involved.

Jurassic boundary. The location of the actual boundary, however, is unknown because the Wingate Sandstone, above the Chinle, is, as would be expected with a desert aeolian deposit, devoid of fossils.

The Pangaea-Panthalassia Margin

Facing onto the **Panthalassic Ocean** (the ancestral Pacific), the western margin of Pangaea had been, from Late Precambrian time, a broad continental shelf, with sandstones and limestones the dominant lithologies. West of the carbonate shelf, however, suites of deep-water sediments frequently contain volcanic deposits derived from one or more island arcs, indicating that oceanic plate subduction was occurring. From time to time and along certain sectors, there is also evidence of thrusting, as seen, for example, in the Antler orogeny that lasted from latest Devonian time until well into the Mississippian. For the most part, however, along both the North and South American segments during the Paleozoic, there had been no major mountain-building movement.

As the Triassic opened, however, continental slope and island arc sediments were thrust eastward onto the craton in a belt extending from British Columbia to the Klamath Mountains of northern California. There was also considerable volcanism. This so-called **Sonoma orogeny** marked the collision of an island arc with North America. It was not a major orogenic event, and no range of fold mountains emerged, but it was the first of a series of collision events that became increasingly pronounced beginning with the Jurassic. Along the entire supercontinent margin from Alaska to South America, over a front of some 10,000 kilometers, there were various collision episodes involving island arcs, ocean plate segments, and continental slivers swept up or accreted as exotic terranes. These collision episodes have been given various names, but separating them into distinct "orogenies" is misleading because, beginning with the Sonoma episode, compressional tectonism prevailed along the whole continental margin more or less continuously over extended periods.

The timing of these compressional tectonic events is likely highly significant because many thousands of kilometers away, in the center of Pangaea, strong tensional forces were beginning to tear the supercontinent apart. This was the turning point in the Worsley, Nance, and Moody cycle. As the great rifts that were to become the Atlantic and Indian oceans of today's world opened and became ever wider, so the edges of the moving Pangaea pieces were overriding subduction zones at their leading margins.

Triassic sedimentation across the western margin of the North American continent was strongly influenced by the Sonoma episode and the plate movements that followed. The regional tectonic picture was not simple, and several models have been proposed. One model suggests, for example, that some shift in direction of plate movement, or plate rotation, resulted in transform faulting and,

for a time, even rifting. That there were some fundamental changes in direction of plate movement is indicated by a marked angular truncation of older Paleozoic structural trends by the newer post-Sonoma trend of regional lineaments.

The European Triassic

Most of what is now Europe was in Triassic time the largely emergent foreland region lying to the north of the Hercynian (Variscan) orogenic belt. Triassic sediments of western Europe and the British Isles are typically of terrestrial type and, particularly in the early Lower Triassic, sediments are dominated by typical molasse lithologies, red-colored conglomerates, sandstones, and shales. Widespread in central Germany and as far west as Britain, they are mapped as the Bunter, the lowest division of the classic German threefold succession that gave the Triassic its name. Where these beds overlie Permian sediments, there is little evidence of an erosional break, indicating that, here, just as in the western North American segment, the hot and semiarid conditions of Permian time, with playa lakes and evaporite basins, carried over, for the most part, into the Triassic.

In the British Isles, many features of Lower Triassic and underlying Permian sandstones are reminiscent of those formed under similar arid conditions that existed when the Devonian Old Red Sandstone was deposited. The resemblances were obvious to William Smith, which is why he named the post-Carboniferous sands the New Red Sandstone.

In Middle Triassic time, a marine incursion from the Tethys Ocean to the south covered most of central and western Europe and extended as far west as the British Isles. Limestone deposited in this sea constitutes the Muschelkalk, the middle division of the Triassic (Figure 17.5). The sea must have brought some alleviation of the aridity because equivalent terrestrial deposits that interfinger with the marine sediments contain the fossils of plants, freshwater fishes, and reptiles. At a few locations, dinosaurs have been found. Biostratigraphic correlations within Muschelkalk successions reveal that many horizons are almost isochronous, suggesting a rapid marine inundation. Whether it was caused by epeirogenic sinking or eustatic sea-level rise or a combination of both is unknown. The extremely flat topography of late Bunter time probably also played an important role.

The inundation of the Muschelkalk Sea was relatively short-lived, and by Late Triassic time, much of western Europe and the British Isles was again emergent. The return of a hot, arid climate is indicated by red sandstones and marls, which are again the predominant lithology. In Germany, they are mapped as the Keuper, the uppermost of the three Triassic divisions.

At the end of the Triassic, the sea returned, and grayish and greenish marls and limestones, together with gypsum deposits, suggest the presence of shallow, exten-

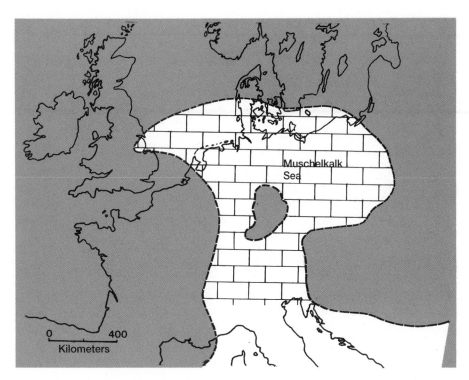

FIGURE 17.5
Paleogeography of the European area in the Triassic,
showing the Muschelkalk Sea.

sive lagoons and mud flats. As the Triassic passed into the
Jurassic, this sea deepened and became more widespread.

The Tethys Ocean

At its fullest development, the configuration of the Pangaea supercontinent was roughly that of a great *V* lying
on its side with the opening to the east (Figure 17.6a).
Inside the *V* was the **Tethys Ocean,** lying as a great inlet
or gulf between the Laurussia portion of the continent to
the north and the Gondwana portion to the south. The
eventual closure of Tethys, as much later continental
movements brought Africa and India northward to collide
with Asia, produced the Alpine-Himalayan fold belt.

Before the concepts of plate tectonics and continental
drift, the essential continuity of Mesozoic marine faunas
along the entire length of the Alpine-Himalayan fold belt
had been very puzzling to paleontologists. The simplest
explanation was to suppose the existence of a great east-
west ocean—the Tethys. Yet, this only answered one puzzle
by producing another. If the Tethys had once existed,
where had it gone? In a nondrifting world, getting rid of
continents and oceans was always a problem! The marine
faunas at locations as widely distant as southeastern Asia
and Morocco were similar because the continental shelves
bordering the Tethys extended at roughly the same latitude within a single zoogeographic province.

The Tethys Ocean has now vanished, although according to some plate-tectonic interpretations, the southeastern Mediterranean can be considered a final vestige

protected as a reentrant at the margin of the African
craton. Similarly, the Black Sea has also been cited as a
Tethyan remnant, but this is less likely.

In marked contrast to the dominantly nonmarine and
redbed sediments of central Europe, the southern European Triassic succession consists of shallow marine sediments dominated by limestones deposited along the
Tethyan margin. Of special interest is the Dachstein
Limestone of southern Germany, made up of a series of
coral reefs that grew along the northern shore of Tethys
and formed part of an extensive series of carbonate platforms (Figure 17.6b). Small patch reefs within the platforms were made up of algae, sponges, bryozoans, and also
corals, which reappeared on the scene in the Middle
Triassic. These were the scleractinian corals that comprise the massive coral reefs of modern tropical seas. Back
in the Triassic, however, this newly evolved group was represented by only diminutive reef structures.

Gondwana Successions

The geologic systems were originally defined by their fossil
content and, for that matter, still are. Because the index
fossils used are almost exclusively of marine organisms,
terrestrial successions always face problems in stratigraphic subdivision and long-distance correlation. In
practice, intercalations of fossiliferous marine horizons
usually provide guide horizons at frequent enough intervals that the problem is not major.

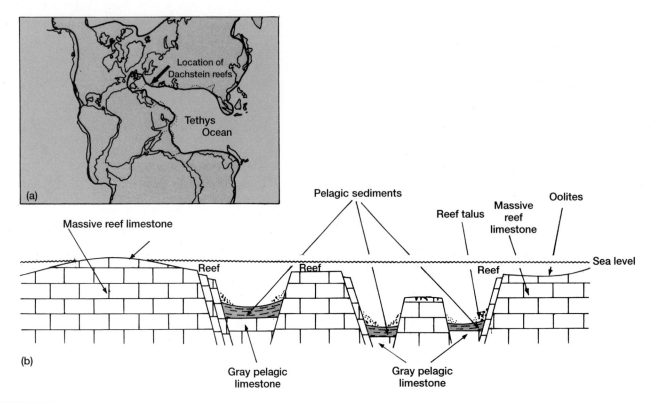

FIGURE 17.6

(a) The configuration of Pangaea was that of a great V, with the Tethys Ocean inside the V. (b) The Dachstein reefs grew on progressively subsiding fault blocks on the northern margin of Tethys.

In the Triassic, with its marked lack of marine successions and its thick and widespread terrestrial formations, stratigraphic classification and correlation, even at the systemic level, is a problem. In South Africa, for example, tremendously thick nonmarine successions have, in effect, been divided into their own systems and series, the boundaries of which do not coincide with those in the standard geologic time scale. The great Karoo Basin, an area of some half million square kilometers, stretching from Cape Province right up into the Transvaal, is underlain by the Karoo System, subdivided into four series (see Table 17.1). Fossils in the Dwyka Series, the lowest unit, indicate an Early Permian age, whereas the uppermost beds, those in the Stromberg Series, are of Late Triassic age, thus covering a time span of more than 70 million years.

Rocks of similar age, lithology, and fossil content are also found in the Parana Basin of South America, while corresponding successions have been described from the other pieces of Gondwana. In India, where the terrestrial successions range in age from Permian to Middle Cretaceous (the time of breakup), they constitute what has been named the **Gondwana System.** Across vast areas on the southern continents, Gondwana-type sediments are strikingly similar, consisting of redbeds made up of sandstone, siltstones, and shales that contain plant fossils and the remains of terrestrial animals (Figure 17.7).

TABLE 17.1

Divisions of the Karoo System

Series	Age
Stromberg	Late Triassic
Beaufort	Late Permian to Triassic
Ecca	Permian
Dwyka	Carboniferous to Early Permian

Triassic Rift Basins in Eastern North America

There is no sedimentary record of Early and Middle Triassic time across much of the central and eastern portions of the North American continent. However, deposits of Late Triassic age are found in a series of narrow basins that are elongated parallel to the Appalachian trend and that extend from the offshore region east of Newfoundland for some 4,000 kilometers southward to northern Florida (Figure 17.8a). The individual basins are not necessarily continuous, but collectively, they form a belt up to 800 kilometers wide. The majority of the basins are buried under thick Mesozoic and Cenozoic sediments of the Atlantic coastal plain, but along the belt's western

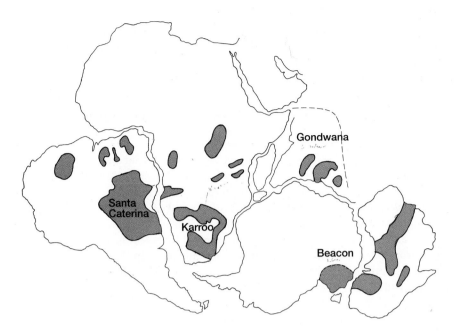

FIGURE 17.7
Distribution of Gondwana facies.

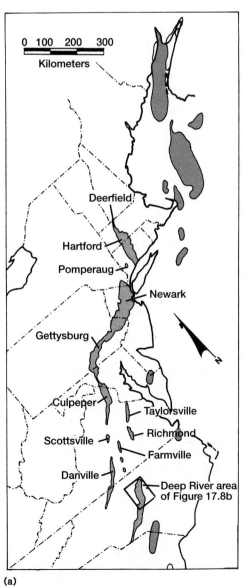

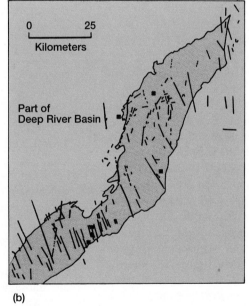

Triassic basins exposed

Triassic basins buried beneath coastal plain and continental shelf deposits

FIGURE 17.8
(a) Location of the major rift basins in eastern North America in the Late Triassic. (b) Detail of dike swarms that crossed the basins.

margin, several basins have been disinterred, as it were, by erosion, and their sedimentary infillings have been studied in considerable detail.

Two areas in Nova Scotia and New Jersey, for example, have particularly well-exposed basins, and in New Jersey, the basin sediments have been mapped as the **Newark Supergroup.** In places, this unit is more than 5 kilometers thick, a clear indication of how recurring movement along the boundary faults caused the basin floor to subside periodically. Facies changes in the sedimentary formations, when traced across the basin, are related to the source of the sediments and their direction of transportation. Along the basin margins, the sediments are typically coarse grained and consist of gravels and feldspathic sands swept down by streams flowing from adjacent highlands, many of which were apparently granitic terrains. Toward the axis of the basin, the sediment becomes progressively finer grained as the gradients of the ancient stream lessened. In places, the siltstone and shales suggest deposition in lakes, and thin coals indicate swampy conditions in some areas. Overall, however, many of the sediments are typically of redbed type; thus, a semiarid to monsoonal climate is generally postulated for this region in the Late Triassic. Some basins may have been better watered than others. On the other hand, at least one basin contains aeolian dune sands.

Many of these fault basins contain both intrusive and extrusive basalts. The chemical composition of these rocks suggests derivation from deep mantle sources, which would be consistent with the general patterns of igneous activity associated with continental rifting. The lava flows and sills are interbedded with the basin-fill sediments at numerous horizons, but none has been found outside the basins. One of the more massive sills forms the well-known Palisades on the Hudson River.

In addition, and cutting across the axial trend of the basins, are numerous dike swarms. In some places, they extend well beyond the confines of the basins, and both isotopic dates and field relationships suggest that they are mainly of Early Jurassic age and postdate the main basinal igneous activity. The most widely accepted interpretation is that such dikes are associated with the regional faulting and tensional stress during the early phase of the North Atlantic rifting (Figure 17.8b).

Triassic Faunas

Invertebrates

After the end-Permian mass extinction, the Triassic opened with greatly impoverished marine faunas but also great opportunities. The brachiopods, for example, had suffered severely, and their many vacant ecologic niches were exploited not only by new brachiopods, but also by bivalves.

Of special importance here was a significant evolutionary step that produced bivalves with siphons. No longer did the animals need to live on the seabed to obtain their food and where they were vulnerable to predatory borers and other enemies. Now they could bury themselves in the sediment and extend only the siphon (a fleshy tube) up to the sediment/water interface for feeding and respiration. The Pleuromyidae were typical of such bivalves, and they became abundant during the Triassic and gave rise to numerous new lineages.

The ammonites survived into the Triassic, but barely, and were immediately successful, undergoing a marked evolutionary radiation that arose apparently from the single genus *Ophiceras*. They were severely decimated at the end of the Triassic, however, and only one family survived into the Jurassic. That the ammonites on two occasions nearly disappeared forever is incredible, given the astounding array of ammonites in Jurassic and Cretaceous strata and the uniquely sophisticated biostratigraphic zonation based upon rapidly evolving ammonite lineages.

The rugose and tabulate corals had disappeared by the end of the Permian, and there is then a mysterious gap in the fossil record of coral history. Arising presumably from a rugose ancestral form or, alternatively, from some unknown soft-bodied group of corals, the scleractinian corals appeared in the Middle Triassic. They are also called hexacorals because their internal radiating septa are inserted as they grow in sixes rather than fours, as was the case in the rugose corals (also known as tetracorals). Through the remainder of the Triassic and into the Jurassic, the scleractinian corals gained in importance as reef builders.

Vertebrates—An Overview

Triassic vertebrate faunas were unique because they were a curious mixture of Paleozoic survivors of the end-Permian "crash" and new progressive forms, many of which were heralding the shape of things to come during the Jurassic and Cretaceous. The labyrinthodont amphibians were still present, as were the cotylosaurs of Permian time. Contemporary with them during the Triassic were rapidly evolving mammal-like reptiles and other groups, including the early archosaurs, a subclass that embraces the dinosaurs, pterosaurs, and crocodilians. The Triassic, then, was likely a time of increased competition, and some workers believe that the disappearance of so many groups by the close of the Triassic (the end-Triassic extinction event, discussed later in the chapter) simply reflected the inevitable disappearance of parent stocks less adaptable than descendant forms.

More important than the disappearances during the Triassic were the many newcomers. Of particular note are those tetrapod groups that are still part of our modern world. They represent some of the most conservative types and have extremely long family trees. The frogs, for example, appeared at the beginning of the Triassic, as did the lizard-like rhynchocephalians, a group that was important during the Triassic but is today represented by the

FIGURE 17.9
Early dinosaurs. (a) *Euparkeria.* (b) *Coelophysis.* (c) The
marine reptile *Placodus.*

single genus *Sphenodon* (also known as the tuatara) of
New Zealand. The turtles appeared about the middle of
the period. The Middle Triassic was marked by the appearance of marine forms, such as the icthyosaurs and
plesiosaurs, while last but not least, the first dinosaurs appeared with both saurischian and ornithischian divisions
represented, as discussed in the next section. All of these
groups were destined for great things in later time. Also
from rocks of Triassic age come fossils of what were likely
the first primitive birds. *Protoavis,* for example, had a very
birdlike skeleton, but whether it had feathers and flew is
not known. Before the close of the Triassic, the first true
mammals also appeared.

The First Dinosaurs

Many of the basic features of some of the most typical
dinosaurs, in terms of their overall body plan, were already discernible in the thecodonts, a diapsid ancestral
stock of the very earliest Triassic and even Late Permian.
Among these thecodonts, the pseudosuchians in particular exhibited many features that were characteristic in
dinosaur lineages of later time. *Euparkeria* from the
Lower Triassic of South Africa is likely close to the main-
line of descent for the dinosaurs (Figure 17.9a). This relatively small animal (less than 1 meter in length) was a
lightly built and active carnivore. Its larger hind limbs and
long tail suggest that it was bipedal, at least when running.

FIGURE 17.10

Cynognathus, a mammal-like therapsid reptile, with a length of about 1.5 to 2.0 meters.

Among other thecodonts were the aetosaurs of Late Triassic time. This group previewed the body plan of the great armored dinosaurs of later time. Not surprisingly, they were all quadrupeds, although even so, their hind legs were larger, indicating a common ancestry with the *Euparkeria* line.

Another body plan—this time very crocodilian in appearance—is seen in the phytosaurs. By Late Triassic time, some of these aggressive carnivores had grown to huge proportions. *Rutiodon,* for example, measured 3 or 4 meters in length. Undoubtedly, they were among the dominant reptiles of the time.

The thecodonts appeared in the Late Permian and as a group did not survive past the Triassic. During that time, however, they anticipated many of the various body plans seen in the dinosaurs of later time, so in some ways, they can be considered the stem dinosaurs.

Arising from a thecodont ancestor that was probably close to *Euparkeria,* the first true dinosaurs appeared in Late Triassic time, and the two divisions traditionally recognized in dinosaur taxonomy—the Saurischia and Ornithischia—were already distinguishable. These divisions are discussed in more detail later in the chapter. One of the best known of these early saurischians was *Coelophysis* (Figure 17.9b). In overall appearance, it was quite similar to some of the thecodonts of Early Triassic time, retaining the large hind limbs, long tail, light body structure, and bipedal gait. The general body plan remained essentially unchanged through the Jurassic and Cretaceous evolutionary radiation of the theropods, the carnivorous dinosaurs.

Other Late Triassic saurischians were clearly ancestral to the giant quadrupedal herbivorous sauropods of the Jurassic. *Plateosaurus,* a herbivore, grew to more than 7 meters in length and thus was already demonstrating the trend toward the enormous size that made some of these Jurassic dinosaurs so spectacular.

Marine Reptiles

During the Triassic, organisms whose ancestors were adapted to life on the land first returned to the sea. By the close of the Triassic, the icthyosaurs, the most fishlike of the marine reptiles, were among the dominant marine predators.

Placodonts, on the other hand, were adapted to life in the shallows, with rather massive bodies, short necks, and tails. The limbs were modified into flattened paddlelike structures. The teeth of placodonts provide some clues as to their diet. The front teeth protruded forward to act as pliers-like nippers, while the teeth behind were broad and adapted to grinding. These adaptations indicate that *Placodus* was a shell eater (Figure 17.9c). Yet another marine reptilian group were the nothosaurs. Their four limbs had become paddles also but were still strong and well muscled enough for locomotion on land if necessary, as with modern seals. They ate fish, and in their general body plan, particularly their long necks, they resembled plesiosaurs, which were their lineal descendants.

The Origin of Mammals

Among the therapsids, one group of carnivores, ranging in size from a small dog to a sheep, were the theriodonts. This group was evolving rapidly in the direction of mammals. By the Early Triassic, there were several groups of the so-called mammal-like reptiles, one of the best known being *Cynognathus.*

About the size of a big dog, *Cynognathus* had a rather large and elongated skull with a prominent temporal opening behind the eye (Figure 17.10). The teeth were differentiated into canines, incisors, and cheek teeth, a very mammal-like feature, and the animal clearly was an efficient predator and could cut up its prey and quickly devour it. A secondary palate separating the mouth from the nasal passage meant that the animal could continue to breathe while swallowing its food. All of these features point to rapid assimilation of food and a high metabolic rate, all very unreptile-like because, as is well known, many reptiles swallow their prey whole and then remain torpid for lengthy periods during the digestion process.

The feet of *Cynognathus* were well adapted for walking and running, as were the limbs that were tucked well under the body, a mechanically more efficient arrangement than the sprawling gait of many reptiles. Although in numerous other skeletal features, *Cynognathus* retained reptilian features, speculation about its exact status continues. Did it, for example, control its body temperature? Did it possess fur? Unfortunately, the fossil record is mute when it comes to answering these questions.

One clue as to the possible mammalian status of these animals is gleaned from a discovery in the Triassic of South Africa of a skeleton of *Thrinaxodon* (a relative of *Cynognathus*) with an immature individual nestled beside it. Is this evidence of parental care? If so, this would certainly weigh the balance in favor of mammalian status for the theriodonts.

In any event, the theriodonts as a group almost completely disappeared at the close of the Triassic. Only one genus—*Stereognathus,* belonging to the tritylodonts, advanced descendants from *Cynognathus* stock—survived into the Middle Jurassic. For a long time, *Stereognathus* and its Late Triassic ancestors were believed to be true mammals. However, recent work places them on a side branch of the evolutionary tree as still mammal-like reptiles, although, admittedly, perhaps the most mammal-like of all. In the meantime, true mammals had appeared by the end of the Triassic but remained a diminutive element in the fauna.

With the exception of the tritylodont *Stereognathus* of the Middle Jurassic, no therapsids are known to have survived beyond the Triassic. Only mammals continued, but for the entire Jurassic and Cretaceous, they failed to evolve into larger forms and remained as small insectivores, carnivores, and herbivores in a variety of ecologic niches.

The End-Triassic Extinction

The Triassic not only began with a mass extinction event, but it ended with one as well. The end-Triassic mass extinction was not as sweeping in its effect as the end-Permian event, but it nevertheless saw some important disappearances. Other animal groups were severely affected.

Among the echinodermata, the inadunate crinoids, which had barely survived the end-Permian extinction with one family, finally disappeared. The conodonts also became extinct, as did many brachiopod groups and nearly half the bivalve genera. Perhaps the most important inverte-

brate group to be involved in the end-Triassic event were the ammonites. While they had barely survived the end-Permian crash, during the Triassic, they had undergone a rapid evolutionary radiation. At the close of the period, they almost disappeared for the second time, and history repeated itself because the Jurassic radiation that followed stemmed from a single family that survived the end-Triassic event.

Although no particular extinctions occurred among the corals, it is noteworthy that, in Tethys, the close of the Triassic marked the end of reef building, perhaps due to a marked cooling.

Among the vertebrates, the stereospondyl labyrinthodont amphibians, a group that had been very successful through the Triassic, suddenly and dramatically disappeared. Among other tetrapods, several reptilian orders became extinct, including the protosaurs, nothosaurs, and placodonts. Noteworthy also was the disappearance of the last of the cotylosaurs. One group of this ancient lineage—the procolophorids (small lizardlike animals)—had survived into the Triassic, but their time had now come also. The thecodonts, which had given rise to the root stock that would lead to the dinosuars, were also among the extinctions.

Finally, for the therapsids, which during the Permian and Triassic had produced numerous lineages exhibiting features of increasingly mammalian aspect, the close of the Triassic saw their near-extinction. Only one genus—*Stereognathus*—survived into the Jurassic.

Recently, some important clues have turned up regarding the cause of the end-Triassic mass extinction. In shales at the Triassic/Jurassic boundary in Tuscany, Italy, grains of shocked quartz were discovered in 1991. This mineral is generally considered an unequivocal indicator of a meteoritic or cometary impact. According to David Bice of Carleton College in Northfield, Minnesota, the impact quartz at the Tuscany location occurs at three closely spaced horizons, which points to multiple impacts, perhaps produced by a cometary shower originating in the Oort Cloud. The next step, of course, is to find the impact site or sites. For one of them, at least, geologists will not have far to look: The Manicouagan impact feature in Quebec, Canada, is a possible candidate. It is 70 kilometers in diameter, and isotopic dating places its age as Late Triassic.

Perhaps the real significance of this recent discovery is the bearing it has on the question of the cause of mass extinctions in general. Of the six important mass extinctions during the Phanerozoic, it now looks as though there is evidence for a contemporaneous cosmic impact in half of them (the Frasnian-Famennian in the Devonian, the end-Triassic, and the end-Cretaceous). Inevitably, the question is asked, if half, why not all of them? Assuming that the timing of mass extinctions and impacts is more

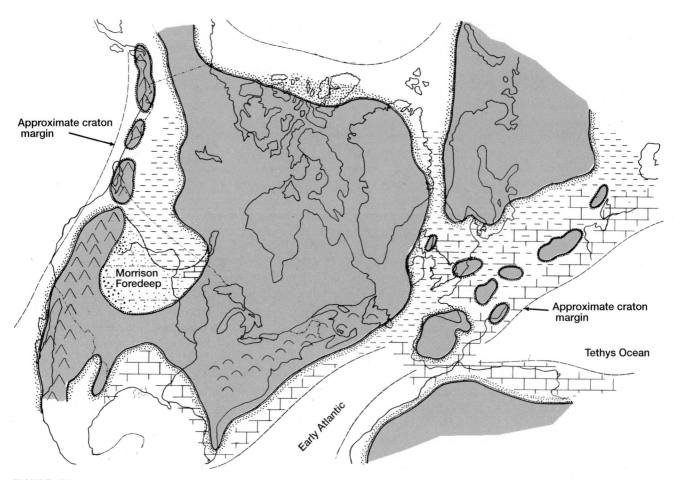

FIGURE 17.11

Paleogeography of Laurussia in the Jurassic.

than coincidence, the problem that remains involves the precise mechanism. Was ecologic catastrophe a consequence of global cooling, global heating, or what? This topic is discussed at greater length in Chapter 18.

The Jurassic

The Jurassic in Western North America

In the western North American region, the latest Triassic/ Early Jurassic was marked by desert conditions, as indicated by the common occurrence of aeolian dunes, such as those preserved in the Wingate Sandstone that unconformably overlies the Chinle Formation (Figure 17.11). The aridity of the region was not total, however, because there is occasional evidence of playa lakes and even streams and freshwater lakes with mollusks and fishes. Ripple-marked sands and shales deposited in such environments have been mapped as members of the Moenave and Kayenta formations that lie above the Wingate Sandstone.

In Arizona, where the Kayenta Formation is best developed, fossils of dinosaurs and mammal-like reptiles are found in addition to the mollusks and freshwater fishes. The general paucity of fossils—particularly the absence of marine fossils—however, make it difficult to determine where in the succession to place the Triassic/Jurassic boundary. Some workers believe that it lies near the base of the Navajo Sandstone, whereas others would place it as low as the Chinle-Wingate contact.

The Navajo Sandstone

Of all the desert sandstones, the **Navajo Sandstone,** with its massive festoon bedding interpreted as formed in aeolian dunes, is perhaps the best known, particularly where it is exposed in the canyon walls of Zion National Park in Utah. Some geologists have suggested that the Navajo sands were laid down in coastal dunes rather than a true desert environment. Unfortunately, the critical area to the west that might contain evidence of interfingering with marine sediments is truncated by the tectonically disturbed belt of the Cordillera.

The Sundance Sea

The Navajo and equivalent formations across the western craton were the final deposits of the Absaroka sequence, the great sedimentary envelope that embraced some 150 million years of earth history and that began in the early Pennsylvanian. When the sea returned in earliest Middle

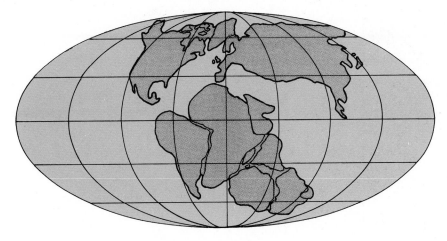

FIGURE 17.12
World paleogeography in the Jurassic.

Jurassic time, it encroached across a widespread unconformity that marks the base of the Zuni sequence. During the remainder of the Jurassic, the sea advanced into the continental interior three times, with brief periods of withdrawal between. At times, the interior seas stretched as far east as Saskatchewan and South Dakota and southward into northern New Mexico and Arizona. The rapidity of the widespread marine advances and retreats suggests that the suberosion surface was of relatively low relief.

Although widespread, the Jurassic seaways apparently never connected with the Gulf of Mexico region, where the proto-Atlantic was going through the earliest stages of rifting. This suggests that the continental divide still lay along the line of the Marathon/Ouachita/Allegheny orogenic belt.

The third and last Jurassic marine incursion was the most extensive, and by the late Bajocian Stage (that is, middle Middle Jurassic), the sea was relatively deep with limestones, sandstones, and shales accumulating over large areas. Various local formation names have been applied, and one of these—the Sundance of Wyoming, Colorado, and South Dakota—gave its name to the sea of this time.

An important source of the sediments deposited in the **Sundance Sea** was a rising range of highlands to the west, the result of increasing tectonic activity, accompanied by the intrusion of massive granite batholiths. This so-called Nevadan orogeny eventually resulted in eastward thrusting and an episode of mountain building. The inevitable flood of clastics spread in great fans eastward. Due to the regional upwarping that accompanied the Nevadan orogeny and likely also due to silting up of the basin, the Sundance shoreline retreated northward.

The Morrison Formation

By the Kimmeridgian stage of middle Late Jurassic age, the basin of the former Sundance Sea was becoming covered by spreads of nonmarine sands, silts, and muds. Al-

though the sediments show considerable local variations in lithology, they have been mapped over large areas as the **Morrison Formation,** the most extensive nonmarine formation in the United States, covering over 1 million square kilometers.

The Morrison Formation is famous for its fauna of Late Jurassic dinosaurs (Figure 17.11). Careful study of the Morrison lithology and depositional environment has revealed much about the habits of these animals. Until quite recently, many of the larger dinosaurs were widely believed to have spent much of their time wallowing in lakes and swamps, rather like the modern hippopotamus. Although lacustrine and swampy facies are known in the Morrison, the overall lithology suggests that the dinosaurs occupied a relatively dry habitat, perhaps similar to the savanna country of eastern and southern Africa with its herds of elephants and other large mammals. Modern studies of dinosuar anatomy support this interpretation.

The Sundance Sea retreated northward, and there is a generally similar diachronous trend for the uppermost Morrison sediments in that direction also. In southern Canada, occurrences of the youngest Morrison sediments are, in fact, of Early Cretaceous age.

The Breakup of Pangaea

Pangaea began to break up during the Jurassic (Figure 17.12). The first cracks had appeared in the Late Triassic in the form of the many rift valleys, but little, if any, true separation had occurred, so the embryo ocean was narrow, perhaps like the modern Red Sea. The first indications that the ocean was flooding in as the pieces of Pangaea moved away from each other are seen in marine deposits. The earliest of these, indicating restricted circulation and evaporating conditions, were salt deposits, such as the **Louann Salt** of the subsurface section in the Gulf of Mexico (Figure 17.13). The Argo Salt in the offshore region near Newfoundland and the Grand Banks is of similar age.

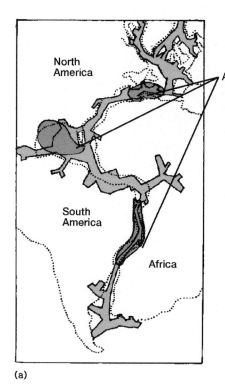

(a)

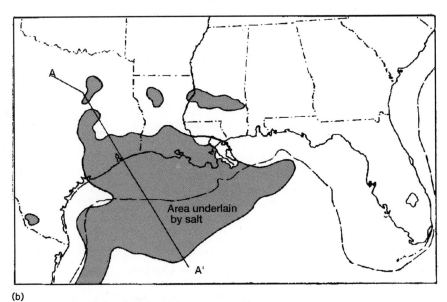

(b)

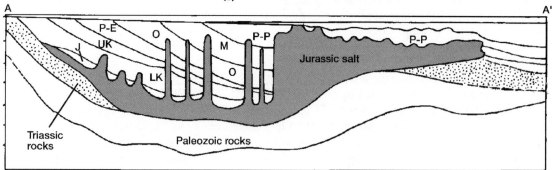

O = Oligocene
P-E = Paleocene - Eocene
UK = Upper Cretaceous
LK = Lower Cretaceous
J = Jurassic
M = Miocene
P-P = Plio - Pleistocene

(c)

FIGURE 17.13

(a) Location of the major rifts that led to the breakup of Gondwana in the Early Jurassic. Note areas of salt deposition during the Red Sea stage of ocean evolution. (b) Location of the Louann Salt in the subsurface of the Gulf coast region. (c) Cross section showing the salt as the source of the many salt plugs of the Gulf coast area.

The breakup of Pangaea, in addition to separating the continental pieces, had an important second effect. The spreading centers in the newly formed ocean/rift basins quickly grew in length and volume, which reduced the volume of the world's ocean basins. Inevitably, this led to a rise in sea level. The tectono-eustatic sea-level rise was more or less continuous from the beginning of the Jurassic until well into the Middle Jurassic. In Bathonian (Middle Jurassic) time, there was a brief marine regression, but then the rise continued even more rapidly until nearly the end of the Jurassic, when there was a relatively sudden retreat as the period closed.

The previous section discussed the results of the Jurassic transgressions in western North America with the incursion of the Sundance Sea. These transgressions would undoubtedly have been larger and more prolonged were it not for the influence of the growing Nevadan orogenic belt on the Sundance Sea's western shore. Thus, eustatic sea-level changes do not always have worldwide impact. Large-scale tectonic and epeirogenic movements on the cratons often have an important modifying effect, which must be kept in mind in assessments of major sea-level changes.

The Early Atlantic

As the early Atlantic became larger and circulation improved, salinity levels normalized, and by Middle Jurassic time, carbonate platforms had appeared along the entire eastern margin of the new North American continent (Figure 17.14). Studies of the lithofacies and fossils suggest that conditions were not dissimilar to those in the modern Great Barrier Reef that lies at the shelf edge off present-day eastern Australia.

Through almost the entire Jurassic, there was, as mentioned in the previous section, a eustatic rise in sea level. This, combined with epeirogenic subsidence of the eastern continental margin, resulted in the accumulation of great thicknesses of shelf margin carbonates through both the Middle and Late Jurassic. Reef-building organisms and reef accumulative processes in general are usually more than capable of matching relative sea-level rises, even glacio-eustatic changes, which, in the context of geologic time, are extremely rapid indeed.

In the Gulf of Mexico, the Louann Salt is overlain by the Norphlet Formation, much of which is interpreted as representing deposition in an arid climate coastal sabkha. Above the Norphlet is the Smackover Formation, a widespread marine limestone, indicating that, in the Gulf region, as along North America's eastern margin, normal marine salinity had become established. Increased stirring by waves and higher-energy bottom conditions is in-

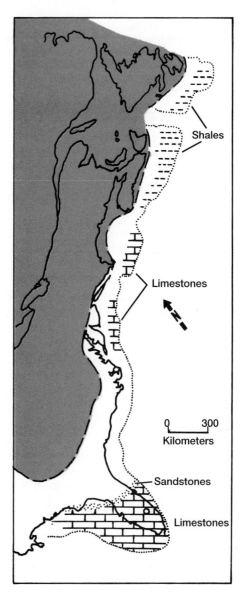

FIGURE 17.14

Facies distribution along the western shore of the early Atlantic in the Jurassic.

dicated in the upper Smackover by cross-bedded oolitic limestone. Good primary porosity, often enhanced by secondary solution, has resulted in the Smackover being an important oil and gas reservoir in the Gulf region.

The European Jurassic

In the classic areas in England where the Jurassic sections and faunas were first described by William Smith, and all across Europe, the Jurassic is dominated by marine shales and limestones, often remarkably fossiliferous. During the whole period, the region was covered by a shallow, epi-continental sea. At times and in such places as the British Isles, water movement was vigorous enough for the development of patch reefs, and oolite shoals formed in environments similar to those on the modern Bahama Banks. At other horizons, organic-rich marls and shales suggest deposition under poorly oxygenated conditions, perhaps caused by density and salinity stratification that can often develop in a hot climate.

The world-famous **Solnhofen Limestone** of Bavaria, renowned for its exquisitely preserved fossils, clearly was laid down under similar unusual bottom conditions. The Solnhofen Limestone is, in fact, only a sparsely fossiliferous formation, but what fossils do occur and the state of their preservation are significant. The Solnhofen has an extremely uniform and fine texture. Such limestone is aptly named "porcellanous" and was originally a fine lime mud deposited under quiet water conditions. Most likely, the mud was laid down in a shallow lagoon protected by adjacent patch reefs made up of stromatolitic algae and sponges. The almost complete absence of an indigenous benthic fauna suggests that the bottom water was either highly saline or deficient in oxygen. The only tracks are of *Paleolimulus,* an ancestor of the modern horseshoe crab, which is tolerant of a wide range of temperature and salinity conditions. The preservation in the Solnhofen of such delicate structures as bird feathers, butterfly and dragon-fly wings, and jellyfish impressions also point to a bottom environment inimical to normal scavenging organisms.

To the south, along the northern margin of the Tethys Ocean, the sedimentary succession from the Triassic into the Jurassic is essentially continuous. Tensional stresses consequent on continental breakup caused widespread normal faulting. The upfaulted blocks became the sites of shallow-water carbonate platforms, while deeper-water sediments, together with submarine breccias, accumulated in the down-faulted basins between. By the Late Jurassic, even the shallow platform areas had begun to subside, and deeper-water deposits became widespread.

Jurassic Faunas

Invertebrates

The great success story in the Jurassic undoubtedly is that of the ammonites. As mentioned earlier in the chapter, only one ammonite family survived the end-Triassic extinction, but this single group experienced one of the most astonishing evolutionary radiations in the history of life. Although largely retaining their plano-spiral (watch-spring) body plan, ammonites varied almost infinitely in size, degree of coiling of the shell, overall shape of the whorls, ribbing, spines, and other ornamental features (Figure 17.15).

While most ammonites measured, perhaps, 10 to 20 centimeters in diameter, some were gigantic with a diameter of 2 meters or more—as large as tractor or jet air-plane tires. Of more significance to taxonomists, however, are the so-called **septal sutures,** which mark on the inside of the shell where the highly convoluted septal wall that divided one chamber in the shell from the next joined the outer shell (Figure 17.15c). The complex pattern of these suture enables taxonomists to distinguish one ammonite species from another.

Detailed evolutionary lineages have been worked out, and ammonites can be used as sensitive biostratigraphic indicators. The average life span of a Jurassic ammonite species has been estimated at 1.2 million years, which allows extremely accurate correlations. Because of their nektonic mode of life, similar to that of modern *Nautilus,* the shells of ammonites are found in virtually every marine sedimentary environment. They also became widely distributed by ocean currents, just as does *Nautilus,* whose shells have been known to float for years after the animal died. The ammonites finally succumbed at the terminal Cretaceous extinction.

Dinosaurs

While the mammals were biding their time, the world belonged to the reptiles, and the lords of creation for over 150 million years undoubtedly were the dinosaurs. Perhaps no other group of animals in the history of life, either living or extinct, has attracted as much interest, judging from the volume of books, television programs, movies, toys, and novelties devoted to dinosaurs. The amazing thing is that, although scientists have studied dinosaurs for nearly 200 years, much is still unknown about these fascinating creatures. In recent years, in particular, a resurgence of studies has led to many new conclusions. In fact, the familiar dinosaurs we grew up with have been replaced by wholly different animals we did not even know existed!

One of the most exciting of these new concepts and supported by a growing body of evidence is the view that the dinosaurs were warm-blooded. Either we have to revise our definition of reptiles or accept the idea that the dinosaurs may not have been reptiles at all. Some researchers have even suggested that the dinosaurs never really became extinct and are still with us in the form of birds! The basis for some of these startling new revelations is discussed a little later in the chapter.

Early Dinosaur Studies and Recent Discoveries The "golden years" of dinosaur hunting were the later decades of the nineteenth century. The two greatest dinosaur hunters were Edward Drinker Cope (1831–1899) and Othniel Charles Marsh (1840–1897) of Yale University.

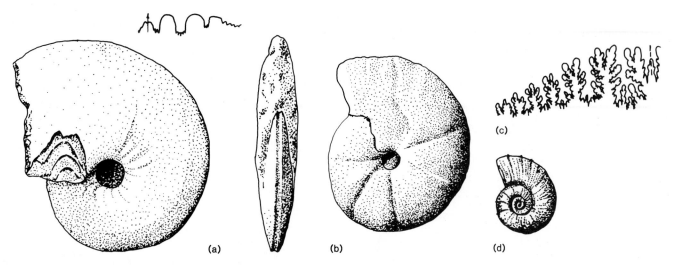

FIGURE 17.15

Triassic and Jurassic ammonites: (a) *Meekoceras gracilitatus*
(Lower Triassic) (b) *Calliphylloceras freibocki* (Jurassic).
(c) Suture pattern of *C. freibocki* (d) *Lytoceras fimbriata*
(Jurassic).

Over the years, a considerable rivalry grew between these two men, manifested apparently in a race to see who could excavate the greatest number of specimens and who could name the most species. Although, on occasion, this may have resulted in skeletal reconstructions and taxonomic determinations that have since required revision, both of these men were very adequate scientists to whom the world of vertebrate paleontology owes a great debt.

Since the first dinosaur discoveries, there has been an ongoing controversy about the reconstruction of dinosaur skeletons and how the animals must have looked in life. Very few large reptiles are ever found with complete and articulated skeletons. Not surprisingly, most of those that *are* found in a more or less complete state are marine forms, such as the icthyosaurs and plesiosaurs, whose remains came to be buried in soft mud on some quiet seabed. Terrestrial forms are often found in alluvial sediments, and quite often, the bones were tumbled about before burial.

Many people viewing a dinosaur mounted in a museum exhibit are surprised to learn that perhaps only a very small proportion of the skeleton was assembled from actual fossil bones dug out of the ground. How then is the skeleton completed? Much of the answer to this question lies in extrapolation. Tetrapod skeletons are, fortunately, bilaterally symmetrical so if, say, a right femur is found, a left one can be constructed as a mirror image. A row of vertebrae along a spinal column and perhaps a long tail beyond that can logically be assumed to be generally similar in form and to become progressively smaller in a regular manner. This means that only one or two vertebrae

are needed, and the rest can be modeled. Lest this all sounds too simple or even a form of cheating, it should be remembered that this "game" of intelligent guessing is not for the amateur. A thorough knowledge of vertebrate anatomy and osteology (the study of bones) is a necessary prerequisite for this sort of paleontological detective work.

One of the biggest problems lies not in reconstructing missing bones but in determining how they articulated with one another. Of particular concern is the way the animal stood or walked. Many early reconstructions showed dinosaurs and other large extinct reptiles to have a sprawling posture, with the limbs emerging from the body as they do in modern alligators and crocodiles. Later workers decided that the legs were likely tucked under the body for greater mechanical efficiency, which is almost certainly the correct interpretation.

The huge size of many dinosaurs (for example, sauropods like *Apatosaurus*) (Figure 17.16) persuaded many paleontologists that their legs could not possibly have supported their weight on land and that, instead, they spent their lives partially immersed in water as swamp- and lake-dwelling herbivores. Studies of the sediments containing the fossils tell a different story, and many scientists now believe that most of the large dinosaurs lived in an environment perhaps not very different from that of modern African elephants.

Just as important as studies of bones and their articulation has been the close attention paid by recent workers to dinosaur footprints. New interpretations based on comparisons with the tracks of modern animals suggest that

FIGURE 17.16

The sauropods (a) *Apatosaurus,* and (b) *Brachiosaurus.*

dinosaurs were much more active than previously supposed. Traditional reconstructions invariably also showed the tail dragging on the ground; in bipedal forms, it presumably formed part of a tripod. In hundreds of dinosaur track fossils, however, only rarely is there a groove made by the tail dragging in the mud. Many dinosaur experts see this as suggesting that bipedal dinosaurs used their tails as balancing organs rather than supports and that they stood like birds rather than kangaroos.

The dinosaurs arose from archosaur ancestors and became prominent toward the end of the Triassic. Many of them, particularly the theropod carnivores, were bipedal, with hind limbs that were markedly larger and stronger than the forelimbs. Although this arrangement enables modern crocodiles and alligators to run rapidly in short bursts either to capture prey or escape from enemies, this may not have been the primary advantage in controlling evolutionary selection. The larger hind limbs

in ancestral archosaurs may have been an adaptation for swimming. Most early archosaurs spent much of their time in and near water, and the larger limbs, together with the powerful tail that invariably goes with the bipedal gait, made them efficient swimmers. The same pattern persists in living crocodiles, and only the hind feet are webbed. Thus, the early advantage of agility seen in dinosaur ancestral groups may have been another case of preadaptation, with anatomical features developed for one purpose becoming, under different circumstances, well adapted to another mode of life altogether.

Dinosaur Classification   The term *dinosaur,* meaning "terrible lizard," was coined by British paleontologist Richard Owen in 1842, and as the collections of specimens grew during the late nineteenth and early twentieth century, the *Dinosauria* seemed a natural and valid taxonomic division to bring together the many and varied

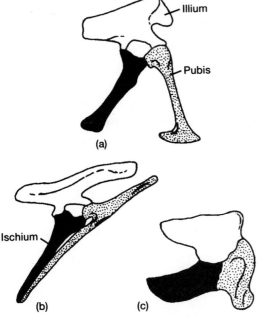

FIGURE 17.17
Pelvic bones of the (a) ornithischian and (b) saurischian groups of dinosaurs, compared with that of (c) a crocodile.

forms. More detailed anatomical studies indicated that all dinosaurs could be placed in one or the other of two divisions, based upon the shape and position of the pelvic bones (Figure 17.17). One group included the dinosaurs in which the pubis diverged from the ischium and extended forward, as in most other reptiles. The other group included the dinosaurs in which the pubis was directed backward to lie alongside the ischium in a manner reminiscent of birds. Despite the striking resemblances in general body plan and mode of life between the dinosaurs in either group, these skeletal differences were held to be justification for erecting two orders: the **Saurischia** (reptile hips) and the **Ornithischia** (bird hips).

Taxonomic arrangements based solely on skeletal features often are artificial, and this is a case in point. Modern dinosaur taxonomists now tend to disregard the twofold division of dinosaurs. In recent years, a revival of interest in dinosaur taxonomy has evolved beyond mere concern with describing and classifying bones and is now moving into an interpretive stage in which more attention is being paid to the dinosaurs' life mode and habitat. In other words, taxonomists are beginning to clothe dinosaurs with flesh and blood and see them as living animals. Some surprising discoveries have been made.

Work by Robert Bakker, Adrian Desmond, Gregory Paul, and others produced strong evidence to suggest that dinosaurs were not the slow, lumbering animals that comparisons with large modern reptiles, such as the crocodiles and turtles, suggest. Instead, studies of dinosaur osteology, gait, and ecology indicate that they were, for the most part, extremely active animals adapted to a wide variety of habitats. It follows from this that dinosaurs could not have been **ectothermic**—that is, cold-blooded—but had

a metabolism that required them to be **endothermic** (warm-blooded). If they were warm-blooded, and if we continue to define reptiles as being cold-blooded, then the dinosaurs and, for that matter, the pterosaurs (flying reptiles discussed later in the chapter), were not reptiles!

Clearly, a whole new approach to the classification of these and other tetrapods is required. In particular, a workable classification scheme must recognize the difference between ectothermy and endothermy (Figure 17.18). During the Triassic, endothermy apparently evolved independently among two distinct groups of early reptiles—the therapsids and a group of thecodonts. The therapsids were mammal-like reptiles, ancestral to the mammalian stock, whereas one line of thecodonts gave rise to the dinosaurs and to the pterosaurs. Early in their evolution, during the Jurassic, the dinosaurs gave rise to the birds, which in terms of modern descendants, are more closely related to the dinosaurs than are the living reptiles. The ectotherms apparently diverged in Late Permian and Early Triassic time, the eosuchians (an ancestral group of early diapsids) eventually giving rise to the snakes and lizards, whereas an early division in basic thecodont stock produced the crocodilians.

Marine Reptiles

One of the difficulties in a narrative of this nature is the question of whether to follow a strictly sequential ordering or to deal with taxonomic/evolutionary entities as they are encountered. If this were a paleontology text, then clearly the dinosaurs, pterosaurs, or any of the taxonomic groupings would be described separately. A book about historical geology, however, must use time units as the primary divisions and thus, in effect, must deal with numerous separate but parallel threads. It is now necessary to pick up one of those threads and return to the subject of marine reptiles.

As described earlier in the chapter, the first return to the sea occurred during the Triassic with the appearance of three major groups: the icthyosaurs, placodonts, and nothosaurs. Of these, the icthyosaurs became the most fishlike and, in the process, most completely divorced from any connections with a dry-land existence (Figure 17.19). Virtually the only unfishlike characteristic they retained was lungs for breathing air. Even reproduction was now a completely subaqueous process. Eggs could not be laid in the water, so the icthyosaurs were **viviparous**—that is, they produced live young—as do some modern lizards and snakes. Occasional fossil remains showing embryos within the mother have been found in Jurassic shales in Germany.

The other important group of Jurassic and Cretaceous marine reptiles were the **plesiosaurs** that arose from nothosaur ancestors. Perhaps the most obvious morphologic trend during the Jurassic and Cretaceous history of this group was an increase in size. Jurassic forms of 5 or 6 meters are fairly common, but they were dwarfed by

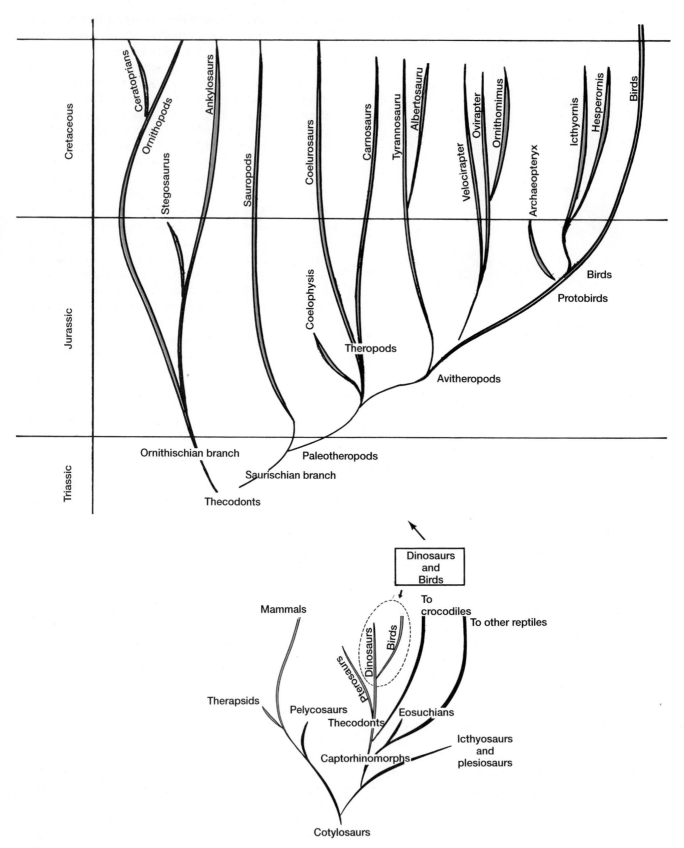

FIGURE 17.18

A classification of the dinosaurs and birds based on
ectothermic and endothermic characteristics. Shaded lines
are endothermic groups; black lines are ectothermic groups.

FIGURE 17.19
Icthyosaurus.

Cretaceous plesiosaurs of more than twice that size. The plesiosaurs must have been powerful swimmers because their limbs were modified into huge paddles. The most typical plesiosaurs had long necks, but another branch, collectively grouped as the pliosaurs, had much shorter necks but greatly elongated skulls.

Flying Reptiles

Among extinct creatures, second only to the dinosaurs in popularity are the pterosaurs, or flying reptiles. From Conan Doyle's *Lost World* to the Hollywood epics in which they are seen carrying off "cavemen" (more usually cavewomen!) to their nests to feed their young, the creatures have clearly made a big impression on human imagination!

The Mesozoic world was dominated by reptiles occupying so many ecologic niches that it would have been surprising if this amazingly versatile class of animals had not also conquered the air. Although the first true fliers capable of sustained flight did not appear until the Jurassic, reptiles had taken to the air as gliders as early as the Late Permian. The wings of *Daedalosaurus* (named after Daedalus of Greek mythology) were formed of a skin membrane stretched across greatly elongated ribs. A similar solution to wing support is seen in *Icarosaurus* from the Triassic and persists in certain of today's flying lizards, such as *Draco*. A much more significant adaptation is seen in *Longisquama* from the Triassic, whose scales were enormously elongated and could be extended on either side of the body to form wings. This bizarre creature could possibly provide support for the idea that bird feathers evolved from reptilian scales.

The first true flying reptiles appeared in the Jurassic, and although they varied in shape and size, they all solved the problem of wing support in the same way. The wing itself was a skinny membrane stretched between the hind limbs and an enormously elongated fourth finger; the fifth digit was lost, while the remaining three were modified to form tiny hooklike structures on the leading edge of the wing. These structures may have fulfilled some kind of grasping function, enabling the pterosaurs to hold onto

branches or rocks. Some paleontologists have even suggested that pterosaurs hung upside down in the same way as do bats.

Just as with the dinosaurs and the way they walked, there has been much discussion as to pterosaurs' flying ability. Most of the early reconstructions pictured pterosaurs as dominantly soaring creatures, swooping down to catch fish from the ocean surface and then crawling painfully back up to a cliff top or other vantage point to repeat the process. In recent years, studies of flying models, experiments in wind tunnels, and computer simulations of the dynamics of pterosaurs have led to a considerable modification of earlier ideas. Pterosaurs are now widely believed to have been quite efficient flyers and capable of wing-flapping flight. They probably also could manage quite well on the ground and could take off from the ground if necessary. In other words, they were probably just as efficient as many birds and almost certainly held their own with the early primitive birds that were their contemporaries.

The earliest pterosaurs were generally less than 1 meter in length. Typically, the rhamphorhynchoids had long tails that presumably had some function in maintaining equilibrium or balance while in flight or perhaps served as rudders (Figure 17.20a).

Arising from Triassic thecodont ancestors, the pterosaurs, like other archosaurs, were diapsids, with two temporal openings behind the large orbits. The skull was additionally lightened by a large preorbital opening. Rhamphorhynchoids had a long snout, and the jaws were equipped with forward-projecting teeth, presumably an adaptation for catching fish.

Toward the close of the Jurassic, the rhamphorhynchoids gave rise to a second group of pterosaurs, the **pterodactyloids.** Pterodactyloid tails were very small, and the teeth were also greatly reduced, trends that became more pronounced as the group evolved through the Cretaceous (Figure 17.20b).

The majority of pterosaur remains have been discovered in marine deposits, and this, together with the teeth designed for catching fish, suggest that the pterosaurs were adapted to life on the seacoast. The fossil record may, however, be biased. Pterosaurs' delicate bones, as with birds, are not the best candidates for fossilization. Significantly, the fossil record of birds is dominated by marine diving birds, and observations of modern birds indicate that this is a skewed representation.

The question of reptilian body temperature control, discussed earlier, persists in the pterosaurs. Here were animals of small size and, presumably, with a fairly high metabolic rate. In addition, their swift motion through the air would have effectively cooled them. In recent years, Upper Jurassic strata in Russia have revealed the preservation of a pterosaur named *Sordes pilosus* in certain fine-grained limestones that is so good that the impression of a hairy covering can be seen, implying that the animal was warm-blooded.

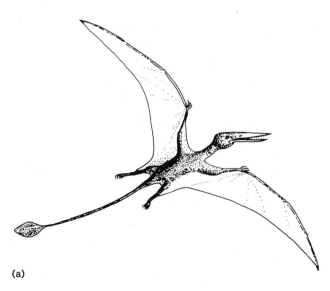

(a)

(b)

FIGURE 17.20

(a) *Rhamphorhynchus*, a pterosaur from the Upper Jurassic. Note its long tail. (b) *Pteranodon*, from the Cretaceous, is tailless.

FIGURE 17.21

What *Archaeopteryx* looked like in life..The skeleton is essentially that of a small carnivorous or insectivorous dinosaur. Only the presence of feathers precludes it from probably being classified as a dinosaur. Note the claws on the front edge of the wing.

Birds

The problem of flight was, of course, also solved by another group that appeared in the Jurassic—namely, the birds. Not surprisingly, the fossil record of the evolutionary steps toward this marvelous ability is extremely fragmentary. The reptilian ancestry of the birds seems to be firmly established by the famous fossils of *Archaeopteryx lithographica* from the Solnhofen Limestone of Bavaria. This animal's skeleton is unquestionably that of a small bipedal thecodont dinosaur, and yet it has feathers (Figures 17.21 and 17.22).

Although often described as the first bird, *Archaeopteryx* probably was not a strong flyer. It was, however, a good climber, and spent much of its life in the trees, with most of its flying done over short distances from branch to branch. *Archaeopteryx* also had teeth and retained claws on its forelimbs, so its dinosaur connections are unquestionable. It is often cited as a classic example of a "missing link," and in the Victorian tradition of such important elements in traditional and gradualistic evolutionary progress, it is seen as "half reptile and half bird." In fact, its only true bird characteristic is the possession of feathers; otherwise, it looks very much like a small, meat-eating dinosaur. Thus, modern taxonomists do not place *Archaeopteryx* on the main line of descent of birds and reject the simple missing-link idea.

Where the first true birds arose is something of a mystery. While they unquestionably were derived from a thecodont ancestor, which one? The evolution of thecodont predators not only produced such giants as *Tyrannosaurus* in the Cretaceous but also many smaller dinosaurs, some of which developed quite birdlike features. Even as early as the Triassic, there was *Protoavis*, which had hollow bones and no back teeth. In fact, in many ways, it had a more birdlike skeleton than *Archaeopteryx*. The fossil record does not indicate whether or not *Protoavis* had feathers, but dinosaur expert Gregory Paul believes it is probable. On more than one occasion among the small tree-climbing dinosaurs, there likely were trends toward the development of a flying ability, and *Archaeopteryx* was almost certainly not the only line of protobird dinosaurs.

An exciting new fossil discovery in Liaoning Province, China, has thrown considerable light into this otherwise extremely dim corner of the fossil record. Found

FIGURE 17.23
Morganucodon, an early mammal from the Late Triassic.

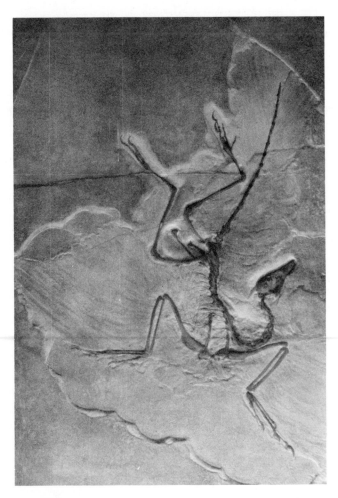

FIGURE 17.22
Archaeopteryx lithographica from the Solnhofen Limestone of Bavaria, Germany.

Mammals

During the Triassic, mammals evolved from the mammal-like reptiles, but the fossil record is poor. The paleobiology of the reptile-mammal transition faces the same difficulties as that of the amphibian-reptile transition. The possession of fur or hair and of mammary glands for the suckling of young are, of course, familiar mammalian attributes, but they leave no fossil record. Instead, paleobiologists must search for skeletal features that are normally considered indicative of the mammalian level of organization.

Perhaps the most important skeletal elements used in these studies are the teeth. Mammalian teeth are normally differentiated into incisors, canines, premolars, and molars, and their relative numbers, shape, and size can be used to determine the animal's diet, as well as play an important role in mammal classification. The lower jaw in mammals is also distinctive. Unlike that in reptiles, the mammalian jaw consists of a single bone, the dentary. Another typically mammalian feature is the greatly expanded brain case. Although fundamentally a synapsid skull, it is clearly adapted to a much larger brain than the relatively small organ of reptiles. Particularly developed in mammals are the cerebral hemispheres, originally dedicated to an olfactory function, but that later formed the higher brain centers required with improved senses and, of course, intelligence.

Not the least of the difficulties encountered in studying the earliest mammals is their small size. During the Late Triassic and Jurassic, no fewer than five different orders of mammals arose, and most were no larger than mice. By the Late Jurassic, one or two forms were the size of a cat, but the skeletons were far from robust. The fossil evidence for many groups, therefore, relies heavily, sometimes solely, upon the teeth.

Among the first mammals were the morganucodonts, based on the genus *Morganucodon,* found in solution hole infillings in Carboniferous limestones in South Wales (Figure 17.23). During Late Triassic time, this region was emergent, and a karst topography, with caverns and sinkholes, developed. Just as in similar current landscapes, sinkholes and fissures were effective traps for unwary animals. Morganucodonts were tiny animals with an undoubtedly mammalian type of skull, but curiously, in the jaw was the remnant of a double jaw joint—a feature reminiscent of its reptilian ancestry.

in lacustrine sediments of latest Jurassic age and some 10 million years younger than *Archaeopteryx,* the Chinese specimen is of a remarkably modern-looking bird about the size of a large sparrow. In contrast to *Archaeopteryx,* the as yet unnamed bird had a well-developed keeled breastbone, so clearly also the muscles for flying. Its short skeletal tail is also very birdlike, but, in contrast, its pelvis still has a dinosaurian shape and there are still claws on the digits supporting the wings. The Chinese fossils suggest either that true birds evolved very rapidly after *Archaeopteryx* or, more likely, arose from an ancestral thecodont dinosaur stock at an earlier date.

Certain ancestral features have not entirely disappeared, even in modern birds. Fledgling hoatzins of the Ecuadorean rain forest are equipped with movable claws on the leading edges of the wings, which considerably aid the young bird as it scrambles about in the branches. This preflight stage provides a fascinating glimpse of how *Archaeopteryx* and other early protobirds probably moved about. The hoatzin, incidentally, has a further claim as a "living fossil" because, at an early stage of development, the hatchlings also have teeth.

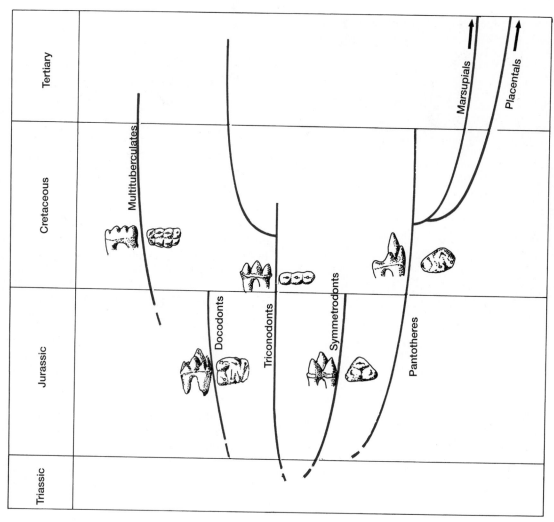

FIGURE 17.24
Evolution of the earliest mammals. Classification is based
largely on the teeth.

The Late Triassic morganucodont fauna is, unfortunately, an isolated lucky find, and only in Middle and Upper Jurassic rocks does the mammalian record reappear with anything more than fragmentary finds. Of the five orders of primitive mammals, the triconodonts, appearing in the Late Triassic and surviving to the Early Cretaceous, were most likely descendants of the morganucodonts. The docodonts, known also from teeth in rocks of Late Jurassic age, may or may not be related. Of the remaining orders, the symmetrodonts—so called because the molar teeth have their main cusps arranged in a triangle—were contemporaries of the triconodonts but, like

them, did not survive long into the Cretaceous. The most successful of the five orders were the multituberculates and the pantotheres. The multituberculates, whose teeth indicate that they were herbivores, had a life-style probably similar to that of the rodents of later time. They lasted well into the Cenozoic but eventually succumbed to more successful competitors. The pantotheres appeared in the Middle Jurassic. They also survived into the Early Cretaceous, where, most paleontologists agree, they gave rise to the marsupial and placental mammals, whose story is continued in the next chapter (Figure 17.24).

Summary

In the Triassic, Pangaea was completely assembled, but by the close of the period, the first rifts were appearing. In the Jurassic, the rifts widened into seaways, and the supercontinent broke apart. During the Triassic and Jurassic, one Worsely, Nance, and Moody cycle ended and another began.

Over large areas of the world, Triassic successions are typified by redbeds, a term that encompasses a wide variety of terrestrial sediments stained by the red iron oxide mineral hematite. Because of the lack of marine successions, the Permian/Triassic boundary is often difficult to define. At the end of the Triassic, the Triassic/Jurassic boundary is similarly often a problem.

In western North America, the Early Triassic is represented by the Moenkopi Formation, made up of sands, silts, and muds transported by streams from easterly sources. In Middle Triassic time, much of the continent was emergent. Sedimentation resumed with the deposition of a widespread conglomerate, the Shinerump, that filled up valleys and hollows in the old land surface. As easterly source areas were eroded down, the Shinerump gave way to the Chinle Formation, made up of muds and silts. The variegated colors of the Chinle are seen in the Painted Desert of Arizona. In the latest Triassic, the Absaroka Sea returned briefly, but the area was largely one of terrestrial deposition as Triassic time passed into Jurassic.

As the Triassic opened, the so-called Sonoma "orogeny" marked the collision of an island arc in the Panthalassic Ocean with North America. This was the first of a series of collision events that became increasingly pronounced during the Jurassic.

Europe was primarily emergent during the Triassic, and hot and semiarid conditions prevailed. Three distinctive divisions—the Bunter, Muschelkalk, and Keuper—characterize European Triassic sediments.

At its fullest development, Pangaea looked like a great *V* lying on its side with the Tethys Ocean inside. The eventual closure of Tethys produced the Alpine-Himalayan fold belt.

In the Triassic, with its marked lack of marine successions and its thick and widespread terrestrial formations, stratigraphic classification and correlation, even at the system level, is difficult. There is no sedimentary record of Early and Middle Triassic time across much of the central and eastern portions of the North American continent, but a belt of narrow basins along the east coast were the first indications of continental rifting.

Latest Triassic to Early Jurassic sediments are dominated by aeolian sands typified in the Wingate and Navajo sandstones. The sea returned in the Middle Jurassic; the marine deposits laid down mark the beginning of the sequence. Sea levels fluctuated during Middle Jurassic time, with the most widespread marine incursion—the Sundance Sea—spreading over much of western North America; it did not connect with the Gulf of Mexico embayment, however.

Along the western shore of the Sundance Sea, a range of tectonic highlands was rising, and large quantities of debris were spilled eastward as molasse deposits. Included in these sediments was the widespread Morrison Formation, famous for its dinosaur fauna.

During the Jurassic, the rifts that had been initiated along North America's eastern margin in the Triassic widened, and the sea entered. At first these incipient oceans had restricted circulation, rather like the modern Red Sea, and salt deposits were laid down. The extensive Louann Salt of the Gulf Coast subsurface and source of the many salt plugs of that region is an example. A similar restricted basin farther north produced the Argo Salt of the Newfoundland offshore area.

By the close of the Jurassic, oceans such as the North Atlantic were large enough for free circulation and normal salinity. As a result, extensive shelf margin reefs formed along North America's eastern seaboard. Much of Europe during the Jurassic was covered by an epeiric sea, and limestones, together with organic-rich shales, were widespread.

Following the end-Permian extinction, Triassic marine faunas were at first impoverished. New bivalves, particularly those with siphons, were exploiting vacant ecologic niches. The ammonoids survived the Permian extinction and underwent an evolutionary radiation during the Triassic. They were decimated at the close of the period, however, and only one family survived into the Jurassic. Following their narrow escape, the ammonites underwent a second evolutionary radiation through the Jurassic and Cretaceous before finally succumbing at the terminal Cretaceous extinction. Among other invertebrates, the scleractinian corals appeared in the Middle Triassic, and through the remainder of the period and the following Jurassic, they gained in importance as reef builders once more.

Among the tetrapods, the labyrinthodont amphibians and cotylosaur and thecodont reptiles were among the Permian survivors to enter the Triassic, where they evolved rapidly. The thecodonts gave rise to the earliest dinosaurs, and before the close of the period, both saurischian and ornithischian lineages were discernible.

The Triassic also marked the first return to an aquatic mode of life of tetrapods of terrestrial stock. The icthyosaurs were the most fishlike, whereas other groups, such as placodonts and nothosaurs, were largely confined to shallow-water and shoreline habitats. Another very successful group of marine reptiles were the plesiosaurs. By the Jurassic, they were evolving rapidly, and two main lineages were apparent: those with long necks and those with short (the latter typified by the pliosaurs).

The history of the dinosaurs during the Jurassic is one of evolutionary radiation and, in most lineages, an increase in size as they moved into a wide variety of habitats. Recent studies of dinosaur locomotion, life-style, and habitat suggest that dinosaurs were warm-blooded rather than cold-blooded animals.

The first flying reptiles appeared in the Triassic, although their flying abilities were limited, and they probably did little more than glide. By Jurassic time, rhamphorhynchoids and other pterosaurs were capable of flapping-wing flight. By the close of the Jurassic, a second group of pterosaurs—the pterodactyloids, with small tails and greatly reduced teeth—had appeared, setting the stage for a Cretaceous radiation.

One of the most important of all Jurassic fossils is *Archaeopteryx* from the Solnhofen Limestone of Bavaria. Although its skeleton is clearly that of a small bipedal dinosaur, it has feathers, and so is classified as a bird. Its skeleton suggests that it probably was not a good flyer, however, and most paleontologists do not place it on the main line of descent of birds.

Recent discoveries in China from rocks only 10 million years younger than *Archaeopteryx* have revealed the oldest true birds found so far. They were clearly good fliers and had birdlike skeletons, although they retained some dinosaur ancestral features.

During the Triassic, the mammals evolved from the mammal-like reptiles of Permian time. The first true mammals are represented by the morganucodonts, small, shrewlike animals found in limestone solution hole infillings in Wales. The later record is poor, but by Jurassic time, five different groups of mammals had evolved. All were extremely small—no bigger than mice—their identification and classification are based largely on differences in their teeth.

Questions

1. Where is the Triassic type area, and why is the system so named?
2. What are redbeds? What is their significance in terms of reconstructing past sedimentary environments?
3. Why is the Triassic unique in terms of Phanerozoic world paleogeography?
4. Describe what happened along the western margin of the North American craton during the Triassic.
5. Describe how the Permo-Triassic nonmarine successions of Gondwana are subdivided. Why is it difficult to recognize the standard divisions used elsewhere in the world?
6. The modern Atlantic Ocean can be said to have had its earliest beginnings in the Triassic. What feature of the North American Triassic would support this statement?
7. What happened to the corals during the Permian and Triassic?
8. Explain why the Triassic and Jurassic were important in the history of marine reptiles.
9. Describe the Sundance Sea and the tectonic events that led to its eventual disappearance.
10. What does the Jurassic succession of eastern North America (Atlantic and Gulf coastal plains subsurface) tell about the early history of the Atlantic Ocean?
11. Explain how the study of dinosaurs and dinosaur classification has evolved since the nineteenth century.
12. Describe some of the evidence that has led some scientists to believe that the dinosaurs were warm-blooded.
13. Discuss the early history of birds, as indicated by the fossil evidence from the Triassic and Jurassic.
14. Why is the transition from reptiles to mammals so difficult to determine from the fossil record?
15. Describe the early history of mammal-like animals during the Triassic and Jurassic.

Further Reading

Alexander, R. M. 1989. *Dynamics of dinosaurs and other extinct giants*. New York: Columbia University Press.

Hallam, A. 1975. *Jurassic environments*. New York: Cambridge University Press.

18

THE CRETACEOUS

Introduction

By Cretaceous time, the earth's surface as it would be seen from space was becoming quite recognizable. What was to become the Atlantic Ocean had its beginning, as mentioned in Chapter 17, in the Jurassic. By the close of that period, a narrow ocean extended between North America and Europe but was not open to the Arctic Ocean. Europe, Greenland, and North America were still joined across what is now the North Atlantic, and the mid-Atlantic rift did not extend northward to separate them until the Early Cenozoic. By the Early Cretaceous, the South American and African continents were barely separated, while India, Australia, and Antarctica formed a single mass as they moved in a generally easterly direction away from Africa. By the Late Cretaceous, India had become separated and was heading northward to a rendezvous with Asia. Australia and Antarctica were still joined and did not separate until the early Cenozoic. In the Cretaceous world, the Tethys Ocean was still conspicuous and essentially separated the northern continents from the southern along a roughly equatorial line. There were no polar ice caps, and the world climate was apparently mild and equable, as it had been during the Jurassic.

The Cretaceous Period spanned some 80 million years, enough time for major changes. These changes might be summarized by saying that, as the Cretaceous opened, the world of the Mesozoic as it had been during the Pangaea phase was still discernible, and reconstruction of the earlier configuration was simple. As the Cretaceous closed, the world as it was going to be was already emerging (Figure 18.1).

The mass extinction event at the close of the Cretaceous tolled the knell of the large reptiles. Henceforward, the world belonged to the mammals, although during the Cretaceous, the mammals' role in vertebrate faunas was negligible.

The Cretaceous in North America

The Atlantic Basin

The eastern margin of North America had now become an important sedimentary province. Beneath the Atlantic coastal plain and out into the subsurface below the continental shelf, the Cretaceous is represented by a great wedge of sediments thickening eastward and whose source was the continental interior to the west (Figure 18.2). This was a passive margin, or **trailing-edge margin,** so compressive tectonic activity and volcanism were conspicuously absent. Traced southward and westward, the Atlantic coastal plain passes into the Gulf of Mexico, and in a great arc surrounding the Gulf, the sedimentary wedge can be traced down into Central and South America. Sediment accumulation in this wedge has continued to the present day, and modern sedimentary environments have close analogies throughout the succession. One consequence of this is that much of the Cretaceous portion of the wedge is buried beneath younger sediments. This means that outcrops are not extensive and are found exclusively along the inland margin, where they comprise a feather edge adjacent to the Paleozoic and older rocks of the Appalachian-Marathon-Ouachita trend.

With the sedimentary source to the west and the ocean to the east, Cretaceous formations as they are traced in boreholes and on seismic surveys become progressively finer grained and show an increasingly marine influence as they pass into the subsurface beneath the coastal plain and continental shelf. At their shoreward extremities, these formations interfinger with freshwater clays, sands, and gravels. Outcrops in Delaware, Maryland, and Virginia have been mapped as the Patuxent, Arundel, Patapsco, and Raritan formations. Fossils of plants, freshwater mollusks, and reptiles, including eight species of dinosaurs, suggest alluvial coastal swamp environments.

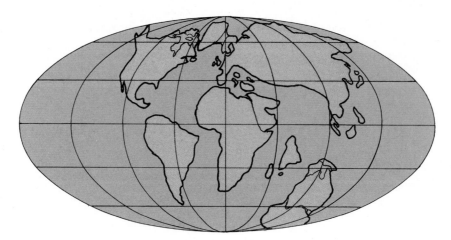

FIGURE 18.1
World paleogeography in the Late Cretaceous.

Out onto the continental shelf, the shelf edge reefs of Jurassic time continued to flourish through the Early Cretaceous (Figure 18.3). Much of the terriginous clastics derived from the continental transport system of streams draining the North American hinterland was deposited inshore. As a result, the outer shelf region remained clear of suspended sediment.

In a carryover from the Jurassic, tectonic controls apparently continued, at least for a time, to play an important role because evidence indicates that some of the rifts of the original Atlantic margin were still active. These movements were manifested in the immediate offshore region in the form of numerous fault-controlled basins, which, acting as sediment traps, prevented terriginous material from reaching the outer shelf.

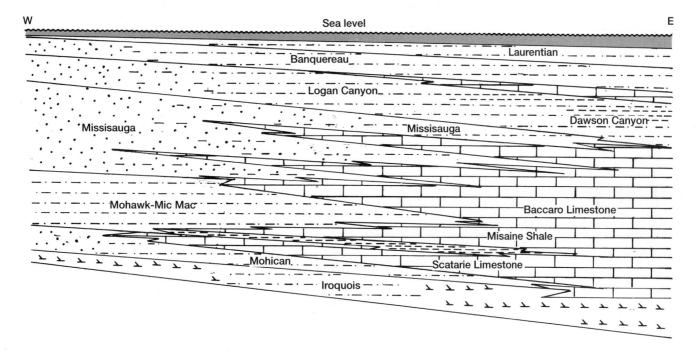

FIGURE 18.2
Cretaceous sedimentary wedge of the continental shelf, Baltimore Canyon area off the eastern United States.

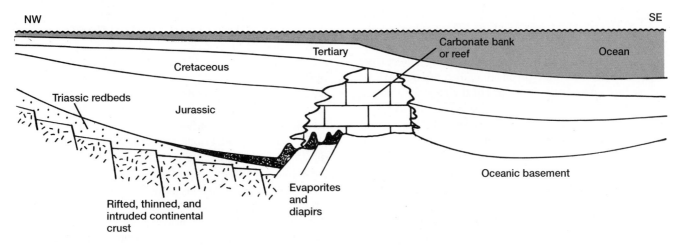

FIGURE 18.3
Schematic cross section, based on seismic reflection surveys through a passive margin continental shelf. The line of section crosses the eastern end of the Long Island platform.

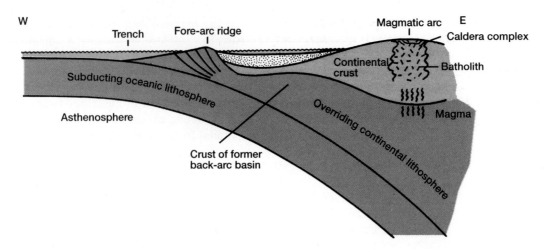

FIGURE 18.4

Schematic section through the western North American craton margin during an early phase of the Cordilleran orogeny.

TABLE 18.1
Phases of the Cordilleran "Orogeny"

Orogeny	Time Period
Laramide	Late Cretaceous to Early Neogene
Sevier	Earliest Cretaceous to end Cretaceous
Nevadan	Late Jurassic to Early Cretaceous

In the overall sedimentary and tectonic setting of the eastern margin, the Early Cretaceous was essentially a continuation of the Middle and Late Jurassic. In the later Cretaceous, however, this changed. Throughout the Cretaceous, eustatic sea level was generally rising, and marine transgressions were widespread on many continents. Along the eastern and southern margins of the North American continent, on the other hand, the sea was regressing, due to the prograding of sediments out onto the continental shelf. By Cretaceous time, subsidence of the continental margin had slowed considerably, as had fault basin activity. This meant that terriginous sediments were encroaching further and further out onto the shelf until they finally engulfed the shelf edge carbonates and reef development largely ceased. Seismic reflectors reached by deep boreholes confirm that this process began, in places, as early as the Hauterivian Stage in the middle Early Cretaceous. Elsewhere, reef development continued into the Late Cretaceous, and in the Florida region, remote from clastic sources, it never really stopped.

The Cordilleran Region

During the Cretaceous along almost the entire western length of the North American continent, there were crustal movements involving uplift and thrusting, together with deep-seated igneous intrusions and volcanic activity (Figure 18.4). These laid the foundations of the great range today called the Rocky Mountains. In South America, the picture was essentially the same, resulting in the Andes Mountains.

Tectonic activity and intrusive phases reached a climax at different times and at different places, so that a series of separate orogenies is recognized. Although they are given different names and ages, the dates of their beginnings and endings overlap so that it is more accurate to think of these orogenies as simply phases during the long history of crustal unrest called the **Cordilleran orogeny** (Table 18.1).

The opening phase of Cordilleran unrest was the **Nevadan orogeny** that began in Late Jurassic time and reached a climax in the earliest Cretaceous. During this time, the great Coast Range, Idaho, Sierra Nevada, and Southern California batholiths were emplaced (Figure 18.5). Later, as intrusions and crustal movements continued through the Cretaceous, the zone of maximum activity migrated eastward, affecting areas of Nevada and Utah during the **Sevier orogeny** (Figure 18.6). In latest Cretaceous and in Early Cenozoic time, during what has been termed the **Laramide orogeny,** the effects of thrusting were being felt as far east as a line from Alberta, through western Wyoming, and into Utah. Why the zone of crustal unrest moved progressively eastward during the Cretaceous is not known for certain, but many geologists now believe that it reflects changes along the boundary between the Pacific and North American plates, with a shift from high-angle to low-angle subduction (Figure 18.7).

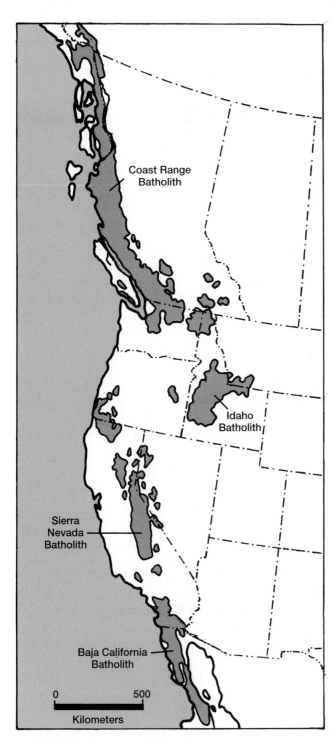

FIGURE 18.5
Batholiths intruded during the Mesozoic crustal unrest in
west-central North America.

Collision Terranes

While the zone of crustal shortening, thrusting, and
compression extended over a vast area, the most intense
deformation was much further west, close to the actual
plate edge. Of particular interest is a melange of rocks of

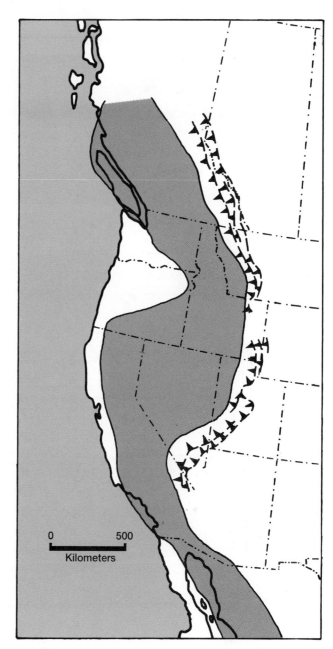

FIGURE 18.6
Area of the Sevier orogenic belt. Major thrust zones
associated with the Sevier orogeny are marked by barbed
lines.

all kinds that forms much of the Coast Ranges of California. Mapped as the **Franciscan Complex,** the origin and
age of these rocks was for a long time, and particularly in
the days before plate tectonics, a complete mystery.

Although a mixture of many different rock types, the
overall aspect of the assemblage is one of deep water.
Indeed, some of the radiolarian cherts have been interpreted as of deep-sea pelagic origin. Associated with the
cherts are graywackes, shales, and pillow lavas, while
embedded in these rocks are exotic blocks of gabbro, ser-
pentinite, and other igneous rocks usually associated with

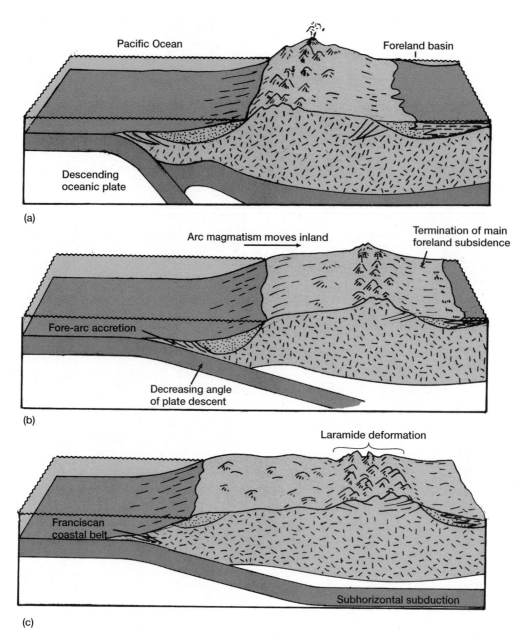

FIGURE 18.7

Inferred plate motions along the western North American craton margin during the Late Cretaceous to Early Cenozoic. (a) 70 to 80 million years ago (Late Cretaceous). (b) 65 to 75 million years ago (Latest Cretaceous). (c) 50 to 60 million years ago (Early Tertiary).

ophiolites derived from oceanic basement sources. Some of the exotic blocks measure several kilometers across and often differ in metamorphic grade from the surrounding rock. Sometimes, they are more metamorphosed, sometimes less.

The most widely accepted explanation for the peculiar rock associations and field relationships is that the Franciscan Complex originated as sediments on the deep ocean floor, perhaps far to the west. Carried eastward on the surface of the Pacific plate, they were then "scraped off" against the North American plate as the oceanic plate descended along a subduction line.

The mechanism postulated for the origin of the Franciscan Complex sets the stage for consideration of similar collision complexes, although on a much larger scale. Just as with the Franciscan rocks, considerable mystery surrounded the so-called **exotic** or **suspect terranes** of a huge area of the Pacific northwest, adjacent British Columbia, and Alaska. The geology of this rugged and often remote region was mapped only relatively recently. However, even the earliest studies indicated that much of the regional

Detailed studies of the fossils and stratigraphy within each of these exotic terranes suggest that some of them, at least, are far-traveled microplates of continental, island arc, or oceanic crustal origin. In some cases, the faunal evidence indicates that certain terranes may even have originated in Asia and traveled on a plate surface clear across the Pacific before becoming accreted to the North American continent.

Some geologists believe that as much as 25 percent of the Cordilleran region of North America may have been acquired in this way. The process took place over a period of time that certainly encompasses the whole of the Mesozoic and may even extend back into the Paleozoic, although the evidence becomes increasingly obscure.

Cretaceous Marine Transgressions

As the pieces of Pangaea drifted apart and broke into smaller pieces, new ocean basins appeared, and new segments were added to the line of spreading centers. These additions to the midocean ridge systems resulted in a eustatic rise of sea level, and during the Cretaceous, greater areas of the continent were being inundated than at any time since the Early Paleozoic.

In North America, although depositional progradation caused marine regression along much of the eastern seaboard, in the Gulf of Mexico, the sea extended well into Texas and northern Mexico (Figure 18.9). The western part of the craton was also widely flooded, and a great arm of the sea encroached southward from the Arctic Ocean, carrying marine conditions into a huge embayment that lay east of the Cordilleran orogenic belt. This so-called **Mowry Sea,** named for the extensive Mowry Shale, extended as far south as Utah but did not connect with the Gulf of Mexico embayment.

In the Middle Cretaceous, world sea level fell briefly but began to rise again almost immediately. This new transgression was even more extensive than the one of Early Cretaceous time. On this occasion, the southwardly encroaching arm of the western sea did finally meet up with the embayment that extended from the Gulf of Mexico. Viewed from space, North America looked like two landmasses separated by what has been called the **Interior Seaway** (Figure 18.10).

The Interior Seaway

The Interior Seaway connected the Arctic Ocean with the Gulf of Mexico and represented one of the greatest inundations of the North American continent in all of geologic history. Although due to its huge area and general shallowness, the Interior Seaway was, technically, an epeiric sea, it differed considerably from the great epicontinental seas of Early Paleozoic time, and many geologists are dubious about using the term *epeiric* at all.

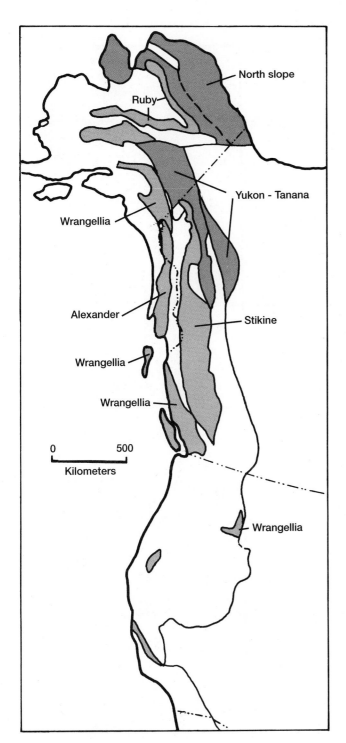

FIGURE 18.8
Exotic terranes in the Pacific northwest region.

stratigraphy and structures did not make much sense. Geologists soon realized that the whole territory was a complex of fault slices and blocks, each of which was different—sometimes totally different—from adjacent blocks (Figure 18.8).

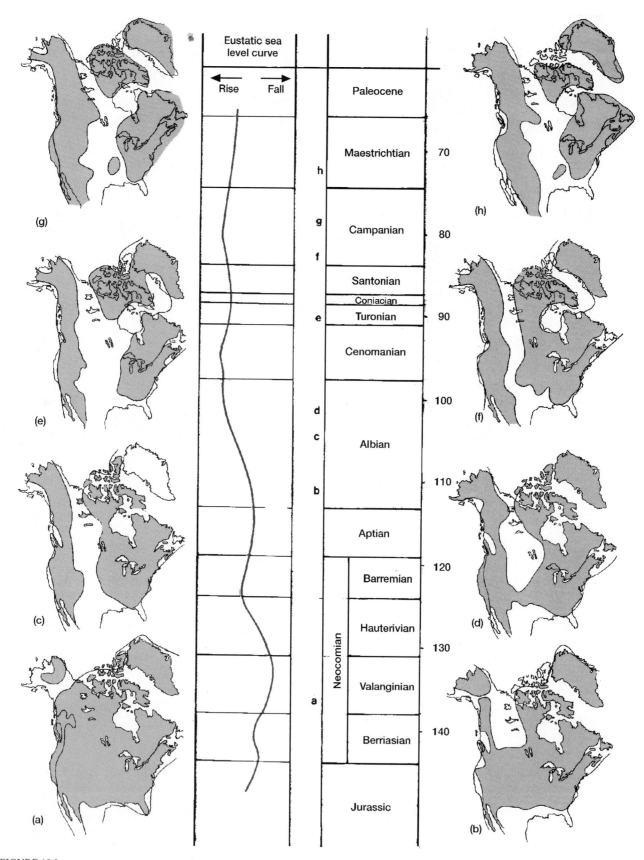

FIGURE 18.9

Fluctuating sea levels and the changing pattern of land and sea on the North American craton during the Cretaceous. (a) Infravalanginian seas. (b) Latest Early Albian seas. (c) Early Late Albian seas. (d) Late Late Albian seas. (e) Late Early Turonian seas. (f) Early Campanian seas. (g) Middle Campanian seas. (h) Early Maestrichtian seas.

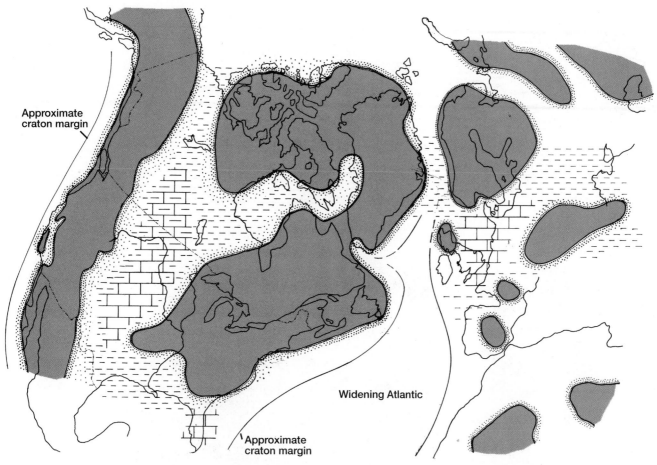

FIGURE 18.10

Paleogeography of the North American and European areas in the Late Cretaceous.

For example, the sea that inundated North America during the Ordovician spread across a stable craton with little structural deformation, clastic sources were far distant, and carbonates were the predominant lithology. In the Cretaceous Interior Seaway, the situation was very different. The sea lay not upon a stable craton but rather flooded what was actually a **foreland basin,** an elongated downwarped region, actively subsiding as a great flood of clastic sediments poured in from a rising orogenic belt to the west. Invariably, all the sedimentary formations filling this subsiding foredeep show essentially the same facies changes. Beginning in the west, where they are thickest, each sedimentary unit is relatively coarse grained, reflecting a nearby source in the rising Cordilleran ranges. Traced eastward, each of the units becomes progressively thinner, and the average grain size falls rapidly. Many of the western formations are of nonmarine sediments and are, in fact, typical molasse deposits (Figure 18.11a). In South America during the Late Cretaceous, all through the Cenozoic, and up to the present day, a similar fore-

deep basin east of the Andes Mountains has been filled by nonmarine sediments derived from the rising Andean Cordilleran belt.

In an easterly direction, many of the foredeep units pass eventually into marine sands, silts, and muds. In the easternmost sections, far removed from suspended sediment, there are even thin limestones. Sea levels fluctuated somewhat during much of the Cretaceous, and this is reflected in repetitive facies changes across the Interior Seaway. Over large areas of eastern Utah, Arizona, New Mexico, and Colorado, for example, are gray marine shales of the Mancos Formation, laid down through a period of marine transgression. Thin sands within the Mancos indicate periods of shallowing, and the formation is overlain by sands, shales, and coals of the Mesa Verde Group, deposited during a period of regression. Detailed facies studies of the Mesa Verde have enabled geologists to construct a picture of advancing and retreating shorelines. The associated facies suggest that extensive coastal swamps were present, and coals are commonly thick and extensive (Figure 18.11b).

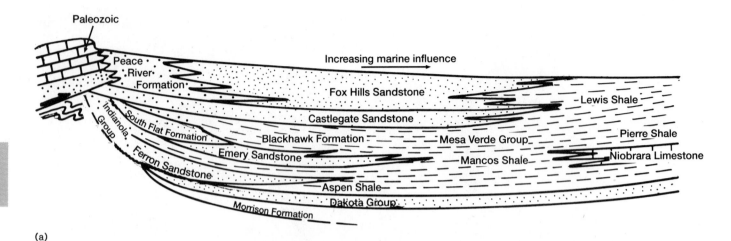

(a)

(b)

FIGURE 18.11

(a) Generalized cross section showing the pattern of facies changes across the foreland basin that lay east of the Cordilleran orogenic belt during the Cretaceous. Marine influence increases, sediments become fine grained, and formations generally become thinner in a west-east direc (b) Sandstones, shales, and coals of the Menepee forma Mesa Verde group, Durango, Colorado.

Cretaceous Flora

Gymnosperms

As discussed in Chapter 14, well before the close of the Paleozoic, the seed plants (gymnosperms) had appeared, and particularly in drier areas, the forests were dominated by gingkoales (the sole living survivor is *Gingko biloba*) cycads, and conifers. During the Triassic and Jurassic, all three of these groups evolved rapidly, replacing the *Lep-* *idodendron* and *Calamites* types that were already declining through the Permian and that finally disappeared in the Triassic and Jurassic, respectively.

Ferns remained prominent, but as undergrowth plants rather than forest trees. Tree ferns and seed ferns formed a forest "middle story," while the tallest trees were conifers, the commonest being a relatively primitive group—the araucarian pines. Today, these plants are, in their natural habitat, confined to areas in the Southern Hemisphere, although they have a worldwide distribution as

(a)

(b)

(c)

(d)

FIGURE 18.12

Living examples of araucarians and cycads. (a) Norfolk Island Pine. (b) Detail of Norfolk Island Pine foliage. (c) Broad-leaved cycad. (d) Detail of cycad flowering structure and foliage.

cultivated plants. The Norfolk Island Pine (Figure 18.12a,b) and the Monkey Puzzle trees are two examples. The trees preserved in the Late Triassic Chinle Formation in the Petrified Forest in Arizona, mentioned in Chapter 17, are dominantly araucarians.

The gingkoales, another group of gymnosperms, had appeared during the Triassic and were fairly common through the Mesozoic. They dwindled during the Cenozoic and until the 1700s were believed to have become extinct in the Neogene. One species remains, however. *Gingko biloba* (the Maidenhair tree) was found surviving

as a cultivated tree in Chinese monastery gardens, the monks apparently having some superstitious regard for the tree. It grew wild in China into historic times but had been largely eliminated in the search for firewood. Since the 1970s, a few wild stands apparently have been located.

Another gymnosperm group that reached its climax during the Mesozoic were the cycads. They had short, stubby trunks, rather like a pineapple in appearance, and a crown of palmlike leaves. Like the gingkoales, they have also survived to the present day but are not common, having a modest distribution through the tropics (Figure 18.12c,d).

BOX 18.1

Life Cycles of Plants

	Ferns	Gymnosperms
Ovules	Produced in archegonia on small gametophyte plant.	Not completely enclosed by tissues of the sporophyte plant. Ovules borne on ovulate cone.
Sperm	Produced in antheridia on small gametophyte plant.	In pollen grains on pollen-bearing cone.
Sperm transfer	Sperms swim through water film.	Within pollen, mainly by wind.
Fertilization	Sperm reaches archegonia and fuses with single egg, producing a zygote.	Pollen reaches exposed ovules and is retained on sticky surface of the scales of ovulate cone.
Development	Zygote grows into embryo plant, which takes root and grows to mature fern.	After pollination, the cone scales grow together to protect the developing ovule.
Seeds		Borne as scales of seed (formally ovulate) cone until ripe; then scales open and release seed.

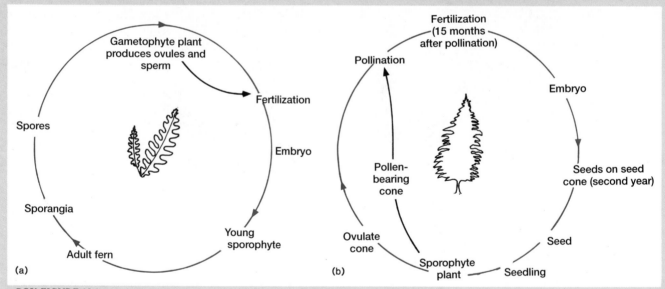

BOX FIGURE 18.1
(a) Fern life cycle. (b) Gymnosperm life cycle. (c) Angiosperm life cycle.

Angiosperms

Ovules enclosed within the tissue of the parent sporophyte (in carpels).

In pollen grains produced by stamens.

Within pollen, some by wind but also by insects, birds, bats.

Pollen reaches specialized structure on the carpel known as the stigma. Pollen pass to ovule down a pollen tube.

On fertilization, the ripening carpels grow into fruit.

The embryo-containing seeds are inside the fruit and are often transported by herbivores.

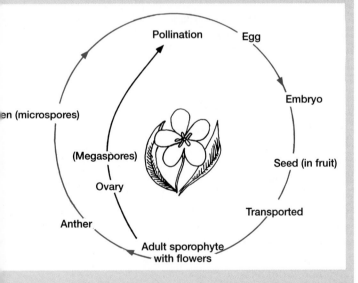

The seed plants, discussed in Chapter 14, represented a great evolutionary step forward in releasing plants from a dependence on moist environments. Seeds are, in effect, fertilized embryos contained within a food supply for the embryo until it has grown leaves and roots to support itself (Box 18.1). For fertilization to occur, sperm-carrying pollen from the male gametophyte (the haploid phase of the plant's life cycle) must be conveyed to the female gametophyte. In conifers and other gymnosperms, pollination is largely by the wind and is an entirely random process. It is also relatively inefficient because enormous quantities of pollen are produced, most of which is wasted.

Angiosperms

The evolution of the angiosperms (a term meaning "covered seed"), or flowering plants, from the gymnosperms, the so-called naked seed plants, is believed to have been a response to mechanisms that improved pollination. Gradually, insects feeding and moving from plant to plant became accidental pollinators by carrying pollen grains on their legs or bodies. Presumably, those plants with the more attractive leaves and scent were involved in a complex selection process involving not only the plants themselves but, through various feedback components, the insects also. The life cycle of many insect species is so finely attuned to specific plant species that the Cretaceous unquestionably was not only a critical time in plant evolution, but for insects, too.

Pollination was only part of the life cycle. Dispersal mechanisms for the fertilized seeds also evolved. In the angiosperms, the seed is contained within a fruit that is invariably edible and is thus carried away, the resistant seeds being eventually voided by the animal. Numerous other mechanisms of seed dispersal—notably sticky coatings and burrlike devices—have also evolved.

Although the earliest flowering plants are believed to have appeared in the Jurassic, certain doubtful fossil remains have been found in rocks of Triassic age. A well-documented fossil record, on the other hand, does not begin until the beginning of the Late Cretaceous, when a rapid phase of evolutionary divergence began.

Apart from spores and problematic structures of various kinds, microfossils have, up to this point, contributed little to paleobotanical studies. However, paleobotanists have been able to collect Cretaceous fossil pollen (Figure 18.13), making palynology (the science of pollen) a feasible working tool for paleontologists and biostratigraphers.

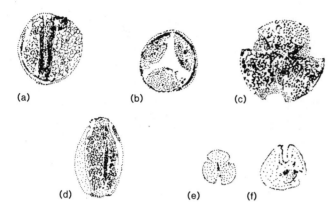

FIGURE 18.13

Typical Cretaceous pollen grains. (a) *Liliacidites dividuus.*
(b) *Liliacidites trichotomosulcatus.* (c) *Tricolpites wilsonii.*
(d) *Fraxinoipollenites venustus.* (e) *Psilatricolpites parvulus.*
(f) *Nyssapollenites albertensis.* Specimens (a), (b), and (d)
are from the Peace River Formation, (c) is from the
Dunvegan Formation, and (e) and (f) are from the
Shaftesbury Formation, all in the Peace River area of
northern Alberta.

Marine Plants

A well-documented record of marine plants, particularly
the phytoplankton, begins in the Cretaceous. Two phyla
of microscopic unicellular marine plants—the Pyro-
phyta, or dinoflagellates, and the Chrysophyta, which include the diatoms and coccolithophorids—dominate the
fossil record. The earliest beginnings of the groups are
wrapped in mystery, although dinoflagellates have been
claimed from rocks as old as Silurian. The earliest un-
doubted diatoms and coccolithophorids are of Jurassic age,
but it was not until the Cretaceous that they began a rapid
expansion that has continued through the Cenozoic. Because both these plants secrete crystalline microscopic
structures—calcium carbonate in the case of coccolithophorids and silica in the diatoms—fossil preservation typically is remarkably good.

Cretaceous Fauna

Invertebrates

A general continuity in marine invertebrate faunas is evident in passing from the Jurassic into the Cretaceous, although during the Cretaceous, important new groups
appeared and the relative importance of others shifted.

Of all the sedimentary rocks, the one most typical of
the Cretaceous is chalk. Indeed, the period was named
from the word *creta,* which is the Latin word for chalk.

Chalk is a remarkably pure and fine-grained limestone
made up almost entirely of the calcareous structures secreted by microscopic planktonic organisms. Chief among
these are the coccolithophorids, a group of algae that
became abundant in the Cretaceous. Also prominent for
the first time were the planktonic foraminifera, such as
Globigerina, a very common genus.

Organic reefs also became much more important
during the Cretaceous, although the balance of the various organisms within the reef communities was different
from that seen in modern reefs. Scleractinian corals were
present, as in modern reefs, but in Cretaceous time, they
took second place as reef builders to a group of odd-looking
bivalved mollusks. These were the rudistid mollusks, some
of which grew to over a meter in length, with shells 10
centimeters thick. Coralline algae and encrusting cheilos-
tome bryozoans were also important constructional elements in the reefs. The brachiopods began to dwindle in
the Cretaceous. During the Jurassic, they had increased
in importance, but a decline now began that has continued
to the present day.

Among the mollusks, the most prominent gastropods
were the high-spired turritellid forms, while *Ostrea, Inoceramus,* and *Exogyra* were important bivalves (Figure
18.14). The ammonites, as in the Jurassic, continued to
evolve rapidly. A second group of cephalopods—the belemnites—were particularly important in the Cretaceous.
Among the echinoderms, the round, regular forms of Jurassic seas were becoming outnumbered by the irregular
"heart urchins," which became adapted to a burrowing
mode of life.

The Continued Evolution of the Fishes

Although fishes are among the most common vertebrate
fossils in older rocks, detailed consideration of their later
evolutionary history has been postponed to this point for
two reasons: One is that, in the Cretaceous, the third and
last of the three main groups of bony fishes—the Teleostei—appeared. The second is that, during the Cretaceous, an evolutionary radiation began in both the
cartilaginous and the bony fishes (Figure 18.15).

Cartilaginous Fishes

The cartilaginous fishes—the sharks and rays—have
always been marine fishes except for a small group of
freshwater sharks—the pleurocanths of Carboniferous and
Permian time. The sharks have also always been largely
active predatory fishes, which is why, throughout their
history, they have retained their streamlined torpedo shape.
Cladoselache, for example, a primitive shark of Late Devonian age, could not be mistaken for anything else.

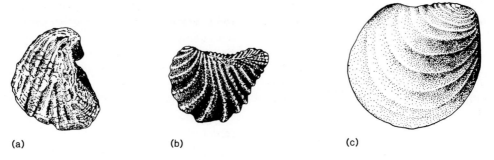

FIGURE 18.14
Cretaceous mollusks. (a) *Exogyra.* (b) *Trigonia.*
(c) *Inoceramus.*

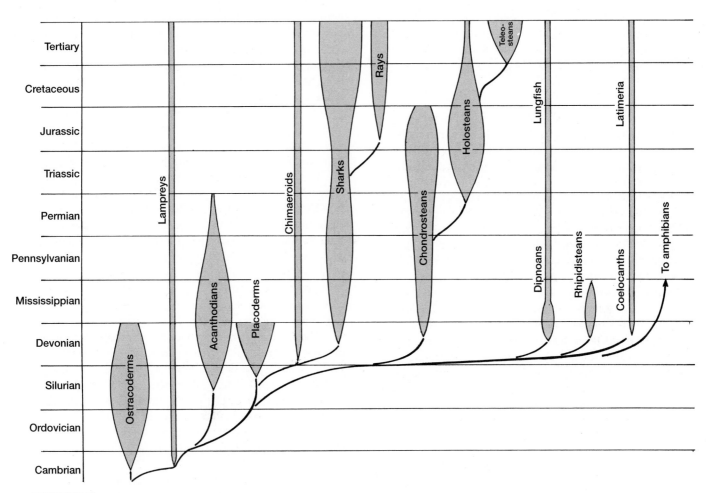

FIGURE 18.15
Evolution of the fishes.

The main line of shark evolution is carried by the so-called **hybodont sharks** that appeared in the Late Devonian and continued to the earliest Cenozoic. Clearly, the sharks had quickly become quite successful animals because the hybodonts retained such primitive features as an early type of jaw attachment and quite primitive teeth. They could thus be considered conservative in terms of evolutionary history. On the other hand, their paired fins were considerably improved in design, and they were efficient swimmers.

By the close of the Permian, the hybodonts were in decline, and although they continued as important elements of marine faunas through the Mesozoic, they were becoming superseded by groups that were clearly ancestral to the "modern" sharks. The most noticeable advance was in the style of jaw suspension. The primitive, so-called amphistylic mode was replaced by a method of jaw suspension in which there was only one attachment point at the back of the skull, a mechanically more efficient arrangement.

By the beginning of the Cretaceous, all three main groups of cartilaginous fishes had appeared: (1) the typical sharks, which retained their torpedo shape from earlier times; (2) the skates and rays, which were adapted to life as bottom dwellers and had greatly enlarged pectoral fins they used as wings to "fly" through the water; and (3) the Chimaerae, a largely deep-water group of fishes that includes the ratfishes.

Bony Fishes

As mentioned in Chapter 14, the first actinopterygeans, or bony fishes, appeared in the Middle Devonian and were adapted to life in freshwater lakes and rivers. The fossil record was largely contained in sediments of the Old Red Sandstone facies, and only later did their descendants move into the oceans. These early bony fishes had only a partially ossified internal skeleton but had heavy rhombic (diamond-shaped) scales, which made efficient armor. Collectively, the bony fishes are classified under the heading of **Chondrostei,** a group that dominated the fish fauna throughout the Paleozoic. A few forms, such as the African genus *Polypterus,* are still living.

Having dominated Late Paleozoic fish faunas, the chondrosteans markedly declined during the Triassic, and their place was taken by fish with much lighter scales and an increased ossification of the skeleton, particularly in the vertebral elements. There were also important modifications in the skull and jaws. Classified as the **Holostei,** this group had begun to decline by the Early Cretaceous, but again, a few have survived to the present day, represented by two genera—the bowfin (*Amia*) of the northeastern states and the gar pike (*Lepisosteus*) of the Mississippi River.

As the holosteans declined, they were progressively replaced by an even more advanced group, the **Teleostei.** In the teleosts, some of the trends discerned in the progression from Chondrostei to the Holostei were continued: Scale weight continued to reduce, while ossification of the skeleton became complete. Further specialized trends in the skull were manifested in such features as a shortening of the jaws. The vertebral column no longer extended into the upper lobe of the tail fins, so the fins became symmetrical, or homocercal, a feature that had also already appeared in some of the more advanced holostean fishes.

As the teleosts expanded in many directions through the Cretaceous, an evolutionary radiation that continues even today, many of the body plans that had appeared earlier in the Holostei and even before then, in the Chondrostei, reappeared. This phenomenon was in some ways an example of parallel evolution, with varying environmental demands in a wide spectrum of ecologic niches being reflected in the same morphologic response in different phyletic lines.

Marine Reptiles

Icthyosaurs and plesiosaurs from the Jurassic continued into the Cretaceous, although icthyosaurs died out well before the end of the period. The plesiosaurs often increased strikingly in size. By the close of the Cretaceous, some of the long-necked plesiosaurs were gigantic in length, if not in bulk. *Elasmosaurus* of Late Cretaceous time had a neck that was twice as long as its body and made up of no fewer than 70 vertebrae (Figure 18.16a).

Perhaps the largest plesiosaur belonged to the short-necked branch, the pliosaurs. In *Kronosaurus* from the Australian Cretaceous, the skull alone was nearly 4 meters long, and the animal's total length was close to 16 meters.

During the Cretaceous, yet another terrestrial group of reptiles—the lizards—returned to the sea. Relatively small forms appeared in the Early Cretaceous, but these early mosasaurs evolved quickly and grew especially in size. By Late Cretaceous time, *Tylosaurus,* for example, was more than 10 meters long (Figure 18.16b). The crocodiles were, incidentally, another group among which there were marine adaptations. The geosaurs, an early marine crocodilian group, had appeared in the Jurassic but were in rapid decline in the earliest Cretaceous.

The Late Cretaceous fossil record shows no particular decline in any of the marine reptiles. On the contrary, virtually all of the groups that had returned to the sea seemed to be flourishing. Nevertheless, when the time came, they shared the fate of the dinosaurs and pterosaurs and vanished from the face of the earth.

Dinosaurs—The Dynasty Continues

Dinosaur faunas appear to be continuous in passing from the Jurassic into the Cretaceous, which reflects a similar continuity in world climatic conditions. Although no major extinctions occurred at the close of the Jurassic, some dinosaur groups clearly had already passed their peak and would disappear well before the end of the Cretaceous. For example, the stegosaurs (quadrupeds with prominent, diamond-shaped plates projecting from the vertebrae) had appeared early in the Jurassic but by its close were already declining. They became extinct by the end of the Early Cretaceous and were, in fact, the first major group of dinosaurs to disappear. Other groups of dinosaurs,

(a)

(b)

FIGURE 18.16

(a) Plesiosaur *Elasmosaurus*. (b) Mosasaur *Tylosaurus*.

however, underwent evolutionary radiation during the Cretaceous and were still diversifying when the terminal Cretaceous event brought about their demise.

One important factor in dinosaur history was linked to plate tectonics. When the dinosaurs first appeared in the Triassic, they were able to spread to all parts of Pangaea. After the breakup of the supercontinent in the Jurassic, dinosaur populations became isolated from one another on the various continental pieces, and evolution went its separate ways on different continents. This trend, of course, continued through the Cretaceous.

Estimates of the abundance of Late Cretaceous dinosaurs indicate that there were between two and three times the number of genera and species in the Late Cretaceous as in any other stage of their history. The herbivorous dinosaurs outnumbered the carnivores, which is the normal balance when comparing herbivorous and carnivorous animals. However, the big increase in herbivorous species likely was due to a concomitant increase in the quality, if not the quantity, of the food supply, since this was also the time of the great evolutionary radiation of the flowering plants.

Dinosaurs and the Fossil Record

Although, to most people, the word *dinosaur* conjures up a picture of massive, lumbering, and for the most part, slow-moving beasts, many, perhaps even the majority of

FIGURE 18.17

The small Cretaceous dinosaur *Ornithomimus*.

dinosaur species, likely were relatively small, agile animals. Some were no larger than birds, and many had the same delicate skeletons, even with hollow bones. In addition, some small dinosaurs were probably insectivores (Figure 18.17). Inevitably, much less is known about these small creatures because their fossils, like those of birds, are rare. Overall, the dinosaur fossil record is undoubtedly biased in favor of the larger species.

Until quite recently, most information about Cretaceous dinosaurs was based upon Late Cretaceous faunas. The few fossils from Lower Cretaceous formations resulted in only about 35 described genera. In recent years, however, the gaps in the record are being slowly filled, in large part due to discoveries in the Sahara Desert of North Africa. Here, in the Gadoufaoua deposit of northeastern Niger, thousands of dinosaur bones, as well as the remains of giant crocodilians and other reptiles, have been collected by several French expeditions. Much of this material has yet to be described.

In contrast to Early Cretaceous dinosaurs, Late Cretaceous dinosaurs were much more abundant and are better known. In fact, during the Late Cretaceous, the dinosaurs and indeed the reptiles as a whole reached the zenith of their evolution. Among the formations most prolific in Late Cretaceous dinosaurs are the Foremost and Oldman formations of the Belly River Group, exposed along the Red Deer River in Alberta, Canada. Farther north and somewhat younger in age are outcrops of the Edmonton Formation, also a prolific source of dinosaur remains. In the United States, formations of roughly equivalent age are the Hell Creek and Lance formations of Wyoming and Montana. The Mesa Verde of Colorado and the Fruitland and Kirkland formations of the Four Corners area (where Utah, Colorado, New Mexico, and Arizona meet) also have yielded significant finds. All of these formations were deposited across broad alluvial plains that lay along the shores of the great Interior Seaway.

Two names that should be added to the roster of dinosaur fossil hunters are American Barnum Brown and Canadian Charles Sternberg, whose sons Charles Jr. and Levi also collected many notable dinosaur skeletons during the first half of the twentieth century. The Sternbergs, in particular, amassed one of the largest collections of Cretaceous dinosaurs in the world, which is now housed in the Royal Ontario Museum in Toronto, Canada. Other fine Canadian collections are in Ottawa and Alberta.

The Saurischians

The saurischian line of sauropods continued from the Jurassic into the Cretaceous with some of the largest land animals ever to have lived. Not surprisingly, they were all quadrupeds, although the hind limbs were all noticeably larger than the forelimbs. These giant animals were herbivores, but another line of saurischians—the theropods—were active, predatory carnivores. They had been successful all through the Jurassic and continued so into the Cretaceous. With powerful hind limbs and massive tails, these bipedal animals could undoubtedly run rapidly. *Deinonychus* ("terrible claw") perhaps attacked its prey with its sharp claws (Figure 18.18a). *Tyrannosaurus,* on the other hand, likely used its awesome teeth with formidable effect (Figure 18.18b).

The Ornithischians

The most notable of the herbivorous dinosaurs of Late Cretaceous time were the ornithischian group, the ornithopods (Figure 18.19). They had already begun to dominate the scene in the Early Cretaceous, but in the Late Cretaceous, the number of genera and species, according to some paleontologists, increased fivefold. Most of these forms can be collectively grouped as duckbilled dinosaurs, although two other groups—the armored dinosaurs or **ankylosaurs** and the horned dinosaurs or ceratopsians—were also common in the Late Cretaceous.

Ornithopods   One of several lines of ornithopod adaptation is typified in *Iguanodon* (Figure 18.18c). Best known in the Early Cretaceous of Europe, an *Iguanodon* specimen found in the Wealden Formation of southern England in 1822, was, in fact, the first dinosaur to be properly described. Dr. Gideon Mantell is credited with this first scientific study of dinosaurs, although his wife actually found the first specimen. This was probably a big mistake on her part because the good doctor's obsessive interest in dinosaurs finally ruined his medical practice!

Iguanodon was a typical herbivorous bipedal ornithischian with powerful tail and hind limbs. Notable in the relatively short forelimbs was a thumb developed into a sharp spike, whose function was presumably in defense. In the earliest museum reconstructions of *Iguanodon,* this spike was mistakenly located as a rhinocerous-like horn growing from the forehead. The discovery of more than 20 complete skeletons at Bernissart, Belgium, many years later revealed the error.

The most successful of the ornithopods were the hadrosaurs or trachodonts of the Late Cretaceous. Many grew to a considerable size, but despite this, they largely retained their bipedal gait. The most distinctive feature in the hadrosaurs was the head region. Typically, the skull was considerably elongated, particularly in the front, where it was also broad and flat. The lower jaw was similarly wide and flattened out so that, together, the upper and lower jaws resembled the bill of a duck. Although the front teeth were suppressed, the cheek teeth were extremely numerous, forming a massive dental pavement in which 2,000 teeth have been counted in some specimens. The teeth were obviously adapted for the grinding of hard and coarse plant material and were continuously replaced as they wore out.

Many trachodonts also experienced considerable modifications of the nasal bones, which became extended back over the top of the skull in a tubelike crest. Trachodonts were once believed to be swamp dwellers, with the greatly extended nasal tube having some kind of underwater breathing function. Today, the suggestion that they

FIGURE 18.18
Cretaceous dinosaurs. (a) *Deinonychus.* (b) *Tyrannosaurus.*
(c) *Iguanodon.*

FIGURE 18.19
A typical ornithopod, *Hypacrosaurus*. Ornithopods are the
so-called duckbilled dinosaurs, and many were characterized
by bony crests on the top of the head, as seen here.

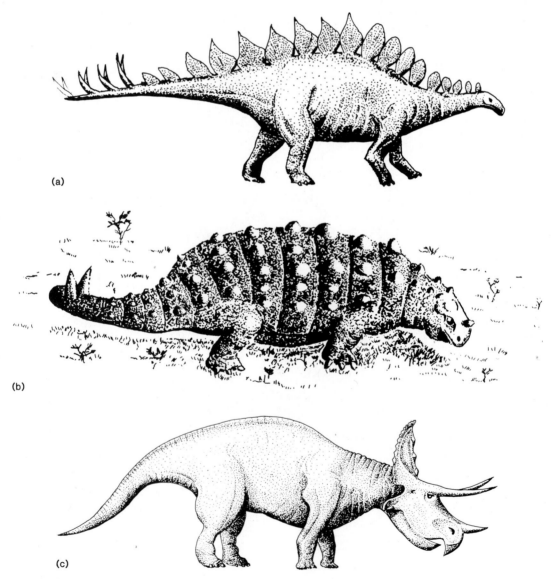

(a)

(b)

(c)

FIGURE 18.20
Armored dinosaurs. (a) *Stegosaurus*. (b) *Ankylosaurus*.
(c) *Triceratops*.

PLATE 63
Archeopteryx as it appeared in life. (From a painting by John
Gurche.)

PLATE 64
A herd of migrating Apatosaurus. (From a
painting by John Gurche.)

PLATE 65

Iguanodon under attack by *Deinonychus*. (From a painting by
John Gurche.)

PLATE 66
Corythosaurus with hatchlings.

PLATE 67

Exposures of the Eocene Wasatch Formation in Bryce Canyon, Utah. The variably colored shales, sandstones, and conglomerates were laid down by streams on alluvial plains.

PLATE 68

Badlands developed on Oligocene clays of the White River Formation in the Badlands National Park, South Dakota. Vertebrate fossils found here include several species of oreodonts, a group of North American artiodactyls.

PLATE 69

The Black Canyon of Gunnison, Colorado. Eroded into Precambrian gneisses, this is the narrowest and deepest canyon in North America, reaching a depth of almost 750 meters and in places only 390 meters wide. This and other spectacular canyons were cut entirely during the Neogene, when the whole region underwent broad epeirogenic uplift.

PLATE 70

Tejon Pass in the Transverse Ranges of California. These mountains were formed by fault blocks in which rocks were contorted and metamorphosed during Mesozoic orogenic movements in the region.

PLATE 71
Lake Elsinore in the Santa Ana Mountains of California. This
lake occupies a downfaulted block.

PLATE 73
Many of the Cenozoic basins of southern California are oil
producers. This is a well on the campus of the University of
California at Santa Barbara.

PLATE 72
Typical scenery in the Basin and Range region in the Sacra-
mento Mountains of southeastern California.

PLATE 74
Faulting in Miocene ash deposits in the Basin and Range region
of Arizona.

PLATE 75
Ship Rock, New Mexico. Note the long dike, one of several that
radiate out from the central vent.

PLATE 76
Cenozoic volcanic plugs are prominent features of the
New Mexico landscape.

PLATE 78
A glacial erratic of Precambrian granite perched on Triassic sandstone, Valecito Lake, Colorado.

PLATE 77
Sunset Crater near Flagstaff, Arizona. This volcano last erupted in 1066 A.D., the year of the Norman conquest of England.

PLATE 79
Precambrian gneisses of the Canadian Shield, smoothed and polished by glacial ice during the Wisconsin glaciation.

lived an aquatic existence has been discarded, so the nasal crests clearly had some other function—perhaps to enhance the olfactory sense, clearly an asset in a relatively defenseless and not very agile herbivore. An alternative suggestion is that the hollow crests were some kind of resonating air chamber and that the trachodonts communicated with trumpetlike calls. Clearly, until someone invents a reliable time machine, the answer will remain unknown!

Another ornithopod line of adaptation involving the head region is seen in *Pachycephalosaurus,* whose skull roof became enormously thickened, so much so that the upper temporal opening became closed, while the lower one was greatly reduced. Again, the purpose of this feature is a mystery. One suggestion is that the head was used as some kind of battering ram, perhaps while fighting in mating rituals.

Ankylosaurs   Although most ornithischian dinosaurs belonged to the ornithopod line, with *Camptosaurus* as an early generalized example, a second line typified by *Stegosaurus* had arisen in the Early Jurassic. *Stegosaurus* barely survived into the Cretaceous, and its extinction marked the first dinosaur group to go (Figure 18.20a). Its place was taken by another group of quadruped ornithischians—the ankylosaurs or armored dinosaurs.

Of moderate size, measuring some 6 or 7 meters in length, ankylosaurs had a squat, massive body with much larger hind limbs than forelimbs, despite its quadrupedal gait. From the top of its head, along its back and flanks, and to the tip of its tail, it was covered by an armor of polygonal bony plates. Long, bony spikes along the sides of the body ensured this animal of virtual impregnability to attack. Squatting to protect its soft underparts, *Ankylosaurus* was presumably as difficult to tackle as a large turtle. In addition, its tail was tipped with a massive knob that must have been an effective club (Figure 18.20b).

Ceratopsians   Another Late Cretaceous descendent from the camptosaur stock and constituting the last dinosaur group to appear were the horned dinosaurs or ceratopsians. The earliest true ceratopsians were relatively small animals, measuring about 2 meters in length. They are represented by *Leptoceratops* in North America and by the generally similar *Protoceratops* from the Upper Cretaceous of the Gobi Desert in Mongolia, where, incidentally, skeletons, together with nests full of eggs (some with embryos), have been unearthed. Evolutionary change again involved increasing size, and later ceratopsians were impressive animals.

Triceratops, for example, weighed up to 8 tons and reached a length of 8 meters or more (Figure 18.20c). Its enormous horny frill behind the head and the presence of a nasal horn plus two wicked horns on the head must have made this herbivore an animal to be reckoned with! *Triceratops* can be considered the rear guard of a great dynasty because its bones are the most common among the very last dinosaur assemblages.

Pterosaurs

The trend toward greater size seen in the later Jurassic pterosaurs continued into the Cretaceous. One of the best known of the Cretaceous forms is *Pteranodon,* with a wing span of more than 7 meters. It had no teeth but possessed a large, sharp beak, presumably for catching fish. To provide aerodynamic stability and a counterweight to the beak, *Pteranodon's* skull projected backward in a long, bony process. In further contrast to the rhamphorhynchoids of Jurassic time, *Pteranodon* was tailless. Clearly, aerodynamic needs in the more advanced Cretaceous forms were solved with a somewhat different body plan.

Of special note among the Cretaceous pterosaurs was the gigantic *Quetzalcoatlus northropi* from the Late Cretaceous of Texas. With a wingspan of more than 15 meters, it was the largest creature ever to have flown.

Birds

Of all the vertebrates, the fossil record of birds is the scantiest. Its extremely fragmentary nature is comparable with that of the insects among the invertebrates. Given the fragility of the average bird skeleton and the habitat of most birds, this lack of fossils is expected.

It is also not surprising that, among fossil birds in the Cretaceous, the only one that is well known is *Hesperornis,* a flightless swimming bird found in the Upper Cretaceous Niobrara Chalk of Kansas (Figure 18.21). The size of a small crane, *Hesperornis* still had teeth, thus retaining a primitive dinosaur feature. On the other hand, its almost complete loss of wings and its change to a swimming mode of life is clearly a secondary adaptation.

Flying birds, some of quite modern aspect, are also found in the Niobrara Chalk, as well as other Cretaceous formations. *Icthyornis* was about the size of a robin, and its skeleton looks quite modern except for the presence of teeth. *Gallornis,* on the other hand, a long-legged, flamingo-type bird from the Lower Cretaceous of Europe, had no teeth.

Mammals

The first evolutionary radiation of the mammals occurred during the Jurassic. It was a time of experimentation and, inevitably, of some failures. Of the five mammal groups recognized among Jurassic fossils, the docodonts disappeared at the close of the Jurassic, while the symmetrodonts and triconodonts barely made it into the Cretaceous before they, too, became extinct.

FIGURE 18.21
The Cretaceous flightless bird *Hesperornis.*

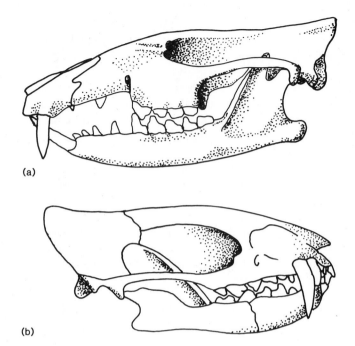

FIGURE 18.22
Cretaceous mammals. (a) The insectivore *Zalambdalestes.*
(b) The creodont *Deltatheridium.* Both of these animals were
about the size of a large rat.

Of the two remaining groups, the multituberculates
were small herbivores whose teeth suggest that they probably filled an ecologic niche that would be later occupied
by the rodents. Indeed, their demise in the Early Cenozoic, after successfully coming through the terminal Cretaceous extinction, was probably due to competition from
rodent ancestral forms.

Last, but not least, were the pantotheres. This group
proved the most successful because, before the close of the
Cretaceous, they gave rise to the first marsupial and placental mammals from which almost all later mammals,
with the exception of the monotremes (egg-laying mammals), were to arise.

The first marsupials in the form of small, opossum-
like animals are not uncommon at some Upper Cretaceous horizons in North America (Figure 18.22). Similarly, small, insectivorous, placental mammals, reminiscent
of modern hedgehogs and shrews, were apparently becoming quite abundant before the close of the Cretaceous.

The Terminal Cretaceous Event

Just as with the end-Permian mass extinction, nineteenth-
century geologists noted the sudden disappearance of many
life-forms at the end of the Cretaceous. The significance
of this discontinuity in the history of life was such that it
marks the boundary between the Mesozoic and Cenozoic
eras. The Cretaceous mass extinction event is second only
to the end-Permian event in the numbers of species that
disappeared.

As with other mass extinction events, there have, of
course, been many attempts to "smooth it out," to prove
that it was merely an artifact of biased collecting, dating,
or stratigraphic determinations. In addition to the question of the validity of the evidence for a mass extinction,
there remains the knotty problem of what caused the event.

Of all the mass extinction events in earth history, and
geologists believe that they can detect at least six, the one
that closed the Cretaceous is by far the best known for
several reasons. One of the most important—even if it has
no special scientific grounds for emphasis—is that the dinosaurs became extinct at this time. Another reason is that
the end of the Cretaceous is not that long ago, at least in
geologic terms, so inevitably, the evidence is better, or put
another way, the trail is fresher! A third reason concerns
the cause. In this event, as in no other, a cause-and-effect
relationship is apparent. The end-Cretaceous extinction
occurred, as far as the accuracy of dating methods per-
mits determination, at the same time as a large meteorite
(or possibly cometary) impact. The possibility that this
was just coincidence seems extremely unlikely.

The Victims

The importance of terminal Cretaceous extinctions can be
assessed by a roll call of the animals concerned. In addition to the dinosaurs, all the pterosaurs and all the large
marine reptiles disappeared. Among the invertebrates, the
ammonites went, as did the rudistid mollusks. The belemnites, another group of cephalopods, are also believed to
have become extinct at this time, although there are some
reports that they may just have survived into the earliest
Paleocene. Although not entirely eliminated, many other
groups were decimated. Whole families of planktonic foraminifera, calcareous phytoplankton, bryozoans, and
echinoderms disappeared.

FIGURE 18.23

Clay layer at the Cretaceous/Tertiary boundary, near Gubbio, Italy. The iridium concentration in the clay is about 30 times higher than in the sediments below and above. Fossil coccoliths are abundant in the limestone below the clay but are only sparsely present above. *(Photograph courtesy of Lawrence Berkeley Laboratories.)*

Likely Cause: Cosmic Impact

Currently, a giant meteorite impact is the favored explanation for the end-Cretaceous extinction, and sedimentary successions containing the Cretaceous–Tertiary boundary have been scrutinized for real evidence. In 1980, Luis Alvarez and his son Walter, working at Berkeley, reported that, at several locations, the Cretaceous/Tertiary boundary horizon is marked by an unusually high concentration of the element iridium. Although not uncommon in certain meteorites, iridium is comparatively rare in the earth's crustal rocks and is typically found in sediments in only tiny amounts, the normal background reading being about 10 to 20 parts per million. Occasional anomalously high concentrations can usually be ascribed to an infusion of iridium-rich volcanic ash. Also, in places—typically on the deep ocean floor, where the rate of sediment accumulation is extremely slow—iridium concentrations can be quite high. Neither of these explanations seems to account for the iridium anomaly at the Cretaceous/Tertiary boundary being found at over 100 locations around the world, and in a variety of depositional environments, both marine and nonmarine (Figure 18.23).

The scenario outlined by the Alvarez team was that the iridium found in cosmic, rather than terrestrial, proportions at the Cretaceous/Tertiary boundary had been derived from fallout from a cloud of dust thrown up by a meteorite impact. They suggested that an **Apollo object,** a large meteorite of perhaps 10 kilometers in diameter,

had impacted the earth and was pulverized. Because meteorites are known to have high iridium concentrations, the origin of the element at the terminal Cretaceous boundary was clearly no mystery. They further suggested that the dust thrown into the atmosphere obscured the sun for a period of months or years, causing widespread decimation of photosynthetic organisms, which caused many food chains to collapse, resulting in mass extinction through a wide spectrum of organisms, both marine and terrestrial (Figure 18.24).

Not surprisingly, the Alvarez hypothesis raised considerable interest, and before long, further data, both in support of the hypothesis and refuting it, began to accumulate. The arguments continue unabated, and the volume of literature on the subject is now so voluminous that anything more than the briefest review is beyond the scope of the present discussion.

Overall, that a cosmic impact of some kind did occur now seems past dispute. While most opinions favor a meteorite, a comet has also been suggested. Supporting the chemical signature of an iridium anomaly is the presence at many locations of the mineral **coesite,** a high-pressure form of quartz. Coesite, unlike iridium, is not found at volcanic eruptions, even violently explosive ones, and is considered an unequivocal indicator of a meteorite impact. A layer of carbon also found at many locations has been interpreted as derived from a fall of soot from global wildfires initiated in the world's forests consequent on the superheating of the atmosphere at the moment of impact.

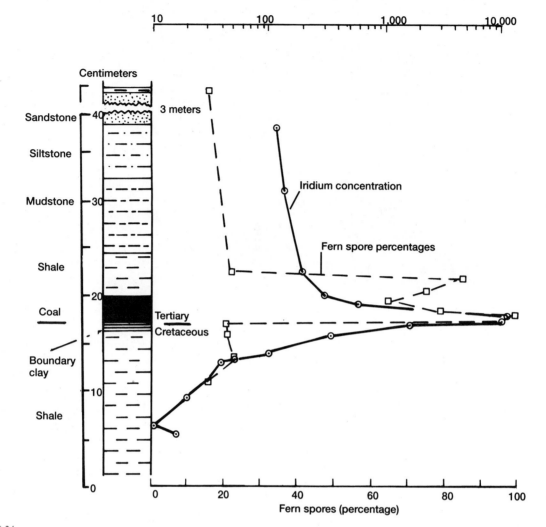

FIGURE 18.24

Diagram showing the stratigraphy of the Cretaceous/Tertiary boundary at Starkville North, Colorado. Plotted also are iridium content values and fern spore counts. The big increase in fern spore proportions at the Cretaceous boundary reflects the disappearance of angiosperms.

Search for the Impact Crater

From the beginning, of course, there has been an avid search for the impact crater. Clearly, if the meteorite had impacted on a continent, the crater could hardly have escaped discovery, so it has been generally assumed that it hit somewhere on the ocean floor—statistically, more likely anyway in view of the relative area of land and sea. Even in an ocean basin, a crater should be large enough to find, and the search has been diligently pursued.

In the late 1980s, when many scientists were beginning to give up and to assume that the crater had been swallowed by a subduction zone or buried beneath a continental shelf wedge, some interesting new information came to light. The first clues came with the discovery of an anomalously coarse-grained, turbulent-water sediment layer in an otherwise fine-grained, quiet water, end-Cretaceous succession at several locations in Texas. This was interpreted as a tsunami deposit produced as the giant wave produced by the impact reached the continental shelf. The hunt was on, and far more spectacular tsunami deposits turned up in Cuba and Haiti. In Cuba, the formation was found to be 450 meters thick, containing blocks up to 2 meters in diameter. Clearly, it was considerably closer to the impact site than were the Texan tsunami deposits. With something less than the whole world's oceans to study, the search became much less of a needle-in-a-haystack affair, and geologists began to pay much closer attention to the Caribbean region.

As it turned out, the impact site had already been found in 1978 by accident. During a routine geophysical survey conducted in the search for oil off the north coast of the Yucatan Peninsula, geophysicist Glen Penfield noticed a large, semicircular magnetic anomaly 120 kilometers in diameter. Further study of old gravity surveys onshore showed that the structure continued beneath the peninsula. It became clear that a large impact crater was buried beneath a cover of Tertiary limestones. Named after Chicxulub, a small town near Merida, the discovery was reported at a professional society meeting in 1981 but apparently went largely unnoticed.

Although buried beneath hundreds of meters of younger sedimentary rock, the Chicxulub crater is, in fact, detectable at the surface because of its effect on the pattern of joints and fractures in the limestone and also because of the way it apparently influences the movement of groundwater. It is doubtful that any structure would have been detectable in surface geological data, but satellite imagery points out subtle differences in the pattern of karstic erosion features that enable the crater rim to be located (Figure 18.25).

In the meantime, closer examination of the terminal Cretaceous sedimentary succession in Haiti turned up examples of tektites, small, glassy droplets produced by the melting of rocks during very high-speed impacts. In addition, the presence of an iridium anomaly and an abundance of shock-metamorphosed quartz grains in the same deposit removed all doubt about its origin. The tektites were particularly important because, for the first time, they allowed direct dating of the deposit. Potassium-argon dating gave an age of 64.5 + 0.1 million years, a value statistically indistinguishable from the 64.6 + 0.2 million years age of coal-bearing boundary beds in Montana.

A distinctive feature of the clay layer that marks the Cretaceous/Tertiary boundary in terrestrial successions at sites throughout western North America is that it always appears as a couplet, the lower clay layer measuring 2 to 3 centimeters in thickness, the upper about 1 centimeter. While it was originally believed that the upper layer was formed by secondary impacts, as debris thrown up by the primary impact fell back to earth, many workers now believe that a smaller crater near Manson, Iowa, may indicate that the impact was a double one. In the original search for the impact crater, the Manson site had been passed over because, although it is the right age, it is too small (32 kilometers). Now, even a third structure at Popigay in northeastern Siberia is being looked at more closely to support a scenario in which the earth was struck by a sort of "shotgun blast." Clearly, other terminal Cretaceous impact structures may be awaiting discovery.

Impact's Role in Mass Extinction: Cause and Effect?

Since a major cosmic impact of some kind at the close of the Cretaceous has now been established, the main focus of discussion has shifted to whether the impact caused the mass extinction that apparently occurred at about the same time. While few would try to argue mere coincidence, opinions differ as to just how important the impact was.

At one extreme is the view that Late Cretaceous faunas and floras give no hint of deteriorating numbers or increasingly stressful environments and that, when it came, the mass extinction was caused by the impact or impacts and was catastrophic. Other paleontologists believe that many groups that became extinct at the close of the Cretaceous were already declining and that the cosmic event was simply the "last straw." According to still other workers, the extinction of many groups was spread over much of the Late Cretaceous and was due to deteriorating climate. Tropical marine invertebrates were particularly susceptible, according to this model. On the other hand, tropical floras, normally the most sensitive to climatic fluctuations, show little if any change, and it seems unlikely that ocean waters could undergo a marked cooling without a global climatic interaction. These apparent contradictions are puzzling.

Of particular interest is the fate of the dinosaurs and other large reptiles. As discussed earlier, although opinions have been divided as to whether the dinosaurs were already doomed well before the close of the Cretaceous, it now looks increasingly likely that their extinction was sudden. One statistically rigorous study of patterns of ecologic diversity in the Hell Creek Formation of Montana and North Dakota, for example, showed no evidence for a gradual decline of dinosaurs at the end of the Cretaceous.

If, as seems likely, one or more meteorite impacts did play a role in the mass extinction event, what mechanism was involved? The Alvarez model, with dust clouds blocking sunlight, seems plausible and is supported by at least one study describing evidence of frost damage in plant fossils. From the degree of the plants' seasonal growth, it was even possible to point to early June as the time the freezing began. On the other hand, other models have been proposed. In one hypothesis, sudden heating of the atmosphere was the main cause of extinction. In another, dust and gases left in the atmosphere after the dust clouds cleared produced a greenhouse effect so that the "impact winter" was followed by a protracted period of hot, wet weather. In yet another model, a greenhouse effect was triggered by the loss of phytoplankton in the oceans. Toxic aerosols produced by the impact are said to have played a vital role in yet another hypothesis. Acid rain and/or changes in the pH of the oceans are among many other recipes for ecologic disaster that can be added to a list that is growing almost monthly.

As the previous discussion indicates, the controversy is by no means over and likely will remain a focus of timely discussion for many years to come.

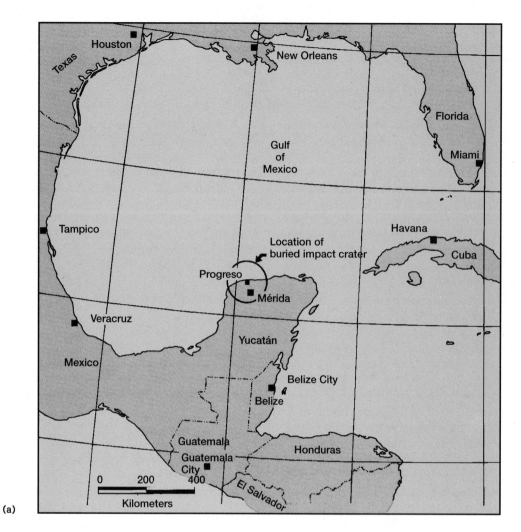

(a)

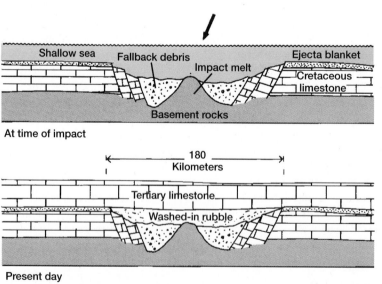

(b)

FIGURE 18.25

(a) There is growing evidence that the meteorite that likely caused the terminal Cretaceous mass extinction impacted at a site on the northern edge of the Yucatan Peninsula,

Mexico. (b) These cross sections show the impact site at the time the crater was formed and at the present day.

Summary

As the Cretaceous opened, the Atlantic Ocean was in existence but still did not extend into the Arctic Ocean, and it was not until the Late Cretaceous that Europe was separated from North America and Greenland. The South Atlantic was still very narrow, and India, Australia, and Antarctica formed a single continent. By the Late Cretaceous, India was separate, but Australia and Antarctica remained joined until the early Cenozoic.

Along the eastern margin of North America, Cretaceous sediments were laid down in a great wedge thickening eastward under the present-day continental shelf. The bulk of the sediments were derived from the continental hinterland to the west and passed from nonmarine facies close to the Appalachians into shallow-water marine sediments to the east. In the Early Cretaceous, extensive reefs formed along the outer shelf margin, aided by still-active block faulting that had marked the initial opening of the Atlantic in the Jurassic. Fault-bounded basins along the continental margin apparently acted as sediment traps and so prevented clastic sediments from reaching the outer shelf. By late in the Early Cretaceous, fault activity had largely ceased and clastic sediments now spread across the entire shelf, smothering the reefs in the process.

Along North America's western margin, the Cretaceous was marked by almost continuous tectonic activity. Several phases of crustal unrest can be recognized and are often described as separate "orogenies," although, in fact, they overlap considerably. The opening phase of Cordilleran unrest was the Nevadan orogeny that began in the Late Jurassic and reached a climax in the Early Cretaceous. At this time, the Coast Range batholith and other large granite masses were intruded. Later, as intrusions and crustal unrest continued in the Sevier orogeny, the zone of disturbance migrated progressively further east. By the close of the Cretaceous, the third orogenic phase, known as the Laramide, was responsible for thrusting and folding as far east as western Wyoming and Utah. A shift from high-angle to low-angle subduction along the Pacific margin is believed to be responsible for the easterly migration of the zone of unrest.

Along the Pacific coast, the peculiar rocks of the Franciscan Complex contain evidence that many of them originated on the deep-sea floor. They are now believed to have been "scraped off" against the North American craton as the Pacific crust descended along a subduction zone. This process exemplifies on a small scale a process of collision and accretion seen along much of the western margin of North America. Some of the so-called exotic or suspect terranes contain evidence of travel over great distance as parts of moving plates. Some are even believed to have originated from as far away as Asia.

Continental rifting and the growth of new oceans resulted in greatly extended midocean ridges. As the ridges grew and reduced the volume of the ocean basins, there was a eustatic rise in sea level, resulting in widespread marine transgressions in the Cretaceous. In North America, the sea at maximum transgression extended as an epeiric sea called the Interior Seaway all the way from the Arctic Ocean to the Gulf of Mexico, dividing North America into two islands. Rising orogenic belts along the seaway's western margin produced vast quantities of clastic sediments that spread eastward into the Interior Seaway.

The Cretaceous was an important time in the history of plants, with a great evolutionary radiation in the flowering plants. Dispersal mechanisms for the fertilized seeds also evolved.

Among marine invertebrates, the rudistid bivalved mollusks were conspicuous reef builders and were, in fact, more important than the scleractinian corals. The ammonites were still abundant and continued to evolve rapidly. Among the bivalves, the large oysterlike *Inoceramus* is particularly characteristic of the Cretaceous.

In the case of the vertebrates, the Cretaceous saw the appearance of the last of the three major groups of fishes: the Teleostei. The Teleostei began an evolutionary radiation that has continued to the present day.

In the seas, also, were the great marine reptiles. From their beginnings in the Triassic and Jurassic, such groups as the icthyosaurs and the plesiosaurs continued their success, and many grew to

enormous size. The mosasaurs, derived from the lizards, also appeared in the sea at this time, and again, some grew to a great size. *Tylosaurus,* for example, was over 10 meters long.

The dinosaurs, of course, dominate the picture of vertebrate life on land. Through the Cretaceous, their evolution continued, and some grew to be the largest land animals of all time. Both the saurischian and ornithischian groups flourished, and there is little indication of serious declines in their numbers as the Cretaceous period drew to a close.

Pterosaurs grew larger in the Cretaceous, with *Quetzalcoatlus* having a wingspan of over 15 meters. The fossil record of Cretaceous birds is scanty, with flightless swimming birds being the most common fossils.

By the Cretaceous, the docodont mammals had become extinct, and they were soon followed by the symmetrodonts and triconodonts. Of the two remaining groups, the multituberculates were small, rodentlike herbivores, while the pantotheres gave rise to both the marsupial and placental mammals before the period closed.

The Cretaceous closed with a major extinction event, second only to the end-Permian event in the numbers of species that disappeared. Among the animals that became extinct were the dinosaurs, the pterosaurs, the large marine reptiles, the rudistid mollusks, the belemnites, and the ammonites. Many other groups, such as the planktonic foraminifera, calcareous phytoplankton, bryozoans, and echinoderms, were decimated.

The cause of the extinction event is believed to have been the impact of an Apollo object or possibly a comet. Among many rival scenarios, one that seems likely involves a pall of darkness caused by immense dust clouds blocking out the sun for months or years. The decimation of photosynthesizing organisms, both large plants and marine phytoplankton, is believed to have caused a widespread collapse of food chains.

Questions

1. Describe the movement and rearrangement of the continents during the Cretaceous.
2. Along North America's eastern margin, the Upper Cretaceous successions are different from those of the Lower Cretaceous. What was the cause of this change?
3. Describe the events during the so-called Cordilleran orogeny.
4. Describe the significance of the Franciscan Complex of California.
5. The Interior Seaway that connected the Arctic Ocean and the Gulf of Mexico in the Cretaceous was an epeiric sea, but it differed considerably in its sedimentary successions and tectonic setting from the epeiric seas of the Early Paleozoic. Discuss and use sketch maps in your answer.
6. Describe the main features of plant evolution from the Triassic through the Cretaceous.
7. Describe the Jurassic and Cretaceous marine invertebrate faunas.
8. Explain the evolution of the bony fishes during the Mesozoic.
9. During the Cretaceous, the fishes provide some good examples of parallel evolution. Explain.
10. Compare the dinosaur faunas of the Cretaceous with those of the Triassic and Jurassic.
11. Describe the evolution of the flying reptiles during the Mesozoic.
12. Of the several Jurassic and Cretaceous groups of mammals, which was the likely ancestor of all later mammals?
13. List the major groups of animals that became extinct at the end of the Cretaceous.
14. What is the evidence for a meteorite (or cometary) impact as a cause of the terminal Cretaceous mass extinction event?
15. Where is the end-Cretaceous meteorite or cometary impact believed to have occurred? Discuss the evidence for this.

Further Reading

Bakker, R. T. 1986. *The dinosaur heresies*. New York: Morrow.

Caldwell, W. G. E., ed. 1975. *The Cretaceous system in the western interior of North America*. Geological Association of Canada, special paper, no. 13.

Desmond, A. J. 1975. *The hot-blooded dinosaurs, a revolution in paleontology*. London: Blond and Briggs.

Langston, W. 1981. Pterosaurs. *Scientific American* 284: 122–36.

Stewart, W. N. 1983. *Paleobotany and the evolution of plants*. Cambridge, England: Cambridge University Press.

19

THE PALEOGENE

Introduction

As the Paleogene opened, Australia and Antarctica were still joined, India had still to collide with Asia, and the great Alpine-Himalayan mountain chain had yet to form. These, and a marked cooling trend in world climates in the Late Paleogene, have been the major events in the world since the Cretaceous (Figure 19.1). Early Paleogene faunas and floras were recognizably modern, but their subsequent evolutionary progress was marked by three major developments: (1) the unprecedented radiation of the mammals through all of the Cenozoic, (2) the appearance of grasses and their significant spread in the latest Paleogene, and (3) the emergence of the advanced primates, who would lead eventually to

humans, with their impact on the environment resulting in the mass extinction event we are now experiencing.

Cenozoic Geologic Time Divisions

The 65 million years of the Cenozoic that have elapsed since the end of the Cretaceous is a period comparable in length to many of the other geologic periods. On the other hand, its relatively recent date and the prolific and easily understandable faunas and floras clearly invite further and more refined subdivision.

To nineteenth-century geologists, a post-Cretaceous division was natural, as was a final chapter to take care of the Great Ice Age. Both the end-Cretaceous extinction

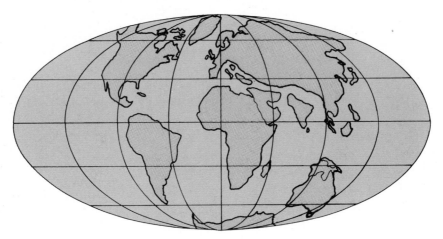

FIGURE 19.1
World paleogeography in the Paleogene.

TABLE 19.1

Evolution of the Cenozoic Time Scale

1833	1833	1839	1854	1867	1874	
Quaternary	Newer Pliocene (Lyell) _____ 4% Extinct sp. 96% Extant sp.	Pleistocene (Lyell)	Pleistocene	Holocene (Lyell) _____ Pleistocene	Holocene _____ Pleistocene	Pleistogene (Harland)
Tertiary	Older Pliocene (Lyell) _____ 58% Extinct sp. 42% Extant sp.	Pliocene	Pliocene	Pliocene	Pliocene	Neogene (Hoernes)
	Miocene (Lyell) _____ 83% Extinct sp. 17% Extant sp.	Miocene	Miocene Oligocene (Beyrich)	Miocene Oligocene	Miocene Oligocene	
	Eocene (Lyell) _____ 97% Extinct sp. 3% Extant sp.	Eocene	Eocene	Eocene	Eocene _____ Paleocene (Schimper)	Paleogene (Naumann)

and the onset of glaciation were clearly indicated in the stratigraphic record. The imbalance between the 63 million years of Tertiary time and the million or two of the Quaternary was simply a reflection of a change of scale in dealing with the wealth of geological and paleontological data that could be so readily interpreted in terms of the modern world.

The abundance of recognizable familiar species led to Charles Lyell's division of the Tertiary as outlined in Table 19.1. Working largely with mollusks from the North Sea and Paris basins, Lyell established the epochs on the proportions of extinct to extant species. By 1874, further divisions were recognized. In 1867, the Quaternary had also been divided into Pleistocene and Holocene under the mistaken impression that the Great Ice Age was over.

None of the various divisions are particularly "natural" ones, and alternatives are not difficult to select. The Paleogene/Neogene division of the Tertiary series, for example, was based on a marked disconformity in the Paris Basin succession at the top of the Oligocene, but this boundary is not particularly discernible elsewhere. Instead, in the global context, the horizon that shows the marked cooling that occurred near the Eocene/Oligocene boundary would unquestionably have made a better Paleogene/Neogene boundary.

Similarly, in approaching the present, the Pliocene/Pleistocene boundary, as marking the close of the Tertiary, is also suspect and simply reflects the old idea that the Pleistocene marked the onset of an ice age. In the same way, the Holocene as marking "postglacial" time is also incorrect. By that definition, modern-day Antarctica and Greenland are still in the Pleistocene.

The Paleogene in North America

The Cordilleran Region

The Laramide Orogeny

The Late Cretaceous to Eocene history of the Cordilleran region is dominated by the effects of the **Laramide orogeny,** or as some people prefer, the Laramide phase of the Cordilleran orogeny. Although a vast area of western North America was affected, the cause of the Laramide disturbance was much further west, along the margin of the North American plate. During the Late Cretaceous, the boundary between the North American and several Pacific plates, the most important being the Farallon plate, lay approximately along the line of North America's west coast. Out in the Pacific, the East Pacific Rise marked a spreading center separating the Farallon plate from the Kula and other plate segments (Figure 19.2). Beginning early in the Cenozoic, the angle of downturn of the Farallon plate, as it was subducted along its collision boundary with the North American plate, became less steep, and the area of hot magma sources beneath the overriding plate

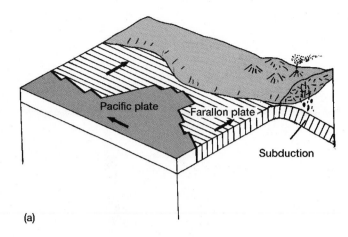

(a)

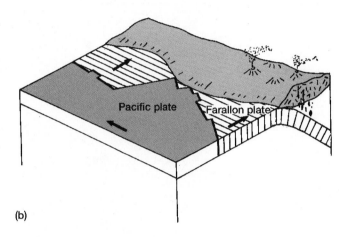

(b)

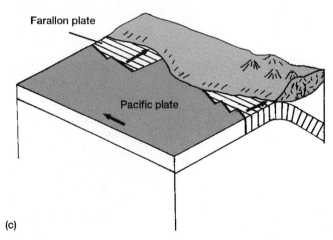

(c)

FIGURE 19.2

Disappearance of the Farallon plate and the beginning of strike-slip movement along the western margin of the North American plate during the Paleogene. (a) 40 million years ago. (b) 30 million years ago. (c) 24 million years ago.

moved further east beneath the continent. The "hot spot" at Yellowstone National Park may be one manifestation.

Structural disturbances associated with the Laramide orogenic phase extended well to the east of the main

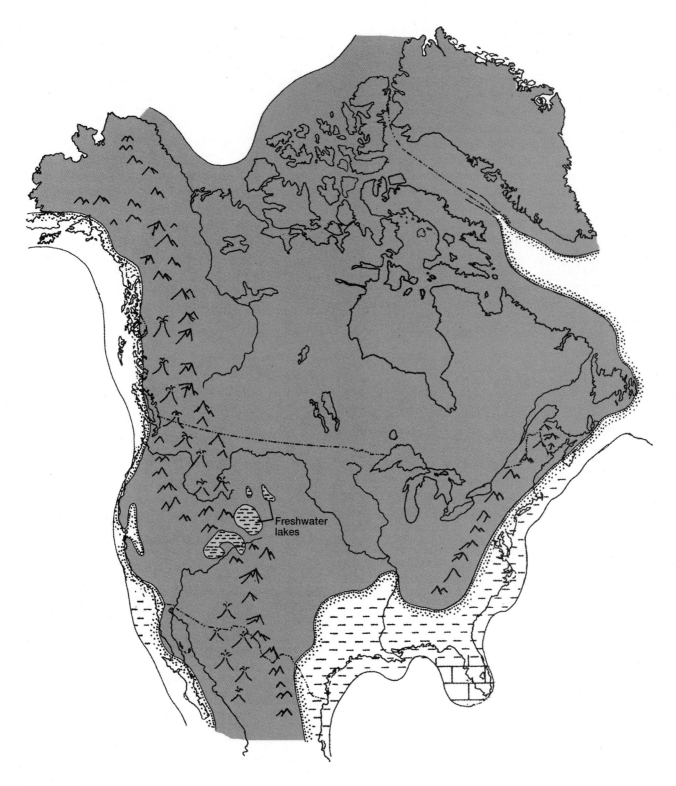

FIGURE 19.3
Paleogeography of the North American continent during the
Paleogene.

Cordilleran ranges and reached as far as Utah. Although
the main climax of activity occurred in latest Cretaceous
into Early Paleocene time, folding and thrusting affecting
rocks as young as Middle Eocene age is found in western
Wyoming and elsewhere. Thereafter, in the waning stages
of the Laramide disturbance, movement largely involved
vertical displacement with block faulting and only minor
folding. Nevertheless, by the Eocene, considerable mountain ranges, extending from Alberta and British Columbia to New Mexico, were spilling sediment eastward
(Figure 19.3).

Paleocene Sedimentary Patterns

Paleocene sedimentary patterns were generally a continuation of those of latest Cretaceous time. They are dominantly of clastics deposited by streams flowing from the newly uplifted highlands. In places, there are indications of swamps, and alluvial successions contain thin coals that were markedly more significant than in Cretaceous time.

Over an extensive area of Nebraska, South Dakota, Montana, and adjacent regions, these Paleocene sandstones, shales, and coals are mapped as the **Fort Union Formation.** The sediments represent deposition under the relatively lowland conditions that existed immediately following the retreat of the Cretaceous Interior Seaway.

The disappearance of the Interior Seaway was, however, not the end of marine conditions in the North American interior. Something of a mystery is a single, isolated area of marine sediments in the middle of the continent in central North Dakota and dated as late Early Paleocene. This so-called **Cannonball Formation**—with up to 100 meters of shales and glauconitic sands—contains a modest marine fauna, but how this sea was connected with the distant ocean across some 2,000 kilometers of intervening continent is a matter of some controversy.

Some paleontologists claim that the mollusks indicate a connection to the Gulf of Mexico region, while others, basing their conclusions on the foraminifera, suggest that the Cannonball fauna has arctic affinities. A connection northward to the Arctic Ocean is possible but equally difficult to prove. A mixture of Gulf and arctic forms could be explained by a third alternative, proposed by geologists William Frazier and David Schwimmer. They suggest that the so-called Cannonball Sea simply represented a lingering vestige of the Cretaceous Interior Seaway, preserved in a structurally downwarped area that was isolated by erosion over the area intervening between North Dakota and the western sea as the Interior Seaway retreated (Figure 19.4).

Basin Filling

By Eocene time, great thicknesses of sediment derived from the rising highlands were accumulating in numerous intermontane basins. The **Wasatch Formation,** magnificently exposed in the towering badlands, buttes, and pinnacles in Bryce Canyon, is typical of these basin-fill deposits and consists of variegated red, pink, orange, and gray sandstones and conglomerates. Comparisons with earlier Paleocene sediments show a notable increase in redbed-type sediments, and there are few coals, indicating that the climate was becoming drier. Most likely, this was a rain-shadow effect in the lee of the Rocky Mountains as moisture-laden winds from the Pacific dumped their rain on the western slopes.

Paleogene Lakes

As new intermontane basins formed and drainage patterns shifted, many lakes of considerable size developed. Chief among these were Lake Gosiute in southwestern

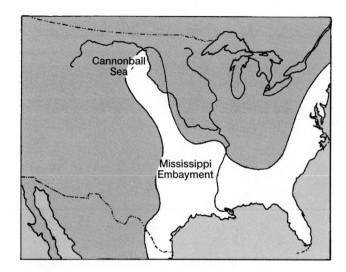

FIGURE 19.4
Sketch map showing the location and a possible seaway connection for the Cannonball Sea.

Wyoming and Lake Uinta in northeastern Utah. As lake levels fluctuated, these two lakes were often joined, and together covered an area of nearly 78,000 square kilometers. Lacustrine sediments, in places, reached 1,500 meters and collectively are mapped as the **Green River Formation** (Figure 19.5).

One of the most characteristic features of these lake-bottom deposits is the repetition of thin laminae in "varved" successions, suggesting a seasonal, probably annual, variation in water temperature and/or chemistry. Algal "blooms" were probably also involved. Particularly important was a seasonal variation in the oxygen content of lake-bottom waters. The very fine and regular laminae and the remarkable preservation of fish, insects, plants, and other life-forms point to a complete absence of scavengers and benthic forms that would normally destroy the laminae through bioturbation.

Also indicative of an anoxic bottom environment is the high organic content of many of the shales. The kerogens contained in these shales were likely derived from algae, spores, and pollen and represent an enormous reserve of hydrocarbons. With current technology, the cost of production is not economical, but this may change.

The economic potential of the Green River Formation is further enhanced by the presence at some horizons of trona ($Na_2CO_3NaHCO_3.2H_2O$) and other evaporite salts. Clearly, at times, water levels were so low that the lakes became areas of inland drainage, and the salinity increased.

The thousands of annual varves in Green River successions have been counted in an attempt to calculate the life span of the lakes as active sediment traps. Various methods of counting and averaging thicknesses resulted in the calculation of a total life span of 6.5 million years for Lake Gosiute.

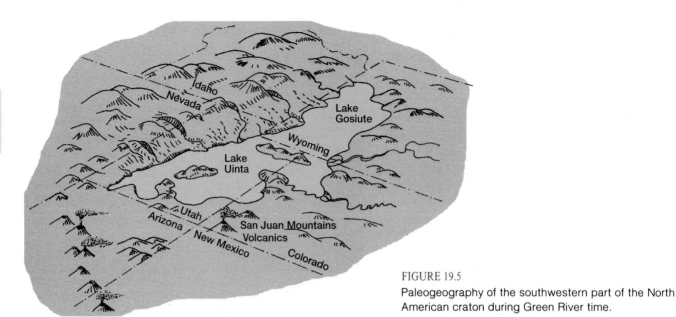

FIGURE 19.5
Paleogeography of the southwestern part of the North American craton during Green River time.

Increasing Volcanic Activity

Eventually, the lakes dried up, and by the close of Middle Eocene time, alluvial and redbed basin-fill deposits were again the area's dominant lithology. In effect, it was a return to the conditions that had existed during the depositions of the Wasatch Formation in the Early Eocene, although there was considerably more volcanic ash fallout, presumably derived from increasingly active volcanoes further west. The Bridger Formation that overlies the Green River Formation is typically a tuffaceous sandstone interbedded with ash deposits.

Volcanic activity throughout the region was clearly on the increase, and as mentioned earlier, the Yellowstone National Park area, at the eastern edge of the Pacific volcanic belt, was apparently one of those areas of localized activity referred to as a hot spot. Catastrophic volcanic eruptions with ash falls and lava flows left a record of repeated devastation. In the Lamar Valley in Yellowstone National Park, for example, no fewer than 27 separate forest layers can be counted, each one buried by a volcanic ash fall. Landslides and slumping of poorly consolidated ash from upper slopes seem to have contributed to the destruction because paleobotanists have noted that, among the generally warm-climate trees, are many cold-climate species. The only real explanation for this odd association is that the cold-climate trees were derived from locations higher up the mountainside.

Eastward Movement of Sediment

Although the mountains produced by the Laramide activity produced enormous volumes of detritus as they rose isostatically and erosion kept pace, little of this material moved far to the east, the intermontane basins apparently having more than enough capacity. This changed in the Oligocene, however, because from that time on, far more sediment began to spread farther eastward from the area of the Front Ranges on the eastern margin of the Rockies

across an erosion surface that was presumably a major pediment cut across rocks of Cretaceous age. This eastward shift of the main depocenters was due most likely to the beginning of subsidence along the trend of the Great Plains from the Dakotas southward into Wyoming, Montana, and eastern Colorado. The finest fractions of this detritus load were carried to the Mississippi drainage system and ended up eventually in the Gulf of Mexico.

The Atlantic and Gulf Coast Regions

Sediment Accumulation during the Cenozoic

As described in Chapter 18, the early history of the great sedimentary wedge lying beneath the eastern and southeastern North American continental margin was largely controlled by its tectonic setting. In Early Cretaceous time, continued subsidence of marginal fault basins had resulted in the entrapment of much of the terrigenous sediments arriving from the continental hinterland, and on the outer shelf, carbonate reefs had formed.

From Late Cretaceous time on, the situation changed. Terrigenous sediments prograding across the shelf smothered the reefs, and with regional subsidence slowing down, the rate of accumulation of sediment on the shelf's upper surface also slowed and continued to do so into the Cenozoic. The consequences of these changes are seen in the relative thicknesses of the Cretaceous and Cenozoic portions of the sedimentary wedge. In the 80 million years of Cretaceous time, some 10 kilometers had accumulated, whereas in the 65 million years since the Cretaceous, the sedimentary pile has grown by only another 2 kilometers. The volume of terrigenous material arriving at the continental shelf had not diminished. Instead, the sediments were swept farther out to sea, and the continental shelf and rise prograded out into the North Atlantic basin.

The major control of sediment accumulation during the Cenozoic has been sea level. During times of rising sea level, coastal erosion increases, whereas the drowning of

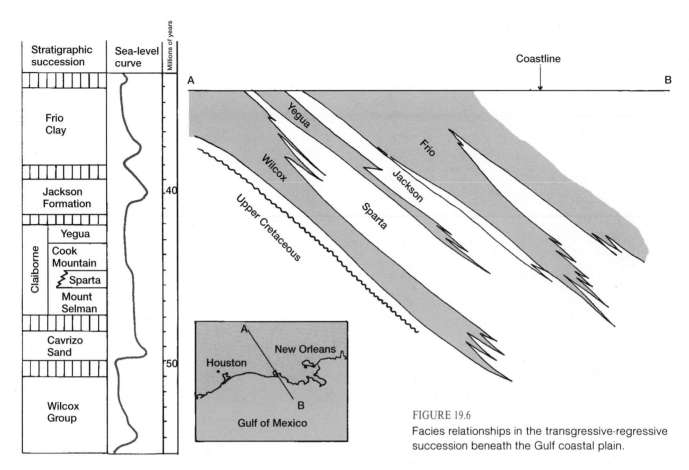

Stratigraphic succession	Sea-level curve	Millions of years

Frio
Clay

Jackson
Formation

40

Claiborne

Yegua

Cook
Mountain

Sparta

Mount
Selman

Cavrizo
Sand

50

Wilcox
Group

A

Yegua

Wilcox

Upper Cretaceous

Coastline

B

Frio

Jackson

Sparta

Houston

New Orleans

A

B

Gulf of Mexico

FIGURE 19.6

Facies relationships in the transgressive-regressive succession beneath the Gulf coastal plain.

the lower reaches of rivers turns them into sediment traps for the silt and mud fractions. Consequently, in continental shelf successions, sandstones are the typical signature of such marine transgressions, while mudstone and siltstones indicate phases of falling sea level. Erosional breaks indicative of periods of actual emergence over areas of the inner shelf have been detected in seismic surveys of the subsurface and have been used, as described in Chapter 9, in the construction of a master curve of eustatic sea-level change.

Far to the south, on the Florida/Bahamas platform, isolated from influxes of terrigenous sediment and bathed by warm, tropical water moving northward, carbonates continued to accumulate through the Cretaceous and into the Cenozoic. Although corals had been important frame builders in the Cretaceous reefs, they suffered a disastrous reduction at the close of the Cretaceous and did not make a comeback until the Eocene. The rudistid mollusks, perhaps an even more important component of Cretaceous reefs, had, of course, been eliminated in the end-Cretaceous extinction.

Influence of the Mississippi

Along the southern North American continental margin in the Gulf of Mexico, the overriding control of regional sedimentary patterns was the Mississippi River. Its enormous sediment supply and the crustal downsagging produced by the sheer mass of material are manifested throughout the entire Cenozoic succession. In a traverse

along the Gulf coast margin, all sedimentary units of the largely paralic (coastal plain) succession thicken markedly as they cross the Mississippi embayment. During the Early Paleocene, marine conditions had penetrated northward into the embayment as far as southern Illinois and even, according to some, had connected with the Cannonball Sea. Since then, there had been a net withdrawal of the sea, although with many minor fluctuations.

As along the Atlantic coast, the Paleocene through Oligocene succession in the Gulf region is dominated by alternating and interfingering terrigenous clastics. Alluvial sediments in the north pass into coastal plain silts and these, in turn, into beach ridges and beach sands. In the vicinity of the axis of the Mississippi drainage, deltaic deposits with bar finger sands laid down in distributary channels, delta plain silts, swamp deposits, offshore muds, and, in fact, all the various lithofacies associated with a major fluvially dominated delta are found. The modern Mississippi delta is, after all, only the latter-day manifestation of a delta that has been in existence since Pennsylvanian time, when it lay many hundreds of kilometers farther north, as described in Chapter 15.

In a traverse along the axis of the river and into the offshore region, the Paleogene succession as a whole consists of interfingering, nonmarine sediments in the north with marine sediments in the south. These, of course, reflect fluctuating sea level but were not caused entirely by eustatic changes. Repetitive sagging, typically accompanied by growth faulting in the delta front region, also influenced facies distribution (Figure 19.6).

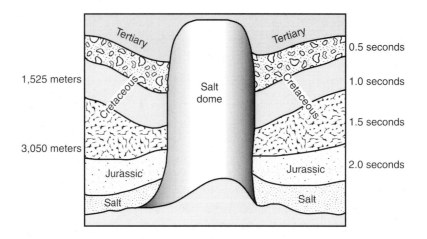

FIGURE 19.7
A reflection seismic profile from the Gulf coast region. Note the salt dome penetrating Mesozoic and Paleogene sediments. *(Source: Data from Morris S. Petersen and J. Keith Rigby,* Interpreting Earth History, *4th ed. Copyright © 1990 Wm. C. Brown Communications, Inc., Dubuque, Iowa.)*

Salt Domes

Over 300 **salt domes** occur in the coastal region of eastern Texas and Louisiana. These salt plug or piercement domes, as they are also called, consist of huge, roughly cylindrical masses of salt that have intruded up from below, rather like a volcanic neck that carries magma up to a vent on the surface. The origin of the salt is the thick Louann Salt of Jurassic age that underlies the Cretaceous and Cenozoic successions over large areas. The tremendous confining pressure of the thousands of meters of sediment lying on top of it enables the salt to behave not as a crystalline substance but rather as a viscous liquid. In other words, the salt *flows,* and, following any crack or fissure, it is squeezed upward toward the surface. In the process, it causes the surrounding rocks to be bent and faulted or folded into broad, domed structures that often are suitable for the entrapment of oil (Figure 19.7). The famous Spindletop Dome gusher in Texas, drilled in 1901, was the first of thousands of producing wells drilled onto similar structures.

The Paleogene in Europe

Across many oceans formed by rifting, opposing continental margins are often similar. Because both their tectonic and sedimentary histories followed the same course, the stratigraphic successions underlying their respective trailing edges are often more or less mirror images of one another. Such is the case with the opposing sides of the South Atlantic, where the Cretaceous through Cenozoic stratigraphic successions on both sides match closely.

Similarly, the Cenozoic history of the southern Australian margin and that of its opposing Antarctic margin are near matches.

Such is not the case in the North Atlantic. On the North American side is a great eastwardly thickening wedge of sediment that, through a succession ranging in age from Jurassic to Recent, has continued to accumulate with only minor interruptions. Cenozoic sediments throughout were largely derived from a hinterland to the west. On the European side, modest and intermittent tectonic activity and upwarping along the western edge of the craton, together with the extrusion of massive lava flows, produced the highland regions of the British Isles, the Breton peninsula, and to the north, Scandinavia. In these highland areas, rocks down to the Precambrian basin are often exposed.

The bulk of European Cenozoic sedimentation took place in basins inland from these peripheral highlands, and a great deal of the sedimentary infilling of these basins was derived from the highlands as well as from the continental hinterland. The North Sea Basin and its extension into the Paris Basin is one of these structures; the Baltic Sea is another. The typical Cenozoic successions in these basins record a series of marine transgressions and regressions, with interfingering of nonmarine sands and marine sands and silts (Figure 19.8).

One of the most sensitive indicators of former land connections is the distribution of terrestrial mammals. In the Paleocene and up to the Early Eocene, for example, the North Atlantic rift clearly had not yet completely separated North America, Greenland, and Europe because the mammal faunas of the two continents are very similar. To the east, however, European and Asian mammal faunas

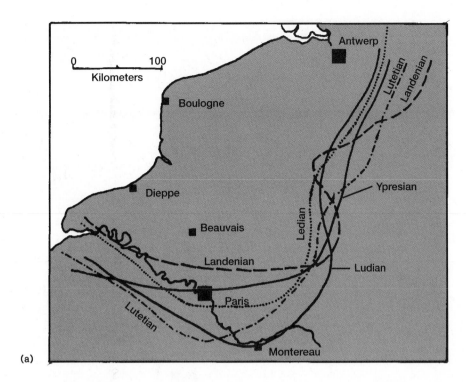

(a)

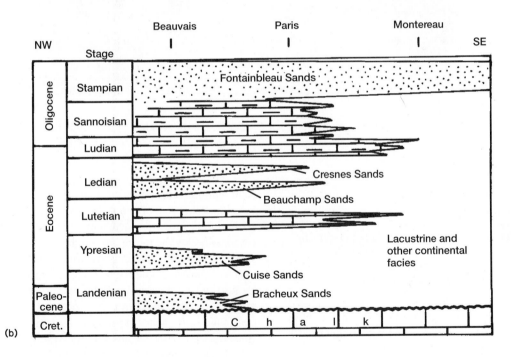

(b)

FIGURE 19.8

(a) Map showing fluctuating shorelines in the Paris Basin.
(b) Diagrammatic cross section through the Paris Basin of
northern France, showing successive transgressive-
regressive facies.

of this time were distinctly different. The Baltic and Siberian shields had collided in Permian time. Nevertheless,
shallow extensions of the Tethys Ocean from time to time
reached as far as the Arctic Ocean. The Turgoi Seaway
(or Strait) in the eastern Urals apparently was one such
connection and proved to be a barrier to the migration of
terrestrial mammals from Europe into Asia and vice versa.
Still further east, the Bering Strait did not exist at this
time, so from time to time, a land bridge existed between
Asia and North America.

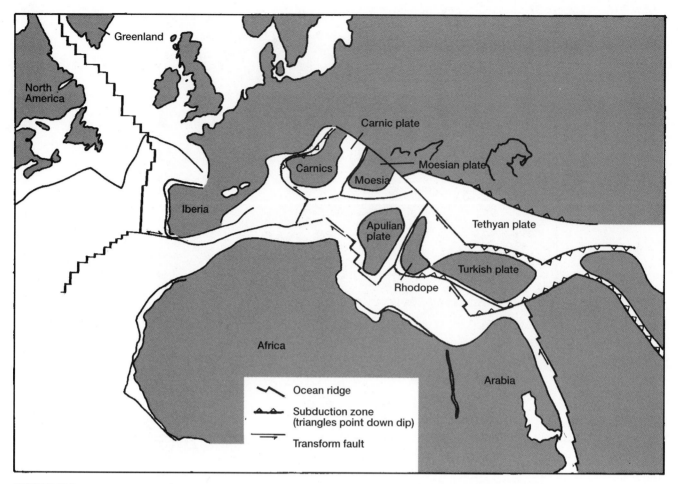

FIGURE 19.9

The numerous miniplates and microcontinental pieces in the western Tethyan region as the African craton moved northward in collision with the European craton to form the Alpine fold mountain belt. This reconstruction shows the approximate distribution in the Paleocene.

The End of Tethys and the Birth of the Alpine-Himalayas

The Tethys Ocean had existed as a great embayment into the Pangaea continent and, through the whole Mesozoic, was an ocean separating the northern and southern portions after the Pangaea breakup. During the Paleogene, it disappeared altogether as plate-tectonic movement brought the African/Arabian block in contact with Europe, while to the east, India closed with Asia (Figure 19.9).

The disappearance of the Tethys resulted in the formation of the enormous Alpine-Himalayan Range of mountains, a fold belt that stretches for some 17,000 kilometers, from Morocco in the west to New Guinea in the east. As with all major fold belts, crustal activity climaxed at different times along its length and even continues today, as a map of modern earthquake epicenters clearly demonstrates.

Some of the earliest activity occurred in the northwestern corner of the Mediterranean, as a thick, marine sedimentary wedge of Paleocene age was folded and thrust into the structures of the Atlas Mountains and Pyrenees. Although northward movement of the African craton was responsible for the major movement, further east, several smaller microplates caught between Africa and Eurasia also were involved, and the Alps, for example, were formed by northward movement of the Adriatic microplate. Beginning in the Oligocene, the so-called **Alpine orogeny** continued up to relatively recent geologic time, and only since the Late Miocene has activity largely ceased. Folding and thrusting in the Jura Mountains have even involved Pliocene sediments.

Meanwhile, to the east, the Indian subcontinent arrived in the Miocene, and its collision with Asia was responsible for the Himalayan Mountains. The great height of the Himalayas and of the Tibetan plateau to the north are generally believed to be due to underthrusting of the Indian crust beneath that of Eurasia to produce a much thicker slab of continental crust, which has risen isostatically.

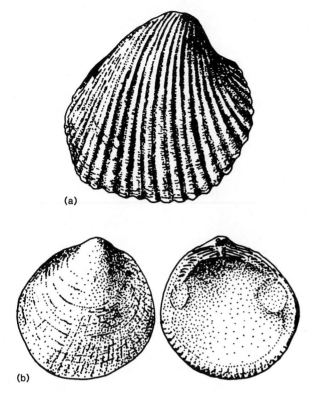

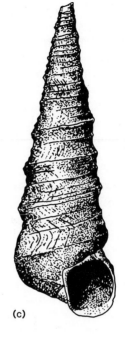

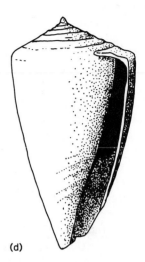

FIGURE 19.10
Typical Early Tertiary mollusks. (a) *Venericardia smithi.*
(b) *Glycimeris idonea.* (c) *Turritella mortoni.* (d) *Conus planiseps.*

Paleogene Flora

In contrast to the history of many animal groups, the Cretaceous/Paleogene transition was not marked by any widespread extinction of plants. Instead, there is a general continuity in terrestrial floras, which were already essentially modern in appearance. Spore and pollen counts from sediments at the Cretaceous/Paleogene boundary show a dramatic drop in many arboreal species and a concomitant rise in the proportion of ferns. This is, however, to be expected if there were, as suggested in Chapter 18, wildfires on a global scale.

The only really important change in terrestrial floras came during the Paleocene, with the appearance of the first grasses. Early species were adapted to swamp environments and were similar to modern sedges. By Late Oligocene time, there had apparently been a significant evolutionary advance with the coming of a continuous growth season. Adaptation to drier conditions assured the success of the grasses during the Oligocene climatic deterioration as the woodlands retreated and open spaces provided unprecedented opportunities. With the spread of grasslands in the Oligocene and Miocene, there was a corresponding evolutionary radiation among the grazing animals.

Paleogene Fauna

Invertebrates

For many invertebrates that survived the end-Cretaceous extinction, recovery during the Cenozoic was relatively rapid, in some instances helped by the disappearance of competitors. For example, although earlier in the Mesozoic, the corals had been important reef builders, during the Cretaceous, they had gradually given way to the rudistid mollusks. Now, with the extinction of that group, the corals were once again able to dominate the reef communities.

Few of the surviving mollusks differed significantly from modern species. Virtually all the major groups found in modern seas arose from recognizable Paleogene ancestors (Figure 19.10). In marked contrast, the brachiopods, already declining in the Cretaceous, continued to lose ground during the Cenozoic, and today are relatively unimportant elements in the marine biota. Among other groups, the bryozoans and echinoderms flourished, and the sand-burrowing sea urchins, such as the sand dollars that first appeared in the Middle Eocene, were particularly successful.

Birds

Sorting out the fossil record and attempting a classification of fossil birds that is meaningful in terms of modern bird classification is not easy. The criteria used by ornithologists are often based on such features as plumage, nest-building habits, and even bird songs. Even between orders, of which most modern classifications recognize 32, the gross skeletal features are often too similar for confident classification of fossil material. Without any attempt at a formal classification, it is possible to divide all birds into three broad groups: (1) the flying birds, (2) the flightless land birds, (the so-called ratites), and (3) the penguins (order Sphenisciforme).

Even a fragmentary fossil record clearly shows that, by Early Cenozoic time, flying birds were already essentially modern in appearance. The basic body plan had become established during the Cretaceous, and evolution through the Cenozoic mainly involved adaptation to a wide variety of habitats and life-styles. Virtually every conceivable ecologic niche was filled.

During the Paleocene and Eocene, some of the large flightless birds were important predators and even competition for the early mammals. Since that time, flightless birds have declined in importance, although they are still represented by the ostrich in Africa, the rheas of South America, and the emus, cassowaries, and kiwis of Australasia.

The oldest penguin fossil remains date from the Paleocene of New Zealand and on Seymour Island of the Antarctic Peninsula. Penguins are and always have been confined to the Southern Hemisphere, the majority living on the coldest and most inhospitable islands and coastlines; hence, the lack of fossil remains is hardly surprising. Penguins evolved in the Early to Middle Cenozoic from the same stock as the tube noses, the family that includes albatrosses, petrels, fulmars, and shearwaters, and progressed through a stage when they could both swim and fly. During their early history, penguins inhabited warm seas but slowly adjusted to a colder environment as Antarctica drifted toward the South Pole and the Southern Ocean became cooler. Some penguins evolved to considerable size (Figure 19.11). The largest modern penguin— the Emperor penguin (*Aptenodytes forsteri*)—stands about 1¼ meters tall, while fossil remains show that *Anthropornis nordeskjoeldi* stood some 2 meters tall and weighed up to 135 kilograms.

In their later evolution, penguins became the most perfectly adapted of all birds to an aquatic existence. Their wings, or flippers, as they are more correctly called, are powerfully muscled, enabling them to "fly" through the water at speeds up to 18 knots. Unlike other birds, their bones are solid, and some are able to dive to depths of 300 meters. A measure of the adaptation to a marine existence is seen particularly in the Emperor penguin, which alone among all seabird species, never goes ashore even to breed, living instead on the pack ice surrounding Antarctica.

FIGURE 19.11
Largest modern penguin, the Emperor penguin (foreground), compared with the largest ancestral form, *Pachydyptes ponderosus* (background) from the Miocene.

Mammals

Kinds of Mammals

Among living mammals, three major divisions, based upon the mode of reproduction, are recognized: (1) the **placental mammals,** which are the most familiar and abundant; (2) the **marsupials,** today confined largely to Australia; and (3) the **monotremes,** or egg-laying mammals, like the duckbilled platypus, also confined to Australia. Although the three groups demonstrate differences in the degree of sophistication in their reproductive systems—with sophistication increasing from monotreme to marsupial to placental—this has not been proven to reflect an evolutionary progression. At least, the fossil record offers no clues on this subject.

The monotremes, for example, are believed to be of ancient lineage and to have arisen from a mammal-like reptile perhaps as early as the Triassic. The docodonts of the Early Jurassic are considered the likeliest of the early mammal groups to lie on the line of descent. Unfortunately, the monotreme fossil record is confined to a few Pleistocene forms and some conjectural material from earlier time.

The marsupial and placental mammals both apparently arose from pantothere ancestral stock in the Early Cretaceous. The two groups differ in the degree of development of the young at birth. In the marsupials, the young appear at a very early stage in their development—in fact,

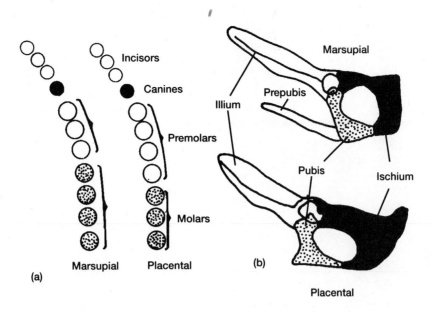

FIGURE 19.12
Comparison of marsupial and placental mammals.
(a) Dentition. (b) Pelvic bones.

they are little advanced from the embryo. They then make their way to the mother's pouch, where they attach themselves to nipples and finish their development. Today, the marsupials are represented by the kangaroos, wallabies, and numerous other groups in Australia, as well as by the familiar Virginia opossum of North America.

In the placental mammals, the embryo is attached to the placenta, a structure formed partly from the mother's uterus wall and partly from the allantoic membrane. The placenta provides oxygen and food to the fetus, and waste products are carried away through the mother's blood. The young are born in a relatively advanced state and are suckled through teats on the mammary glands.

Fortunately, certain skeletal elements of placental and marsupial mammals are diagnostic (Figure 19.12). Marsupial teeth, for example, have an archaic triangular arrangement of the cusps. Other marsupial features include an inwardly bent posterior angle on the jaw bone and a generally smaller brain case for a given size of animal.

Mammalian Evolution

Several distinct stages of mammalian evolution are recognized, each one characterized by a similar sequence of events. Each stage apparently began with a period of evolutionary experimentation, during which some lineages were successful and underwent radiation and expansion, whereas others were less successful and eventually died out, perhaps as evolutionary "dead ends" without descendent lineages.

First Evolutionary Stage   The first evolutionary stage occurred during the Triassic and Jurassic with the appearance of the first probable egg-laying mammals. The modern monotremes—represented, for example, by the egg-laying duckbilled platypus (Figure 19.13)—are remarkable survivors and provide insight into what the early mammals probably looked like. These early mammals were small: Fossil remains, often consisting only of teeth, indicate that none was larger than a mouse. Five orders of Jurassic mammals have been recognized, but of these, only three survived into the Cretaceous.

Second Evolutionary Stage   During the Cretaceous, and representing the second stage in mammalian evolution, the primitive multituberculates, symmetrodonts, and pantotheres were joined by two other groups that probably rose from pantothere stock: the first marsupials, and the insectivores, the first placental mammals. They survived in a largely reptilian world by virtue of their small size and lack of specialization. Although, during the Cenozoic, they gave rise to the root stock for an unprecedented evolutionary radiation, their original recipe for success also served them well because they are still found today in the form of such diminutive and retiring animals as moles, shrews, and hedgehogs. By the Late Cretaceous, a moderate radiation of these groups had produced some larger mammalian species, but they were still no bigger than cats. In a world completely dominated by reptiles, size clearly was no particular advantage. While the fossil record naturally offers no proof, these early mammals were likely nocturnal in their habits.

Before the close of the Cretaceous, the insectivores had given rise to at least two other branches: the creodonts, a group of flesheaters, and the **condylarths,** whose teeth showed modifications adapted to a diet of plants. The condylarths were the first **ungulates** (hoofed mammals) and formed the root stock of the hoofed animals of later time.

FIGURE 19.13
A present-day monotreme, the duckbilled platypus of Australia. *(Photograph courtesy of the Australian Overseas Information Service.)*

Third Evolutionary Stage   The third stage of mammalian evolution began with the terminal Cretaceous event, and from this time on, there is an essential continuity in the story of mammals. As the Cenozoic opened, the world, emptied of dinosaurs, pterosaurs, and large marine reptiles was, literally, a place of opportunity. Of those mammals that survived the end-Cretaceous mass extinction, none was larger than a cat, and many were still relatively generalized in their basic limb structures and dentition. On the other hand, the many and various ecologic niches were being filled: There were carnivores in the form of the creodonts, herbivorous primitive ungulates, and, last but not least, the insectivores, the least specialized of all and which quite early in the Paleocene gave rise to the first primates. Like their parent stock, the primates continued through much of their subsequent history to remain quite unspecialized in many of their anatomical features.

Paleocene Mammalian Expansion

The first major evolutionary expansion of the mammals began in the Early Paleocene, and 11 new orders appeared (Figure 19.14). Among these were the first edentates (sloths and armadillos), rodents, lagomorphs (rabbits), carnivores, and, of course, the primates, all of which are still part of the modern world.

Contemporaneous with them were certain other groups whose future was less certain. These groups included the less successful experiments, such as the taeniodonts and tillodonts, both large, rather bearlike herbivores with teeth reminiscent of the rodents, a stocky build, and heavy, clawed feet. Neither group survived past the Eocene.

Another of the less successful groups were the amblypods, an early offshoot from the evolving ungulate line, herbivores that had arisen from the same root stock as the creodonts during the Late Cretaceous. By the Eocene, some amblypods were quite large; *Uintatherium* of Early Eocene time, for example, was very rhinoceros-like in size and appearance (Figure 19.15a). Its most distinctive features were no fewer than six horns and extremely large, tusklike, upper-canine teeth. Amblypods were contemporaries of other more successful ungulates, but they became extinct before the Middle Oligocene.

Geographic Isolation

During the Early Paleocene mammalian evolutionary radiation, when the early mammals were ranging far and wide to exploit their newfound world, certain groups in the further reaches of their dispersal eventually became geographically isolated. This happened most noticeably in South America and Australia.

South America   During the Early Cenozoic, South America was connected to North America by the Panamanian isthmus, but by Eocene time, the isthmus had foundered, and a land bridge was not reestablished until the Pliocene. During much of the Cenozoic, therefore, South America was isolated from the rest of the world, and the earliest mammal immigrants evolved along many different lines, often resulting in animals that demonstrated a remarkable similarity to species in similar ecologic niches on other continents but whose ancestry was quite different. Among the earliest South American mammals were marsupials that, as time passed, came to fill many ecologic niches. Among them, for example, was *Borhyaena,* a Miocene carnivore that was very wolflike.

Among the first immigrants to arrive in South America were primitive ungulates belonging to the order Condylarthra, and before long, and in the isolation of the southern continent, they gave rise to three orders of distinctive South American ungulates, the Notoungulata (Figure 19.15b), the Litopterna (Figure 19.15c), and the Astrapathera. Of these, the Astrapathera were short-lived, but the other two orders survived into the Pleistocene, their demise likely due to competition with more advanced mammals newly arrived via the Panamanian isthmus, which became emergent again in the Pliocene.

Among the most numerous mammalian fossils in South America are those of the various notoungulates that underwent their own separate radiation isolated from the rest of the world. The earliest forms were relatively small,

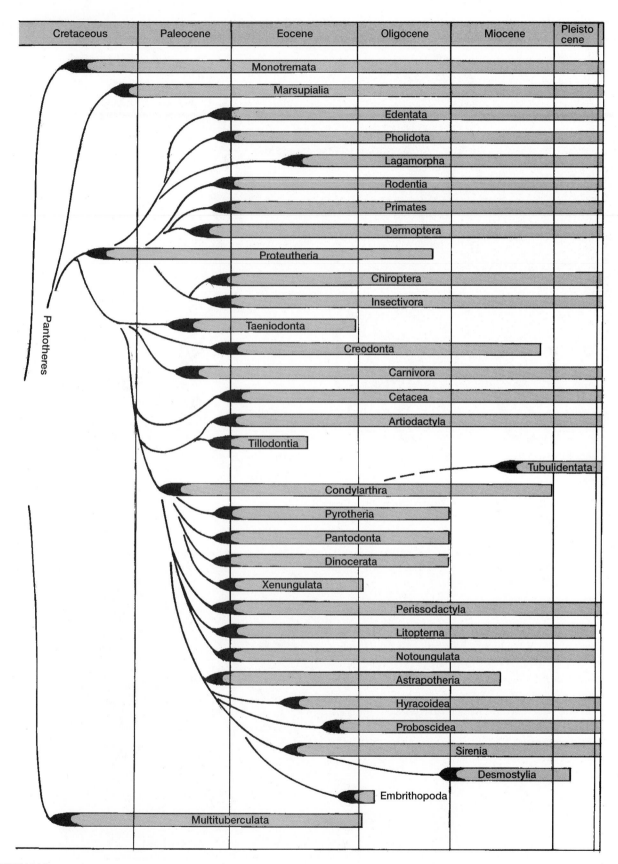

FIGURE 19.14
Evolutionary radiation of the mammals, beginning in the
Paleocene.

(a)

(b)   (c)

FIGURE 19.15
Early Cenozoic mammals. (a) *Uintatherium*. (b) The
notoungulate *Thomashuxlia*. (c) The litoptern *Macrauchenia*.

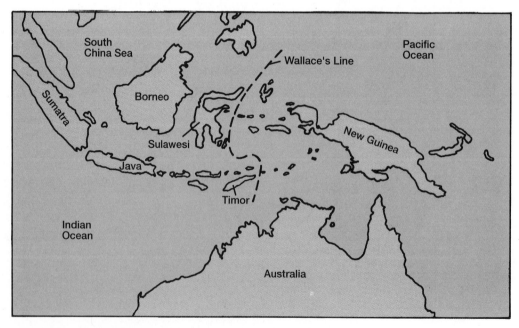

FIGURE 19.16
Sketch map of portion of East Indian archipelago, showing
the location of Wallace's Line.

FIGURE 19.17
The best-known marsupial, the kangaroo. *(Photo courtesy of Australian Overseas Information Service.)*

hoofed animals that arose from a condylarth stock in the Late Paleocene. During later evolution, many grew to be quite large, and *Nesodon* of the Miocene, for example, was as large as a rhinoceros and had the same heavy build. Other notoungulates were very much like horses and underwent a series of changes that in many ways were reminiscent of those seen in the true horses.

Australia   Australian faunas provide the most striking examples of the effects of geographic isolation. Australia's isolation from other continents has been longer and more complete than that of South America. The separation began in the Cretaceous, when the Australian and Antarctic cratons together moved away from the rest of Gondwana. In the Early Cenozoic, further splitting resulted in Australia's complete separation, and from that time on, it drifted northward into warmer latitudes. In the Middle Miocene, it was making first contact with the Asian plate, but from a zoogeographic point of view, it remained isolated because land animals were still surrounded by water. In latest Miocene into Pliocene time, the islands of the New Guinea-Indonesia archipelago became emergent as possible stepping stones for migration. Even without human interference, Australia's isolation was no longer complete.

In prehistoric time, a small interchange of Australian and Asian species began, although the zone of overlap was extremely narrow. Minor island hopping by land mammals had occurred, but Asian and Australian biota were markedly separate, as noted by Alfred Russel Wallace, the eminent Victorian biologist and co-discoverer with Charles Darwin of the idea of natural selection. Wallace established what became known as **Wallace's Line,** a demarcation between the islands of Borneo and Sulawesi that denoted Asian fauna on one side and Australian on the other (Figure 19.16). The presence of a marsupial on Sulawesi placed Sulawesi on the Australian side of the line, even though certain Asian elements, including two species of monkeys, a pig, a porcupine, one deer species, and several insectivores had immigrated. After later studies, Wallace decided that the Sulawesi marsupial was itself an immigrant heading toward Asia and so revised his line to place Sulawesi on the Asian side.

The islands north of Australia were only a partial bridge, or filter, and the Australian mainland at the time of the coming of early humans, presumably in the Late Pleistocene, held no placental mammals. These early humans brought with them only the Australian wild dog, or dingo, and possibly also rats.

Virtually every mammalian ecologic niche in Australia became filled by marsupial species of one kind or another, a remarkable example of adaptive radiation. Often, the marsupials that were adapted to certain habitats and life-styles were strikingly similar to their placental contemporaries in other parts of the world.

For example, the Tasmanian wolf *Thylacinnus,* which survived right up to about 1930, when senseless slaughter eliminated it, was not only very similar to the true wolves in general form but also closely resembled its South American marsupial cousin, the extinct *Borhyaena.* Further examples of what is termed **evolutionary convergence** are seen in Australian phalangers or opossums that show very squirrel-like features. Rabbitlike marsupials are represented by bandicoots, and *Notoryctes,* a small burrowing animal, is molelike in appearance and life-style. The major herbivores are represented by the best-known of all marsupial mammals—the kangaroos and wallabies (Figure 19.17).

Eocene Mammalian Expansion

The mammalian evolutionary expansion obviously was gaining momentum. While the taeniodonts and tillodonts became extinct during the Eocene, at least seven new mammalian orders appeared. In fact, of the 15 orders of mammals still extant, only two had yet to appear by the close of the Eocene. Significant also is the fact that of the seven Eocene newcomers, all have survived to the present day. The Eocene was a time of modernization, and the major evolutionary patterns apparently had become largely established by that time.

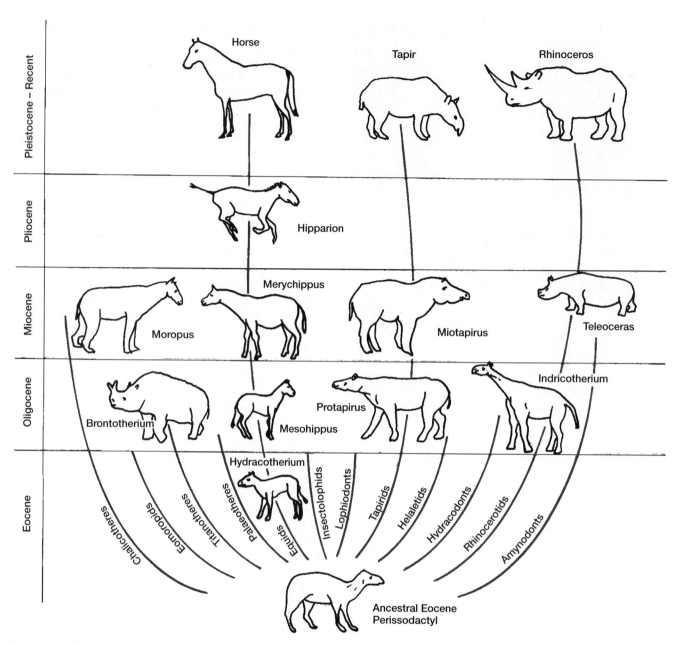

FIGURE 19.18
Evolution of the perissodactyls.

As with the reptiles, the mammalian herbivores were among the most numerous animals and underwent some of the most spectacular evolutionary changes. The perissodactyls, the odd-toed ungulates that include the modern tapirs, rhinos, and horses, reached their climax during the Late Eocene into the Oligocene and showed a wide range of morphologic divergence (Figure 19.18). The evolutionary history of the horse is particularly well documented and often cited as a classic example of evolutionary change (although invariably oversimplified). The earliest horse, named *Hyracotherium*—later, popularly, although incorrectly, labeled *Eohippus*—first appeared in the Early

Eocene. It was a relatively small creature about the size of a dog, but during successive changes through Eocene and Oligocene time, it became larger, while at the same time, the number of toes was reduced to three. By the Early Oligocene, *Mesohippus* looked very horselike and during the Miocene gave rise to four separate lineages (Figure 19.19).

Back to the Sea Again—The Marine Mammals

The magnitude of the mammalian evolutionary radiation during the Cenozoic was so great that some mammals, like many reptiles before them, returned to an aquatic

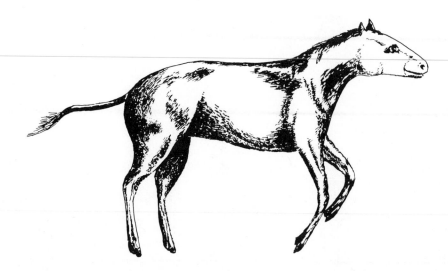

FIGURE 19.19
The Oligocene three-toed horse *Mesohippus*. This animal stood about 1/2 meter tall at the shoulder and thus was no larger than a sheep.

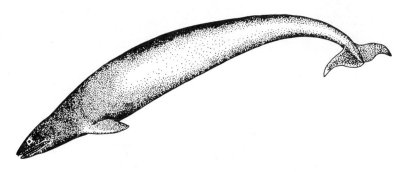

FIGURE 19.20
Zeuglodon, an early whale.

mode of existence in a fully marine habitat. This happened in three groups, producing creatures of widely differing size and degree of marine adaptability. The greatest degree of adaptation is seen in the **cetaceans,** which include the whales and dolphins. The **pinnipeds,** including the seals, sea lions, and walruses, and the **sirenians,** or sea cows, must return to land for breeding. The evolutionary history of these groups is not well known because, although marine organisms generally leave a better fossil record than do terrestrial organisms, the fossil remains of marine mammals have been disappointingly few.

The whales and porpoises, the most fishlike of the mammals, have completely severed their connection with the land and produce young in the water. They still have to surface to breathe, but many remain submerged for up to an hour and can dive to great depths. Only the forelimbs remain as paddles, and the massive and powerful tail provides the main propelling power. A fleshy dorsal fin acts as a stabilizer to prevent rolling. The pelvic bones and hind limbs have been reduced to mere vestigial structures. All whales are carnivores, although in one group—

the so-called whalebone whales—the teeth are suppressed and replaced by a series of plates, or baleen, that hang from the roof of the mouth and whose function is to strain microscopic plankton from the water.

The earliest fossil record of whales appears in rocks of Middle Eocene age. They were already of considerable size, and *Zeuglodon,* typical of the archaeocetaceans, or primitive whales, was, for example, some 20 meters long (Figure 19.20). The modern whales appeared during a radiation that began in the latest Eocene to the Early Oligocene, and the ancestors of the modern whale families had appeared by the Miocene.

The origins of the second group—the pinnipeds—are somewhat of a mystery because, when they first appear in the fossil record in rocks of Miocene age, they were already differentiated into two or possibly three different groups. Their adaptation to a marine existence is less advanced than the cetaceans because they have to return to land for breeding. All four limbs have been retained as paddles, with webs between the toes.

FIGURE 19.21
A modern sirenian, the manatee. *(Photograph by courtesy of
Florida Game and Freshwater Fish Commission.)*

FIGURE 19.22
Prosimian primates. (a) Tree shrew. (b) Lemur. (c) Tarsier.
*(Photographs by courtesy of Wisconsin Regional Primate
Research Center.)*

The last group of marine mammals—the sirenians or sea cows—include the manatees and dugongs (Figure 19.21). With a fossil record beginning in the Eocene, the earliest sirenians looked much like their modern descendants. The skull was slightly more pointed, and the pelvis still retained tetrapod features, but otherwise, little has changed. The sirenians' closest living relatives are the elephants, because they came from the same ancestral stock—the proboscideans. Like all proboscideans and related groups, they are herbivores.

Early Primate Evolution

The **primates** are an order of mammals that includes humans, apes, monkeys, and related forms. Not surprisingly, in view of their habitat, generally small size, and light build, the fossil record of early primates leaves much to be desired. On the other hand, some likely evolutionary pathways can be discerned from a study of living primates. For example, modern tree shrews, although looking little like primates, are probably similar to the early ancestral primates of Paleocene time. The lemurs and tarsiers, as more advanced primates, presumably represent a later stage in evolution (Figure 19.22). What fossil record there is confirms these determinations.

The evolution of the primates provides a good example of a phenomenon mentioned in earlier chapters—namely, **preadaptation.** In the case of the primates, it was rather a lack of specialization that led to important advances. Probably all the small, tree-shrew-like forms lived an arboreal existence in which they rarely, if ever, came to the ground. Life up in the forest canopy was much safer, particularly for small species that could run from tree to tree. As new and larger species evolved, running out on the furthest twigs to cross to an adjacent tree became increasingly difficult, and progression through the canopy required leaps from one secure branch to another. Good muscular coordination, grasping limbs, a sense of balance, and, above all, depth perception were, as with any trapeze artist, necessary prerequisites for survival. The retention in these early primates of a primitive, five-toed foot now stood them in good stead. In some forms, the development of a prehensile tail was an additional adaptation.

This arboreal life clearly called for a different emphasis in the senses, with sight more important than smell. As a result, a long, snouted skull gave way to a shortened snout, and a flattened skull resulted in the eyes moving to the front for stereoscopic vision. The need for better muscular coordination probably set the early primates on the road to an expansion of the higher centers of the brain that would eventually lead to intelligence. These trends were very much in evidence by the Oligocene, and the first representatives of what have been called the higher primates, or prosimians, had appeared. The final steps along the road to humankind are described in the next chapter.

Paleogene Climatic Deterioration

The division between the Paleogene and Neogene, placed at the Oligocene/Miocene boundary, is in many ways an arbitrary selection and not particularly justified by marked faunal discontinuities. The close of the Eocene would have been a preferred boundary, for example, because many marine invertebrates had been considerably reduced by a global refrigeration event. The evidence is seen in such groups as the planktonic foraminifera, which, apparently, were particularly susceptible, and also in the terrestrial floras. There was also a eustatic fall of sea level at this time.

As we have seen on many occasions throughout this text, most important events of earth history ultimately have been due to plate-tectonic movements, and the end-Eocene event is no exception. On this occasion, however, the effects of plate movements on oceanic circulation are clearly demonstrated. The most important factor was the splitting apart of the Australian and Antarctic continents in the Eocene. Prior to this time, the Antarctic area had lain approximately at the South Pole, and an ice cap likely was already in existence there. Indeed, some authors have suggested a southern ice cap as early as latest Cretaceous. The huge Australian/Antarctic continent certainly had plenty of room in the interior for an ice sheet, even though ocean currents from warmer latitudes maintained a mild coastal climate. This changed after the sundering of Australia and Antarctica. With the isolation of Antarctica and a redirection of ocean currents, the ameliorating effect of a warm ocean was gone, and the ice cap grew rapidly. Ice-rafted material in deep-sea sediment cores show that, by Oligocene time, the ice front had reached tidewater and was calving icebergs, although sea ice probably had appeared earlier, in the Late Eocene (Figure 19.23a).

The growth of ice pack and coastal ice shelves introduced a new factor into the global marine environment as extremely cold, dense water produced in the Southern Ocean sank to the sea floor and moved equatorward, beginning a major system of thermohaline oceanic circulation that continues to the present day. In the modern oceans, what is known as the Antarctic Bottom Water is still detectable as a distinct water mass north of the equator. The immediate result of the formation of this deep layer of cold water, or **psychrosphere** (Figure 19.23b), as it is known, was an extinction of many benthic marine organisms, and by the Oligocene, there were considerable repercussions throughout the food chain.

Meanwhile, events in the north polar regions also influenced climatic conditions. As discussed in Chapter 18, despite the birth of the Atlantic Ocean, North America and Europe remained joined until Early Eocene time. The Arctic Ocean lying at the North Pole was undoubtedly covered by pack ice for most of the year, but its water was more or less isolated from the world's oceans. With the

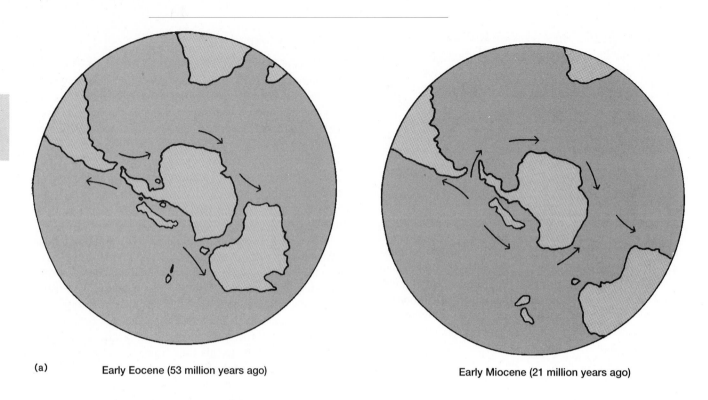

(a)   Early Eocene (53 million years ago)   Early Miocene (21 million years ago)

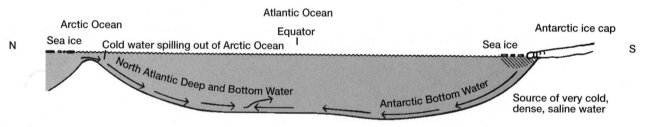

(b)

FIGURE 19.23

Origin of the psychrosphere. (a) The separation of Antarctica and Australia led to the thermal isolation of Antarctica as a circumpolar ocean current system developed. (b) The appearance of pack ice (sea ice) around Antarctica began the intense cooling that produced the Antarctic Bottom Water. This dense, salty water sank to the ocean floor and moved northward as part of a general thermohaline circulation pattern that persists today.

extension of the mid-Atlantic ridge northward, separating Greenland and Europe, this isolation ended, and cold arctic water began to spill southward, as it does today. Oceanographers call this water the North Atlantic Deep and Bottom Water (Figure 19.23b). This development intensified the effects of the psychrosphere, and the global cooling that resulted set the stage for further climatic deterioration, which culminated in the Late Cenozoic Ice Age in which we currently live.

Summary

Although post-Cretaceous geologic time has been divided into the Paleogene and Neogene, the more traditional division has been into the Tertiary and Quaternary. One of the disadvantages in this latter approach is the large imbalance in the magnitude of the two divisions. In any case, all the various divisions are more or less artificial, and the only "natural" boundary discernible is the marked global climatic deterioration in the Late Eocene to Early Oligocene.

In North America's Cordilleran region, Late Cretaceous to Eocene time is dominated by the Laramide orogeny, during which the area of crustal disturbance extended much further east than ever before. This was likely due to a lessening of the angle of descent of the Farallon plate beneath the North American plate.

As the Laramide orogeny came to an end, the western interior of North America underwent considerable uplift, and easterly flowing streams spread sediments over extensive areas of Nebraska, South Dakota, and Montana, where they are mapped as the Fort Union Formation. In central North Dakota, the Cannonball Formation is a marine deposit, indicating that the sea lingered here long after the retreat of the Cretaceous Interior Seaway.

By the Eocene, intermontane basins were becoming filled with sediments, such as those of the Wasatch Formation, and the climate apparently was becoming drier. Shifting drainage patterns frequently resulted in the formation of large lakes. Two of these were Lake Gosiute in southwestern Wyoming and Lake Uinta in northeastern Utah. As lake levels fluctuated, these two lakes often became joined, and in places, lacustrine sediments are 1,500 meters thick. Mapped as the Green River Formation, the deposits include "varved" laminae believed to represent annual or seasonal cycles. The Green River Formation is famous for its well-preserved fossils, particularly fish. By Oligocene time, most of the intermontane basins were filled with sediment, and streams began spreading sands and silts further east across a major pediment surface.

Along the Gulf and Atlantic margins, Paleogene sediments form part of the great wedge of terrigenous material derived from the continental interior. Much of this material was deposited sequentially basinward—that is, into the Gulf and the Atlantic—rather than upward, as had been happening during the Cretaceous when the continental margin was still subsiding. Only in the south, in the area of the Florida/Bahamas platform, which is remote from clastic sources, did large-scale carbonate accumulation continue. Along the southern North American continental margin in the Gulf of Mexico, the overriding control of regional sedimentary patterns was the Mississippi River. In the Gulf coast region are numerous salt domes derived by the squeezing upward of the Louann Salt of Jurassic age.

In Europe, Paleogene sediments accumulating in the North Sea and Paris basins were derived both from the continental interior to the east and from the peripheral highland areas of western Britain and Scandinavia. Plate-tectonic movements involving the northward movement of Africa and the movement of the Indian peninsula toward Asia closed the Tethys Ocean and caused the folding and thrusting that resulted in the Alpine-Himalayan range of mountains.

Plants came through the Cretaceous-Paleogene boundary with little change, and recovery was rapid. The first grasses appeared during the Paleocene and by the Late Oligocene were expanding rapidly as the cooling and drying of world climate provided opportunities for the spread of grasslands.

Among the invertebrates that survived the end-Cretaceous extinction, recovery was rapid, and the aspect of faunas was essentially modern.

The fossil record of birds is fragmentary but nevertheless shows that Paleogene species included many flying birds that were quite modern in appearance. Some of the large flightless birds were important predators but eventually lost in competition with evolving mammals. Penguins, which have always been confined to the Southern Hemisphere, slowly adjusted to a colder environment, and in their later evolution, became the most perfectly adapted of all birds to an aquatic existence.

The Paleogene saw a marked evolutionary radiation of the mammals. In a world now devoid of most large reptile groups, opportunities for expansion into many vacated ecologic niches were numerous. During the Paleocene, 11 new orders of mammals appeared, including the edentates, rodents, lagomorphs, carnivores, and primates, all of which have survived to the present. Other groups were less successful, and the taeniodont and tillodont herbivores, for example, did not survive past the Eocene. The amblypods, another group of herbivores, died out before the Middle Oligocene.

Notable examples of parallel evolution occurred when early Cenozoic faunas became geographically isolated, as they did in South America and Australia. Many of the ecologic niches became occupied by marsupial mammals that came to look remarkably similar to placental mammals in other parts of the world.

The mammalian evolutionary expansion gained momentum during the Eocene, and at least seven new mammalian orders appeared, all of which have survived to the present day. Major evolutionary patterns apparently had become largely established by that time.

As part of the mammalian evolutionary radiation, many forms returned to a marine existence. Three main groups were involved: the cetaceans, pinnipeds, and sirenians.

Early primate evolution provides a good example of the phenomenon of preadaptation. In the case of primates, a lack of specialization led to important advances. In addition, the need for better muscular coordination probably set the early primates on the road to an expansion of the higher centers of the brain.

By the end of the Oligocene, global climate deteriorated, largely because of changes in oceanic circulation. These changes were, in turn, largely due to the separation of Antarctica from Australia, which resulted in the thermal isolation of Antarctica and the rapid expansion of its ice cap. The appearance of sea ice around the margin of Antarctica in the Eocene and the eventual formation of ice shelves and icebergs in the Oligocene produced very cold and dense water to form the psy-chrosphere. Events in the north polar regions had a similar effect. The northward extension of the mid-Atlantic ridge system finally split Greenland away from Europe, allowing the cold arctic waters to spill southward into the North Atlantic. This set the stage for the further cooling that resulted in the Late Cenozoic Ice Age in which we live today.

Questions

1. Describe the plate-tectonic movements that were largely responsible for the Laramide orogeny.
2. Why is there some mystery surrounding the Cannonball Formation?
3. The Green River Formation of Wyoming and Utah is famous for its remarkable fossils, notably of freshwater fishes and plants. Describe the conditions under which this formation accumulated and why the fossils were so well preserved.
4. What influence did the Mississippi River have on the Gulf coast sedimentary successions of Tertiary time?
5. Describe events that led to the disappearance of the Tethys Ocean.
6. Give some account of the way in which reef communities changed in passing from the Cretaceous to the Paleogene.
7. Describe the highlights of bird evolution during the Paleogene.
8. List as many marsupial mammals as you can, and indicate a placental mammal group that approximately fills the same ecologic niche.
9. Why did the first major evolutionary expansion of the mammals begin in the Paleocene? What animals appeared at this time?
10. Give some account of the work of Alfred Russel Wallace and how it relates to the question of the geographic distribution of animals.
11. Describe briefly the return of certain mammal groups to a marine existence. Which ones are most dependent upon a periodic return to the land, and which ones are less so, or not at all?
12. The evolution of the primates provides a good example of preadaptation. Explain.
13. What changes in world climate were becoming evident by the close of the Eocene?
14. What evidence is there for the timing of the beginning of an Antarctic ice cap?
15. What is the psychrosphere? How did it form?

Further Reading

Kurten, B. 1971. *The age of mammals.* New York: Columbia University Press.

Pearson, R. 1964. *Animals and plants of the Cenozoic era.* London: Butterworth.

Pomeral, C., and I. Premoli-Silva, eds. 1986. *Terminal Eocene events.* Amsterdam: Elsevier.

Woodburne, M. O., ed. 1987. *Cenozoic mammals of North America.* Berkeley: University of California Press.

20

THE NEOGENE

Introduction

And so we come to the final chapter in the story of our planet. This segment of geologic history began only 25 million years ago and embraces the Miocene, Pliocene, Pleistocene, and Holocene epochs; within the great sweep of geologic time, it is a relatively brief period.[1]

An overview of the material in this chapter shows events occurring at three different scales of time. First, over periods measured in tens of millions of years, major geologic events during the Neogene have simply been a continuation of what had been happening during the Paleogene. The world in terms of the distribution of land and sea looked recognizably modern. No large areas of the continent were submerged, so the stratigraphic record of Neogene time is largely contained in nonmarine successions laid down in interior basins and across floodplains. Marine sediments, largely confined to narrow belts along coastal margins, record relatively rapid fluctuations of sea level that, except in regions of tectonic activity, provide a record of glacio-eustatic fluctuations.

Second, on a time scale measured in hundreds of thousands of years, geologic processes have been largely controlled by climatic fluctuations. By Miocene time, a major ice cap covered the South Pole, and there is abundant evidence for the beginning of a northern ice cap as well. Clearly, the world was rapidly entering a full-blown ice age.

Third, in a time scale measured in only tens of thousands of years, the human species has emerged as a geologic agent. Humans' role in shaping this planet has not been confined to the use of bulldozers and explosives, but began with the depredations of early hunters, which many believe were responsible for a mass extinction event rivaling anything in the geologic past and that continues today with the ever-increasing destruction of habitats.

Just as important is humans' influence on the atmosphere. The burning of fossil fuels since the beginning of the Industrial Evolution has increased the carbon dioxide content of the atmosphere by 10 percent. That this will result in a greenhouse effect and cause world temperatures to rise is a growing concern.

---

1. The Neogene Period, as the upper division of the Tertiary, by definition includes only the Miocene and Pliocene, leaving out the Quaternary with its Pleistocene and Holocene divisions. On the other hand, the glacial/preglacial boundary that was the base for the original Quaternary has lost much of its significance, so the obvious solution is to extend the Neogene upward to the present, as it is done here, albeit unofficially (see Table 19.1).

Strictly speaking, the Quaternary as a division of period rank should be used only with the Tertiary. If the Paleogene and Neogene divisions are to replace the Tertiary, then another name is required for the Pleistocene and Holocene together. British geologist William Harland has proposed the term *pleistogene*, but it has not found wide acceptance.

The Neogene in North America

The Cordilleran Region

Beginning in the Oligocene and continuing to the present day, the whole of the western margin of the North American continent has been profoundly influenced by intense faulting and widespread volcanism. To the east has been a broad uplift and rejuvenation of streams. Much of the record of these events is contained not in sedimentary successions, as with earlier geologic history, but in landforms and erosional features. Because most of the processes that sculpted the landscapes are ongoing, they can be easily understood.

During the Oligocene, the overall compressional style of plate margin tectonics all along the Pacific border gave way to shearing or translational movement in which the North American and Pacific plates began to slide past one another. The effects of this movement are, for example, seen today in the activity along the **San Andreas fault** system. Throughout the Neogene, the effects elsewhere have been profound and widespread. Because these new plate movements have affected different sections of the Cordilleran region in different ways, their histories must be discussed separately.

The Pacific Coast

In the Pacific coast region, the effects of the changed plate relationships can be seen. During the earlier Cenozoic along the western margin of North America, an easterly dipping subduction zone was consuming what has been called the **Farallon plate.** Farallon plate crust was being generated along a spreading center—the East Pacific Rise—that lay to the west in the Pacific Ocean, but apparently at a slower rate than it was being consumed beneath the North American plate. This imbalance resulted in a net relative movement of the North American plate toward the spreading center until the plate eventually overrode it altogether. In the process, the Farallon plate largely disappeared and is today represented only by two small fragments: the Juan de Fuca miniplate off Washington and Oregon and the Cocos plate off Mexico (Figure 20.1).

The Pacific plate at this time was generally moving in a north-northwesterly direction, so that, on meeting the North American plate, its contact relationship was one of translational movement rather than collision. The San Andreas and other similar faults are a manifestation of this translational movement (Figure 20.2). Because the trace of the faults is rarely straight, it follows that relative lateral movement across the fault results in an irregular alternation of zones of compression with zones of tension along the fault's length. When the local structural style is one of tension, so-called **pull-apart basins** may form (Figure 20.3a). In southern California, these fault-controlled basins both onshore and offshore become filled with sediments, and many are prolific oil and gas producers. (Figure 20.3b).

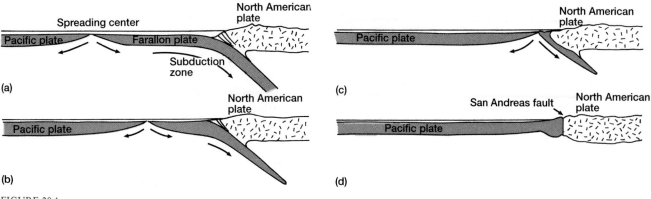

FIGURE 20.1

Progressive disappearance of the Farallon plate as the spreading center separating it from the Pacific plate moved toward the North American plate. (a) Latest Cretaceous. (b) Early Tertiary. (c) Late Tertiary. (d) Present.

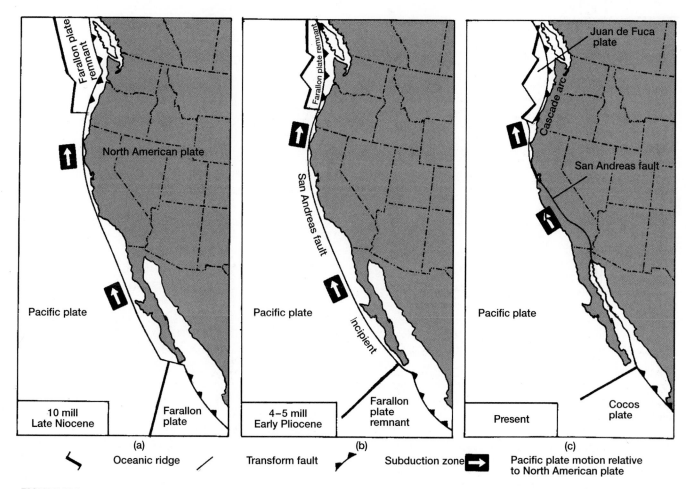

FIGURE 20.2

Evolution of the San Andreas transform fault system. (a) Late Miocene (10 million years ago). (b) Early Pliocene (4.5 million years ago). (c) Present.

The Sierra Nevada

The **Sierra Nevada** is one of the youngest mountain ranges in the world, nonexistent even as late as the Pliocene. At this time, moisture-carrying winds from the Pacific were reaching the area that is now Nevada, and plant fossils from sediments of Pliocene age indicate an abundance of moisture. Beginning in the Late Pliocene, however, there are indications of a change to a dry savanna climate, which could only have been caused by the rain-shadow effect of a rapidly rising range of mountains to the west.

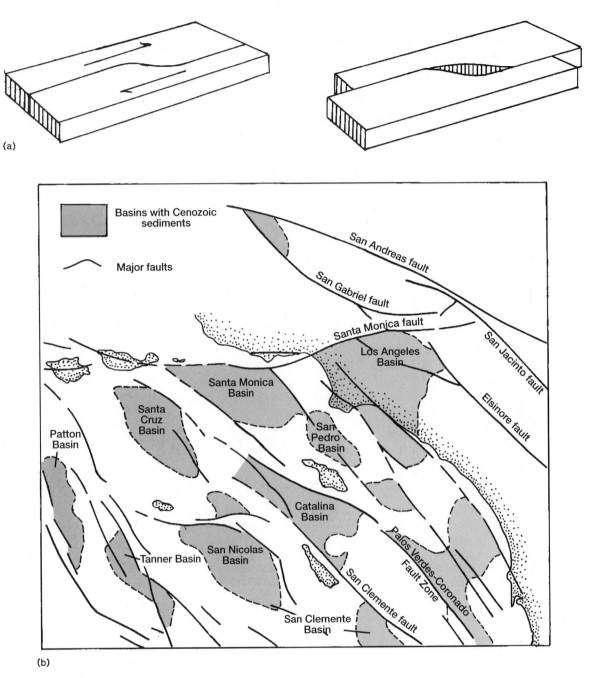

FIGURE 20.3

(a) Strike-slip fault pattern and the origin of pull-apart basins.
(b) Cenozoic offshore basins in southern California as pull-

apart basins. *(Based on map by D. L. Durham, U.S. Geological Survey.)*

Uplift of the Sierra Nevada block was not uniform but involved a marked westward tilt (Figure 20.4). Most of the movement occurred along major faults that form the eastern boundary of the region, while the western side of the block was depressed to form the California trough. Uplift of the Sierra Nevada was probably related to the major change that had occurred earlier in plate-tectonic motion as active subduction along the plate margin ceased. The change from a compressive structural style to a largely translational one allowed isostatic recovery of deeply

buried granitic material. The upward flotation of such a block of granitic crust is what pushed the Sierra Nevada up so rapidly.

The Columbia Plateau

During the Miocene, enormous fissure eruptions resulted in the greatest lava outpourings in North America since the Precambrian, covering an area of southeastern Washington and northeastern Oregon totaling some 300,000

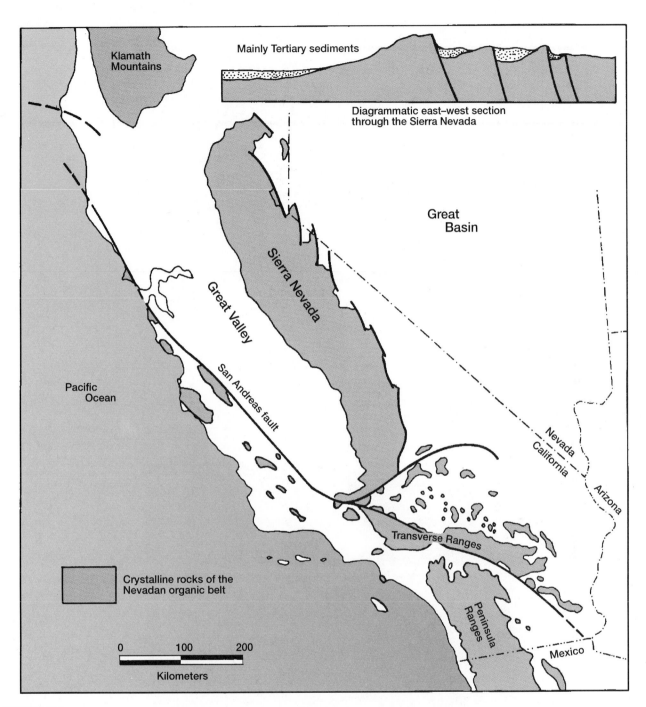

FIGURE 20.4
Regional geology and structure of the Sierra Nevada.

square kilometers and called the **Columbia Plateau** (Figure 20.5). The estimated volume of the flow is 200,000 cubic kilometers, with the bulk of the lava extruded over an interval of 3.5 million years. The lavas are basalts of a type know as tholeiite. With a low (47 to 50 percent) silica content, they are extremely fluid, and individual flows can be traced for over 300 kilometers. Some flows, channeled along river valleys of the ancestral Columbia River drainage, even reached the Pacific coast! Today, the succession of flows is exposed in the walls of river gorges, and interbedded with them are ancient soils, the fossil remains of forests that grew on them, and ancient river and lake deposits (Figure 20.6). Clearly, after each flow, landscapes and drainage patterns became reestablished for considerable intervals before being overwhelmed by the next fiery outpouring.

The Columbia Plateau was not the only center of volcanic activity at this time. There were also outpourings to the north in British Columbia and to the south in southern Oregon and northern California.

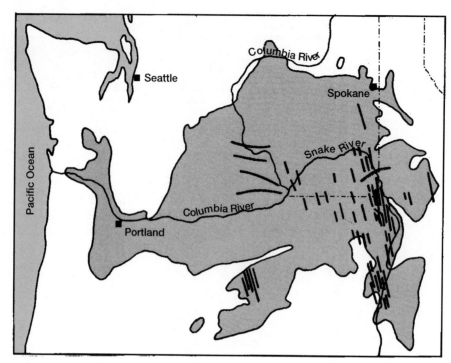

FIGURE 20.5
Distribution of the Columbia Plateau basalts. The black bars
mark the location of the major fissures feeding the lava flows.

FIGURE 20.6
Basalt flows of the Columbia Plateau at Soap Lake at the
south end of the Grand Coulee in Washington State.
(Photograph courtesy of Washington State Tourism Division.)

The cause of all this basaltic volcanic activity is still
controversial. One model suggests that an acceleration of
seafloor spreading in the Middle Miocene resulted in
crustal stretching and the opening of the fissures that supplied the basalt.

The Basin and Range Province

At the beginning of Neogene time, the **Basin and Range
Province** was an area of only moderate relief, having
undergone broad uplift and erosion during the Paleocene.
Considerable volcanic activity resulted in much of the area

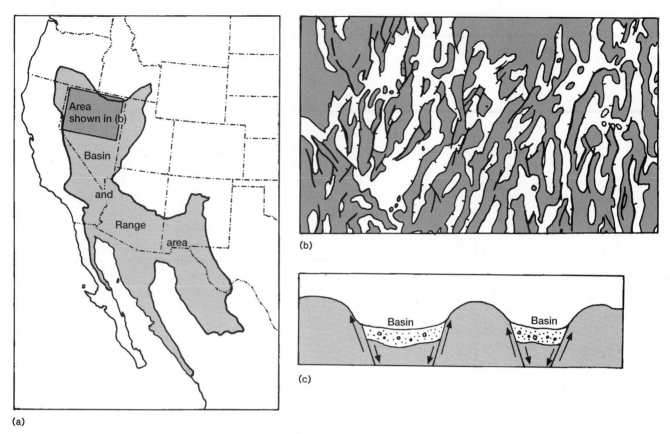

FIGURE 20.7
Location and structures of the Basin and Range Province.

being flooded in Early Miocene time by rhyolitic lava flows. In Late Miocene time, crustal movements that indicated tensional forces at work resulted in a broad upwarping and, at the same time, block faulting and the extrusion of basaltic lavas. Between the major faults, most of which have a roughly north-south orientation, the down-faulted blocks subsided to form the *basins* between the *ranges* of the up-faulted blocks (Figure 20.7). Erosion of the rising ranges supplied sediment that was transported into neighboring basins.

The cause of these structural movements is not clear. In some ways, the tensional structural style and down-faulting of various blocks are reminiscent of continental rifting. This may have been associated with the East Pacific Rise spreading center, part of which had been overridden by the North American plate.

In an alternative hypothesis, the faulting was associated with regional deformation involving transform faulting along the North American plate boundary. This movement continues to the present day, as manifested in the San Andreas and associated faults.

The crust is markedly thinner than average beneath the Basin and Range Province, while heat flow is about twice that of regions to the east. Thus, deep-seated mantle activity and stretching of the crust may have been important factors.

The Colorado Plateau

The **Colorado Plateau** forms a vast upland area, with average elevations of 2,000 meters and more, and is centered approximately on the Four Corners area, where Utah, Colorado, New Mexico, and Arizona meet (Figure 20.8). Except for broad warping and some normal faulting, it was little affected by the crustal deformation of the Mesozoic and earlier Cenozoic along its western flank, and it has remained more or less as a single structural entity.

In early Neogene time, the Colorado Plateau was largely a lowland region, and sedimentary successions dating from that time indicate that it was an area of inland drainage. Beginning in the Pliocene, broad uplift of the area was accompanied by faulting, volcanism, and extensive mineralization. The eroded remnants of the volcanic necks and the associated dikes are common topographic features throughout the region. Ship Rock in northwestern New Mexico is one of the most famous of these features.

Volcanic activity is by no means over, and several vents with impressive cinder cones, such as Sunset Crater in the San Francisco Mountains north of Flagstaff, Arizona, have been active in historical times. The last eruption occurred at about the same time as the Norman conquest of England in 1066.

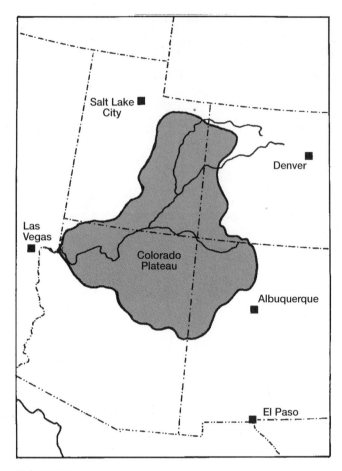

FIGURE 20.8
Location of the Colorado Plateau.

eastward-thinning wedges derived from the mountains and carried by easterly flowing streams (Figure 20.9).

During Oligocene through Miocene time, the mountains were eroded to an area of modest relief, and a broad erosion surface, known as the **Sherman Surface,** is widely recognized in the coincidence of many summit levels. Projected eastward, the Sherman Surface coincides with the broad depositional plain capping the sedimentary wedges that butt up against the mountains.

With the Pliocene to Pleistocene uplift of the region to the west and the initiation of canyon cutting, mentioned earlier, the easterly flowing streams also began downcutting as they were rejuvenated. They quickly dissected the old pediplain erosion surface, excavating down to Cretaceous and older rocks in some places. The remnants of the Oligocene through Pliocene sedimentary wedge now constitute the **High Plains**. West of Cheyenne, Wyoming, one High Plains segment still lies up against the mountain flank, and the Sherman Surface can be seen in continuity with the High Plains depositional surface. It also, incidentally, provides a conveniently graded transportation route known as the "gangplank," which carries the tracks of the Union Pacific Railroad westward up into the Laramie Range (Figure 20.10).

The most extensive deposits of the Great Plains are, not surprisingly, the youngest and of Pliocene age. Much of this vast sheet of mixed alluvial, lacustrine, and playa sediments, largely unconsolidated, is mapped as the Ogallala Formation (or Group). Much of the Ogallala was laid down in streams, across floodplains, and in lakes, and so was full of fresh water, making it one of the greatest reservoirs in the world (Figure 20.11). Unfortunately, irrigation agriculture is depleting the Ogallala at a rate many times faster than the replenishment rate.

The Gulf and Atlantic Coastal Plains

Neogene sedimentary patterns along the Atlantic and Gulf of Mexico margins were essentially a continuation of those in Paleogene time. The stratigraphy reveals a series of intertonguing wedges of marine and brackish-water sediments, recording alternating marine transgressions and regressions. Because the Miocene lasted for over 18 million years, the Miocene Series dominates the succession. In the area affected by the downwarping associated with the Mississippi Delta, the series is over 6.5 kilometers thick. Except in the Florida region, most of the sediments, from up-dip nonmarine facies to down-dip marine facies, are dominantly clastics with few carbonates.

Miocene strata are widely exposed in northern and central Florida and occur in the subsurface in southern Florida and across the Bahamas platform (Figure 20.12). Although carbonates dominate the Cenozoic succession of this region as a whole, during Late Miocene time, there was an influx of clastic material as far south as central and even southern Florida. In southern Florida, the clayey

Uplift of the region was accompanied by rapid downcutting by streams, producing many spectacular canyons. The most famous, of course, is the Grand Canyon of the Colorado River, where erosion has now penetrated to the underlying Precambrian basement rocks some 2,500 meters below the canyon rim. Although exposing a calendar of earth history stretching back 2 billion years or more, the canyon itself is, geologically, a young feature. Radiometric dating of volcanic pebbles in gravels of precanyon age indicate that the time of the uplift that rejuvenated the Colorado River to begin the canyon-cutting process was only between 5 and 10 million years ago.

The Interior Lowlands

As mentioned in Chapter 19, a remnant of the epeiric sea of the Zuni sequence lingered in North Dakota as the Cannonball Sea of Paleocene time. On the sea's withdrawal, the whole of the interior region became dry land and an area of erosion or of terrestrial deposition. Dominating the sedimentary patterns of the entire region were the rising Cordilleran ranges to the west, and the sediments that now underlie the Great Plains constitute large,

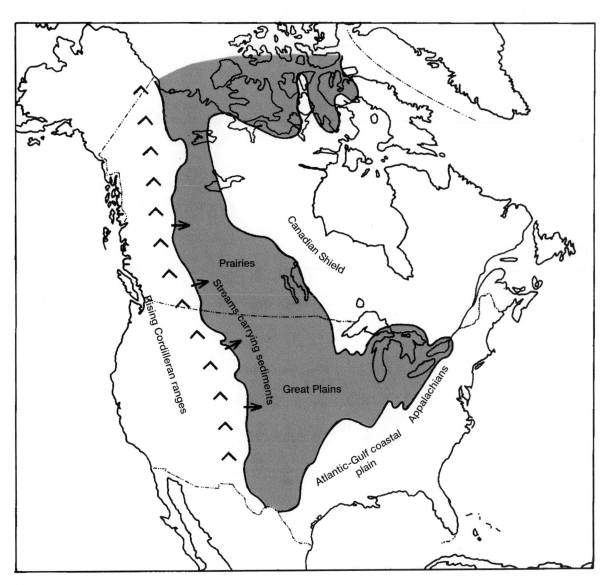

FIGURE 20.9

The interior lowlands are underlain largely by alluvial
sediments derived from streams flowing from the rising
Cordilleran ranges to the west.

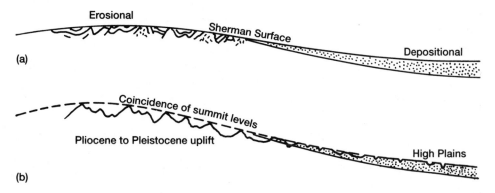

FIGURE 20.10

Evolution of (a) the Sherman Surface and (b) the High Plains.

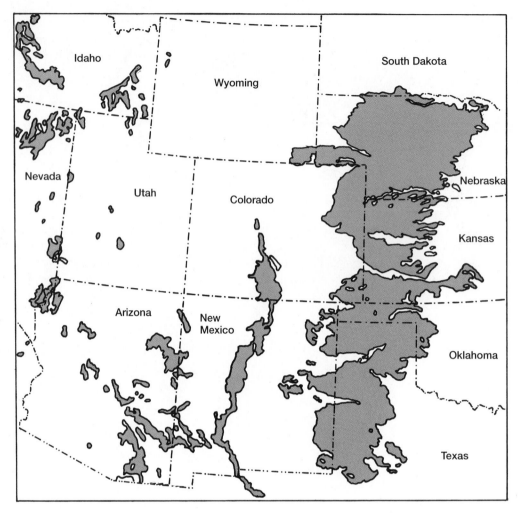

FIGURE 20.11
Area underlain by sediments of Neogene age in the western
United States. Under the Great Plains areas of Nebraska,
western Kansas, and West Texas, this area is mapped as
the Ogallala Formation.

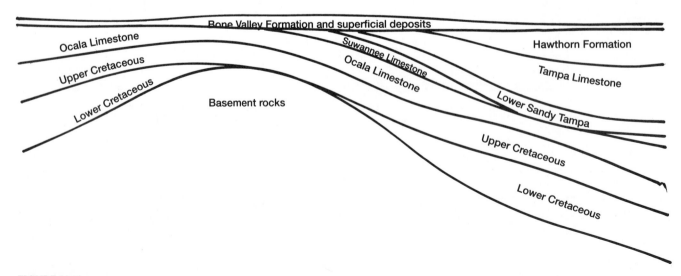

FIGURE 20.12
Diagrammatic north-south cross section through central
Florida, showing chief stratigraphic units.

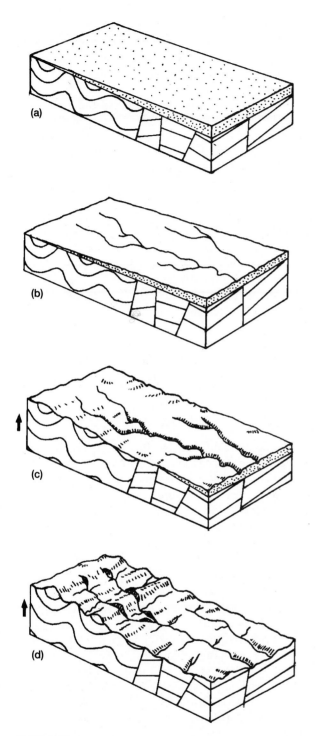

FIGURE 20.13

Physiographic evolution of the Appalachian region from the Late Cretaceous to the present. (a) Cretaceous sediments laid down on a surface eroded across Triassic and Jurassic rocks, the Fall Zone Surface. (b) Initial drainage across emergent Cretaceous sediments in a general southeasterly direction, the beginning of the Schooley peneplain. (c) Cretaceous sediments now largely stripped away, with streams eroding down into older rocks as the region is uplifted. (d) Underlying northeast-southwest trending structures begin to influence the drainage pattern of small streams. These tend to follow the outcrops of softer rocks aligned in that direction. Only the major streams are able to maintain their original courses in a southeasterly direction.

Hawthorn Formation is an important confining bed, separating the deep Floridan aquifer, here largely containing brackish water, from the surficial aquifers tapped by municipal well fields.

The Appalachians

Although the rocks that comprise the Appalachians range in age from Precambrian to latest Paleozoic, the modern topography is the result of differential erosion of Paleozoic structures and dates only from the Late Cenozoic. Largely a history recorded by erosion, rather than the deposition of strata, it is not easily deciphered.

The erosional story begins in the Cretaceous, when sediments laid down during a major marine transgression were deposited across a surface of low relief beveled across the Triassic and older structures of the region (Figure 20.13). This early sub-Cretaceous erosion surface is called the **Fall Zone Surface.** During the Cenozoic, as the region became emergent, the drainage pattern established across the veneer of Cretaceous and Early Cenozoic sediments, laid down on the Fall Zone Surface, was controlled largely by major streams flowing southeastward into the Atlantic. Because they were buried beneath the Cretaceous and Cenozoic sediments, the complex northeast-southwest trending structures of the Appalachians had no influence on the drainage.

Geomorphologists like William Morris Davis noticed over a century ago that the majority of Appalachian summits were approximately the same elevation and that a projection between them would form a smooth plain. In other words, the coincident summits represent erosional remnants of a peneplain (an ancient landscape with little relief) that had been beveled across the varied Appalachian rocks, just as the Fall Zone Surface had. This **Schooley Peneplain,** as it is called, was clearly younger than the Fall Zone Surface because it cut across it.

As uplift continued into the Neogene, the streams established across the Cretaceous-Paleogene sediments eventually stripped the sediments away and began carving valleys into the older rocks of the Appalachian fold structures. Now, the differences between the hard Paleozoic sandstones and the softer limestones and shales began to influence the drainage. The majority of the smaller streams now tended to flow along northeast-southwest trends, following the outcrops of the softer rocks, while the harder rocks—dominantly sandstones—stood up as ridges. Only the major streams, with their greater erosive power, continued to flow along the original northwest-southeast trends established before the Appalachian structures had been disinterred. Many such streams, such as the Pigeon River in the Great Smokies, now flow through spectacular gorges.

The Miocene Mediterranean—A Vanishing Sea

Scientific investigation occasionally becomes particularly exciting when several problems can apparently be solved using the same explanation. At such times, all the pieces seem to drop into place, and the likelihood of the explanation being correct is greatly enhanced. An example of just such an occasion involved investigations of what were some of the more puzzling aspects of the Late Cenozoic history of the Mediterranean.

One of the earliest problems concerned the origin of certain submarine canyons around the margins of the basin. When an origin for submarine canyons was being sought during the 1950s, the Mediterranean canyons seemed to provide convincing proof of being drowned river valleys. However, as a general explanation for submarine canyons worldwide, the large fluctuation of sea level required quickly eliminated this suggestion, and alternative models were sought.

A second problem arose during exploratory drilling by Soviet engineering geologists working on the Aswan Dam project on the River Nile. They found that the Nile had at some time in the recent geologic past cut a deep canyon, now filled with latest Cenozoic alluvial sediments. A similar deeply buried canyon had been located below the modern floodplain of the Rhone River in France. Such evidence caused geologists to suspect that these rivers had been downcutting to a base level controlled by a Mediterranean Sea level far below its current one.

The final pieces began to drop into place when strong seismic reflections obtained from the subsurface sediments in several places on the Mediterranean sea floor proved, on exploratory drilling, to be salt. These evaporite deposits of gypsum, halite, and other salts had been laid down in the not-so-distant geologic past, when the Mediterranean apparently had dried up. More precisely, during most of the Messinian Stage at the very end of the Miocene, the Mediterranean had been a vast, deep evaporating basin, with conditions akin to those seen in the modern Caspian Sea and the Dead Sea.

This drying-up episode has come to be known, rather dramatically, as the **Messinian Salinity Crisis.** The cause is not hard to find. As the configuration of continents and oceans slowly changes in response to plate-tectonic movements, narrow land bridges and seaways connecting larger bodies of land and sea are sometimes formed. The effects of such changes on oceanic circulation and the distribution of marine and terrestrial organisms are often considerable. In many cases, sea-level changes also play a critical role, and if they are glacio-eustatic fluctuations, the effects may be rapid and even catastrophic.

Just such a scenario is indicated for the Mediterranean basin in the Late Miocene. At this time, a narrow seaway connected the Mediterranean with the Atlantic, just as it does today, but a glacio-eustatic sea-level fall was apparently sufficient to produce a land bridge that severed the oceanic connection (Figure 20.14). With a semiarid climate and insufficient inflow of major streams, the Mediterranean dried up, producing a vast, inland evaporite basin similar to the modern Caspian and Dead Sea basins.

An estimate based on the volume of the Mediterranean basin indicated that a single drying episode would produce a layer of salt about 200 meters thick. On the other hand, deep drilling has shown that the salt deposits are, in places, over 2,000 meters thick, so there must have been repeated infusions of the salt-bearing water between the evaporation phases. Over a period of some 2 million years, there may have been as many as 40 such saltwater floodings. Apparently, the entrance sill at the Straits of Gibraltar was at a critical depth in relation to the magnitude of glacio-eustatic sea-level changes.

Aridity and salt deposition were not continuous throughout the basin because, at some horizons, are interbedded freshwater and brackish-water lake deposits. These indicate some inflow of water from spillover channels that, from time to time, were connected to the ancestral Black Sea, Caspian Sea, and Aral Sea basins, which at that time were large freshwater or brackish-water lakes.

The Big Freeze—The Late Cenozoic Ice Age

The climatic deterioration that had become pronounced at the beginning of the Oligocene continued, with warmer intermissions, through the Miocene and into the Pliocene, and became increasingly severe in the Pleistocene (Figure 20.15). The Ice Age that began at the end of the Pliocene is often referred to as the "Pleistocene Ice Age," but this is not really true. If an ice age is defined as a period when large ice caps existed at one or both poles and there was a global deterioration of climate, the present Ice Age began in the Oligocene or earlier. There is evidence that glacial centers in the Northern Hemisphere were growing by the Late Miocene and Early Pliocene, and by the latest Pliocene, the northern ice caps were large enough to influence weather patterns, plant distribution, and animal migrations over large areas. In Europe, for example, the Plio-Pleistocene stratigraphic boundary in marine successions is placed at the first incoming of cold-water species and is not based on direct evidence of glaciation.

The Neogene provides, perhaps, the best example of the interaction between the planet's dynamic systems. Plate-tectonic movements clearly influenced climate, and changing climate, in turn, was reflected in profound changes in a whole host of biologic linkages, from plants through insects, herbivorous animals, carnivorous animals, and finally, humans.

By the Late Neogene, continental ice sheets were expanding and reaching limits unattained during previous advances. On the North American continent, the ice front extended south of the Great Lakes, reached the Atlantic

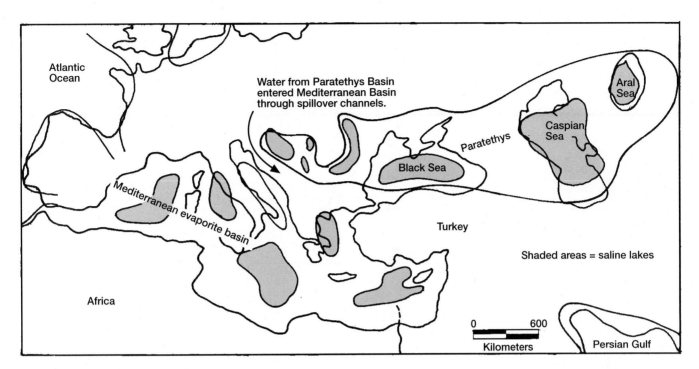

FIGURE 20.14

Sketch map of the Mediterranean region, showing the location of the chief evaporite basins at the time of the Messinian Salinity Crisis. *(Source: Redrawn from data in "When the Black Sea Was Drained" by K. J. Hsu. Copyright © 1978 by Scientific American, Inc.)*

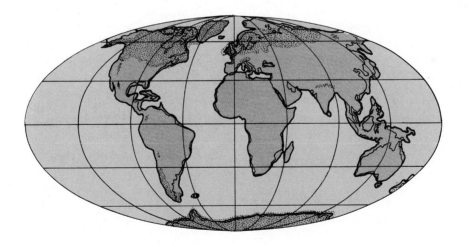

FIGURE 20.15

World paleogeography in the Pleistocene. Shaded areas were covered by ice caps.

Coast at Long Island, New York, and in the west finally met and coalesced with the growing piedmont glacier advancing out of the Rocky Mountains. At the maximum advance of the most recent glaciation, the Wisconsin, Laurentide, and Greenland ice caps, joined by the Cordilleran ice cap in the west, covered an area of 18.06×10^6 square kilometers (Figure 20.16). In Europe, the Fenno-Scandian ice cap covered all of Scandinavia and the Baltic Sea, and extended across central Europe, with a total area of 6.66×10^6 square kilometers, although it never joined the extensive Alpine ice sheet. Mountain glaciers everywhere around the world expanded, and extensive mountain glaciation is evident even into lower latitudes. The Antarctic ice sheet was, of course, considerably larger, although because its margins reached the oceans, its previous extent is unknown.

FIGURE 20.16
Climatic fluctuation, ice advances, and recessions during the
last glaciation.

Beyond the actual ice margins in the areas directly affected by meltwater streams and outwash deposits, the influence of the ice sheet was manifested in two ways: Over much of the nonglaciated continental areas, the climate was cooler and, in many areas, wetter than it had been in preglacial time. In coastal regimes, the most obvious effects of glacial episodes were glacio-eustatic sea-level fluctuations. At times of glacial advance, sea level stood at some 60 meters below its present level (Figure 20.17).

In the present context, the last glacial advance and its subsequent retreat is a primary concern because we are presently living in an interglacial interval, and the Late Cenozoic Ice Age is ongoing. The deposits and landforms left behind after the retreat of the last major ice sheet are not even 20,000 years old and, therefore, have been little modified by subsequent geologic processes.

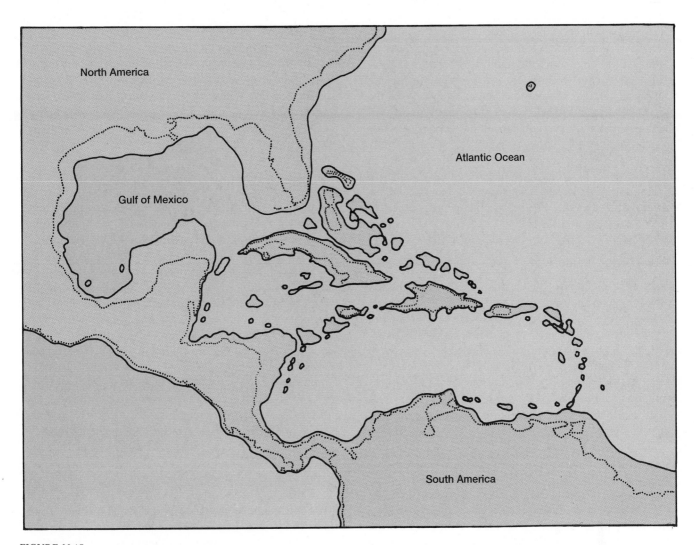

FIGURE 20.17

Map of the Caribbean and Gulf of Mexico showing configuration of coastlines during a glacial lowstand of sea level.

Cause of the Late Cenozoic Ice Age

While the advance and retreat of ice sheets during an ice age is now generally ascribed to the mechanism controlled by the insolation cycles first suggested in the Milankovitch-Köppen hypothesis, the cause of an ice age itself is less easily explained. Clearly, a model that explains the Late Cenozoic Ice Age might also explain other ice ages of the past.

The hypothesis that currently seems most popular involves plate tectonics and the configuration of the continents with respect to the poles. According to this theory, if a continental mass or ocean is situated at a pole and is thermally isolated in terms of global climatic patterns, then an ice cap or ice-covered sea will result. While this model is, in effect, tailor-made for the present Ice Age, it does not work as well in explaining the Permo-Carboniferous ice age. At that time, Pangaea stretched from the pole to the equator and therefore was not thermally isolated.

By the Miocene, a permanent ice pack likely was present in the Arctic Ocean, thereby enormously increasing the albedo, the fraction of the sun's energy reflected back into space. This is obviously a self-generating mechanism. An increase in albedo cools the climate, which, in turn, results in increased snow and ice over a longer winter, producing a feedback effect and another increase in albedo. (The refrigeration of the Arctic Ocean and its influence on the development of the psychrosphere and in accentuating global climatic deterioration were discussed in Chapter 19.)

Although a climatic feedback mechanism probably was important, the giant northern ice caps of Pleistocene time would not have grown without the influence of yet another factor. Again, plate tectonics played a role. Tectonic movements related to the Caribbean plate finally resulted in the emergence of the Panamanian land bridge about 3.5 million years ago, in the Middle Pliocene. Quite apart from its effect on the migrations of land animals between North and South America, as described in Chapter 19, the isthmus closed off the connection between the Atlantic and Pacific Oceans. The warm, westerly flowing Equatorial Current was now deflected northward into the North Atlantic and is believed to have greatly increased the flow of moisture-carrying air into the region. Glaciers not only require cold climates—they also must be nourished by snowfall that comes from such moisture-laden air. Once the Gulf Stream had been rerouted, the growth of the Laurentide ice sheet was probably inevitable. This model may not answer all the questions, but is probably correct in its essentials.

Evidence for an Ice Age

Because the climate has fluctuated markedly over a period embracing only the past 20,000 years or so, the geologic evidence in terms of glacially modified landforms and spreads of glacial and meltwater sediments is all around, particularly in those midlatitude areas where there were actual ice caps and glaciers. Despite their prominence, a proper understanding of the significance of these features was late in coming, and only within the last century and a half has there been any awareness of past pronounced climatic changes.

Throughout Europe, spreads of sands and gravels and erratic boulders had been the subject of speculation for centuries. During the Dark Ages, strange boulders that obviously did not match adjacent rocks were usually ascribed to witchcraft, the devil, or giants. Later, during serious attempts to reconcile geologic phenomena with the biblical account, such glacial deposits were ascribed to Noah's Flood. Seeking a scientific explanation and edging closer to the truth, Charles Lyell suggested that glacial deposits had been transported by icebergs in seas that formerly covered the land. For this reason, such deposits came to be called *drift,* a term still used today.

The true nature of glacial deposits was discovered by Swiss zoologist Louis Agassiz (1807–1873), although from his own account, the idea actually came from an alpine shepherd with whom he was talking one day. Following the age-old seasonal cycle of moving his flock up to the alpine meadows for summer pasture and down to the valleys in the winter, the shepherd probably saw rock debris and boulders associated with modern glaciers high up in the mountains and recognized the same materials at lowland localities.

In terms of recent geologic history, the **Great Ice Age,** as it was called, came to be accepted as a period that was virtually synonymous with the Pleistocene Epoch. This meant that, in effect, any succession underlying the oldest glacial deposits was, by definition, of Pliocene age. Later,

more evidence, such as glacial deposits and geomorphic features that were not all the same age, clearly indicated that there had been several glacial advances and recessions—that is, more than one Ice Age.

Incidentally, scientists also assumed that the Ice Age was over and that we were now living in "postglacial time." The total length of the Ice Age was usually believed to be about a million years.

Ice Age Chronology

German geologist Albrecht Penck was the first to attempt to establish a chronology of glacial events. He noticed that the terminal moraines left behind by Alpine glaciers at their furthest extent were associated with a flood of gravel carried by meltwater streams and that filled the valleys below the moraines. When the ice retreated, the meltwater streams eroded deep channels into the gravel, leaving erosional remnants as terraces perched in a steplike fashion on the valley sides (Figure 20.18). Working in the northern foothills of the Alps, Penck eventually concluded that there had been four major glacial advances, which he named Günz, Mindel, Riss, and Würm (in alphabetical order from oldest to youngest), after four northward-flowing streams in the area west of Munich (Figure 20.19). The various terrace gravels showed no stratigraphic ordering relative to each other but were recognized on the basis of their height above the valley floor. The oldest terraces were high up the slope, the younger lower down.

The four separate advances and retreats of the Alpine glaciers came to be the basis for a division of Pleistocene time, and Günz, Mindel, Riss, and Würm became, in effect, time terms. Along the southern fringe of the Fenno-Scandian ice sheet that had covered northern Europe, Eduard Bruckner, working on the central German plain, also found evidence of four major local advances. In North America, Louis Agassiz had little difficulty demonstrating to American and Canadian geologists the reality of ice ages in the New World, and in the classic areas south and southwest of the Great Lakes, again, four glacial episodes could be recognized. The glaciations were named Nebraskan, Kansan, Illinoian, and Wisconsin,[2] from older to younger. As with the Fenno-Scandian ice sheet, there was a tacit understanding that the fourfold division reflected global climatic fluctuations and that the various glacial successions could be matched up sequentially.

---

2. Also referred to as the Wisconsinan or (Wisconsinian). Purists have long sought to standardize the endings of stratigraphic names. Sometimes, it works (as with Mississippian, Kansan, and so on). Sometimes, it definitely does not (as with Black Riveran, Two Creeksian, and so on). The tendency in recent years has been to allow inconsistency if it sounds better.

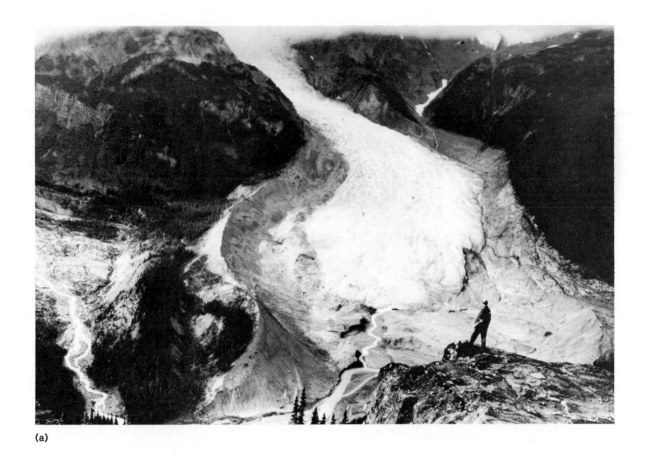

(a)

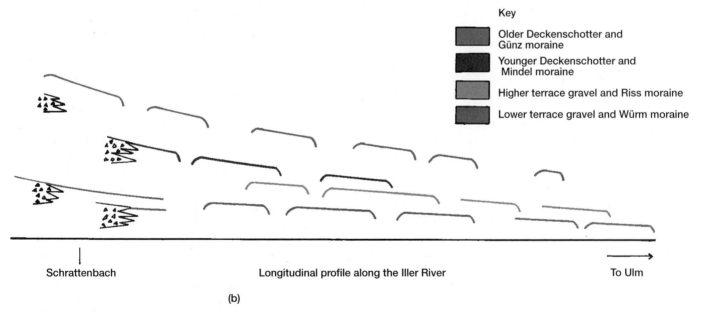

Key

Older Deckenschotter and Günz moraine

Younger Deckenschotter and Mindel moraine

Higher terrace gravel and Riss moraine

Lower terrace gravel and Würm moraine

Schrattenbach   Longitudinal profile along the Iller River   To Ulm

(b)

FIGURE 20.18

(a) Valley glacier with outwash gravels at the terminus, Ball Creek, northern British Columbia. (b) Distribution of the four alluvial terraces described by Albrecht Penck in the northern Alps. (Deckenschotter: a *schotter* is an outwash terrace, while *decken* means "cover.")

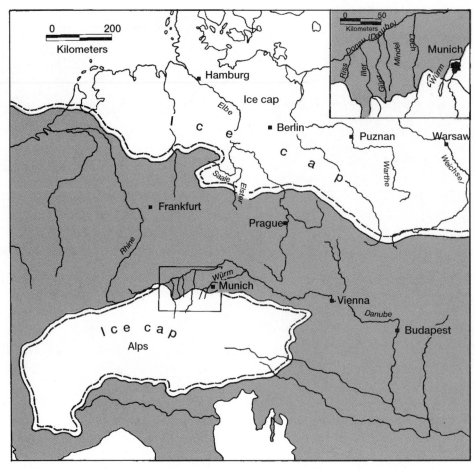

FIGURE 20.19
Location map for the classic alpine glacial successions
described by Albrecht Penck and for the European lowland
successions described by Eduard Bruckner.

Unfortunately, things were not as simple as they
seemed. From the first investigations in the classic Alpine
areas, earlier (that is, pre-Günz) glaciations had been suspected. Scattered, high-level terrace, gravel remnants
suggested that there had been an earlier so-called Donau
glaciation, and in a few places, traces of even older gravels
pointed to an even more ancient glacial episode. In addition, the Wisconsin glaciation in North America was
determined to have actually occurred in two phases, and
during each of these phases, the ice had made numerous
advances and retreats (Figure 20.20). The older glaciations probably also had been multiple in character, although direct evidence was scanty.

As new discoveries were made, the whole subject of
glacial history, far from becoming easier to understand
was, instead, growing ever more complex. A particular
problem concerned the correlations between glacial episodes in different parts of the world. Clearly, correlations
could not be made by simply counting backward through
the successive glacial till sheets and moraines. The most
recent studies of the climatic cycles involved, together with
an increasing number of radiocarbon and other radiometric dates, have shown, for example, that the Kansan
and Nebraskan glaciations actually correlate with the
Donau and Günz, respectively, of the Alpine succession.
At the same time, no corresponding lowland glaciation

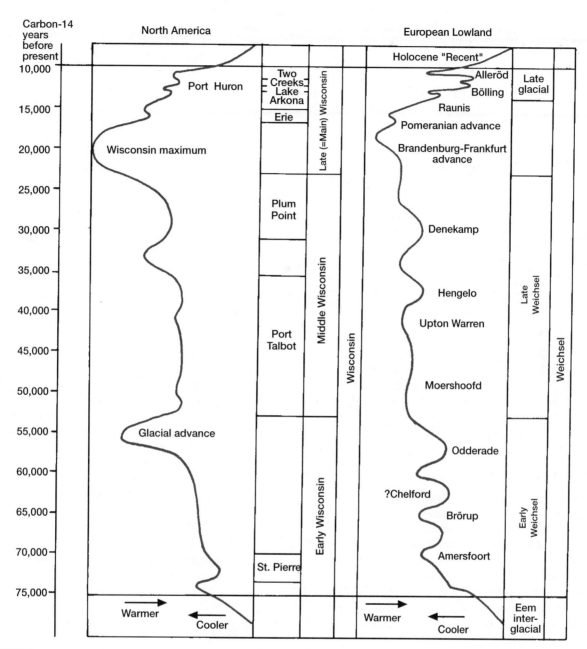

FIGURE 20.20

Climatic fluctuation, ice advances, and recessions during the last glaciation.

apparently occurred in northern Europe, although, as shown in Table 20.1, there were at least three older glacial advances. The earliest major glaciation there is the Elster, which corresponds with the Mindel of the Alpine succession and the Illinoian of North America.

Thus, although the climatic cycles in North America and Europe were essentially synchronous, the effects in terms of glacial development were not always the same. Almost certainly one factor was the much greater size of the North American, or Laurentide, ice cap. The key to

TABLE 20.1

Major Divisions of the Pleistocene Glacial Successions in Europe and North America*

Alps	Northern Europe	British Isles	North America
Würm	Weichsel	Weichsel-Devensian	
R/W	*Eem*	*Ipswich*	Wisconsin
Riss	Saale	Wolstonian	
M/R	*Holstein*	*Hoxnian*	*Sangamon*
Mindel	Elster	Anglian	Illinoian
G/M	Cromer	*Cromer*	*Yarmouth*
		Beestonian	
		Pastovian	
Günz	Menapian		Kansan
D/G	*Waale*		*Aftonian*
Donau	Eburonian		Nebraskan
	Tiglian		
Biber	Praetigilan		

*Interglacials are in italics.

global climatic fluctuations is now suspected to lie in the Laurentide ice cap, where the main center of ice accumulation changed quite quickly and huge domes of ice migrated from one place to another. Both the short-term and long-term effects of these changes on the weather patterns of the time are still being evaluated.

Climatic Cycles

Although the advancing and retreating ice sheets of the past might appear to leave an adequate record of changing climate, direct evidence of glacial episodes in terms of deposits and landforms is extremely poor for an obvious reason. Glaciers and ice sheets are among the most powerful and destructive of all agents of erosion; thus, as an ice mass advances, it destroys everything in its path. Not only are the landscape features and sediments of earlier glaciations obliterated, but even the preglacial landscape is typically remolded. Only the deposits and landforms that mark the latest and furthest advance of the ice are left behind when the ice retreats. Also preserved are the features that mark the net recession of the ice with time, which is why a detailed picture of the ice sheet's final withdrawal is possible, but only a fragmentary picture of earlier events.

For example, in North America, the last glacial episode—the Wisconsin—was also one of the most intense, and in many areas, this ice front advanced to positions never reached before. The glacial tills and moraine features of earlier glacial advances thus are found only in those few areas that were not buried by the Wisconsin ice.

Although glaciers and ice sheets are the most obvious manifestation of glacial episodes, a detailed chronology of the climatic fluctuations involved is found in the deep-sea succession. This is because the deep sea floor is a repository for biogenic sediments, predominantly calcareous oozes made up of the skeletons of microscopic planktonic foraminifera that lived in the surface waters. World climatic changes of the past were inevitably mirrored in oceanic water temperatures, and these, in turn, were documented by the presence of warm-water or cold-water species. It follows, therefore, that successive layers of deep-sea sediment containing the fossil remains of temperature-sensitive organisms also contain what is, in effect, a record of changing ocean temperatures. One method of establishing a **paleotemperature curve** is described in Box 20.1.

The Great Lakes

The Great Lakes, together comprising the largest body of fresh water in the world, owe their existence to glacial action and did not exist before the Late Cenozoic glaciation. Indeed, the lakes in their present form came into being only since the end of the Wisconsin glaciation and so are geologically young features.

Lake Superior occupies a structural depression in Precambrian rocks, and the other lakes were likely lowland areas, forming part of what was originally a gently undulating terrain. This whole region in Pliocene time was drained by rivers that were tributaries to an ancestor of a northern segment of the Missouri River, which in those

BOX 20.1

Oxygen Isotopes—Key to Ancient Temperatures

Oxygen has three isotopes: O^{16} (ordinary oxygen), O^{17}, and O^{18}; of these, O^{17} occurs in only minute amounts, but O^{18} constitutes about 0.2 percent of natural oxygen. The isotopes have different atomic weights, so in chemical reactions involving oxygen, a certain fractionation occurs. In 1947, Harold Urey discovered that this fractionation was temperature-dependent. This means that oxygen-containing compounds, such as CO_2 and $CaCO_3$, that form at low temperature contain a measurably higher proportion of the heavy isotope O^{18} than do the same compounds produced at higher temperature.

Of particular interest are the shells and tests of lime-secreting organisms because it follows that, if the oxygen isotope ratio of skeletal carbonates can be determined, then this value, measured against a standard sample, could be used to determine the temperature of the water in which the animal lived.

As a stratigraphic tool in deep-sea successions, the oxygen isotope method was pioneered by Cesare Emiliani of the University of Miami. Using the tests of the planktonic foraminiferan *Globigerina saculifera* in sediment cores from the Caribbean and Atlantic, Emiliani constructed a record of changing ocean water temperature during the time the sediments in the cores were deposited (Box Figure 20.1). Emiliani was finally able to construct a paleotemperature curve that extended back to about 800,000 years before present, a time interval embracing the last two glacial advances (in North America, the Wisconsin and Illinoian) and even part of the one previous (the Kansan).

This paleotemperature curve could also be considered a paleoglacial curve because, during glaciation, when there is a eustatic fall of sea level, ocean waters become slightly more saline and also relatively enriched in O^{18}.

An obvious drawback with the oxygen isotope method as a stratigraphic tool is that there is nothing unique about each cold/warm cycle to distinguish it from another. This means that the absence of one or more complete cycles, through a lack of deposition or through erosion, is difficult to ascertain. In practice, biostratigraphic and magnetostratigraphic indicators are used to supplement the paleotemperature log.

Spectral analyses of the oxygen isotope curve show a marked periodicity at 23,000, 41,000, and 100,000 years, and these numbers agree closely with those of the Milankovitch-Köppen insolation cycle.

From Nancy Healy-Williams, ed., *Principles of Pleistocene Stratigraphy Applied to the Gulf of Mexico*, p. 80, © 1984 International Human Resources Development Corporation. Adapted by permission of Prentice-Hall, Englewood Cliffs, New Jersey.

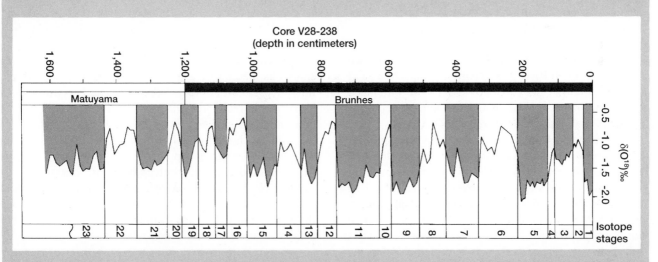

BOX FIGURE 20.1
Succession of oxygen isotope stages as determined in deep-sea core V28–238 from the equatorial Pacific (depth scale in centimeters), with age estimates for stage boundaries. Shaded portions of curve represent temperature maxima.

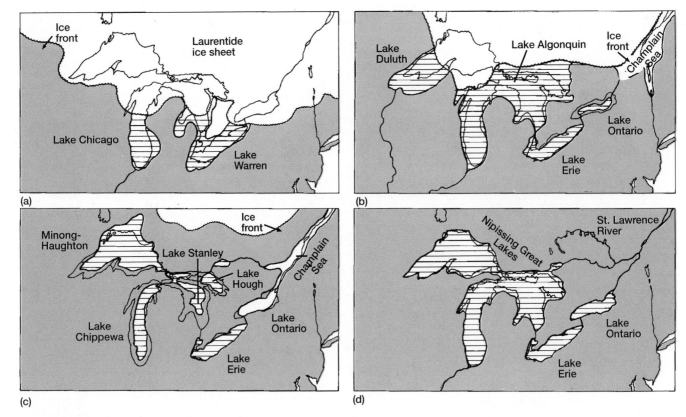

FIGURE 20.21
Glacial history of the Great Lakes region in the last 13,000 years. Ruled areas are freshwater lakes. (a) 13,000 years ago. (b) 11,500 years ago. (c) 9,500 years ago. (d) 6,000 years ago.

days, flowed northward into Hudson Bay. The northern reaches of the Ohio River flowed northeastward into what was later to be the St. Lawrence River. The watershed between the Mississippi basin and the Hudson Bay lowland lay to the south of the present Great Lakes.

As the succession of ice sheets advanced and retreated over a time span of a million years, the lowland areas became deeply excavated to form the lake basins. During times of ice withdrawal, when the climate was as warm or possibly warmer than the present day, large lakes, ancestral to the present lakes, undoubtedly existed, but no trace of their form and drainage relationships remains.

The modern Great Lakes only took shape during the waning stage of the Wisconsin ice sheet (Figure 20.21). In many ways, they are textbook examples of the numerous effects of continental glaciation. Not only do they demonstrate how old drainage patterns were rearranged and, in many cases, completely turned around, but they also show the effects of massive ice dams, glacial scour, and the dumping of enormous masses of glacially transported rock debris.

Glaciation is not just a surface phenomenon; the enormous loading by a mass of ice thousands of meters thick depresses the crust. When the ice disappears, the crust rises in rebound. This isostatic effect also played an important role in the evolution of the Great Lakes.

The first lakes formed as the ice front retreated from the glacially scoured depression that now forms Lakes Michigan and Erie. The only way out for drainage was southward; thus, what geologists have called Lake Chicago drained into the Mississippi system. Lake Warren, the ancestor of Lake Erie, drained across the "thumb" of Michigan into Lake Chicago.

As the ice retreated still further northward, eastern outlets eventually became uncovered. For a time, some of the drainage was via the Mohawk gap (between the Adirondacks and the Catskills) and then the Hudson River valley, the St. Lawrence outlet still being blanketed by ice. Finally, about 12,000 years ago, the shrinkage of the ice caps left the St. Lawrence lowland uncovered, but because of isostatic depression of the crust under the load of ice, it was drowned by the sea. For a time, the so-called

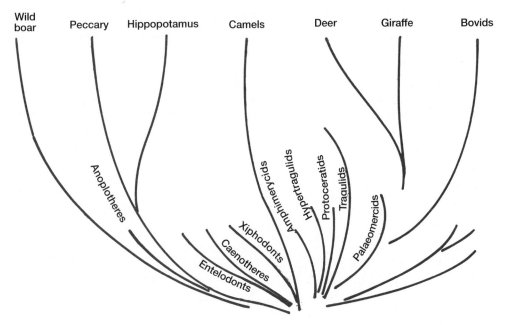

FIGURE 20.22
Generalized family tree of the artiodactyls.

Champlain Sea extended up to Lake Ontario, and an arm also stretched southward into what is now Lake Champlain. By this time, the southern outlets to the Mississippi had been abandoned as lake levels dropped.

The final phase saw the isostatic rebound of the whole area marginal to the ice caps, which by now had shrunk to become a series of separate ice centers, one of which was centered on Quebec and Labrador. With this crustal uplift, the sea withdrew from the Lake Ontario/St. Lawrence lowland and from Lake Champlain so that by about 6,000 years ago, the lakes took on an essentially modern form. The only major difference was the reestablishment for a time of the southern outlet to the Mississippi, but because erosional downcutting of outlet streams to the east was more rapid, it was finally abandoned as lake levels fell. The southern outlet has, in fact, been reopened in modern time by the construction of a barge canal, and it is now possible to sail from the Great Lakes to the Gulf of Mexico.

The Modern Biosphere Emerges

From the Oligocene on, world climates not only became cooler, they also became drier. Large areas formerly covered by forest now became open savanna or prairie. These changes profoundly influenced the plants, and through them, a whole host of terrestrial animals. Many familiar species of nonarboreal plants can be dated from the Miocene; this is when the modernization of the plant kingdom began.

With the retreat of forests came a corresponding increase in the opportunities for low-growing shrubs and herbaceous plants, including those that gardeners refer to as "annuals" and that die back after producing their seeds. Such plants are particularly successful at colonizing open ground in the absence of other larger plants, which is why many are referred to as "weed" plants. Grasses, as mentioned in Chapter 19, had already appeared in the Paleocene, but their big opportunity came with the climatic changes at the close of the Paleogene. By the Miocene, the world's grasslands were rapidly expanding, and with them, the potential habitats for many new animals.

The low-growing herbaceous plants underwent an evolutionary explosion during the Early Neogene, and with thousands of new flowering species inevitably came a corresponding radiation among insects. With new vegetable and insect food supplies, many small-animal groups, such as rodents, and also the songbirds underwent spectacular adaptive radiation. Two successful groups whose numbers also increased at this time were the frogs and toads, who benefited from the increase in their insect food supply, and also the snakes, probably the chief predatory foe of the rodents.

With the expanding grasslands, evolutionary success was also assured for the second group of ungulates, the so-called odd-toed ungulates or **artiodactyls** (Figure 20.22). Beginning in the Miocene, the deer and the Bovidae, which includes cattle, sheep, goats, and antelopes, also began an expansion that has continued to the present. Other groups, such as the pigs and giraffes, were also

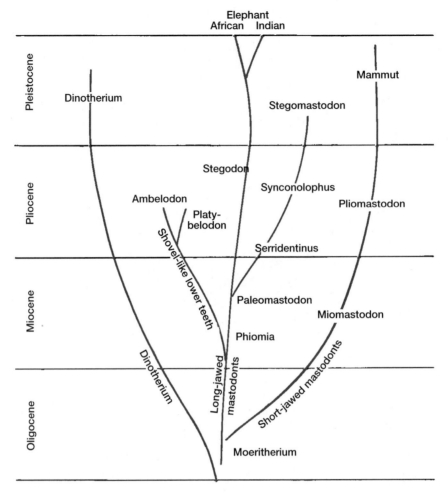

FIGURE 20.23
Evolution of the proboscidians leading to mammoths and modern elephants.

markedly successful, although compared with Miocene time, the number of species is currently somewhat reduced. The elephants also diversified during the Miocene and Pliocene, and their decline to the two elephant species of today largely reflects the Late Pleistocene extinctions discussed later in the chapter (Figure 20.23). Not surprisingly, the expansion and diversification among the herbivores was accompanied by the appearance of new carnivores, notably the hyena and the bears.

In the refugia of Australia and South America, evolution of many marsupial groups during the Neogene was marked by an increase in size. By the Pliocene, the South American carnivore *Thylacosmilus,* for example, was as big as a tiger and indeed had a feline appearance. Of particular interest were its large, knifelike, upper-canine teeth, which were remarkably similar to those seen in the famous saber-toothed tiger *Smilodon* of the North American Pleistocene. With the emergence of the Panamanian land bridge, South America's isolation ended, although not all of the native South American species were exterminated by the Pliocene immigrants from the north. In a few cases,

some survived up to Recent times before finally succumbing to the depradations of the most dangerous species of all, humans.

Evolution of the Higher Primates

At its most fundamental level, taxonomy, as discussed in other parts of this text, is concerned with the sorting and classifying of organisms on the basis of their differences and also their resemblances. In paleontology, time relationships are also important. Thus, forms that are apparently unlike must sometimes be grouped into the same taxon because fossil evidence indicates that their respective ancestors did look alike and presumably arose, in turn, from a common root. By the same token, apparently similar forms that resemble one another but that can be shown arising from different ancestral stocks must be separated.

On the basis of fossil evidence, the broad divisions of the **anthropoids** (the suborder of primates that includes the monkeys, apes, and humans) can be fit into a "family

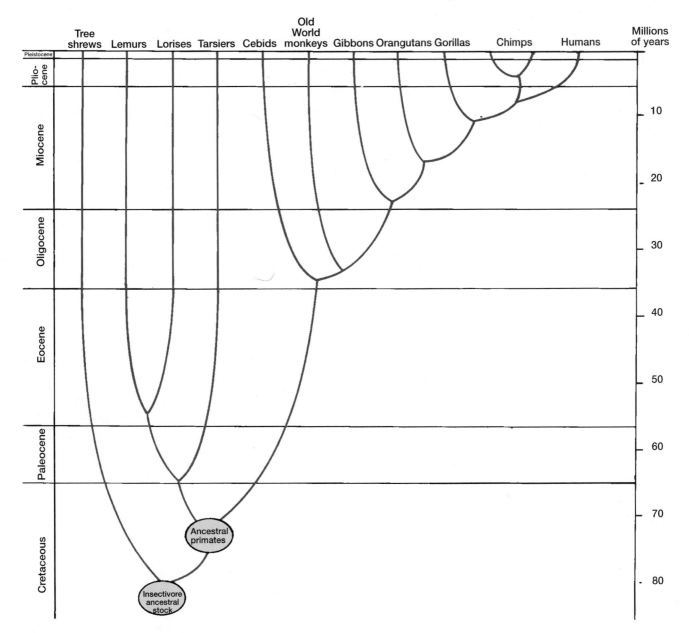

FIGURE 20.24
Evolution of the primates, showing major phylogenetic relationships.

tree," as shown in Figure 20.24. In the case of the monkeys, the two groups—the Cercopithecoidea, or New World monkeys, and the Ceboidea, or Old World monkeys—had already diverged from a common primitive primate, or prosimian, ancestor at some time earlier in the Oligocene. The phenomenon of evolutionary convergence, discussed in Chapter 19, can probably account for the many similarities between the two groups of living monkeys. These resemblances place them in some classifications as superfamilies in the single suborder Anthropoidea, but this may be misleading.

In any event, higher up the family tree, by Late Oligocene time, the divergence between the Old World monkeys and the apes is manifested in two separate genera identified in a rich fauna unearthed at Fayum in Egypt. *Oligopithecus* seems to be the ancestor of all Old World monkeys, whereas *Aegyptopithecus* exhibits apelike features. Of particular significance is the pattern of cusps in certain molar teeth. Monkeys have four cusps, while apes and humans have five.

The Fayum discoveries provide clues to the probable start of the hominoid line, which led eventually to apes and humans. However, these discoveries are followed by

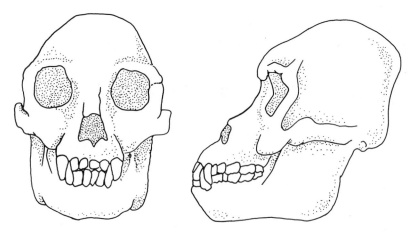

FIGURE 20.25
Dryopithecus (Proconsul).

a gap in the fossil record extending over some 10 million years. The next clues come from the Early Miocene in East Africa, where interest centers on *Pliopithecus,* an ape already well advanced along the hominoid line, and on a second group of primates, including *Dryopithecus* (Figure 20.25).

Dryopithecus

First discovered in 1930 on Msangano Island in Lake Victoria and named at that time *Proconsul, **Dryopithecus*** was clearly more advanced than *Pliopithecus* but at the same time retained certain primitive features. By Middle Miocene time, the dryopithecines had spread from East Africa into Eurasia and showed considerable diversification. In many ways, they remained quite generalized, and although they were undeniably apes with, among other features, the typical projecting canine teeth, they still retained some monkeylike features. On the other hand, some experts believe that certain features of dryopithecine dentition hint at human characteristics, and these became more manifest in *Ramapithecus,* which eventually arose from the dryopithecine line.

While many paleontologists consider *Dryopithecus* to have been a ground dweller of the open savannah, an alternative view holds that they were still largely arboreal, retaining more monkeylike habits. In any event, dryopithecines were an adaptable group and clearly a considerable success, surviving through the greater part of the Miocene over an interval of some 10 million years.

Ramapithecus

The main ape line of descent may have become established in a group that arose from *Dryopithecus* about 17 million years ago. Known as *Ramapithecus,* this animal was smaller and more lightly built than *Dryopithecus,*

ranging in weight from about 20 to 70 kilograms and probably averaging a little over 1 meter in height. The canine teeth were smaller, the molars flatter, and the overall appearance of the dental arch, or arcade, as it is known, quite humanlike.

These features, together with a foreshortened face, originally persuaded many paleontologists that *Ramapithecus* should be considered the first hominid. The current view, however, is that *Ramapithecus,* together with the closely similar form *Sivathecus* (some workers consider them the same), predate the human/ape split by at least 4 million years. Unfortunately, from about 7 million years ago, the age of the last *Ramapithecus,* there is a 3-million-year gap before the record resumes in the Pliocene.

Ancestral Relationships of the Apes

Fossil evidence does not indicate for certain whether apes arose from the dryopithecine or ramapithecine lines. New nonpaleontologic evidence, however, suggests that whatever line gave rise to the apes also provided the ancestors of humans, a finding that would, at least, clearly eliminate *Dryopithecus* and place it on a side branch of the evolutionary tree.

In recent years, biochemical studies that have produced what has been termed a **molecular clock** have provided a new approach to the problem of ancestral relationships. Since differences in amino acid residues in proteins accumulate at measurable rates, the observed differences between different animal taxa can be quantified in terms of the elapsed time since the animals arose from a common ancestor. These studies indicate that the line leading to gibbons was the earliest to split off, about 10 million years ago in the Middle Miocene, and that about 8 million years ago, the orangutan line split off. While providing useful data on timing, these studies tend to confirm conclusions already reached from fossil evidence.

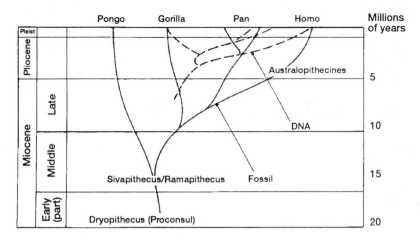

FIGURE 20.26
Hominoid evolution as determined from fossil and DNA hybridization dates.

When it comes to the three final branches of the tree—involving gorillas, chimpanzees, and humans—the split that set humans off on their own line occurred about 4 million years ago, while the gorilla and chimpanzee lines split about 3.2 million years ago (Figure 20.26). That these splits occurred so recently is surprising. Even more surprising is additional biochemical evidence based on the analysis of the sequence of 7,100 nucleotides in a DNA segment from the hemoglobin gene. This evidence suggests that humankind's nearest relative is the chimpanzee and that the match between the genes of humans and chimpanzees is closer than that between gorillas and chimpanzees. Together, all of these matches are close enough, it is argued, to justify placing gorillas, chimpanzees, and humans in the same genus.

Australopithecus

The oldest hominids belong to the genus *Australopithecus*, whose fossil remains have been found in many parts of eastern and southern Africa in deposits ranging in age from about 4 million to 1.3 million years. During this interval, several species evolved, and although some were evolutionary dead ends, considerable evidence suggests that, within this group, are the ancestors of modern humans.

Perhaps the most characteristic feature of *Australopithecus* was that here, for the first time, was an animal with a true bipedal gait. The shape of the pelvic bones leaves no doubt that *Australopithecus* walked upright. Despite this, *Australopithecus* retained many apelike features, with heavy brow ridges, a low forehead, and a forward-jutting jaw. The incisor, canine, and molar teeth were small and much less differentiated than those of an ape so, while still not human, were indicative of a considerable advance.

The earliest australopithecine—*A. afarensis*—was first discovered in 1974 by David Johanson in the Hadar region of Ethiopia (Figure 20.27a). At that time, the greater than 3-million-year age of these fossils made them the oldest known true hominids, and the discovery aroused much interest. The individual unearthed was a young female, and she quickly became known as "Lucy." Since 1976, the Hadar Formation has yielded the bones of over 60 individuals, while associated with other finds at Laetoli in Tanzania is a volcanic ash bed with australopithecine footprints. The prints were clearly made by someone walking upright, confirmation of the bipedalism of Lucy and her kinfolk. Although about the size of a chimpanzee, even the earliest australopithecine *A. afarensis* was probably more intelligent, the cranial capacity ranging from 380 to 450 cubic centimeters, compared with 300 to 400 cubic centimeters for the chimpanzee. New discoveries have pushed back the age of the earliest examples of *A. afarensis* to almost 4 million years, some half-million years before Lucy lived.

To date, *A. afarensis* is the earliest and most primitive australopithecine species, but at least three other species have been recognized. Arising from the *afarensis* line about 3 million years ago was *A. africanus*. Somewhat taller than *A. afarensis*, this species likely was also more intelligent, having a cranial capacity of 400 to 600 cubic centimeters. The face was also flatter and the teeth still further reduced.

Two other species of *Australopithecus*—*A. robustus* and *A. boisei*—show a trend toward increased stature and heavier build, also with a brain capacity of 400 to 600 cubic centimeters (Figure 20.27b). Especially noticeable are the unusually massive jaw and the broad, flat molars adapted to chewing coarse plant material. Additional attachment area for powerful jaw muscle was provided by a bony crest on the top of the skull, similar to that seen

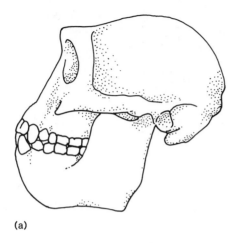

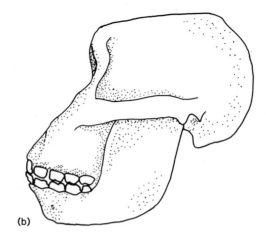

(a)   (b)

FIGURE 20.27
Two species of *Australopithecus*. (a) *A. afarensis.* (b) *A. boisei.*

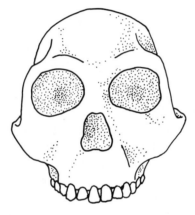

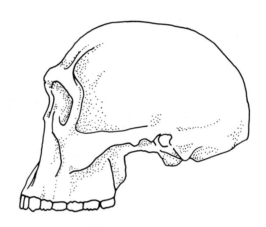

FIGURE 20.28
Partial reconstruction of a skull of *Homo habilis.*

in the gorilla. These features strongly suggest that, unlike *A. africanus,* which was probably more or less omnivorous, these more robust species were vegetarians.

The time ranges of the several species of *Australopithecus* show considerable overlap, typically 300,000 to 600,000 years. This would be expected in any evolutionary scheme based on the punctuated equilibrium mechanism. An ancestral species often continues to live alongside a descendent species before finally succumbing to competition or to a changing environment to which the descendent species is better adapted.

The relationship between *Australopithecus* and the genus *Homo* is still largely unresolved, and several different evolutionary pathways have been proposed. In one scheme, *A. afarensis* is considered the ancestral form, giving rise some 3 million years ago to three distinct lines. One contained a progressively evolving lineage, with *A. africanus* followed by *A. robustus,* and another with *A. aethiopicus* and *A. boisei,* both being evolutionary dead ends. The third line contained a creature with undoubt-

edly australopithecine links but who was nevertheless able to use tools. Although as an advanced australopithecine, it is labelled *Australopithecus habilis* (meaning *able*) by some paleonanthropologists, other workers prefer the designation *Homo habilis* (Figure 20.28). In an alternative proposal, Richard Leakey suggests that all of the australopithecines were already on an evolutionary sideline and that the ancestor common to both *Australopithecus* and *Homo* existed much earlier, perhaps 5 or 6 million years ago, and has yet to be discovered.

The Genus Homo

Following the publication of Darwin's *Origin of Species,* there was, quite naturally, an avid search for "ape-men" who would provide the "missing link" postulated in Darwin's thesis. The first discovery of fossil humans had been made in 1856, with the unearthing of a skull in a cave in the Neander Gorge of the Düssel River near Düsseldorf, Germany. The large cranial capacity of this so-called

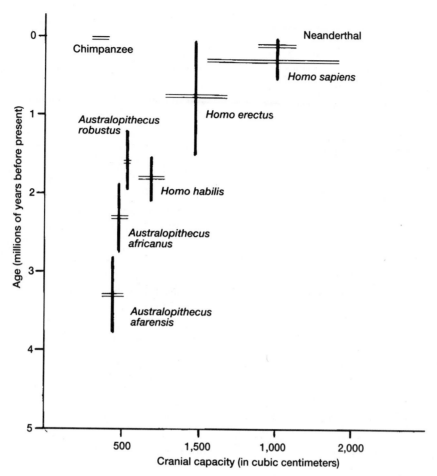

FIGURE 20.29
Evolving cranial capacity in hominids.

Neanderthal man, however, already placed him well beyond any apelike animal and so close to modern humans that he was at least in the same genus. The missing link was still missing, much to the delight, of course, of Darwin's opponents.

More than 30 years passed before any further discoveries. Then, in 1891, Eugene Dubois, a Dutch anatomist working in Java, found an apelike skull and, in the following year, additional remains, including a thigh bone. From these finds, Dubois was able to construct a picture of a bipedal animal with a brain roughly intermediate in size between ape and human. To recognize its missing-link status, this creature was named *Pithecanthropus* (meaning ape-man) *erectus.*

In the years since the Dubois discovery, similar fossils have been found in numerous other places in China, Europe, and Africa. Modest differences between the various groups were considered by earlier workers sufficient justification for the recognition of separate species and even genera. So *Pithecanthropus erectus* was joined by *Paleanthropus heidelbergensis, Sinanthropus pekinensis,*

Cypraeanthropus rhodesiensis, and so on. Even the specimens from a second collection from Java, excavated on the Solo River quite close to Dubois's original find, were named *Javanthropus soloensis.* This multiplicity of names and only the vaguest notions as to the relative ages of all these fossils were, to put it mildly, not conducive to a proper understanding of hominoid taxonomy.

In recent years, a detailed comparison of the various fossils has indicated the need for a new approach. The morphologic differences between the various fossil populations are largely of the kind and degree readily discernible within present-day human populations and ascribed to no more than racial differences. In some features, these fossil variations seem to be time-related—that is, when properly ordered as to geologic age, trends from a primitive to a more advanced state may be discerned. For example, whereas older skulls might have a cranial capacity of around 775 cubic centimeters, skulls from younger strata are significantly larger, with capacities of 1,000 to 1,300 cubic centimeters—in fact, overlapping with the 1,200- to 1,300-cubic-centimeter range of modern humans (Figure 20.29).

Paleoanthropologists now generally agree that the taxonomy of these various fossils would be greatly simplified and make more sense if they were all recognized as belonging to a single species. Under the rules of zoological nomenclature, the original discovery of Dubois takes precedence, and so the trivial name *erectus* applies to all the fossils. As to the generic name, the abandonment of the plethora of earlier names and the placement of *erectus* in the single genus *Homo* is justified not only on skeletal resemblances, but also on evidence that all these animals used fire and tools. To most workers, this represents the crossing of a significant threshold.

To modern humans, *Homo erectus* would still look very apelike, with a heavy supraorbital ridge in a massive and rather flattened skull. The forehead sloped, and the jaws were prognathous—that is, they projected forward at the tooth line and there was no distinct chin. On the other hand, the teeth and the shape of the dental arcade were essentially modern.

The origins of *Homo erectus* are somewhat obscure. The possible relationships between *Homo erectus* and the australopithecines are particularly intriguing. The gap between the two groups may be partly filled by *Australopithecus* (or *Homo*) *habilis,* mentioned earlier. Discovered in 2-million-year-old sediments in the Olduvai Gorge in East Africa, skull fragments suggest a cranial capacity of 600 to 752 cubic centimeters, intermediate between that of *Australopithecus* and *Homo erectus.*

Although the association of skeletal remains with primitive (Oldawan) tools suggests that *habilis* belongs in the genus *Homo,* the picture remains confused because of a relatively recent discovery of tools that are some half a million years older than *habilis.* No bones have been found associated with the artifacts, so either there was an earlier and as yet unknown species of our genus, or the australopithecines were also tool users. Skull fragments discovered in 2.4 million-year-old sediments in Kenya in the 1970s, but overlooked in a museum until 1992, have since been shown as belonging to the genus *Homo.* This would suggest that the former supposition is correct.

Neanderthal Man

The final stages of human evolution also are sketchy because of serious gaps in the fossil record. The youngest examples of *Homo erectus* so far dated are about 400,000 years old. The oldest remains of creatures generally considered to be human (Neanderthal man) are only 100,000 years old, which leaves a void of 300,000 years.

After the initial Neanderthal discovery, similar remains were found at places scattered across much of the Old World. The unearthing of a complete skeleton at Lachapelle-aux-Saints in southwest France in 1908 resulted in a reconstruction of Neanderthal man as a squat, rather heavily built being, with a stooping, shambling gait. Even though Neanderthal's cranial capacity of 1,300 cubic centimeters was as large or larger than the average for modern

humans, most people preferred to think of him as dimwitted and brutish. This view is particularly surprising in that Neanderthal man produced the superbly crafted stone stools of the Mousterian culture. Be that as it may and human ego being what it is, Neanderthal was not considered human and so was classified as the separate species *Homo neanderthalensis.*

As it turned out, much of the original interpretation of Neanderthal man was incorrect because the 1908 skeleton was later found to be that of an elderly individual afflicted with a chronic arthritic condition. Data from hundreds of subsequent finds have set the record straight. Although having a more massive and larger skull than modern humans and a somewhat more protruding jaw, the differences in the lower skeleton were negligible. Neanderthal man was undoubtedly more stockily built, but this could be attributed to the climate in which he lived. Just as modern Eskimos' adaptation to life in a cold climate is seen in their stocky stature, so Neanderthal was living in Europe during the third interglacial and into the following glacial period.

Neanderthal man was often a cave dweller but also built primitive shelters of stone. His intellectual capacity has been a subject of considerable debate and, naturally, not easy to determine. Neanderthal's fine Mousterian culture and the fact that he buried his dead with weapons and ornaments, suggesting a belief in an afterlife, point to a creature of considerable intellectual stature. For these reasons, most taxonomists now prefer to see Neanderthal as a member of our own species, *Homo sapiens.*

Cro-Magnon Man

The disappearance of Neanderthal man is something of a mystery. At about 35,000 years ago, he seems to have been abruptly replaced by a new race that, to all intents and purposes, were modern humans. Where this so-called **Cro-Magnon man**[3] came from is also a mystery. Cro-Magnon man may simply have evolved from Neanderthal man. If so, the process was a rapid one, but not impossible within a punctuated equilibrium model. Certainly, the Cro-Magnon culture contains many features to suggest that it "evolved" from the Mousterian culture of the Neanderthals. In an alternative hypothesis, Cro-Magnon man migrated into Neanderthal territory from outside (his likely place of origin being Africa) and then simply replaced Neanderthals through warfare.

Whether the two races interbred is an open question. Evidence from a comparison of the Aurignacian industry of Cro-Magnon man and the Chatelperronian industry of later Neanderthals indicates considerable population interaction. In the Middle East, where the record begins some 5,000 years earlier than in western Europe, the evidence is somewhat stronger for a mixing of the two races.

3. Named for the first discovery in 1868 of a skull in a limestone cave at Cro-Magnon, a small village near Les Eyzies in the Dordogne area of France.

Some anthropologists claim to see in occasional modern individuals certain skull features and cranial measurements that point to Neanderthal origins. Many such examples occur among the peoples of the so-called Celtic fringe of western Europe, which supposedly demonstrates that Neanderthals retreated before a wave of incoming Cro-Magnons in much the same way as in later times indigenous peoples retreated before successive invaders from the east.

Which explanation for the origin of modern humans is correct? If Cro-Magnon man did come from Africa, he may have arisen as a line from *H. erectus* ancestors in Africa, whereas the Neanderthals may have been derived from *H. erectus* who had migrated to Europe at a much earlier date.

Eve, the Common Ancestor of All Humans

As mentioned earlier, molecular biology is making some significant new, if controversial, contributions to the understanding of human evolution. The technique involves tracing family trees by means of mitochondrial DNA. Mitochondria are energy-supplying structures in the cell, and they contain DNA that is not involved in the mixing of parental genes during meiosis but is derived only from the egg, not the sperm. Thus, a lineage can be traced back from mother, to grandmother, to great-grandmother, and so on. Mitochondrial DNA is changed only by mutations, which are passed on matrilinearly to the next generation. Given the assumption that mutations occur at a fixed rate, different DNA types can be compared and the number of generations that separate the different types from a common ancestral type calculated. In other words, all humans alive today share mitochondrial DNA derived from a single female ancestor.

That the genetic stock of all humans perhaps arises from a single ancestral female, or "Eve," as she has been called, conforms to basic genetic theory. What is surprising, however, is that calculations show that Eve lived only about 200,000 years ago. This is before the modern human races arose, which implies that, from a common African homeland, carriers of Eve's genes spread to most parts of the world and that it was their descendants who gave rise to the modern races. In other words, the various races did not, as some anthropologists have argued, arise independently from different *Homo erectus* lineages.

This model, announced by the late Allan Wilson and colleagues at the University of California at Berkeley in 1987, not surprisingly aroused a storm of controversy. For one thing it contradicted the very considerable evidence from the fossil record that pointed to a common ancestor no younger than about a million years. The technique used in DNA analysis was also criticized, as was the choice of study subjects. Finally the computer program and the method used were also called to question as statistically flawed. The debate continues, but amid the conflicting views it still looks as though an African origin for modern humans seems likely.

Pleistocene Extinctions

By the Late Pleistocene, the Cenozoic evolutionary radiation had produced a rich fauna of mammals, both large and small, in virtually every ecologic niche. In North America, for example, the fossil evidence points to an assemblage of large mammals as abundant and varied as those in modern Africa up to very recent time. Their decline—both in populations and number of species—since that time has been so rapid that, in the context of geologic time, it can be considered a North American mass extinction event.

The cause of the extinctions is a matter of considerable controversy, with two main schools of thought: On the one hand, the coincidence of the time of the extinctions with the rapid retreat of the Wisconsin ice sheet supports an environmental cause, with the disruption of food chains linked to climate-caused vegetational changes. On the other hand, there is considerable support for the idea that early human hunters were responsible. The time of arrival of the early waves of humans from Asia across the Bering land bridge and their subsequent spread through

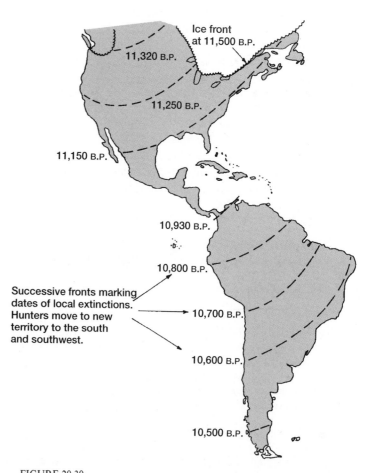

FIGURE 20.30

Map showing the timing of major post-Pleistocene mammal extinctions in North and South America. (B.P. = before present.)

both North and South America is claimed to coincide with the time of local extinction of many large mammals (Figure 20.30).

One weakness of the environmental argument is that similar extinction events apparently did not occur after earlier glacial retreats, all of which were accompanied by similar rapid climatic/vegetational changes. The human hunter hypothesis, however, also has its weaknesses. For example, dating techniques may not be accurate enough to support the connection in time between the archaeological evidence and the disappearance of the mammals. In addition, the extinctions were apparently selective because some large mammals, like bison, musk oxen, and moose, have survived to the present day. This point is countered by the suggestion that the mammals with the slowest regeneration rates were the most vulnerable. And so the argument continues.

Epilogue: The Terminal Holocene Event

In coming to the close of an account such as this, some sense of perspective is needed. We must look at the modern world and the world of the near future in terms of what has gone before. Particularly important is that part of earth history involving humankind as potentially the most devastating species ever to have evolved.

Sadly, the mass extinction event that began in the Late Pleistocene continues to the present day. If, indeed, early humans were responsible, their actions might be explained as necessary for survival. They probably knew nothing of the consequences of their actions. No such excuse is possible today. A recent example was the senseless slaughter of the North American Passenger Pigeon that, even as late as the mid-nineteenth century, numbered in the millions. The last survivor died in the Cleveland Zoo in 1915. The millions of plains buffalo almost met a similar fate and had been reduced to mere hundreds after incredible slaughter, much of it for sport. Often, the

tongue was the only part of the animal taken. Politicians sometimes invited European royalty to a buffalo "hunt," and they would shoot the animals from train observation cars. Tiger hunts in India were organized for visiting dignitaries as a gesture of hospitality, while African safaris were organized for the express purpose of acquiring trophies to hang on the wall. The poaching of elephant-tusk ivory and rhinoceros horns for aphrodisiacs are other examples of human activities that, until quite recently, were accepted as normal behavior.

Humans' attitudes regarding their place in the universe, and particularly their role as an earth-dwelling species, have only begun to change in the last few years. Unfortunately, religious and ethical teachings have been the last to recognize that there is a problem. Only very belatedly has it become fashionable to introduce some reference to caring for the environment. The reason for this delay is found in the teachings handed down through the ages. The idea that humans were "given dominion over the fowl of the air and the beast of the field" and, for that matter, the whole earth as some God-given right might seem to some people all the justification they need.

Apart from diminishing natural resources, pollution, and the destruction of natural habitats, the problem that completely dwarfs all others is that of human population. As we near the close of the millenium, world population growth is still completely out of hand, and unless this Malthusian monster, now part of human awareness for some 150 years, is overcome, the future for our planet is not bright. If, even with this knowledge of the likely consequences, humans as a species continue to proliferate and to destroy the global environment, then they may go the way of the dinosaurs—perhaps, given the circumstances, a fate they deserve!

To quote Finnish paleontologist Bjorn Kurten, "There can be nothing more urgent than finding the way back to a sane interaction between man and his surroundings."

Summary

The Neogene encompasses the past 25 million years, a period during which not only the modern world in terms of oceans and continents emerged, but also the many and varied species of plants and animals that inhabit the world of today.

In the Cordilleran region of western North America, the period was marked by widespread faulting and volcanic activity. In particular, there were vast outpourings of tholeiitic lavas in the Columbia Plateau area of parts of Washington and Oregon. Crustal movements along the Pacific coast, including the uplift of the Sierra Nevada, were due to important

changes in plate relationships. During the earlier Cenozoic, the western margin of the North American craton had been marked by a subduction zone, along which the Farallon plate was dipping down below the North American plate. Beginning in the Oligocene, the overall compressional style of tectonics was replaced by a translational movement in which the North American and Pacific plates were sliding past each other, rather then colliding. This translational movement, with the Pacific plate moving in a north-northwesterly direction, continues to the present day and is manifested in the San Andreas and other fault systems.

To the east, in the Basin and Range Province, tensional crustal forces became more pronounced in the Miocene, resulting in block faulting along trends aligned roughly north–south. The erosion of the ranges comprising the upfaulted blocks supplied sedimentary infillings of the basins between the ranges.

Still further east, the Colorado Plateau remained a structural entity through much of the Cenozoic. Broad uplift and extensive volcanism began in the Pliocene, some of it continuing into recent times. One consequence of the broad regional uplift of the plateau region was rejuvenation of streams, resulting in the downcutting of some spectacular gorges, including the Grand Canyon.

Toward the center of the North American continent were the interior lowlands. Much of this area is underlain by broad sheets of alluvial sands and silts derived from the eroding and isostatically rising mountains to the west. One of the world's great aquifers—the Ogallala Formation—was laid down at this time in the Pliocene. The Ogallala is an important freshwater irrigation source throughout the Southwest, but, unfortunately, it is being depleted at a faster rate than it is being replenished.

Along the Gulf and Atlantic coastal plains, Neogene sedimentation shows an essential continuity from the Paleogene. Sedimentary facies reflect fluctuating sea levels, mainly of glacio-eustatic origin. The present-day configuration of the Appalachian Mountains is due to continued uplift through the Cenozoic with streams cutting down differentially into softer rocks.

In the Mediterranean basin, the Messinian Stage of the Miocene saw periodic drying-up episodes, and large evaporite basins formed. The cause of this was a glacio-eustatic fluctuation of sea level that periodically left the Straits of Gibraltar emergent.

One of the most important features of the Neogene was an intensification of the cooling trend that had begun in the Early Oligocene. By Late Miocene time, ice caps existed in both the Southern and Northern hemispheres. The cause of this Late Cenozoic Ice Age is hypothesized to

involve plate tectonics and the configuration of the continents with respect to the poles. A climatic feedback mechanism and episodes on different continents are sometimes difficult. A detailed chronology of the climatic fluctuations involved in glacial episodes is found in the deep-sea succession. The Great Lakes owe their existence to glacial action and did not exist before the Late Cenozoic glaciation.

The last 25 million years have seen the emergence of the modern biosphere. Both the plants and animals of this period were very modern looking. During this time, advanced primates evolved rapidly, and the first hominids appeared in Africa.

Among the advanced apes, *Ramapithecus* was the most likely ancestor of humans. Appearing about 17 million years ago, *Ramapithecus* showed many advanced features. The first hominid with a true bipedal gait was *Australopithecus*, which appeared about 4 million years ago. Several australopithecine species have been recognized, with *A. afarensis* the earliest. Whether the *Australopithecus* line produced the ancestors of humans or was an evolutionary side branch is still a matter of some controversy.

The first species to be considered as belonging to the genus *Homo* was originally discovered in Java in 1891 and named *Pithecanthropus erectus*. In the years that followed, many similar finds were made, and each was assigned its own genus and species name. Recent work has shown that all these individuals likely belong to a single genus and species—*Homo erectus*—and that the differences

the emergence of the Panamanian land bridge may also have been involved. Major divisions of the glacial successions have been identified in different parts of the world, but correlations between glacial between them are no more than one would expect between members of different races.

The oldest members of the human species date from about 100,000 years ago and are represented by Neanderthal man. Originally classified as a separate species, *Homo neanderthalensis,* many now agree that he really belongs to *Homo sapiens.* The disappearance of Neanderthal man about 35,000 years ago and his replacement by Cro-Magnon man, essentially a modern man, is something of a mystery but is generally believed to be a consequence of the migration of Cro-Magnon man into Europe from Africa. Whether Cro-Magnon man simply eliminated Neanderthal man in warfare or whether the two groups interbred is still unknown.

A molecular biology technique involving mitochondrial DNA indicates that the genetic stock of all humans perhaps arises from a single ancestral female. If this is true, then the various human races did not arise independently from different *Homo erectus* lineages.

The Late Pleistocene saw the beginning of a mass extinction event that continues to the present day. This may have been caused by environmental changes due to glacial retreat or by the depredations of early human hunters. More recently, it has continued as a result of modern humans' destruction of habitats, deliberate hunting, and sometimes senseless slaughter.

Questions

1. Explain why the present definition of the Neogene as a stratigraphic division is unsatisfactory. Discuss some possible alternative ways of dividing up the past 25 million years.
2. What major geologic events have occurred in the Pacific coast region since the beginning of the Neogene?
3. The rocks at the bottom of the Grand Canyon are nearly 2 billion years old; yet, the canyon itself is probably less than 10 million years old. Explain.
4. What is the "gangplank"? How is it significant in understanding the depositional and erosional history of the High Plains?

5. Give some account of the Late Cenozoic history of the Appalachians.
6. To what does the Messinian Salinity Crisis refer?
7. In comparing the Late Cenozoic Ice Age with those of earlier geologic history, there are both resemblances and differences. In particular, the differences seem to suggest that we as yet have no satisfactory model to explain all ice ages. Discuss.
8. What were the changes, particularly in the oceans, during the Neogene that likely led to the Late Cenozoic Ice Age?

9. What role did land bridges in the Panama region play in influencing the distribution of mammals in the Americas?
10. Describe the glacial advances and retreats in North America, and compare them with those in Europe.
11. Write a brief history of the Great Lakes.
12. What special features do paleoanthropologists use in looking for likely ancestors to modern humans?

13. What contributions have studies of amino acids in the so-called molecular clock made to the understanding of evolutionary relationships among the higher primates?

14. After the initial discovery of Neanderthal man, why did early paleoanthropologists believe him to be an apelike subspecies?

15. What direct evidence of the Wisconsin glaciation is closest to your area? Describe the major geologic/topographic features involved.

Further Reading

Berggen, W. A., and J. A. Van Couvering. 1974. The Late Neogene: Biostratigraphy, geochronology, and paleoclimatology of the last 15 million years in marine and continental sequences. *Palaeogeography, Palaeoclimatology, Palaeoecology* 16:1–216.

Bowen, D. Q. 1978. *Quaternary geology: A stratigraphic framework for multidisciplinary work.* Oxford, England: Pergamon.

Flint, R. F. 1971. *Glacial and quaternary geology.* New York: Wiley.

Johanson, D. C., and M. A. Edey. 1981. *Lucy, the beginning of humankind.* New York: Simon & Schuster.

Leakey, R. E. 1981. *The making of mankind.* New York: Dutton.

Martin, P. S. 1973. The discovery of America. *Science* 179:969–74.

Tattersall, I., and N. Eldredge. 1977. Fact, theory, and fantasy in human paleontology. *American Scientist* 65:204.

Weaver, K. F. 1985. The search for our ancestors. *National Geographic Magazine* 168:560–623.

Appendix A
Formation Correlation Charts

Series	Stages	S.E. Newfoundland	Vermont	New York	E. Tennessee	North Illinois	N. Park Range, Canadian Rockies	North Wales (type section)	Europe Epoch	Europe Age
		Ordovician	Ordovician	Ordovician	Ordovician	Ordovician	Ordovician	Ordovician	Epoch	Age
Croixan	Trempealeauan	Elliott Cove Group	Clarendon Springs Formation	Briarcliff Dolomite	Copper Ridge Dolomite	Eminence Dolomite	Lynx Group	Lingula Flags — Dolgelly Beds	Merioneth	Dolgellian
Croixan	Franconian	Elliott Cove Group	Clarendon Springs Formation	Briarcliff Dolomite	Copper Ridge Dolomite	Potossi Dolomite	Lynx Group	Lingula Flags — Ffestiniog Beds	Merioneth	Maentwrogian
Croixan	Dresbachian	Elliott Cove Group	Danby Formation	Pine Plains Dolomite	Copper Ridge Dolomite	Franconia Formation	Lynx Group	Lingula Flags — Maentwrog Beds	Merioneth	Maentwrogian
						Ironton Formation				
						Galesville Sandstone				
						Eau Claire Formation				
						Mount Simon Sandstone	Arctomys Formation			
Albertan		Manuels River Formation	Winooski Dolomite	Stissing Dolomite	Honaker Dolomite / Conasauga Formation		Pika Formation	Menevian Beds — Clogan Shales	St. David's	Menevian
Albertan		Chamberlins Creek Formation	Winooski Dolomite	Stissing Dolomite	Honaker Dolomite / Conasauga Formation		Titkana Formation	Menevian Beds	St. David's	Solvan
Albertan		Chamberlins Creek Formation	Winooski Dolomite	Stissing Dolomite	Honaker Dolomite / Conasauga Formation		Tatei Formation	Cefn Goch Grits	St. David's	Solvan
							Chetang Formation		?	
							Adolphus Formation			
Waucoban		Brigus Formation	Monkton Quartzite	Poughquag Quartz	Rome Formation		Mahto Formation	Harlech Grits	Caerfai	Lenian
Waucoban		Brigus Formation	Monkton Quartzite	Poughquag Quartz	Shady Dolomite		Mahto Formation	Harlech Grits	Caerfai	Atdabanian
Waucoban		Brigus Formation	Dunham Dolomite	Poughquag Quartz	Shady Dolomite		Mural Formation	Harlech Grits	Caerfai	Atdabanian
Waucoban		Smith Port Formation	Cheshire Quartzite		Chilhowee Group		McNaughton Formation	Harlech Grits	Caerfai	Tommotian
Waucoban		Bonavista Formation	Cheshire Quartzite		Chilhowee Group		McNaughton Formation		Caerfai	Tommotian
(Below) →		(Precambrian)	(Precambrian)	(Precambrian)	(Precambrian)	(Precambrian)	(Precambrian)	(Precambrian)		

A1 CAMBRIAN

		East Ontario	New York	Lexington, Virginia	Upper Mississippi Valley	Arbuckle Mountains	Ouachita Mountains	Roberts Mountain, Nevada	Epochs
		(Silurian)	(Silurian)	(Silurian)	(Silurian)	(Silurian)	(Silurian)	(Silurian)	
Cincinnatian	Gama-chian	Queenston Red Shale	Queenston Shale	Juniata	Maquoketa Formation		Polk Creek Shale	Hanson Creek Formation	Ashgill
	Richmond	Russell Dolomite				Fernvale Limestone			
	Maysville	Carlsbad Shale	Oswego Sandstone						Caradoc
	Eden		Lorraine Group	Martinsburg Formation					
Champlainian	Mohawkian — Trenton	Billings Shale / Eastview Shale	Utica Shale		Galena Dolomite	Viola Limestone	Big Fork Chert		
		Ottawa Limestone	Trenton Limestone	Collierstown Limestone				Eureka Quartzite	
	Black River		Black River Limestone	Edinburg Formation	Platteville Formation	Simpson Group	Wamble Shale		
	Chazy	St. Martin Limestone / Rockcliffe Formation		Lincolnshire Limestone / Whistle Creek Limestone / New Market Limestone	St. Peter Sandstone				Llandeilo / ?
									Llanvirn
Canadian	(Undivided)		"Beekmantown Formation" / Ogdensburg Dolomite		Prairie du Chien Group	Upper Arbuckle Group	Blakeley Sandstone	Pogonip Limestone	Arenig
							Mozarn Shale		?
		Oxford Dolomite / March Dolomite / Nepean Sandstone	Tribes Hill Dolomite				Crystal Mountain Shale		Tremadoc
(Below) →		(Precambrian)	(Precambrian)	(Cambrian)	(Cambrian)	(Cambrian)	(Cambrian)		

A2   ORDOVICIAN

North America		Nova Scotia	Pennsylvania-Tennessee	Central New York	West New York/South Ontario	North Utah	Mackenzie River	Central Nevada	European Stages
Series	Stage	(Devonian)	(Devonian)	(Lower Devonian)	(Devonian)	(Devonian)	(Devonian)		
Cayugan		Stonehouse Formation	Keyser Limestone	Manlius Limestone		Sevy Dolomite	North Nahanna River Dolomite		Pridolian
				Rondouts Limestone					
				Cobleskill Dolomite	Cobleskill Limestone				
			Tonoloway Limestone		Salina Group — Bertie				
				Salina Group	Camillus				
					Syracuse				
			Wills Creek Shale		Vernon				
			Bloomsburg Redbeds		Pittsford				
Niagaran	Lockport	Moydart Formation	McKenzie Formation		Guelph Dolomite			Love Mountain Limestone	Ludlovian
				?			?		
				Lockport Dolomite	Lockport Dolomite				
			?					?	
	Clifton	McAdam Formation	Clinton Group		Clinton Group — Rochester Shale	Laketown Dolomite	Mount Kindle Formation		Wenlockian
				Clinton Group	Irondequoit			?	
	Clinton	Ross Brook Formation			Merriton			Roberts Mountain Formation	
				Clinton Group	Neahga		?		
					Thorald			?	
Medinian (Alexandrian)		Beechill Cove Formation	Tuscarora (Clinch) Sandstone	Grimsby Sandstone	Cataract — Grimsby		Franklin Mountain Formation		Llandoverian
					Power Glen				
					Whirlpool				
(Below) →		(Ordovician)	(Ordovician)	(Ordovician)	(Ordovician)	(Ordovician)	(Ordovician)	(Ordovician)	

A3 SILURIAN

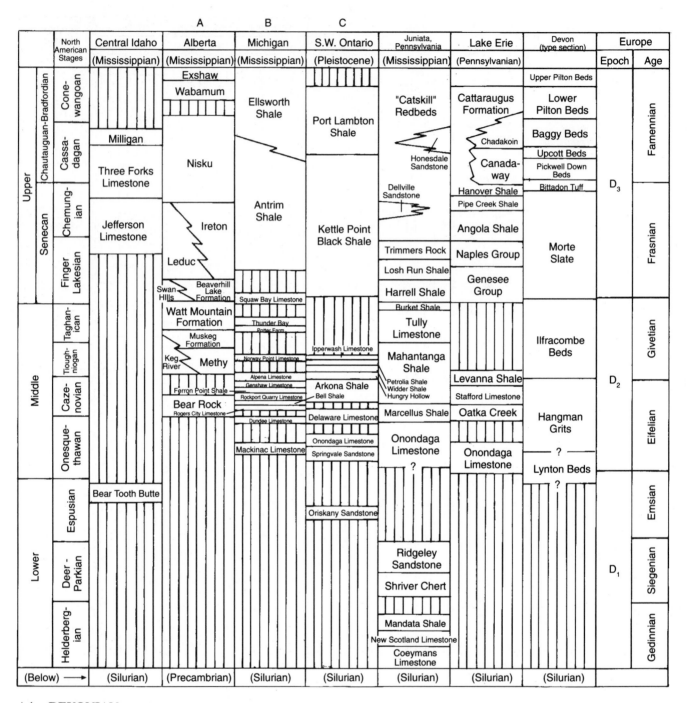

A4   DEVONIAN

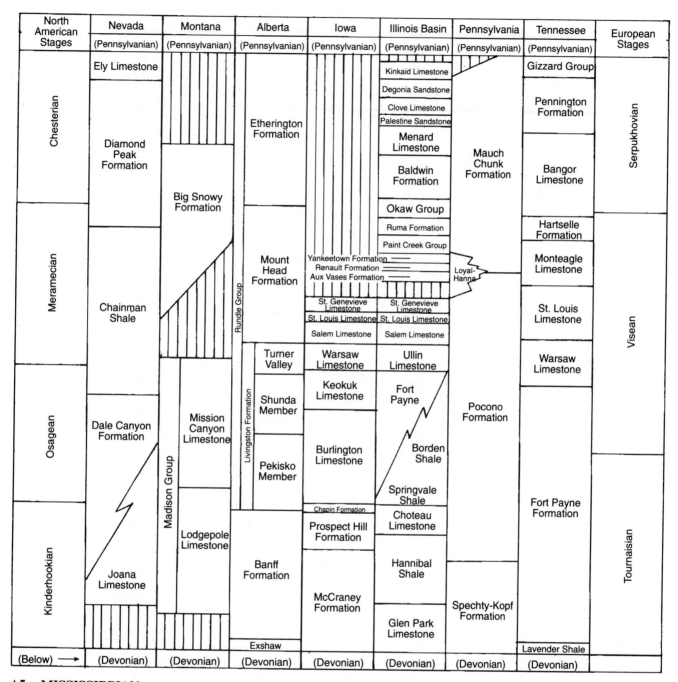

North American Stages	Nevada (Pennsylvanian)	Montana (Pennsylvanian)	Alberta (Pennsylvanian)	Iowa (Pennsylvanian)	Illinois Basin (Pennsylvanian)	Pennsylvania (Pennsylvanian)	Tennessee (Pennsylvanian)	European Stages
Chesterian	Ely Limestone		Etherington Formation		Kinkaid Limestone		Gizzard Group	Serpukhovian
	Diamond Peak Formation	Big Snowy Formation			Degonia Sandstone	Mauch Chunk Formation	Pennington Formation	
					Clove Limestone			
					Palestine Sandstone			
					Menard Limestone		Bangor Limestone	
					Baldwin Formation			
Meramecian	Chainman Shale		Mount Head Formation		Okaw Group		Hartselle Formation	Visean
					Ruma Formation		Monteagle Limestone	
					Paint Creek Group	Loyal-Hanna		
				Yankeetown Formation				
				Renault Formation				
				Aux Vases Formation				
				St. Genevieve Limestone	St. Genevieve Limestone		St. Louis Limestone	
				St. Louis Limestone	St. Louis Limestone			
				Salem Limestone	Salem Limestone			
Osagean	Dale Canyon Formation	Mission Canyon Limestone	Turner Valley	Warsaw Limestone	Ullin Limestone	Pocono Formation	Warsaw Limestone	
			Shunda Member	Keokuk Limestone	Fort Payne			
			Pekisko Member	Burlington Limestone	Borden Shale		Fort Payne Formation	
					Springvale Shale			
Kinderhookian	Joana Limestone	Lodgepole Limestone	Banff Formation	Chapin Formation	Choteau Limestone			Tournaisian
				Prospect Hill Formation	Hannibal Shale			
				McCraney Formation	Glen Park Limestone	Spechty-Kopf Formation		
			Exshaw				Lavender Shale	
(Below) →	(Devonian)	(Devonian)	(Devonian)	(Devonian)	(Devonian)	(Devonian)	(Devonian)	

A5 MISSISSIPPIAN

North American Stages	Wyoming (Permian)	New Mexico (Permian)	Central Texas (Permian)	Missouri (Permian)	South Illinois (Permian)	Southwest Pennsylvania (Permian)	Nova Scotia (Permian)	European Stages	
Virgilian	Tensleep Formation	Wild Cow Formation (Madera Group)	Cisco Group	Waubaunsee Formation	McLeansboro Formation	Monongahela Series	Pictou Group	Gzhelian	Stephanian
				Shawnea Group					
				Douglas Group					
Missourian			Canyon Group	Pedee Group		Conemaugh Series		Kasimovian	
				Lansing Group					
				Kansas City Group					
				Pleasanton Group					
Desmoinesian	Amsden Formation	Los Moyos Formation	Strawn Group	Marmaton Group	Carbondale Formation	Allegheny Series		Moscovian	Westphalian
				Cherokee Group					
Atokan		Sandia Formation	"Atoka"	Riverton Formation	Tradewater Formation	Pottsville Series	Shulie Formation		
				Burgner Formation					
				McLouth Formation			Joggins Formation		
			Smithwick Facies	Cheltenham Formation					
Morrowan	Sacajawea Formation			? Hale Formation	Caseyville Formation		Bass Point Formation	Bashkirian	"Namurian" (part)
			Marble Falls Formation				Claremont Formation		
							Shepody Formation		
(Below) →	(Mississippian)	(Mississippian)	(Mississippian)	(Mississippian)	(Mississippian)	(Mississippian)	(Mississippian)		

A6   PENNSYLVANIAN

North American Stages	S.W. Montana	North Arizona	Permian Basin	S.W. Texas	Nebraska	South Africa	Germany	European Stages
	(Triassic)	(Triassic)	(Triassic)	(Triassic)	(Triassic)	(Triassic)	(Triassic)	
Ochoan	Phosphoria Formation		Dewey Lake / Rustler / Salado / Castile	Tessey Limestone	Freezeout Shale	Beaufort Series	Zechstein	Tatarian
Guadalupian			Bell Canyon Formation / Capitan Limestone	Capitan Limestone	Forelle Limestone			Kazanian
Guadalupian			Goat Seep Limestone / Cherry Canyon Formation / Brushy Canyon	Word Formation	Glendo Shale		Kupferschiefe / Upper Rotliegende	Kungurian
Leonardian	City Park Formation	Kaibab Limestone	Bone Springs Limestone / Victorio Peak Limestone	Leonard Formation	Minnekahta Limestone	Ecca Series	Lower Rotliegende	Artinskian
Leonardian		Toroweap Formation			Opeche Shale			
Leonardian		Coconino Sandstone			Cassa Group			
Leonardian					Stone Corrall Formation			
Leonardian		Hermit Shale			Ninnescah Shale			
Wolfcampian		Supai Formation	Hueco Limestone	Wolfcamp Formation	Broom Creek Formation	Dwyka Series		Sakmarian
Wolfcampian								Asselian
(Below) →	(Pennsylvanian)	(Pennsylvanian)	(Pennsylvanian)	(Pennsylvanian)	(Pennsylvanian)	(Carboniferous)	(Carboniferous)	

A7 PERMIAN

Series	S.E. California (Cretaceous)	Utah (Jurassic)	Wyoming (Jurassic)	North Arizona (Jurassic)	New Mexico (Jurassic)	New Jersey (Cretaceous)	Germany (Jurassic)	European Stages
Upper		Ankareh Formation: Stanaker Member / Garta Grit / Mahogany Member	Chugwater Group: Popo Agie Formation / Alcova Limestone	Chinle Formation / Shinarump Conglomerate	Dockum Group: "Chinle" / Santa Rosa Formation / Pierce Canyon Formation	Newark Group: Portland Arkose / Meriden Formation / New Haven Arkose	Keuper: Rhät / Gyes-keuper / Letten-kohle	Rhaetian / Norian / Carnian
Middle	Volcanics	Thaynes Formation	Red Peak Formation				Muschelkalk	Ladinian / Anisian
Lower	Inyo Formation	Woodside Formation	Dinwoody Formation	Moenkopi Formation			Bunter	Scythian
(Below) →	(Permian)	(Permian)	(Permian)	(Permian)	(Permian)	(Lower Paleozoic)	(Permian)	

A8   TRIASSIC

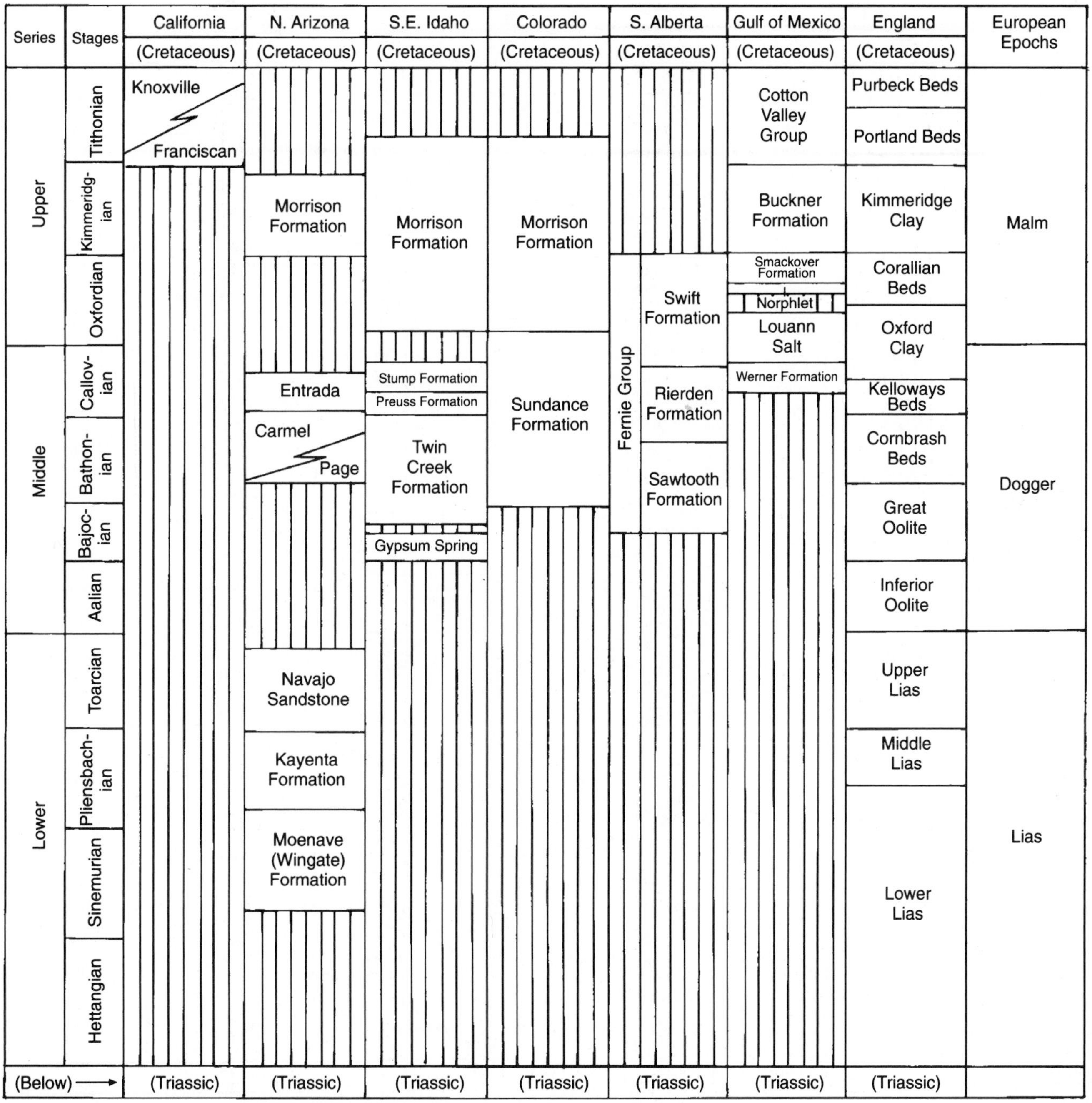

Series	Stages	California (Cretaceous)	N. Arizona (Cretaceous)	S.E. Idaho (Cretaceous)	Colorado (Cretaceous)	S. Alberta (Cretaceous)	Gulf of Mexico (Cretaceous)	England (Cretaceous)	European Epochs
Upper	Tithonian	Knoxville / Franciscan					Cotton Valley Group	Purbeck Beds	Malm
Upper	Tithonian						Cotton Valley Group	Portland Beds	Malm
Upper	Kimmeridgian		Morrison Formation	Morrison Formation	Morrison Formation		Buckner Formation	Kimmeridge Clay	Malm
Upper	Oxfordian					Swift Formation	Smackover Formation / Norphlet	Corallian Beds	Malm
Upper	Oxfordian					Swift Formation	Louann Salt	Oxford Clay	Malm
Middle	Callovian		Entrada	Stump Formation / Preuss Formation	Sundance Formation	Rierden Formation	Werner Formation	Kelloways Beds	Dogger
Middle	Bathonian		Carmel / Page	Twin Creek Formation				Cornbrash Beds	Dogger
Middle	Bathonian					Sawtooth Formation		Great Oolite	Dogger
Middle	Bajocian			Gypsum Spring				Inferior Oolite	Dogger
Middle	Aalian							Inferior Oolite	Dogger
Lower	Toarcian		Navajo Sandstone					Upper Lias	Lias
Lower	Pliensbachian		Kayenta Formation					Middle Lias	Lias
Lower	Sinemurian		Moenave (Wingate) Formation					Lower Lias	Lias
Lower	Hettangian							Lower Lias	Lias
(Below) →		(Triassic)	(Triassic)	(Triassic)	(Triassic)	(Triassic)	(Triassic)	(Triassic)	

Note: "Fernie Group" appears as a vertical label spanning the S. Alberta column.

A9   JURASSIC

	A.						B.	

Series	Stages	California	Colorado	Montana	South Dakota	Alberta	East Texas	Maryland	England
		(Tertiary)	(Tertiary)	(Tertiary)	(Tertiary)	(Tertiary)	(Tertiary)	(Tertiary)	(Tertiary)
Upper	Maestrichtian		Animas	Hell Creek	Hell Creek	Edmonton	Navarro Group	Monmouth	
	Campanian	Franciscan Sequence	McDermott / Kirkland / Fruitland / Picture Cliffs / Lewis / Mesa Verde	Fox Hills / Bearpaw / Judith River / Parkman / Claggett / Eagle / Telegraph Creek (Montana Group)	Fox Hills / Pierre Shale	Bearpaw / Belly River / Wapiabi (Alberta Group)	Taylor Group	Matawan	Upper Chalk
	Santonian		Mancos Shale	Niobrara (Colorado Shale)	Niobrara	Cardium	Austin Chalk	Magothy	
	Coniacian								
	Turonian			Carlile	Benton Formation	Blackstone	Eagle Ford Formation		Middle Chalk
	Cenomanian		Dakota Sandstone	Greenhorn / Belle Fourche / Mowry Shale		Buda Limestone / Del Rio Clay	Woodbine Formation	Raritan	Lower Chalk
Lower	Albian			Muddy Sandstone / Thermopolis Shale	Dakota Sandstone	Blairmore	Edwards		Upper Greensand
	Aptian		Burro Canyon	Kootenay		Rodessa / James / Pine Island	Glen Rose	Patapsco	Lower Greensand
	Barremian (Neocomian)						Sligo (Pettett)	Arundel	
	Hauterivian (Neocomian)					Travis Peak (Hosston)	Patuxent (Potomac Group)	Wealden
	Valanginian (Neocomian)								
	Berriasian (Neocomian)					Kootenay			
(Below) →		(Jurassic)	(Jurassic)	(Jurassic)	(Jurassic)	(Jurassic)	(Jurassic)	(Jurassic)	(Jurassic)

A10 CRETACEOUS

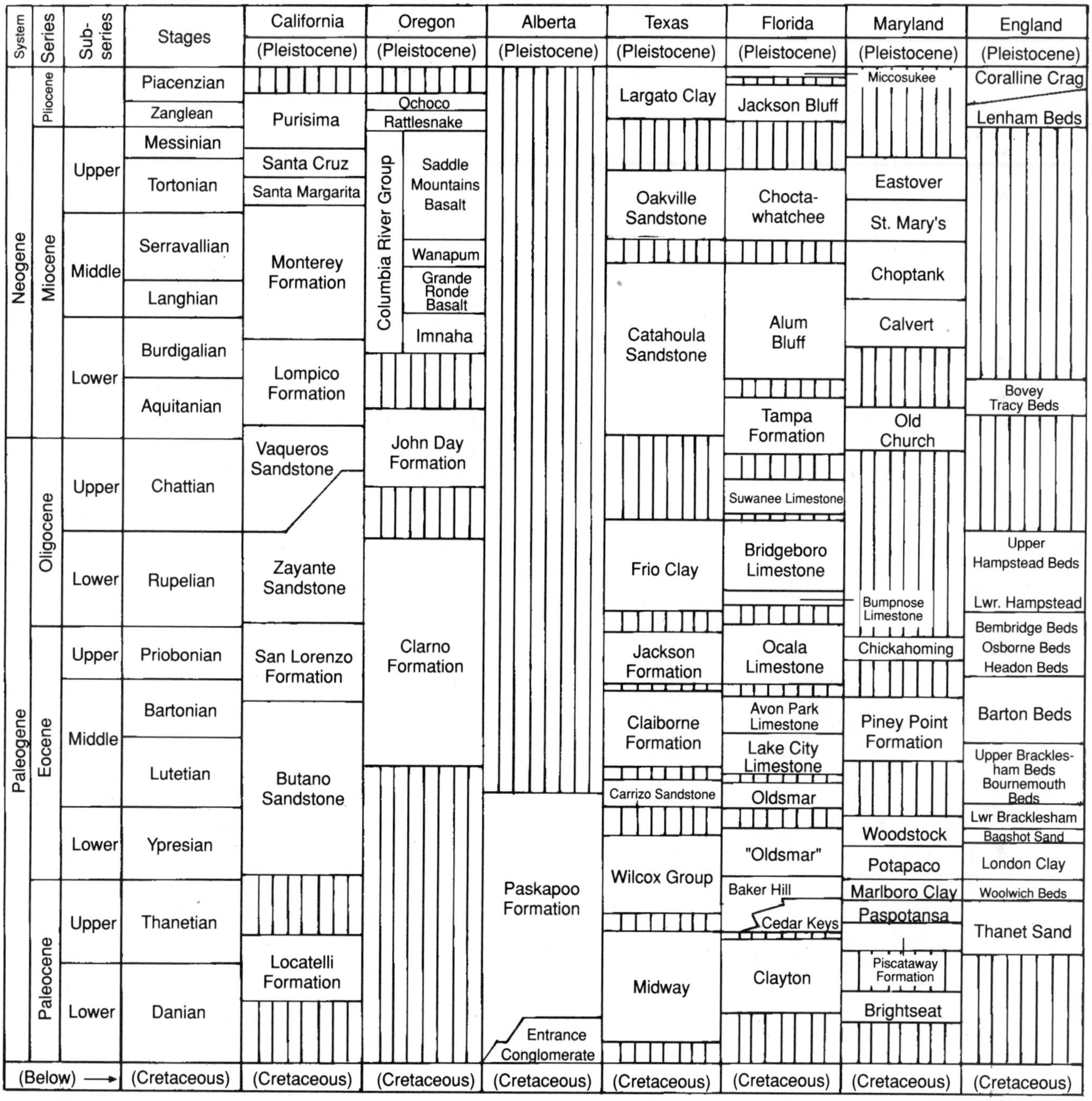

System	Series	Sub-series	Stages	California	Oregon	Alberta	Texas	Florida	Maryland	England
				(Pleistocene)	(Pleistocene)	(Pleistocene)	(Pleistocene)	(Pleistocene)	(Pleistocene)	(Pleistocene)
Neogene	Pliocene		Piacenzian	Purisima	Ochoco		Largato Clay	Jackson Bluff	Miccosukee	Coralline Crag
			Zanglean		Rattlesnake					Lenham Beds
	Miocene	Upper	Messinian	Santa Cruz	Saddle Mountains Basalt		Oakville Sandstone	Choctawhatchee	Eastover	
			Tortonian	Santa Margarita					St. Mary's	
		Middle	Serravallian	Monterey Formation	Wanapum		Catahoula Sandstone	Alum Bluff	Choptank	
			Langhian		Grande Ronde Basalt				Calvert	
		Lower	Burdigalian	Lompico Formation	Imnaha					Bovey Tracy Beds
			Aquitanian					Tampa Formation	Old Church	
Paleogene	Oligocene	Upper	Chattian	Vaqueros Sandstone	John Day Formation		Frio Clay	Suwanee Limestone		Upper Hampstead Beds
		Lower	Rupelian	Zayante Sandstone				Bridgeboro Limestone	Bumpnose Limestone	Lwr. Hampstead
									Chickahoming	Bembridge Beds / Osborne Beds / Headon Beds
	Eocene	Upper	Priobonian	San Lorenzo Formation	Clarno Formation		Jackson Formation	Ocala Limestone		Barton Beds
		Middle	Bartonian	Butano Sandstone			Claiborne Formation	Avon Park Limestone	Piney Point Formation	Upper Bracklesham Beds / Bournemouth Beds
			Lutetian					Lake City Limestone		Lwr Bracklesham
		Lower	Ypresian				Carrizo Sandstone	Oldsmar	Woodstock	Bagshot Sand / London Clay
	Paleocene	Upper	Thanetian	Locatelli Formation		Paskapoo Formation	Wilcox Group	"Oldsmar"	Potapaco	Woolwich Beds
								Baker Hill	Marlboro Clay / Paspotansa	Thanet Sand
								Cedar Keys		
		Lower	Danian				Midway	Clayton	Piscataway Formation / Brightseat	
						Entrance Conglomerate				
(Below) →				(Cretaceous)	(Cretaceous)	(Cretaceous)	(Cretaceous)	(Cretaceous)	(Cretaceous)	(Cretaceous)

A11 CENOZOIC

Note: Oregon Miocene/Pliocene columns include the "Columbia River Group" vertical label spanning the Saddle Mountains Basalt, Wanapum, Grande Ronde Basalt, and Imnaha units.

Appendix B
Classification of Organisms

Kingdom MONERA (unicellular: nonnucleated cell structure)

Division[1] Schizoycophyta—bacteria; Archean-Holocene

Division Cyanophyta—cyanobacteria (blue-green bacteria), stromatolites; Archean-Holocene

Kingdom PROTISTAE (unicellular: nucleated cell structure)

Phylym Protozoa

Class Sarcodina

Order Foraminiferoida—foraminifera; most commonly with calcareous tests; Cambrian-Holocene; planktonic forms—Cretaceous-Holocene

Family Fusulinidae—fusulinids; Mississippian-Permian

Order Radiolaroida—radiolarians; siliceous, perforate shell; Cambrian-Holocene

Kingdom FUNGI

Division Zygomycota

Division Ascomycota

Division Basidiomycota

Kingdom PLANTAE (unicellular and multicellular [metaphyte]: nucleated cell structure; photosynthetic)

Subkingdom Thallophyta—primarily aquatic forms lacking true root systems; some unicellular algal groups

Division Chlorophycophyta—green algae; Archean(?)-Holocene

Division Rhodophycophyta—red algae; Archean(?)-Holocene

Division Phaeophycophyta—brown algae (seaweeds); Archean-Holocene

Division Chrysophycophyta—diatoms; Jurassic(?)-Holocene

Division Euglenophycophyta—euglenids; Cretaceous-Holocene

Division Charophycophyta—charophytes; Silurian-Holocene

Subkingdom Embryophyta—terrestrial plants

Division Rhyniophyta—Silurian-Devonian

Division Zosterophyllophyta—Silurian-Devonian

Division Psilophyta—Devonian-Holocene

Division Microphyllophyta—club mosses; Devonian-Holocene

Division Arthrophyta—horsetails and sphenopsids; Devonian-Holocene

Division Pteridophyta—ferns; Devonian-Holocene

Division Pteridospermophyta—seed ferns; Devonian-Jurassic

Division Coniferophyta—conifers; Devonian(?)-Holocene

Division Cycadophyta—cycads; Mississippian(?)-Holocene

Division Ginkgophyta—maidenhair tree; Pennsylvanian(?)-Holocene

Division Gnetophyta—Permian(?)-Holocene

Division Anthophyta—flowering plants; Triassic(?)-Holocene

Kingdom ANIMALIA (multicellular [metazoan]:
    nucleated cell structure;
    nonphotosynthetic)
Phylum Porifera—sponges; Cambrian-Holocene
    including the stromatoporoids—important
    mid-Paleozoic, lime-secreting reef
    builders
Phylum Archaeocyatha—soft-tissue structure
    unknown; conical, double-walled skeleton;
    extinct; Early and Middle Cambrian
Phylum Cnidaria—Ediacarian(?); Cambrian-
    Holocene
    Class Anthozoa—corals and sea anemones
        Order Tabulata—extinct forms without (or
        with poorly developed) septa; horizontal
        tabulae supported the animal; important
        contributors to Paleozoic reefs;
        Ordovician-Permian
        Order Rugosa—extinct forms with septal
        development; includes horn corals; major
        Paleozoic reef builders; Ordovician-
        Triassic
        Order Scleractinia—coral reef builders of
        Mesozoic and Cenozoic times;
        predominantly colonial types; Triassic-
        Holocene
    Class Hydrozoa
    Class Scyphozoa—jellyfishes
Phylum Bryozoa—colonial encrusting or branching
    forms; Ordovician-Holocene
Phylum Brachiopoda—marine forms with bivalved
    shell; Cambrian-Holocene
    Class Inarticulata—two valves lacking tooth-and-
    socket hinge structure; chitino-phosphatic
    shell composition; Cambrian-Holocene
    Class Articulata—two valves with well-developed
    hinge structure; typically calcareous shell;
    Cambrian-Holocene
Phylum Mollusca—diverse group of both fossil and
    modern forms; Cambrian-Holocene
    Class Bivalvia—two-hinged, mirror-image shells;
    muscular, creeping foot; clams, oysters,
    scallops; Cambrian-Holocene
    Class Gastropoda—most with single, coiled shell;
    muscular, creeping foot; distinct head;
    snails; Cambrian-Holocene
    Class Cephalopoda—shelled or shell-less forms;
    shelled forms commonly with chambers
    and sutures; jet-propulsion system of
    locomotion; extinct ammonoids comprise
    one of the most important guide-fossil
    groups; late Cambrian-Holocene
        Subclass Nautiloidea—Cambrian-Holocene
        Subclass Ammonoidea—fluted sutures
        Subclass Coleoidea—Mississippian-Holocene
        Order Belemnoidea—belemnites;
        Mississippian-Eocene
    Class Scaphopoda—curved, tusk-shaped shells
    open at both ends; common as Cenozoic
    fossils; Ordovician-Holocene
    Class Polyplacophora—segmented shell of the
    chiton; Cambrian-Holocene
    Class Monoplacophora—conical shell, typically
    with several pairs of muscle scars on its
    inner surface; biologically an important
    form, suggesting common ancestry of
    mollusks, annelids, and arthropods;
    Cambrian-Holocene

Phylum Annelida—segmented worms (earthworm an example); trace fossils as burrows and trails; Ediacarian(?); Cambrian-Holocene

Phylum Arthropoda—segmented bodies and jointed appendages; diverse forms; most abundant phylum—80 percent of all known animals; Ediacarian(?); Cambrian-Holocene

Class Trilobita—trilobites; Cambrian-Permian

Class Crustacea—ostracodes, barnacles, lobsters, and crabs; Cambrian-Holocene

Class Insecta—insects; relatively rare as fossils, although the most abundant of living invertebrate classes; Silurian-Holocene

Class Arachnoidea—including spiders

6 Order Eurypterida—eurypterids; Ordovician-Permian

Phylum Echinodermata—internal skeleton; commonly, five-rayed symmetry; Ediacarian(?); Cambrian-Holocene

Subphylum Crinozoa—mainly sessile (attached to the sea floor) echinoderms

4 Class Crinoidea—crinoids; Ordovician-Holocene

Subphylum Echinozoa—mainly vagrant (not attached) echinoderms; Ordovician-Holocene

Class Echinoidea—sea urchins; Ordovician-Holocene

Class Asteroidea—starfish; Ordovician-Holocene

Phylum Hemichordata—some affinity to chordates; small, dorsal stiffening rod

4 Class Graptolithina—graptolites; Cambrian-Mississippian

Phylum Chordata—most often, with a segmented vertebral column, as in subphylum Vertebrata; diverse; Ordovician-Holocene

Subphylum Vertebrata

Class Agnatha—jawless fish; Ordovician-Holocene

Class Placodermii—primitive armored fish; Ordovician-Mississippian

Class Chondrichthys—cartilaginous fish (sharks and rays); Silurian-Holocene

Class Acanthodii—may be ancestral to bony fish; spiny sharks; Silurian-Permian

Class Osteichthys—bony fish; Silurian-Holocene

Class Amphibia—amphibians; water-dependent stages in life cycle; Devonian-Holocene

Class Reptilia—reptiles; Pennsylvanian-Holocene

Subclass Anapsida—includes turtles; Pennsylvanian-Holocene

Subclass Synapsida—includes extinct pelycosaurs and therapsids; Pennsylvanian-Triassic

Subclass Euryapsida—extinct marine forms, including icthyosaurs and plesiosaurs; Triassic-Cretaceous

Subclass Diapsida—most diverse subclass; includes lizards, snakes, crocodiles, extinct thecodonts, dinosaurs, pterosaurs; Triassic-Holocene

Class Mammalia—mammals; Triassic-Holocene

Subclass uncertain—includes docodonts and triconodonts; Triassic-Jurassic

Subclass Protoheria—monotremes; Pleistocene(?)-Holocene

Subclass Allotheria—includes multituberculates; Jurassic-Eocene

Subclass Theria—includes symmetrodonts, marsupials, insectivores, pantotheres, and all Cenozoic placental; Jurassic-Holocene

Class Aves—birds; Jurassic(?); Cretaceous-Holocene

Glossary

The Key Terms listed in each chapter are defined in this Glossary, as are numerous other geological terms. Most of the terms listed here are also found in the Glossary of Geology by R. L. Bates and J. A. Jackson (3d ed., 1987), published by the American Geological Institute. Italicized words within definitions are themselves defined elsewhere in the Glossary.

Absaroka sequence
A widespread succession of Pennsylvanian and Permian sediments overlying a regional unconformity that cuts across rocks of Mississippian age or older. In form, its upper boundary is a regional unconformity overlain by sediments of the *Zuni sequence*, containing rocks of Middle Jurassic age and younger.

absolute time scale
Geologic time scale measured in real time—that is, in years before the present (BP), where the present is defined as A.D. 1950. Ages determined by *isotopic dating* methods give real-time dates.

abyssal plain
The flattest part of the deep ocean floor at depths of around 4000 to 5000 meters. Formed by the blanketing effect of *turbidity current* and *pelagic* deposition over older topographic features.

Acadian orogeny
A mountain-building episode, or possibly several episodes, in the northern Appalachians during the Devonian and caused by the collision of the Baltic craton with the North American craton, marking the final closing of the *Iapetus Ocean*. One or more microcontinental slivers may also have been involved.

Acanthodian
A fish belonging to a subclass of the Osteichthys (bony fishes) and including the earliest jawed fishes. Ranged from the Late Silurian to the Early Devonian.

accumulation clock
An *isotopic* age determination method that depends upon the measurement of the ratio of the accumulated radiogenic *daughter isotope* to that of the *parent isotope*.

acritarch
Unicellular, thick-walled, microscopic organism of doubtful affinities, although many are probably of algal origin. An artificial group embracing fossils from Precambrian to Recent.

active continental margin
Collision plate margin close or adjacent to a *subduction zone*. Characterized by vulcanism and compressional and thrust tectonics.

actualism
The uniform control of geologic processes by the actual laws of nature that are invariant as to character and rate of operation.

adaptation
A feature of an organism that better enables it to live in its environment.

adaptive radiation
The expansion of organisms arising from a common ancestral stock into new habitats. Typically is reflected in numerous speciation events.

aeolian
Pertaining to the wind (for example, aeolian dunes of windblown sand). Also spelled *eolian*.

aerobic organism
Organism that can only function in the presence of oxygen.

age
Time (geochronologic) division smaller than an *epoch*. The time represented by the time stratigraphic (chronostratigraphic) unit *stage*.

Agnatha
Jawless fishes, including living lampreys and hagfishes and the extinct *ostracoderms*.

algal mat
Interwoven mass of various species of algae (mostly *cyanobacteria*) that forms

a skinlike coating on the surface of sediments in shallow marine, intertidal, *lacustrine,* and similar environments.

Allegheny orogeny
The orogenic event that deformed the rocks of the central and southern Appalachians during the Pennsylvanian and Early Permian.

allopatric species
A species that is geographically isolated from other species.

alluvial
Pertaining to river deposits.

alluvium
Sediment deposited by a stream.

alpha particle
Helium nucleus (of two protons and two neutrons) emitted from an atomic nucleus during *radioactive decay.*

Alpine orogeny
Episode of mountain building affecting southern Europe and northern Africa during the Late Mesozoic-Cenozoic.

amber
Fossilized resin, the yellowish, sticky substance that oozes from the bark of coniferous trees.

amino acid racemization
A dating method depending upon the chemical transformation of *amino acids* from organisms. After death, there is a slow, time-dependent change (racemization) from one type of amino acid to another.

amino acids
The building blocks of proteins. Consist of various configurations of carbon, hydrogen, oxygen, and nitrogen.

ammonoid
An extinct group of cephalopods with chambered shells that typically were coiled in a plano-spiral (watch spring).

amniotic (cleiodic) egg
An egg in which the growing embryo is nourished and protected by such structures as the yolk, amnion, and allantois. The type of egg produced by reptiles, birds, and monotremes.

amphibian
Vertebrates that use gills in the early stages of development but lungs as adults. Like reptiles, they are cold-blooded; unlike reptiles, however, they require water in which to reproduce.

anaerobic organism
An organism that can function in an environment with no oxygen (*anoxic* environment).

angular unconformity
An *unconformity* in which the upper (younger) strata lie upon a surface eroded across a lower (older) succession of strata that were folded and tilted prior to erosion.

ankylosaur
Armored *ornithischian* dinosaur of Cretaceous age.

anoxic
Oxygen deficient.

anthropoid
The primate group that includes monkeys, apes, and humans.

Anthropoidea
The suborder of primates that includes the monkeys, apes, and humans.

Antler orogeny
Late Devonian to Mississippian mountain-building episode that affected part of the Cordilleran *mobile belt* extending from central Nevada to southwestern Alberta.

aphelion
When the earth is farthest from the sun, it is said to be at aphelion.

Apollo object
General term for earth-orbit-intersecting meteorite, larger than 10 kilometers in diameter.

Archaeocyatha
Phylum containing primitive spongelike animals. Ranged from the Lower through Middle Cambrian.

Archean Eon
The early part of the Precambrian, beginning about 4.0 billion years ago (the date of the earliest dateable minerals) and ending 2.5 billion years ago.

Archimedes Limestone
Early name for Mississippian limestones of the midcontinent region. So-called for the great abundance of the bryozoan *Archimedes.*

argillite
Slightly metamorphosed argillaceous (clayey) sediment, such as shale, but with no developed slaty cleavage.

arkose
Sandstone in which feldspar is the dominant mineral. Typically derived from weathering of nearby granite.

articulate brachiopod
Brachiopod with teeth and sockets along the hinge line and that articulate with each other.

Artiodactyla
Order of herbivorous mammals, including goats, pigs, sheep, camels, bison, deer, and musk-oxen. The so-called even-toed *ungulates.*

asthenosphere
That part of the upper mantle lying below the *lithosphere.* Known to seismologists as the "low-velocity channel." It behaves as plastic, and this is where the convectional movement involved in the plate-tectonic mechanism is believed to occur.

atomic number
Number of protons in the nucleus of an atom.

atomic weight
The average relative weight of the *isotopes* of a given element, as compared with carbon-12, the accepted standard.

autotroph
An organism that synthesizes nutrients from inorganic substances. Bacteria and plants that do this by utilizing sunlight as an energy source in a photosynthetic process are termed photoautotrophs.

Avalonian terrane
One of the *exotic terranes* within the Appalachian region. Named after the Avalon Peninsula of southeastern Newfoundland and believed to have been derived by rifting of African (Gondwana) crust.

backarc
In an arc-trench system, refers to structural features on the sides of volcanoes and away from the trench.

background extinction
The continuous extinction of a small proportion of species within a fauna or flora. They are replaced by new species that appear as a consequence of ongoing speciation events.

back reef
Sheltered, shallow lagoon on the shoreward side of a barrier reef.

Baltica
A Paleozoic craton comprising Russia west of the Ural mountains, Poland, north and central Germany, and Scandinavia.

banded iron formation (BIF)
Interlaminations of ferric iron oxide (dominantly hematite) and *chert*.

barrier beach
Beach ridge separated from the mainland by a narrow and shallow lagoon or by tidal marshes. See also *barrier island*.

barrier island
Essentially the same as a barrier beach. Normally, barrier islands are segments of a barrier beach that is cut by tidal inlets. See also *barrier beach*.

basal transgressive sand
During a *marine transgression,* the sand reworked as the coastal zone advances across the land.

basement
The oldest rocks in an area and that underlie younger successions. Basement rocks are often complexly folded, intruded, faulted, and/or metamorphosed. Typically, they lie below a marked erosional discontinuity and are genetically unrelated to the rocks above. In many cases, they are of Precambrian age.

basin
The site of deposition of great thicknesses of sediment, often with indications of prolonged structural downsagging.

Basin and Range Province
Physiographic province in the southwestern United States and adjacent Mexico characterized by tilted fault blocks, typically elongated in a north-south direction, and which form highland areas with lowland basins between.

Beck Springs Formation
Proterozoic formation of southern California containing what is claimed to be the first fossil evidence for *eukaryote* cells.

bed
Layer or stratum of sedimentary rock. The smallest formal *lithostratigraphic* unit. Beds thinner than 1 centimeter are often called *laminae.*

bedding plane
Surface of a bed. The plane of *stratification.*

benthic
Adjective referring to *benthos.*

benthos
Bottom-dwelling organisms that live on a sea floor or lake bed (*epifauna*) or burrow below the sediment-water interface (*infauna*). *Sessile* benthos are attached in their adult life (for example, corals); vagrant benthos move about.

bentonite
Clay derived from alteration of volcanic ash.

beta particle
Electron emitted during *radioactive decay.*

bioclast
A fragment of skeletal material incorporated in sediment.

biocoenosis
A life assemblage. A group of animals (or plants) that lived together. See also *thanatocoenosis.*

biofacies
That aspect of a rock concerned only with its fossil content rather than its lithologic features. See also *lithofacies.*

biogenic
Referring to any sediment or structure in a sediment produced by organic activity.

bioherm
A reefoid rock mass built from the skeletal remains of organisms and having a moundlike form.

biostratigraphic unit
A body of rock defined on the basis of its fossil content. The basic unit is a *biozone.*

biostratigraphy
The study of *stratigraphy* as it relates to the *fossils* contained in the rocks. Fossils' most important function is as a means of establishing time correlation.

bioturbation
Mixing and disturbance of sediment by organisms—typically, burrowing *infaunal* species.

biozone
Succession of sediments characterized by the presence of one or more species or other taxa. The fundamental *biostratigraphic unit.*

bipedal
Walking on two legs. See also *quadrupedal.*

bittern salts
Salts precipitated from seawater in the final stages of evaporation when little water remains. Include magnesium sulfate, magnesium chloride, calcium chloride, and various iodides and bromides.

Bitter Springs Formation
Australian Proterozoic formation containing what is claimed to be the first direct evidence of sexual reproduction.

Bivalvia
Class of the phylum Mollusca. Contains aquatic animals that secrete a calcareous exoskeleton, consisting of two valves that articulate along a hinge line. Also known as pelecypoda.

black dwarf
The burnt-out cinder of a star after it has expended all of its nuclear fuel.

blocking temperature
In a cooling igneous rock body, the temperature at which a mineral containing radioactive *isotopes* becomes a closed system and there is no further leakage of *daughter isotopes.*

Brachiopoda
Phylum of marine animals that secrete two valves. All are *sessile benthic* in habit.

bracketing
The determination of relative ages in the relationship between igneous intrusions and country rock. Thus, a sedimentary rock is older than the igneous body that intrudes it, but younger than any rock that it overlies.

Bryozoa
Phylum of colonial animals of small size that form branching, lacy, or encrusting colonies. May locally be minor *reef* builders.

Burgess Shale
Thin, black-shale member of Middle Cambrian age in British Columbia. Contains unusually well-preserved invertebrate fossils, the majority of unknown affinities.

Burgess Shale fauna
The *fossils* of the *Burgess Shale*.

Bushveld Complex
Major basic intrusion in the Precambrian of southern Africa.

Caledonian orogeny
A mountain-building episode during the Silurian and Early Devonian resulting from the collision of part of the Baltic craton with the northern margin of the North American/Greenland craton. It produced the Caledonide mountain chain that today extends from Ireland, through Scotland, to Norway and Sweden.

Canadian Shield
The largest expanse of exposed Precambrian rocks in the world. Underlies most of central and northern Canada. Also known as the Laurentian Shield.

Cannonball Sea
A relict of the Late Cretaceous sea that covered large areas of western North America apparently survived into the late Early Paleocene. It is marked by the Cannonball Formation, a marine unit of glauconitic sands and shales isolated within and surrounded by nonmarine units in central North Dakota and surrounding areas. Connections to the Pacific and/or the Gulf of Mexico are problematic.

Capitan Reef
Massive basin-margin reef in the Permian basin area of west Texas. Of Middle Permian (Guadalupian) age, it is built primarily of sponges, algae, and bryozoans.

carbon-14 (radiocarbon) dating
A dating method based on measuring the carbon-12 to carbon-14 ratio in samples of charcoal wood, shells, calcareous cave deposits, and so on.

carbonate coastline
A coastline dominated by *reefs* built up by lime-secreting organisms, such as corals and algae, and typically also with shallow-water carbonate clastic shoals.

carbonate platform
Extensive, shallow-water area of carbonate deposition. Sediments may include *reefs,* oolite shoals, and fecal-pellet muds.

carbonate rock
General term for limestone, consisting of calcite and/or aragonite, $CaCO_3$, and *dolostone* consisting of dolomite $CaMg(CO_3)_2$.

carbonate zone
Depth zone where carbonate sediments preferentially accumulate.

cast
The infilling of a *mold* by a secondary mineral or by sediment.

catastrophism
The doctrine that earth's history has been marked by a succession of catastrophic endings and new creations.

Catskill Delta
A large, clastic wedge of *molasse* deposits derived from the highlands produced by the Acadian orogeny in the northern Appalachians. The sediments are of middle Late Devonian age and extend westward into Pennsylvania and western New York.

Ceboidea
The New World monkeys.

Central Basin Uplift
Positive region lying between the Delaware and Midland basins of the West Texas area during the Permian.

Cephalopoda
Class of the phylum Mollusca. Includes octopus, squid, nautilus, and the extinct ammonoids.

Cercopithecoidea
The Old World monkeys.

cetacean
Whale or porpoise.

chalk
A fine-grained variety of limestone dominantly made up of the calcareous tests of microscopic marine planktonic organisms, typically the *coccolithophoridae.* Color is invariably white to pale gray.

Charnian fauna
Fossils in the Late Proterozoic of the Charnwood area of central England.

chelogenic cycle
Cycle of *orogenies* that resulted in the accretions of a *craton.* Literally, a *shield*-forming cycle.

Chengjiang assemblage
Fossils in the Middle Cambrian of the Chengjiang area of China. Similar to but a little older than the *Burgess Shale fauna.*

chert
Amorphous or cryptocrystalline silica. Most typically occurs as nodules in limestones or as beds in shale successions.

Chinle Formation
A formation consisting of varicolored shales, sandstones, and conglomerates deposited in an *alluvial* environment in Late Triassic time in the northern Arizona and adjacent areas. It is the formation that outcrops in the Painted Desert and that contains the silicified tree trunks in the Petrified Forest of Arizona.

chitino-phosphatic shell
Shell made up of phosphorus-rich chitin.

choana
Third nostril opening in the skull.

Choanicthyes
Group of fishes that includes *crossopterygians* and *dipnoans.*

Chondricthyes
The cartilaginous fishes, including sharks, skates, and rays.

chondrostei
The most primitive of the three infraclasses of the bony fishes. This group dominated the fish faunas from Devonian through the Permian. A few forms survive to the present day.

chronostratigraphic unit
Time-rock unit. A body of rock formed during a specific period of time and bounded by *isochronous* surfaces. Used as the basis for defining a specific time interval.

Churchill Province
One of the major *tectonic provinces* of the Canadian Shield.

cladogenesis
Speciation by phylogenetic splitting or branching.

clast
Piece or fragment of an older rock derived by weathering and breakdown.

clastic
Pertaining to a sedimentary rock or sediment composed of broken fragments derived from preexisting rocks or minerals.

clay
General term for hydrous aluminum silicate minerals. Related to the micas. Typically, the crystals are small (average 2 to 4 microns).

Cnidaria
Phylum that includes jellyfishes, hydrozoa, and corals. Also known as Coelenterata.

coacervate
Substance with a tendency to form discrete droplets.

coal ball
A mineralized concretion occurring within a coal bed. Often contains well-preserved plant fossils.

coalification
The process whereby peat is turned into coal as a consequence of increasing heat and pressure as it becomes more deeply buried.

coesite
A high-pressure form of quartz. Considered diagnostic of impact-crater origin.

Colorado Plateau
Extensive area of uplifted but largely undeformed rocks centered on the Four Corners region. Characterized by deep canyons (including the Grand Canyon) and many Late Cenozoic volcanic centers.

Columbia Plateau
Plateau area in the northwestern United States built up of successive outpourings of basaltic lavas that are over 2,800 meters thick in places.

concordant
Describes strata that are parallel and structurally *conformable*, but within which there may be a *hiatus*.

concordia
Time curve joining graphed points plotted for ages derived from the ratios of lead-208/uranium-238 and lead-207/ uranium-235 values.

concurrent range zone
Stratigraphic interval between the first appearance of one taxon and the last appearance of a second or additional taxa—that is, the interval of overlap of two or more ranges. Hence, it is sometimes called an overlap zone.

condylarth
Early herbivorous mammal, the most primitive of the *ungulates*. Characteristic of the Paleocene.

conformable
Describes strata that lie one above the other in parallel and apparently continuous succession. There may be evidence of some interruption in sediment accumulation, provided no erosion or disturbance of the earlier strata occurred.

connate water
Water trapped in the pore spaces of sedimentary grains at the time they were first deposited in a *subaqueous* environment.

conodont
Small, toothlike fossil derived from an animal believed to have been an eel-like pelagic hemichordate.

continental drift
The change in position of continents as they travel on the moving surface of *lithospheric plates*.

continental margin
The sea floor between the shoreline and the deep ocean floor. Includes the *continental shelf, continental slope,* and *continental rise.*

continental rise
Gently sloping surface that extends up from the *abyssal plain* to the foot of the *continental slope.*

continental shelf
Gently inclined submerged margin of the continent. Extends from the shoreline to where there is a sudden increase in slope (the shelf break), typically at about 200 meters depth.

continental slope
Sloping surface lying between the *continental shelf* and the *continental rise.*

convection cell
In a liquid, the internal movement consequent on differential heating.

convergent evolution
Over time, groups from different ancestral stocks may come to look more and more like each other as a consequence of progressive *adaptations* to a similar environment. For example, porpoises, icthyosaurs, and fishes.

convergent plate boundary
The boundary between two plates that are approaching one another through plate-tectonic convectional movement.

coprolite
Fossilized feces.

Cordilleran orogeny
General term to cover a series of orogenic episodes affecting the *mobile belt* of the western margin of the North American craton from Jurassic into the Early Cenozoic. Three separate phases have been identified; the *Nevadan, Sevier,* and *Laramide* orogenies.

Cotylosaur
Member of the order Cotylosauria, originally considered primitive reptiles, now classified as amphibians.

craton
Central stable core or nucleus of ancient *basement* rocks of a continental block, consisting of exposed *shield* areas and adjacent *platforms* covered by younger sediments and/or modern shallow-marine water.

Crinoidea
Division of phylum Echinodermata. The cup-shaped animal has an upper surface surrounded by tentacle-like arms. Most species are attached to the seabed by a long, articulated stem.

Cro-Magnon man
The name given to the earliest examples of modern man. Anatomically, almost identical to present-day Europeans.

cross-bedding
Inclined beds of sediment laid down by water currents or the wind, each bed lying downstream (or downwind) from the previously laid bed.

Crossopterygians
The group of *choanicthyan* lobe-finned fishes ancestral to the *amphibians.*

Curie point
During the cooling of a melt or cooling after metamorphism, the temperature at which a magnetic mineral acquires *thermoremanent magnetism.*

Cutler Formation
A *redbed* formation of Permian age found in the Four Corners region of Colorado, Utah, Arizona, and New Mexico.

cyanobacteria
Unicellular or multicellular photosynthesizing organisms containing chlorophyll. Formerly termed blue-green algae, they are the group mainly responsible for the formation of *stromatolites.*

cyclical uniformitarianism
The uniformitarian idea modified to suggest that the essential continuity implied in the concept is manifested in recurring cycles, rather than as a straight line.

cyclothem
Sedimentary unit laid down during a single cycle of deposition. Each cycle is usually one of a series of rhythmically repeated changes in the environment, such as water depth, alteration of brackish and marine conditions, sediment supply, and so on. The presence of coal was implicit in earlier definitions based on Pennsylvanian examples.

daughter isotope
The radiogenic *isotope* produced by decay of a radioactive element.

decay clock
An *isotopic* age determination method that depends upon the measurement of the amount of a radioactive *isotope* remaining after a given interval of decay.

decay constant
Constant value for each radioactive *isotope* that is a measure of the rate of spontaneous *radioactive decay*.

decay series
The succession of *daughter isotopes* that appears during the decay of a radioactive element until a stable isotope is reached.

decollement
Compressional deformation feature associated particularly with thrust structures when rocks above a plane of weakness (the decollement surface) break away or are detached from the rock below and exhibit their own style of deformation different from the rock below the plane of detachment.

Delaware Basin
A northwest-southeast trending basin that existed in the West Texas area during the Permian.

delta
An accumulation of alluvial sand and mud at the mouth of a river.

depositional cycle
Normally, a single cycle of sea-level rise (*marine transgression*) and fall (*marine regression*), particularly as it pertains to the resultant sedimentary envelope.

depositional progradation
Outward building of the coastline by sediment accumulation.

derived fossil
Fossil originating in an older formation and which has been weathered out and redeposited in a younger formation.

desert
An arid region with less than 25 cm (10 inches) of rainfall per year.

detrital magnetism
Remanent magnetism in sedimentary grains of magnetic minerals aligns the grains with the direction of the main field at the time and place of deposition of the sediment.

diachronous
Said of a rock unit or geologic boundary that is of different ages in different places—that is, is time-transgressive.

diagenesis
Encompasses all changes—chemical, physical, and biological—that occur in a sediment subsequent to its deposition but prior to its destruction by weathering or alteration by *metamorphism*.

diamictite
Poorly sorted, coarse, clastic deposit.

diastem
Relatively brief interruption in sedimentation, typically with no removal of previously deposited sediment.

diastrophic cycle
Cycle of crustal unrest or mountain building.

diatom
Unicellular plant of the class Bacillariophyceae. Of microscopic size, diatoms secrete a frustule (supporting structure) of silica and are found in both marine and freshwater environments.

dike swarm
Large number of subparallel dikes. Typically of regional extent and likely related to an episode of crustal tension.

Dipnoi
The order to which lungfishes belong.

disconformity
An *unconformity* that demonstrates a marked *hiatus* within a sedimentary succession but in which the *beds* below and above the break are parallel.

discordia
The curve formed when the lead-206/uranium-238 ratio is graphed against the lead-207/uranium-235 ratio.

divergent plate boundary
The boundary between two lithospheric plates that are moving apart. Also termed a spreading center, such a boundary is characterized by a tensional structural style and vulcanicity. On the ocean floor, spreading centers are where new oceanic crust is formed.

DNA molecule
A molecule of deoxyribonucleic acid, the genetic material of all organisms.

dolomitization
In limestones, the transformation of calcite into the mineral dolomite. The rock is then termed a *dolostone*.

dolomitization
The partial or complete conversion of limestone to dolomitic limestone or *dolostone*. The process involves the replacement of the original calcium carbonate by magnesium carbonate.

dolostone
A sedimentary rock composed of more than 50 percent of the mineral dolomite $(CaMg(CO_3)_2)$.

drift
A general term applied to all sediment transported by ice or by meltwater emanating from a glacier.

dropstone
A large *clast* dropped into deep-water deposits after release from floating ice that has melted.

drowned coastline
A coastline with morphology caused by rising sea level. Typically with *barrier beaches* and *barrier islands*. Deeply indented estuaries mark the drowned lower reaches of rivers.

dryopithecus
Generic name for species belonging to the Dryopithecidae, a family of apelike species found in Africa from the Early to Late Miocene and in Europe in the Middle to Late Miocene.

Echinoidea
Division of the phylum Echinodermata. Includes sea urchins and sand dollars.

echo sounder
An instrument that measures the depth to the bottom of a lake or ocean by recording the travel time of sound waves emitted from a vessel and reflected back from the bottom.

ecologic niche
The place of a species or population within its environment.

ecology
The study of the relationship between organisms and their environment.

ectothermic
Describes an animal with a variable body temperature. These are the so-called "cold-blooded" animals that acquire heat from their environment. See also *endothermic.*

Ediacaran fauna
General term for a Late Proterozoic fauna of *metazoans,* many of doubtful affinities. Named after the Ediacara Hills of South Australia.

effect hypothesis
The idea that a given area is able to support numerous, highly specialized species, but only one or two generalized species. Essentially, it involves the competition for food.

electron
Small, subatomic particle with a negative charge that revolves around the atomic nucleus.

electron spin resonance
Dating method utilizing trapped electrons produced by particle collisions during radioactive decay.

endemic
Refers to organisms that are restricted in their geographic range or confined to a specific region or environment.

endothermic
Describes an animal with a constant body temperature maintained by its metabolic processes. A "warm-blooded" animal. See also *ectothermic.*

end-Permian extinction
The mass extinction event that marked the close of the Permian Period. Approximately 90 percent of animal species became extinct.

eolian
Alternative spelling of *aeolian.*

eon
The largest time (geochronologic) unit used in geologic classification.

eonothem
Succession of rocks formed during an *eon.* The largest *chronostratigraphic unit.*

epeiric sea
Shallow sea covering the continental interior.

epeirogeny
Large-scale and relatively slow upwarping or downwarping of the continental crust. Involves little or no folding and faulting.

epicontinental sea
Synonym for *epeiric sea.*

epifauna
Benthic organisms that live on the sea floor or lake bed.

epoch
(1) Geologic time (geochronologic) unit of lesser rank than a *period.* (2) Time interval of about 1 million years, characterized by normal or reversed magnetism.

era
Geologic time unit.

erathem
Succession of rocks formed during a specific *era.*

eugeosyncline
Outer (oceanward) part of a geosynclinal belt along a craton margin. Typified by deep-water clastics (such as *turbidites*) and associated volcanics derived from *island-arc* vulcanism.

eukaryote
A type of cell that contains a nucleus as well as other cell structures, including mitochondria, within a membrane.

eurytopic
Describes organisms that have a tolerance for a wide range of environmental conditions.

eustatic
Pertaining to worldwide sea-level change. For example, glacio-eustatic change caused by variations in the size of ice caps.

evaporite
Minerals or sediment produced by evaporation of sea or lake water and the precipitation of salt crystals.

evaporite
Sedimentary rock formed by the precipitation of salts, such as gypsum, anhydrite, and halite, as a result of partial or complete evaporation of the saline solution.

evolutionary convergence
The process whereby similar morphologic features arise in animal groups of different origins and taxonomic affinities, as a consequence of their becoming adapted to similar habitats.

evolutionary radiation
The relatively rapid appearance of many new taxonomic groups arising from a single ancestral stock.

exotic terrane
Region consisting of rocks that are markedly different in type and/or age from those in surrounding terranes. Believed to have originated as microcontinental or island-arc fragments and to have been transported by lithospheric plate movement and accreted to a stable *craton.* Also called *suspect terranes.*

facies
Overall aspect or set of characteristics of a rock that reflects the rock's particular depositional environment. Features that set a rock off from adjacent facies within the same rock unit.

Fall Zone Surface
The early sub-Cretaceous erosion surface of the eastern margin of North America and across which Cretaceous sediments were deposited during a series of marine transgressions.

Farallon plate
The lithospheric plate lying between the North American plate and the East Pacific rise during the Tertiary.

fault
A fracture in crustal rocks along which there has been a relative displacement of the rocks.

felsic
A mnemonic for feldspar plus silica.

field relationships
The gross relationships between bodies of rock as they occur together at the earth's surface.

Fig Tree Group
Lithostratigraphic unit within the Swaziland *sequence* of the Archean of southern Africa.

fissility
Refers to the way in which rocks, particularly shales, split into thin *laminae* parallel to the *bedding.*

fission-track dating
Dating method based on measurement of the length of the trail of collision damage produced by decay emissions.

floodplain
Flat floor of a river valley that is covered by water when the river is in flood.

fluvial
Pertaining to a stream or river.

flysch
Marine shales and *turbidites* characteristic of deposition in a *foredeep* adjacent to a rising mountain belt during the early stages of an *orogeny.*

fold mountains
Mountains produced by the differential erosion of hard and soft rocks folded and squeezed during plate collision events.

foraminifera
Single-celled marine protozoans that secrete calcareous tests. Mostly of microscopic size. Many are planktonic, and their tests accumulate on the deep sea floor as foraminiferal *ooze.*

forearc basin
The basin formed by crustal sagging above a descending *lithospheric plate* between a trench and volcanic belt.

foredeep
Downwarped trench adjacent to an *island arc* or orogenic belt.

foreland
Stable portion of a *craton* adjacent to a collision margin and toward which the rising orogenic belt is being thrust.

foreland basin
A subsiding area adjacent to an orogenic belt.

formation
The fundamental rock (lithostratigraphic) unit in *stratigraphy.* Distinguishable from adjacent formations by specific physical characteristics and large enough to be a mappable unit. A *type section* is recognized in the area or at the locality where the formation is most typically developed and likely where it was first defined.

Fort Union Formation
Nonmarine gray shale and sandstone formation, locally with coals. Derived from streams flowing east from the rising Cordillera and widespread through the Dakotas, northern Wyoming and eastern Montana.

fossil
The remains of an organism from the geologic past preserved in the rocks.

Franciscan Complex
Chaotic assemblage of deformed and metamorphosed shales, siltstones, *graywackes,* basalts, and radiolarian *cherts,* together with exotic blocks of gabbro and other basic rocks. Generally believed to represent oceanic crust "scraped off" at a descending plate contact along a *subduction zone.*

fringing reef
Elongated organic reef that lies along a shoreline, normally with no lagoon behind it.

fusulinid foraminifera
Foraminifera belonging to the family Fusulinidae.

Gastropoda
Class of the phylum Mollusca. Includes snails and slugs.

geanticline
In the classic geosynclinal model, a belt of regional uplift dividing a *miogeosyncline* from a *eugeosyncline.*

gene
A structure on the chromosome that governs the transmission and development of inheritable characteristics.

gene pool
Sum total of genetic material of a species population.

genetics
The study of inheritance from generation to generation.

geochronologic unit
A unit used in the measurement of geologic time.

geochronology
Science of geologic time, especially its measurement in terms of real time in years.

geographic isolation
The isolation of one population, or part thereof, from another by uncrossable geographic features, such as wide oceans, land barriers, deserts, mountain ranges, and so on.

geographic range
The areal extent of the distribution of a species or a population.

geologic map
A map that shows the areal distribution and the structures of rocks as they are exposed at the earth's surface.

geosyncline
Large, elongated trough marginal to a continent. Over long geologic periods, it subsides and accumulates great thicknesses of sediment. See also *eugeosyncline* and *miogeosyncline.*

gill arch
In fishes, a group of small bones arranged in a *V* pattern and pointing forward and immediately behind the head region. They function as supports for the gill openings.

glaciation
The formation and movement of an ice sheet or glacier.

global boundary stratotype section and point (GBSSP) The stratigraphic horizon and locality selected by international consensus as being the best and most representative example of a particular stratigraphic boundary.

golden spike
The popular name for a GBSSP.

Gondwana
Ancient supercontinent comprising the present-day southern continents together with peninsula India. Named after the Gondwana System of India, Gondwana means "land of the Gonds."

Gondwana System
A succession of rocks of Permo-Triassic age in India.

Gowganda Conglomerate
Early Proterozoic conglomerate of the *Canadian Shield.* Generally interpreted as of glacial origin.

graded bed
Individual bed of clastic sediments having a gradual, upward change of grain size—typically, from coarse to fine, as in *turbidites.*

gradualism
See *phyletic gradualism.*

Grand Cycle
One of eight major sea-level cycles, presumably of eustatic origin, detected in the Cambrian and Lower Ordovician of North America.

granulite
High-grade metamorphic rock with a coarse, granular texture.

graptolite
Extinct colonial marine organism of the class Graptolithina of the phylum Hemichordata. Many species were

planktonic or pseudoplanktonic in habit and became widely dispersed, being found mainly in black-shale successions. Ranged from Middle Cambrian to Carboniferous.

Graptolithina
Class of the phylum Hemichordata. Colonial animals that secreted a chitinophosphatic, sawtooth-like colony. Ranged from the earliest Ordovician to the Mississippian.

graywacke
Poorly sorted sandstone with abundant feldspar, lithic clasts, and clay. Typically, dark gray. Often described as "dirty sandstone."

Great Ice Age
The name given to the Late Cenozoic glaciations by nineteenth-century geologists when it was believed that there had been only one glacial episode.

Green River Formation
Widespread formation of Eocene age dominated by *lacustrine* deposits, including oil shales and "varved" successions believed to mark seasonal algal blooms in lakes.

greenstone belt
Belt of associated metasediments and metavolcanics found in all Archean terrains.

greenstones
Metavolcanics and metasediments found in all Archean terrains.

group
In the hierarchy of lithostratigraphic units, contains two or more contiguous formations.

guide fossil
An easily recognized and geographically widely distributed species, having a short species life span and preferably not confined to one particular sedimentary facies. Used as a biozonal indicator to correlate or date the containing strata. Also known as *index fossil* and *zone fossil*.

Gunflint Chert
Proterozoic *chert* of the Great Lakes *Canadian Shield* where the first Precambrian microfossils were discovered.

gymnosperm
Naked seed plant. That is, seeds are commonly in a cone and not enclosed in an ovary.

habitat
Environment to which an organism is best adapted.

Haeckel's Law
The recapitulation idea that states that features seen in a growing embryo recapitulate the form of ancestral forms during *phylogeny*.

hairpin
On an apparent *polar-wandering curve,* a sudden change in direction.

half-life
Time required for half of a given amount of radioactive *isotope* to decay.

halmyrolysis
Changes in the rocks of the seafloor as a result of chemical reaction with seawater. Literally, submarine "weathering."

Hercynian orogeny
A mountain-building episode that affected southern Europe during the Pennsylvanian and Permian.

heterotroph
An organism that depends for nutrients upon existing organic molecules in the surrounding environment.

hiatus
A gap within a stratigraphic succession. An interval of time not represented by sediments. A hiatus may be due to nondeposition, erosion of previously deposited sediment, or both.

High Plains
Largely undissected area of the Great Plains region along the eastern flank of the Rocky Mountains. Elevations typically above 600 meters.

holostei
An infraclass of bony fishes that reached a maximum development from the Triassic to the Cretaceous, but with a few forms surviving to the present.

homeomorph
Species that closely resembles another species even though the two are not related below the family level. A consequence of *convergent evolution.*

homogeneous differentiation
Model to describe the early evolution of the earth, with iron settling toward the center and lighter silicate material forming the outer layers.

homologous organs
Organs that have similar structure and skeletal elements but in different

organisms serve different functions. For example, the forelimbs of tetrapods and the wings of birds.

hot spot
A localized area of the crust with very high heat flow, presumably due to a rising plume of hot mantle material below. Hot spots are often the sites for volcanic activity (for example, Hawaii).

Hudsonian orogeny
An episode of mountain building that affected parts of the *Canadian Shield* during the Proterozoic, approximately 1.9 to 1.8 billion years ago.

Huronian System
Major division of the *Canadian Shield* Proterozoic.

hybodont shark
A group of sharks ranging in time from Late Devonian to Early Cenozoic. The most primitive of the modern sharks.

Iapetus Ocean
The ancestral Atlantic that existed from the Late Proterozoic to Early Ordovician until its final closure with the Acadian orogeny.

ice sheet
A mass of glacial ice of regional or even continental extent thick enough to completely blanket most of the topography beneath. Also known as ice cap.

igneous rock
Rock formed as a consequence of the cooling and crystallization of a magma or lava.

Iguanodon
Large *ornithopod* dinosaur from the Early Cretaceous.

immature sand
Sand characterized by poor sorting, angular grains, and a large proportion of minerals of low resistance.

inarticulate brachiopod
Primitive brachiopod with no teeth and sockets along the hinge line where the two valves are joined.

inclination
See *magnetic inclination.*

index fossil
See *guide fossil.*

industrial melanism
When tree bark and other surfaces are blackened by soot from industrial smoke, black or dark-colored varieties of organisms, such as moths, are more invisible to predators and consequently enjoy a statistical swing toward a higher survival rate.

infauna
Benthic organisms that live within the sediments of the sea floor or lake bed.

inner clastic zone
Near-shore, shallow-water zone where clastic, noncarbonate sedimentation is predominant.

insolation cycle
Cycle of variations in the relationship of the earth and the sun. Affects the amount of the sun's energy reaching the earth's surface.

interglacial
Time between two major glacial advances.

Interior Seaway
During the maximum Cretaceous marine advance onto the North American craton, the *epeiric sea* that lay between the emergent cordilleran region to the west and the Appalachian region land area to the east.

intermontane basin
A sedimentary basin within or surrounded by mountains.

interstade (interstadial)
Short-lived recession of the ice during a period of glacial advance.

intracratonic basin
Basin on a craton surface.

island arc
Curving line of islands of volcanic origin and adjacent to an oceanic trench. The curve is convex toward the trench and ocean beyond. For example, the Aleutian and Kurile islands in the northern Pacific.

isochron
Line on a chart or map that joins points of the same age.

isochronous
Having the same age. A synonym for *synchronous.*

isochronous surface
A time horizon. A theoretical concept that only rarely can be demonstrated by stratigraphic phenomena. On a local scale, a volcanic ash band is isochronous, as is a single bed laid down by a *turbidity current.*

isostasy
Mechanism whereby areas of crust sink or rise until they reach a buoyancy equilibrium in "floating" on the denser mantle.

isotope
One of two or more species of the same chemical elements. Isotopes have the same number of protons in the nucleus but different numbers of neutrons.

isotopic dating
Calculating the age of rocks and minerals by measuring the ratio of the amount of a radioactive element to the amount of accumulated decay product. For example, potassium-40/argon-40, a so-called *accumulation clock.* In *decay clocks,* the amount of the radioactive material remaining is measured. For example, carbon-14 dating. Also known as *radiometric dating.*

joint
Crack or fracture in a rock, across which no relative displacement has occurred.

Karoo System
A thick succession of largely terrestrial sediments in southern Africa. The age range is from Permian to Early Jurassic.

karst topography
Topography typical of areas underlain by major limestone formation. Solution of the limestone by groundwater produces caverns, sinkholes, subsurface drainage, and dry valleys.

Kaskaskia sequence
A succession of sediments laid down in the Kaskaskia Sea as it advanced over a regional unconformity cut across Pre-Devonian sediments. The transgressive-regressive cycle began in the Early Devonian and ended in the Early Permian.

Keewatin Series
In the classic area of the Great Lakes, the name given to the lower, metavolcanic succession in a *greenstone belt.*

Kenoran orogeny
An episode of mountain building on the *Canadian Shield* about 2.5 billion years ago. Generally taken as marking the boundary between the Archean and Proterozoic.

Klamath Arc
An *island arc* that lay off the western margin of the North American craton until it collided with the craton during the Late Devonian to Early Mississippian. The collision event was marked by the *Antler orogeny.*

labyrinthodont
General term for amphibians of latest Devonian to Triassic age characterized by teeth with complexly infolded (labyrinthine) enamel.

lacustrine
Pertaining to lakes.

lagoon
Shallow body of water behind a *barrier island, barrier beach,* or *reef.*

Lamarckism
The idea that supposes that characteristics acquired through the life of an individual can be passed on to the individual's offspring.

lamina
Layer of sediment less than 1 centimeter thick. See also *bed.*

land bridge
An area of land connecting two continents.

Laramide orogeny
Episode of mountain building that deformed the western margin of the North American craton during the Late Cretaceous to Early Cenozoic.

Laurasia
The name given to the northern supercontinent comprising present-day North America, Greenland, Europe, and part of Asia during the Late Paleozoic, as suggested by Alfred Wegener in 1915.

Laurentia
The name applied to the supercontinent consisting of the Laurentian (Canadian) Shield and Greenland, together with part of northern Scotland and possibly fragments of the northern Baltic Shield.

Laurentian Shield
See *Canadian Shield.*

Laurussia
The supercontinent consisting of *Laurentia* and the Baltic Shield (*Baltica*) and formed during the *Acadian orogeny.*

law of original continuity
Law suggested by Nicolas Steno that sedimentary strata on one side of a valley were once continuous with a similar succession of strata on the other side. Although once continuous, the two occurrences have been isolated from one another by the erosion of the valley.

law of original horizontality
Steno's law that states that rock strata now tilted and folded were formed originally as horizontal strata.

law of superposition
Steno's law that states that, in any undisturbed succession of sedimentary strata, the oldest are at the bottom and the youngest at the top.

Lipalian interval
The supposed worldwide discontinuity at the base of the Cambrian.

lithification
The process whereby unconsolidated sediment is converted into solid rock typically by the introduction of a secondary mineral into the pore spaces that cements the grains together. In mud rocks, the lithification process is mainly due to the welding of clay particles as water is squeezed out.

lithofacies
That aspect of a rock concerned with its lithic character (mineralogy, grain size, texture, bedding characteristics, and so on).

lithosphere
The rigid outer layer of the earth. Lying above the *asthenosphere,* it comprises the outer mantle and crust. Typically about 100 kilometers thick.

lithospheric plate
A portion of the rigid outer layer of the earth, comprising the upper mantle and the crust.

lithostratigraphic unit
A rock unit. A body of rock defined on the basis of its lithic characteristics (lithology)—that is, grain size, mineral composition, texture, and so on.

Louann salt
Thick *evaporite* deposit of late Middle to early Late Jurassic age underlying the northern Gulf of Mexico. The source of the many salt plugs in the Gulf Coast region.

lycopsid
Group of herbaceous plants with a fossil record dating back to the Carboniferous. Modern representatives include *Lycopodium* and *Phylloglossum.*

mafic
A mnemonic for magnesium plus ferric.

magnetic anomaly
Measurement of the intensity of polarity of the earth's magnetic field that is a departure from the normal average or anticipated value or direction.

magnetic declination
The horizontal angle between the geographic (that is, the "true" or rotational) pole and the magnetic pole.

magnetic inclination
The vertical angle between the magnetic lines of force of the earth's magnetic field and the earth's surface. This "dip" angle, as it is also known, is 90° at the magnetic poles and becomes progressively less in moving into lower latitudes until it is 0° (horizontal) at the magnetic equator.

magnetic polarity
The direction of the north or south magnetic pole, as indicated by a compass needle.

magnetic reversal
A 180° change of polarity of the earth's magnetic field—from normal (as at present day) to reverse, or reverse to normal.

magnetostratigraphy
The study of the magnetic polarity direction and field strength, as they can be used to aid the time correlation of sedimentary strata.

main-sequence star
A star that has reached an equilibrium state in which gravitational collapse and expansion by heating are balanced.

marginal basin
A basin of sediment accumulation at or near the margin of a continental block.

marine regression
A retreat of the sea either due to a fall in sea level or an emergence of the land.

marine transgression
An advance of the sea either due to a rise in sea level or a sinking of the land.

marsupial mammal
The mammal group in which the young are born at a very early stage of development and which then move to the mother's pouch to complete their growth. Living examples are kangaroos, wallabies, and opossums.

mass extinction
The sudden extinction of large numbers of species across a wide spectrum of ecologic niches.

massif
General term for rigid mass of crystalline rocks.

mass number
The total number of protons plus neutrons in the atomic nucleus.

mass spectrometer
An instrument used for separating ions of different mass but equal charge whereby molecular weights and relative abundance of different *isotopes* can be measured.

mature sand
Sand made up entirely of quartz grains—well rounded and well sorted.

meiosis
Cell division involving two successive divisions that reduce the number of chromosomes by half. In plants, this type of division produces *pollen* and ovules, and in animals, sperm and eggs. See also *mitosis.*

member
In the hierarchy of lithostratigraphic units, a subdivision of a *formation.*

mesosphere
The rigid zone of the earth's mantle below the *asthenosphere.*

Messinian salinity crisis
The name given to the period during the Late Miocene when the Mediterranean region became an evaporating basin.

metallic catalyst
Substance that speeds up chemical reactions without being consumed itself.

metamorphism
Change produced in rock, usually at some depth below the surface, by pressure or by exposure to hydrothermal fluids. Such change results in new minerals and textures. For example, shale is turned into slate, granite into gneiss, limestone into marble, and so on.

metazoa
Multicellular animals.

metazoan
Multicellular animal.

midocean ridge
A chain of submarine mountains formed by vulcanism and thermal expansion above a zone of hot mantle material rising from below within a convectional system.

Milankovitch Köppen effect
Cycle of world climatic change linked to the so-called *insolation cycles* caused by fluctuations in the amount of the sun's energy delivered to the earth. These fluctuations, in turn, are due to cyclical variations in the tilt of the earth's rotational axis, eccentricities in the earth's orbit around the sun, and the time of the year when the earth is at *perihelion* (closest to the sun).

miogeosyncline
In the classic geosynclinal model, the inner *geosyncline* lying next to the continent.

mitosis
Cell division producing two cells, each having the same number of chromosomes as the parent. See also *meiosis*.

mobile belt
An elongated belt subject to folding, faulting, and igneous activity during one or more mountain-building episodes. Invariably, mobile belts lay along a continental margin during the period they were active and were due to the influence of a *subduction zone* and collision tectonics.

Moenkopi Formation
Widespread *redbed* formation of Early and Middle Triassic age. Outcrops throughout the Colorado Plateau region and adjacent areas.

molasse
Sediments, typically nonmarine or sometimes shallow marine, laid down in front of tectonic highlands and filling a subsiding *foredeep*. Typically, molasse deposits mark the waning stages of a mountain-building episode.

mold
The impression made in rock by the external and/or internal surface of a shell or other skeletal element.

molecular clock
Dating method based on the fact that the differences in the amino acid residues in proteins accumulate at a measurable rate. Thus, the degree of difference is proportional to the time elapsed since different taxa arose from a common ancestor.

Monera
The kingdom that contains the most primitive life-forms: single *prokaryote* cells with no nuclei or other internal structures. Includes the bacteria.

monotreme mammal
Egg-laying mammal. Living examples include the platypus and spiny anteaters.

moraine
An accumulation of unsorted, unstratified *till* transported by a glacier or ice sheet and deposited at its terminus or along the margin as ice melts.

morphospecies
Supposed species recognized in paleontology and defined on the basis of skeletal morphology alone and assuming that such morphologic features reflect the genetic features that would normally differentiate one biological species from another.

Morrison Formation
Of Jurassic age, the most widely distributed formation in North America, consisting of *alluvial* and *lacustrine* deposits and best known for its dinosaur fauna.

Mowry Sea
An Early Cretaceous (Albian) extensive inland sea formed by an embayment from the Pacific and covering a large area of Montana, Wyoming, and parts of Colorado and the Dakotas. Named from the Mowry Shale, a siliceous, bentonitic shale with type section in Wyoming.

mutation
An inheritable change in a gene. One of the sources of variation in a genetic population that supplies the potential for natural selection.

natural selection
Evolutionary mechanism proposed by Charles Darwin and Alfred Russel Wallace whereby the effect of the environment on a population is seen in the higher survival rates and reproductive potential of those varieties within a species that are better adapted to their environment.

Navajo Sandstone
Jurassic sandstone of Utah and surrounding area. Contains striking *cross-bedding* features indicative of deposition as desert dunes.

Neanderthal man
An early race of *Homo sapiens* with a fossil record extending from about 100,000 to 35,000 years before present.

nebular hypothesis
The theory suggesting that the solar system evolved from a rotating cloud of gas.

nekton
Free-swimming organisms, such as squids, fish, whales, and so on.

Nemesis star
A hypothetical star that supposedly passes close to the sun every 26 million years and in so doing disturbs the orbits of comets, some of which impact the earth.

Neptunism
The theory proposed by Abraham Gottlob Werner that all rocks were formed by precipitation in a worldwide ocean.

neutron
Elementary particle in the atomic nucleus having the mass of one proton and no electrical charge.

Nevadan orogeny
A phase of mountain building that affected the western margin of the North American craton during the Jurassic and Early Cretaceous.

Newark Supergroup
Succession of Late Triassic nonmarine sediments filling the fault basins of the northeastern region. Typically developed in the New Jersey area.

New Red Sandstone
The name given by William Smith to reddish sandstones of Permian age occurring in northeastern England.

nonconformity
That type of *unconformity* where sedimentary rocks overlie an eroded surface of igneous or metamorphic rocks.

notoungulate
A member of a group of *ungulates* that underwent an evolutionary radiation in South America during the Cenozoic due to the geographic isolation of that continent.

novaculite
Light-colored form of *chert*.

nuclide
Atoms defined by the number of protons and neutrons in its nucleus.

obduction
The overthrusting of oceanic crust onto continental crust during plate collision.

offlap
Relationships between *strata* as they are deposited during a *marine regression* as successively younger beds are laid down basinward of older beds and leave the landward extent of older beds progressively emergent. See also *onlap*.

Old Red Sandstone
The name given by William Smith to a succession of reddish sandstones and shales that occur in South Wales, Scotland, and elsewhere and that contain fossils of terrestrial plants and freshwater fishes. Later shown to be of Devonian age.

olistostrome
A sedimentary deposit showing chaotic bedding and indications that it was laid down as a consequence of submarine sliding and slumping.

onlap
Basal relationship of beds laid down during a *marine transgression* as they terminate progressively further inland as sea level rises. Each bed encroaches successively landward over previously deposited beds. See also *offlap*.

ontogeny
The growth and development of an organism from conception to maturity.

Onverwacht Group
The basal group of the Swaziland Series of the Archean of southern Africa.

oolith
Spherical grains of calcium carbonate, approximately 0.5 to 1.0 millimeters in diameter and formed initially by the precipitation or accretion of aragonite crystals around a nucleus. Typically, a small bioclast or quartz grain. Ooliths form in warm, shallow-marine, moderately agitated water. Lithified deposits form oolitic limestone.

Oort Cloud
Supposed ringlike swarm of comets around the sun in an orbit beyond that of the outer planets.

ooze
A *pelagic* (typically, deep-ocean) sediment consisting of at least 30 percent skeletal remains, such as *foraminifera, diatoms, radiolaria,* and so on, with the remaining 70 percent being clay.

ophiolite suite
A suite of basaltic lavas and *ultramafic* rocks (peridotite) believed to originate in the oceanic lithosphere together with *pelagic* muds, radiolarian cherts, and other indicators of a deep ocean floor origin.

opportunistic species
Those species that are apparently successful in adapting to new ecologic niches arising as a result of environmental changes.

Ornithischia
A taxonomic subdivision of the dinosaurs in which the pelvic bones are birdlike.

orogeny
A phase of mountain building marked especially by compressional tectonics—that is, folding and thrust faulting—to produce fold mountains.

ostracoderm
Jawless fishes of Late Cambrian to Late Devonian time. Typified by bony armor, especially in the head region.

Ouachita-Marathon orogenic belt
See *Ouachita orogeny*.

Ouachita orogeny
An orogeny that deformed the Ouachita region during the Pennsylvanian and that was caused by the collision of *Gondwana* and *Laurussia*.

outer detrital zone
Somewhat deeper water zone, out beyond the depth of wave influence, where fine clastic sediments accumulate.

outgassing
The process whereby volcanic eruptions eject gases from the earth's interior. This process produced the first terrestrial atmosphere during the Archean.

outlier
When erosional stripping on an areal scale removes higher and younger formations, locally, remnants of the younger rocks remain as erosional remnants surrounded by the older rocks that underly them. Such remnants are termed outliers.

outwash
Deposits of glacial meltwater streams.

paleoclimate
A climate that existed in the geologic past.

paleocurrent
An ancient stream current direction preserved in the sediment by such structures as *cross-bedding,* current ripples, and other features having some directional significance.

paleoecology
The study of fossil organisms and their relationship to their life environment.

paleogeography
Using geologic data, the study of the distribution of continents, oceans, mountains, deserts, and so on in the geologic past.

paleomagnetism
Ancient remanent magnetism preserved in the rocks by magnetic minerals oriented within the main field at the time they were formed or when they came to be deposited in their present attitude.

paleotemperature curve
A graphical presentation of past world temperature changes. Typically, such curves are based upon paleoecologic evidence or methods involving oxygen isotopes.

palinspastic map
A map in which rocks that are now folded, faulted, and moved by thrust faults during compressional tectonic events are restored to their original position and attitude.

pandemic
Describes an organism that has an extensive geographic range. Most likely this indicates tolerance to a wide variety of environmental conditions.

Pangaea
The name given by Alfred Wegener for a supercontinent comprising all of the continents before breakup.

Pangaea Hemisphere
When all the continental masses are joined to form a single supercontinent, almost a whole hemisphere is occupied.

Panthalassia Hemisphere
The hemisphere opposite the Pangaea Hemisphere. Occupied only by ocean.

Panthalassic Ocean
The name given to the world ocean at times when the continents were merged into a single Pangaea supercontinent.

paraconformity
An obscure *unconformity* representing a discontinuity, perhaps with no greater magnitude than a *bedding plane*. Although, typically, there are no indications of erosion, the biostratigraphic evidence points to a more considerable time gap.

parallel evolution
The development of similar structures in two or more related species as they evolved within separate lines of descent. The similarity of form is a consequence of adaptations in a similar way to a particular environment. See also *convergent evolution.*

parent isotope
The radioactive isotope that produces *daughter isotopes* during radioactive decay.

parent stock
The ancestral population from which new species arise.

passive continental margin
Continental margin located within a *lithospheric plate.* Tectonic movements are dominantly of vertical type. Some uplift occurs at initial rifting, followed mainly by a history of subsidence as the two plate edges move away from the spreading center (see also *seafloor spreading*) and from one another.

patch reef
Small, isolated reef mound or pinnacle growing in a lagoon or on a shallow platform.

peat
Unconsolidated swamp deposit of dead and partially decayed vegetation. Represents the first stage in the formation of coal.

pelagic
Describes the open ocean environment as distinct from the ocean bottom.

pellet limestone
Limestone comprising a consolidated deposit of fecal pellets excreted by mud-ingesting *benthic* organisms, commonly worms, gastropods, and so on.

pelycosaur
Belonging to a group of synapsid reptiles of Late Pennsylvanian to Permian age. Includes the edaphosaur fin-backed reptiles.

peneplain
Extensive, low, almost featureless landscape. In the original nineteenth-century concept, supposedly a result of long-continued *subaerial* erosion. A landscape in old age.

perihelion
When the earth is closest to the sun, it is said to be at perihelion.

period
Fundamental time (geochronologic) unit. A subdivision of an *era.*

peripatric isolates
Portions of a gene pool that become isolated from the surrounding population.

peripheral isolate
Member of a population near the geographic limits of the species range that is likely, in the course of geographic/climatic changes, to become isolated from the main gene pool.

permeability
Ability of a rock or sediment to transport fluid through pore spaces and cracks.

Permian Basin
General name for the region of Permian rocks in the West Texas region. Includes many important oil and gas fields.

permineralization
The addition of mineral matter into the structure of hard skeletal material.

Permo-Carboniferous ice age
A major glacial episode that began in the Carboniferous and lasted through most of the Permian. A continental ice sheet was centered on Gondwana at this time, and evidence of glacial erosion and deposition is found on all the southern continents.

photic zone
In the ocean and lakes, the water depth to which sunlight will penetrate. Varies with latitude and the turbidity of the water.

photosphere
The thin, gaseous, outer layer of the sun's atmosphere that emits light.

photosynthesis
The utilization of light energy in the synthesis of compounds from carbon dioxide and water.

phyletic gradualism
Evolutionary model in which a new species gradually evolves from an ancestral form over a long period of time. Supposedly, speciation is the result of the progressive accumulation of many small changes wrought by microevolutionary shifts or genetic drift.

phylogeny
The line of descent in a given group of organisms.

pinnacle reef
Isolated, stromatoporoid-algal reef in the Middle Silurian of the Michigan Basin.

pinniped
Animal group that includes seals, sea lions, and walruses. The fossil record begins in the Miocene.

placental mammal
Mammal in which the embryo is nourished through the placenta and is born at a comparatively advanced state of development.

placoderm
Primitive, jawed fish of the Paleozoic.

planetary nebulae
Stars in a post-*red-giant* stage, surrounded by an expanding cloud of gas.

planetismal
Asteroid-sized body. Gravitational clumping of many planetismals produced *protoplanets.*

planetology
The study of planets, particularly their "geologic" rather than cosmic characteristics.

Planet X
A supposed tenth, and as yet undiscovered, planet lying beyond the orbit of Pluto. Some evidence for its existence is claimed in certain observed perturbations of the orbits of the outer planets.

plankton
Animals and plants that float passively in the surface water. Many are microscopic in size.

plate tectonics
The model that describes movement of the surface of *lithospheric plates* as due to convectional overturn within the mantle.

platform
That part of a *craton* where the basement rocks are covered by younger sediments.

playa lake
Temporary lake in an arid or semiarid region with internal drainage. When such lakes dry up, *evaporite* salts are deposited.

plesiosaur
Belonging to a group of large marine reptiles that evolved during the Jurassic and Cretaceous. A typical plesiosaur had four paddlelike limbs, and many, but not all, had long necks.

Plutonist
Someone who believed that many rocks originated in a molten state deep within the earth. Also known as *Vulcanist*.

point bar
Accumulation of sand or gravel on the inside of a bend in a meandering stream.

polar-wandering curve
The sinuous line joining the locations of the north and/or south magnetic poles as they have apparently progressively shifted through time.

pollen
Microgametophytes. Microspores of seed plants (*angiosperms* and *gymnosperms*), each containing a microscopic male gamete.

Porifera
The phylum that contains the sponges.

porosity
Percentage of the total rock volume that constitutes pore spaces.

potassium-argon dating
Dating method based on the measurement of radiogenic argon produced during the decay of the unstable potassium-40 isotope.

preadaptation
When morphologic features of an organism prove to have survival potential different from that for which they originally developed.

Precambrian
Geologic time preceding the beginning of the Cambrian. Comprises about 90 percent of all earth history.

precession of the equinoxes
An approximately 22,000-year cycle in the wobble of the earth's axis. This wobble causes a systematic change in the time of the year that the earth is closest to the sun.

primate
Belonging to the mammal group that includes the prosimians (tree shrews, lemurs, and tarsiers), Old World and New World monkeys, apes, and humans.

primitive atmosphere
The earliest atmosphere surrounding a newly formed planet. Formed of stellar material, dominantly hydrogen and helium.

prodelta
The gentle slope beyond the front of a delta. The surface is below *wave base*.

productid brachiopod
Belonging to a group of brachiopods characterized by a strongly convex pedicle valve and a flat to concave brachial valve. Common during the Mississippian through Permian.

progradation
Outward building of the coastline by sediment accumulation, such as in deltas, mangrove swamps, or beaches.

progymnosperm
Primitive ancestor of gymnosperms.

prokaryote
A primitive type of cell that lacks a cell nucleus. This type of cell is found in cyanobacteria and bacteria. See also *eukaryote*.

protein
A chain of *amino acids* joined by peptide bonds.

Proterozoic
The younger of two divisions of the Precambrian.

Protista
The kingdom containing diverse phyla with *eukaryotic* cells—that is, cells with nuclei and other internal structures.

proton
Elementary particle in the atomic nucleus. Has a positive charge.

protoplanet
Asteroid-sized object formed by nucleation of solid debris in orbit about the early sun.

protostar
A very young star not yet hot enough to emit light.

psychrosphere
The cold, deep zone of the ocean. Formed by convectional movement of cold water generated in polar regions. Temperatures are typically only a few degrees above freezing.

Pteridospermaphyta
The seed ferns.

pterodactyloid
General term for flying reptiles that appeared in the Late Jurassic. Unlike the rhamphorynchoids of the earlier Jurassic, the pterodactyloids had no tails.

pull-apart basin
Along a lateral fault, irregularities in the shape of the fault plane result in sections along the fault where tensional stresses cause subsidence.

punctuated equilibrium
The concept that evolution takes place in a series of steps and that a new species arises as a result of rapid change over a few thousand generations. Thereafter, the species remains unchanged, perhaps for millions of years.

pyroclastic
Clastic material derived from volcanic eruptions. The ejecta from a volcano, including blocks, cinders, ash, and so on.

quadrupedal
Walking on four legs. See also *bipedal*.

Queenston Delta
The clastic wedge of dominantly Ordovician age sediments that spread

westward across northwestern New York and adjacent areas. Composed of *molasse* material derived by erosion of the tectonic highlands to the east, uplifted during the *Taconic orogeny.*

radioactive decay
The spontaneous transformation of atoms of one element into atoms of another element as a result of emission of a particle (alpha or beta) from the atomic nucleus, or through electron capture.

radioactivity
The spontaneous breakdown, or decay, of certain unstable *isotopes.*

radiolaria
Planktonic marine protozoans of microscopic size that secrete a skeleton of opaline silica.

radiometric dating
See *isotopic dating.*

radionuclide
Radioactive *isotope.*

range zone
A *biozone* based on the total stratigraphic range of a species or other taxon, or of an assemblage of taxa.

real time
Time measured in years before the present (B.P.). The present is defined as A.D. 1950.

recrystallization
The solid state transformation of mineral grains in a rock into new crystals, often larger than the original grains. Mineralogical composition may remain the same or be different.

redbeds
Sediments of any type, but typically shales, siltstones, and sandstones that are reddish in color due to the presence of ferric iron (hematite). Such sediments usually are deposited in a continental environment.

red giant
As a star's hydrogen fuel becomes exhausted, the star expands and cools to become a red giant.

reef
Rocklike mass made up of skeletons of sedentary calcareous marine organisms and built up as a wave-resistant structure from the sea floor. Internally,

the reef consists of the remains of frame-building organisms, such as corals, together with calcareous algae and many other reef dwellers. In a general and largely nongeological sense, the term *reef* also applies to any rock in shallow water that is a hazard to navigation.

regional unconformity
An erosional break of widespread regional significance.

regolith
The layer of rock debris and soil derived from weathering and breakdown of rock and forming a largely untransported blanket of varying thickness on top of the bedrock.

regression
See *marine regression.*

relative time scale
A time scale in which geologic events are set out in the order they occurred, without reference to the actual time measured in years.

relict sediment
Sediments characteristic of and originally laid down in a different depositional environment from the one in which they presently occur.

resistate
Sediment or sedimentary grains of minerals that are resistant to weathering and abrasion.

rhizome
A horizontal underground stem.

Rhynie flora
A fossil flora of Early Devonian age found near the village of Rhynie in Aberdeenshire, Scotland.

rift valley
A valley formed by the subsiding of the surface between boundary faults.

ripple marks
The wavelike undulations formed on the surface of unconsolidated sands by water currents, waves, or in deserts, by the wind. Frequently preserved as *bedding-plane* features in sedimentary rocks.

rock cycle
The cycle involving the life history of a rock from its original formation to its destruction by weathering and erosion. The debris (*clasts*) then becomes redeposited to form a new generation of sediments and begin the cycle anew. If

the rocks become deeply buried, part of the cycle may involve metamorphism and even melting to produce a magma. Cooling and crystallization of the magma produces igneous rocks, which again begin a cycle.

Rothliegende Sandstone
In the North Sea area, a succession of desert sandstones with *evaporites* laid down in a westward extension of the German-Dutch basin of Permian time.

rubidium-strontium dating
Dating method based on the decay of radioactive rubidium to the *daughter isotope* strontium-87.

rudistid mollusks
Peculiar, bivalved mollusks in which one valve became greatly thickened and elongated to produce a shape reminiscent of the rugose horn corals. The other valve became a sort of lid. Flourishing during the Mesozoic, especially in the Cretaceous, when they formed considerable reefs, they became extinct during the terminal Cretaceous mass extinction event.

sabkha
Extensive supratidal flat in an arid region and on which accumulates a variety of *evaporite* minerals.

saltation
The movement of sand grains or pebbles along the bed of a stream by bouncing. Sand grains transported across the desert surface by the wind also move in this fashion.

salt dome
A domelike anticlinal structure, or diapir, in sedimentary strata pushed up by a rising salt plug. Frequently, such structures are traps for commercial quantities of oil and gas.

San Andreas Fault
The name given to the major fault system in western California that is the surface manifestation of differential movement between the North American and Pacific *lithospheric plates.*

saturated rock
Rock containing sufficient silica to have produced some quartz during crystallization of magma.

Sauk sequence
The succession of sediments laid down during the transgression of the Sauk Sea across the North American craton from Late Proterozoic through Early Ordovician time.

Sauk Transgression
The first of the major marine incursions onto the North American continent during the Paleozoic. Began in the latest Precambrian and ended in the Early Ordovician.

Saurischia
A taxonomic subdivision of the dinosaurs in which the pelvic bones are lizardlike.

scale tree
General term for treelike ferns and seed ferns in which the bark of the tree consists of closely spaced, stubby leaves that overlap like the scales of a fish.

Schooley Peneplain
The name given to an erosion surface that beveled the Appalachian region during the Tertiary. Later regional uplift caused its dissection by stream erosion, but its former existence is seen in the coincidence of many summit elevations in the Appalachians.

seafloor spreading
The movement of the sea floor away from a *spreading center (midocean ridge)*, where new oceanic crust is generated along a series of fissures in the oceanic crust.

sea-level curve
Graphical representation of the cycles of sea-level rise and fall through time at a given location.

sedimentary rock
Rock formed by the *lithification* of a sediment, such as sand or mud, to produce rocks such as sandstone and shale.

seismic stratigraphy
The study of *stratigraphy* and sedimentary *facies* as interpreted from seismic reflection data.

selection pressure
In a changing environment, new factors tend to select those forms better adapted to the change.

septal suture
In the *ammonoid* and nautiloid *cephalopods,* the curving or convoluted trace on the outer shell of the line marking the join or bond between the internal septa (walls separating the shell chambers) and the outer shell.

sequence
The name given to a major lithostratigraphic unit bounded below and above by regional unconformities.

series
Time-rock (*chronostratigraphic*) unit of lesser rank than a *system*. The time unit equivalent is an *epoch*.

sessile
Describes bottom-dwelling aquatic organisms that spend their adult lives attached to the substrate. For example, corals, bryozoa, many mollusks, and so on.

Sevier orogeny
An episode of mountain building affecting the western margin of the North American continent during the Cretaceous.

Sherman Surface
The name given to the old pediplain erosion surface developed across the interior lowlands during the Tertiary. In the Pliocene and Pleistocene, this surface was dissected by streams flowing eastward from the rising cordilleran ranges.

shield
Extensive area of exposed basement rocks of Precambrian age in the interior of a *craton*.

sial
A mnemonic for silica and aluminum.

Sierra Nevada
Mountain range in California developed on rocks of a major fault block uplifted and tilted during the Late Cenozoic.

siliceous
Formed of silica. Typically describes the amorphous or cryptocrystalline form of *chert*.

sirenian
The mammal group that includes the dugongs and manatees, or sea cows.

Slave Province
One of the major structural provinces of the *Canadian Shield*.

small shelly fossils
Small invertebrate fossils of calcium phosphate from the Tommotian Stage of the Early Cambrian.

solar nebula hypothesis
The model describing the origin of the solar system from a rotating nebula of dust and gases that eventually condensed to form the sun and planets.

solar wind
The outpouring of high-energy particles from the sun.

Solnhofen Limestone
Fine-grained, porcellanous limestone of Late Jurassic age that occurs in southern Germany. Deposited in a quiet lagoon and likely *anoxic* environment, the limestone is famous for the beautifully preserved fossils found as flattened impressions on the *bedding planes*. Included are the only known fossils of *Archaeopteryx,* one of the earliest ancestral birds.

Sonoma orogeny
Episode of crustal unrest and structural movements that affected western Nevada and adjacent areas during the Permian.

sorting
Refers to size distribution in a population of clastic grains. If all the grains are approximately the same size, the sediment is well sorted. In poorly sorted sediment, a wide range of grain sizes is represented.

sphenopsid
Belonging to a group of plants having jointed stems. The horsetail *Equisetum* is a living example.

spicule
In sponges, tiny, rigid, siliceous or calcareous supporting structures. Often needle- or rod-shaped, or with a stellate, radiating structure.

spreading center
The boundary between two diverging *lithospheric plates*.

stade (stadial)
Subdivision of a glacial episode (*stage*), when a climatic cooling caused a brief readvance of the ice.

stage
(1) A chronostratigraphic unit of lesser rank than a series. (2) In Quaternary stratigraphy, a glacial or interglacial episode.

stasis
The absence of any morphologic change from generation to generation through the life of a species.

stegosaurus
A plated, quadrupedal, *ornithischian* dinosaur. Primarily a Jurassic group, stegosaurs became extinct in the Early Cretaceous, the first major dinosaur group to disappear.

stenotopic
Said of an organism that is relatively intolerant of environmental change and that can only survive within a narrow range of ecologic conditions.

stratigraphic section
An exposure of stratified rocks in vertical succession.

stratigraphy
The science of stratified rocks.

stratotype
See *type section.*

stratum (pl. strata)
A layer or bed of sedimentary rock.

strike-slip fault
A fault in which the movement is in a direction parallel to the strike of the fault.

stromatolite
Organosedimentary structure made up of fine sedimentary layers trapped or secreted by successive generations of cyanobacteria, bacteria, and algae that form so-called *algal mats* on sediment surfaces.

stromatoporoids
Primitive sponges that secreted calcareous structures that were built up in layers, like the leaves in a cabbage.

subaerial
At the ground surface. For example, weathering processes, deposition of desert sand dunes, and so on. See also *subaqueous.*

subaqueous
Submerged below the water. For example, marine, *lacustrine,* and *alluvial* environments.

subduction zone
The inclined surface of a descending slab of oceanic crust along a plate margin. Marked at the surface by an oceanic trench and an associated volcanic *island arc.* In the subsurface, characterized by a so-called Benioff zone, marked by the distribution of moderately deep focus to deep focus earthquakes.

submarine canyon
A steep-sided valley that cuts back into the continental shape and shelf.

Sundance Sea
A widespread marine embayment transgressing from the Pacific in the Late Jurassic and covering much of the area of the western United States.

supergroup
In the hierarchy of lithostratigraphic units, a division containing two or more contiguous *groups.*

superinterval
A division of geologic time based upon the spacing of *hairpins,* sharp kinks in the apparent *polar-wandering curve.*

Superior Province
One of the major *tectonic provinces* of the *Canadian Shield.*

supernova
Explosion of a large star after the runaway expenditure of its nuclear fuel.

suspect terrane
See *exotic terrane.*

sympatric species
Related species that occupy the same or overlapping geographic ranges.

system
Fundamental and original *chronostratigraphic* (time-rock) unit. Equivalent to the time (geochronologic) division of *period*—that is, it was formed during a *period.*

Taconic orogeny
The episode of mountain building that affected the northern Appalachians during the Ordovician.

taphonomy
The study of the fossilization process and the postmortem events that lead to fossilization.

tar seep
Natural surface seep of heavy oil or bitumen.

taxonomy
The study of the relationships and the classification of plants and animals, living and fossil. Also known as systematics.

tectonically positive area
A more or less localized area that subsides at a slower rate than adjacent areas, or alternatively, shows a tendency for uplift.

tectonic province
An areal division of a Precambrian *shield* set off from adjacent provinces by a characteristic structural style, tectonic trends, and clusterings of radiometric dates.

Tejas sequence
The sedimentary succession laid down during *marine transgressions* onto the eastern margin of North America into the Mississippi enlargement, and into parts of California during the Cenozoic.

teleostei
The most advanced of the four infraclasses of the bony fishes. Cretaceous to Recent.

temporal fenestra
Openings in the skull to provide room and additional attachment area for jaw muscles.

tephra
Generic term for all *pyroclastic* material.

tephrochronology
The study of stratigraphic correlation and the dating of *tephra.* Invariably, the dated tephra are ash falls, typically in deep-sea successions.

terminal moraine
A *moraine* that forms at the margin of a glacier or ice sheet and marks the furthest advance of the ice.

terrain
General term applied to an area or tract of the Earth's surface, particularly with concern for its topography.

terrane
A fault-bounded geological entity or body of rock that has stratigraphic and structural features that are distinctive from those of adjacent terranes. Typically both the origin and geologic history of contiguous terranes are quite different from one another.

terrestrial
Refers to the continent surface—that is, terrestrial sediment would include desert and glacial deposits, as well as *lacustrine,* swamp, and *alluvial* sediments.

terriginous
Derived from the land and, in the case of sediment, likely deposited in shallow offshore water.

Tethys Ocean
The ocean that lay between *Laurasia* and *Gondwana* during Paleozoic and Mesozoic time. Its closure by plate movements resulted in the formation of the Alpine/Himalayan chain of fold mountains.

Tetrapod
Four-legged animal.

thanatocoenosis
A death assemblage. Fossil remains brought together after death simply as clasts by sedimentary processes. See also *biocoenosis*.

therapsid
Belonging to a group of synapsid reptiles of Middle Permian to Jurassic age that had many mammal-like features.

thermal dome
A supposed doming of the crust when a Pangaea configuration produces an insulating effect, preventing mantle heat dissipation.

thermal isolation
Describes a continental mass surrounded by ocean at or near a pole, or conversely, an ocean more or less surrounded by continental areas.

thermoluminescence
Dating method based on measurement of light emitted as electrons, displaced by particle collisions, return to an ordered state when heated.

thermoremanent magnetism (TRM)
Magnetism acquired by certain minerals (for example, magnetite) in igneous rocks as they cool through the *Curie point* in the presence of the earth's magnetic field.

thin-skinned tectonics
In fold mountain belts, highly contorted strata may be bodily thrust laterally on a *decollement* surface that cuts across relatively undisturbed strata below. In other words, the folds seen at the surface may extend only a very short distance downward and thus form a "thin skin" lying on top of terrain with a completely different structural style.

thorium-230 dating
Dating method based on measurement of the decay of radioactive thorium-230.

tidalite
A sediment deposited in the intertidal zone or in subtidal locales subject to tidal currents that scour and redistribute the sediment.

till
Unconsolidated, unstratified, and poorly sorted accumulation of boulders and pebbles, together with claylike rock flour, transported and deposited by glacial ice.

tillite
Lithified *till*.

Timiskaming Series
In the classic Great Lakes Precambrian, the upper, metasedimentary unit of *greenstone belts*.

Tippecanoe sequence
The succession of sediments laid down across the North American craton during a major marine transgression/regression cycle from late Early Ordovician to Early Devonian time.

trace fossil
An indication preserved in the rock of the presence of life activity of an organism, although with no remains of the organism concerned. Dinosaur footprints and worm tubes and borings are typical trace fossils. Also known as ichnofossils.

tracks
Along an apparent *polar-wandering curve*, the more or less straight portions lying between the sudden kinks or *hairpins*.

trailing-edge margin
In plate tectonics, a continental margin formed by oceanic rifting and facing onto a spreading center.

Transcontinental Arch
An uplifted region trending from the Great Lakes area in a southwesterly direction to Arizona. It was emergent as an extensive peninsula at the beginning of the Sauk transgression but was likely reduced to a series of small islands during maximum transgression. Thereafter, its influence persisted during several subsequent floodings of the continental interior.

transform fault
A *strike-slip fault* associated with *spreading centers* and trenches. Trending roughly at right angles, it causes offsets and displacement of the trend of *midocean ridges* and trenches.

transgression
See *marine transgression*.

translational boundary
A boundary between two *lithospheric plates* where they are sliding past each other in opposite directions.

Triceratops
Ceratopsian or horned dinosaur. This group evolved through the Late Cretaceous and were the most abundant dinosaurs at the time of the terminal Cretaceous extinction.

Trilobita
A class of the phylum Arthropoda. Contains animals with a distinctive, longitudinally three-lobed carapace. Laterally, the animal had a head shield (cephalon), a thorax, and a tail shield (pygidium).

turbidite
A sedimentary layer deposited from a *turbidity current*. Typically, turbidites exhibit fining upward *graded bedding*.

turbidity current
A type of density current laden with suspended sediment that flows down *subaqueous* slopes.

type section
The standard section and locality selected in defining and describing a given *lithostratigraphic* (rock) *unit*, such as a formation. Also known as a *stratotype*.

ultramafic
Describes igneous rock composed mainly of mafic (that is, dark-colored ferromagnesian) minerals.

unconformity
Surface between a lower (older) succession of rocks and an upper (younger) succession, representing a considerable break in the succession and interruption of sediment accumulation.

underclay
The clay that occurs typically below a coal seam and believed to represent the soil in which the coal-forming plants grew.

undersaturated rock
A rock containing minerals with low silica content.

ungulate
An informal term referring to hoofed mammals, including several extinct orders and the living Artiodactyla and Perissodactyla.

uniformitarianism
The principle that suggests that all of past geologic history can be interpreted and understood in terms of geologic processes going on and, in many cases, observable at the present day. The strict uniformitarian doctrine of nineteenth-century geologists has now been modified to emphasize the processes themselves. This modified model has been labeled *actualism*.

uranium-lead dating
Dating method based on the measurement of the ratio of uranium remaining, after a given period of decay, to a stable *isotope* of lead.

Vail curve
The eustatic sea-level curve proposed by Peter Vail and associates at Exxon. Based largely on seismic data from the subsurface of the continental margins.

varve
Annual (or possibly monthly or daily) sedimentary increment—typically, a thin *lamina* laid down on a lake bed and controlled by seasonal changes. A glacial varve, for example, consists of a couplet containing a relatively coarse-grained summer layer, produced by meltwater streams, and an overlying fine-grained winter layer, deposited when melting has ceased.

vestigial organ
An organ that has no apparent function, but which in other species still does have a function.

viviparous
Bearing live young.

Vulcanist
See *Plutonist*.

Wallace's Line
The line drawn by Victorian biologist Alfred Russel Wallace in the East Indian archipelago to separate those islands with an Asiatic fauna from those with an Australian fauna.

Walther's Law
The principle that, when depth-related depositional environments migrate laterally, as they do, for example, during a *marine transgression* or *regression,* the sediments of particular environments come to lie in vertical succession in the same order that the environments are arranged adjacent to each other in the horizontal direction of the sea floor.

Wasatch Formation
Formation consisting of fluvial, shales, sands, and conglomerates, typically with variegated colors. The sediments were laid down in easterly flowing streams originating in the Cordillera during the Eocene.

wave base
The maximum depth to which bottom sediment is stirred by normal ocean waves. Typically, about 10 meters on most shorelines.

white dwarf
A very late stage in a star's existence. The star is small and intensely hot.

whole rock method
In fine-grained rocks, separating individual mineral grains for measurement of radioactive decay products is impossible, so, instead, the entire rock is dated.

Wilson Cycle
Cycle of plate-tectonic events, from continental rifting to produce an ocean basin to closing of the basin and continental collision.

Worsley, Nance, and Moody Cycle
A cycle of about 440 million years, during which the continents come together into a single Pangaea configuration and then break apart again to reach maximum dispersal with up to six or seven continental pieces.

yoked basin
A sedimentary basin associated with fault-bounded highland areas and which were the source of the sediments filling the basin.

Zechstein Sea
A restricted seaway that involved an area from eastern Greenland, the North Sea, and into central Germany in Late Permian time. At least four cycles of transgression-regression left thick *evaporite* deposits.

zone
Body of rock characterized by the presence of distinctive and particular unifying features, such as *fossils,* heavy minerals, and so on.

zone fossil
See *guide fossil*.

Zuni sequence
A succession of sediments laid down over large areas of the North American craton during the Early Jurassic to Early Paleocene transgressive-regressive cycle of the Zuni Sea.

Credits

Chapter 2

2.5 From *Earth and Life Through Time,* by Steven M. Stanley. Copyright © 1988 by W. H. Freeman and Company. Reprinted by permission. **2.8** Reprinted with the permission of Macmillan Publishing Company from *Principles of Stratigraphy* by Roy R. Lemon. Copyright © 1990 Merrill Publishing Company an imprint of Macmillan Publishing Company, Inc. **2.17** Adapted from E. G. Purdy, "Recent Calcium Carbonate Facies of the Great Bahama Bank, Petrography and Reaction Groups," *Journal of Geology,* Vol. 71: 334–335. Used by permission of The University of Chicago Press. **2.18** Reprinted with the permission of Macmillan Publishing Company from *Principles of Stratigraphy* by Roy R. Lemon. Copyright © 1990 Merrill Publishing Company an imprint of Macmillan Publishing Company. **2.19** Reprinted with the permission of Macmillan Publishing Company from *Principles of Stratigraphy* by Roy R. Lemon. Copyright © 1990 Merrill Publishing Company an imprint of Macmillan Publishing Company.

Chapter 3

3.12 Reprinted with the permission of Macmillan Publishing Company from *Principles of Stratigraphy* by Roy R. Lemon. Copyright © 1990 Merrill Publishing Company an imprint of Macmillan Publishing Company.

Chapter 4

4.10 Reprinted with the permission of Macmillan Publishing Company from *Principles of Stratigraphy* by Roy R. Lemon. Copyright © 1990 Merrill Publishing Company an imprint of Macmillan Publishing Company. **4.11** From A. Williams, *Treatise on Invertebrate Paleontology,* Pt. H, Geological Society of America and University Press of Kansas. Reprinted by permission of University Press of Kansas, 2501 West 15th Street, Lawrence, KS. **4.12** Reprinted with the permission of Macmillan Publishing Company from *Principles of Stratigraphy* by Roy R. Lemon. Copyright © 1990 Merrill Publishing Company an imprint of Macmillan Publishing Company.

Chapter 5

5.6 After Ian McDougall, et al., (1977) *Geological Society of America Bulletin,* vol. 88, fig. 4, page 11. Used by permission. **5.7** Reprinted with the permission of Macmillan Publishing Company from *Principles of Stratigraphy* by Roy R. Lemon. Copyright © 1990 Merrill Publishing Company an imprint of Macmillan Publishing Company. **5.9** Redrawn after L. L. Sloss, "Sequences in the Cratonic Interior of North America," *Geological Society of America Bulletin,* vol. 74, 1963. Used by permission of the author. **5.10** Source: After S. W. Petters, "West African Cratonic Stratigraphic Sequences," *Geology,* vol. 7, p. 530, 1979.

Chapter 6

6.4 From K. R. Ludwig and J. S. Stuckless, *Contributions to Mineral Petrology,* Vol. 65, pp. 243–254. Copyright © 1978. Reprinted by permission of Sprisnger-Verlag, Heidelberg. **6.7** Reprinted with the permission of Macmillan Publishing Company from *Principles of Stratigraphy* by Roy R. Lemon. Copyright © 1990 Merrill Publishing Company an imprint of Macmillan Publishing Company.

Chapter 7

7.4 From C. D. Gebelein, "Distribution, Morphology and Accretion Rate of Recent Sub-tidal Stromatolites," *Journal of Sedimentary Petrology* 39:60. Copyright © 1969 Society for Sedimentary Geology. Used by permission.

Chapter 8

8.5 Source: Data from E. J. Petuch, *Neogene History of Tropical American Molluskus.* Copyright © 1988 Coastal Education and Research Foundation, Charlottesville, VA. **8.8** Source: After G. M. Kay, "North American Geosynclines," *Geological Society of America Memoir 48,* 1951. **8.9** Source: After Schuchert, "Sites and Nature of the American Geosynclines," *Geological Society of America Bulletin,* vol. 34, 1923.

Chapter 9

9.2 Reprinted by permission from *Nature* vol. 321, pp. 739–743; Copyright © 1986 Macmillan Magazines Limited. **Box Figure 9.1** From E. Irving and J. X. Park, "Hairpins and Superintervals," *Canadian Journal of Earth Sciences,* vol. 9, p. 1320. Copyright © 1972 National Research Council Canada. Used by permission. **9.5** From P. R. Vail et al., 1984, "Jurassic Unconformities, Chronostratigraphy and Sea Level Changes Seismic Stratigraphy and Biostratigraphy," *AAPG Memoir* 36:132. Reprinted by permission of the American Association of Petroleum Geologists. **9.7** From D. M. Raup and G. E. Boyakian, "Generic Extinction in the Fossil Record," *Paleobiology* 14:116. Copyright © 1988 The Paleontological Society. Used by permission.

Chapter 11

11.4 Redrawn from C. H. Stockwell, *Geological Survey of Canada Paper 64–17.* Reproduced with permission of the Minister of Supply and Services Canada, 1992.

Chapter 12

12.11 Reprinted with the permission of Macmillan Publishing Company from *Principles of Stratigraphy* by Roy R. Lemon. Copyright © 1990 Merrill Publishing Company an imprint of Macmillan Publishing Company.

Chapter 13

13.5 From A. V. Cohee, 1948, "Cambrian and Ordovician Rocks in Michigan Basin and Adjacent Areas," *AAPG Bulletin* 32:1428–1429. Used by permission of the American Association of Petroleum Geologists. **13.8** From Rowley and Kidd, "Plate Tectonic Model of the Taconic Orogeny," in *Journal of Geology* 89:212. Used by permission of The University of Chicago Press. **13.9** From H. Williams and R. D. Hatcher, Jr., "Suspect Terranes and Accretionary History of the Appalachian Orogeny," *Geology* 10:530, 1982. Used by permission. **13.15** From Mesolella et al., 1974, "Cyclic Depostion of Silurian Carbonates," *AAPG Bulletin* 58:34. Used by permission of the American Association of Petroleum Geologists. **13.16** From H. L. Alling and L. A. Briggs, 1961, "Silurian Evaporite Basins," *AAPG Bulletin* 45:517–547. Reprinted by permission of the American Association of Petroleum Geologists.

Chapter 14

14.26 From P. E. Playford, "Iridium Anomaly in the Upper Devonian of the Canning Basin, Western Australia," *Science,* Vol. 226, pp. 437–439, October 16, 1984. Copyright © 1984 by the AAAS. Used by permission.

Chapter 15

15.16 After P. B. King, *Evolution of North America.* Copyright © 1959 Princeton University Press.

Chapter 18

18.9 After Williams and Stelck, "Speculations on the Cretaceous Paleogeography of North America," in *The Cretaceous System in the Western Interior of North America,* edited by W. G. E. Caldwell, Special Paper 13, Geological Association of Canada, 1975. Reproduced with permission of the Minister of Supply and Services Canada, 1992.

Chapter 19

19.9 Source: After Dewey, et al., *Geological Survey of America Bulletin,* vol. 84, pp. 3137–3180, October 1973.

Chapter 20

20.20 Reprinted with the permission of Macmillan Publishing Company from *Principles of Stratigraphy* by Roy R. Lemon. Copyright © 1990 Merrill Publishing Company an imprint of Macmillan Publishing Company.

Index

472